001.64
K961

S0-AKW-017

938 001/938002

tutorial on
PARALLEL PROCESSING

ROBERT H. KUHN
DAVID A. PADUA

LMSC LIBRARY   PALO ALTO
Return to LMSC Library. Do not destroy
or transmit to another person or office.

DISCARDED
FROM
LMSC LIBRARY

LIBRARY DUE RECORD

DUE	BORROWER	DUE	BORROWER
9-17-87	H.C. Kancler		
9-21-87	J. Walsh		
4-4-88	Dulo		
4-18-88	Frederickson		
5-31-88	Retd - EN		
12-9-88	retd		
2-4-89			
5-23-89	aoto		
5/6/90	F. PANG		
5-25-90	Returned (M)		
Returned	G 7-3-90		
5/23/91	Robert		
6/4/92	Razeggi		
7/10/92			

ORM LMSC 6527-3   LOCKHEED MISSILES & SPACE COMPANY

Published by IEEE Computer Society Press
1109 Spring Street
Suite 300
Silver Spring, MD 20910

Copyright and Reprint Permissions: Abstracting is permitted with credit to the source. Libraries are permitted to photocopy beyond the limits of U.S. copyright law for private use of patrons those articles in this volume that carry a code at the bottom of the first page, provided the per-copy fee indicated in the code is paid through the Copyright Clearance Center, 21 Congress Street, Salem, MA 01970. Instructors are permitted to photocopy isolated articles for noncommercial classroom use without fee. For other copying, reprint or republication permission, write to Director, Publishing Services, IEEE, 345 E. 47 St., New York, NY 10017. All rights reserved. Copyright © 1981 by The Institute of Electrical and Electronics Engineers, Inc.

IEEE Catalog Number EHO182-6
Library of Congress Number 81-82820
IEEE Computer Society Order Number 367
ISBN 0-8186-0367-4 (soft)
ISBN 0-8186-4367-6 (microfiche)

Order from: IEEE Computer Society
Post Office Box 80452
Worldway Postal Center
Los Angeles, CA 90080

IEEE Service Center
445 Hoes Lane
Piscataway, NJ 08854

 The Institute of Electrical and Electronics Engineers, Inc.

Table of Contents

1. Introduction

Whenever a computer designer has reached for a level of performance beyond that provided by his contemporary technology, parallel processing has been his apprentice. This point will be demonstrated in two ways in this introduction: by an outline of the historic achievements of parallel processing and by a review of the taxonomic types into which the spectrum of parallel processors can be divided. This point also leads to a consideration of the theoretical obstacles to extensive parallel processing that various researchers have proposed. Note, however, that the remainder of this tutorial testifies to the power of parallel processing, in spite of these theoretical roadblocks.

Historical Achievements

There is evidence that even Babbage considered parallel processing to be a powerful design technique (Kuck, 1977). He saw the need to process the digit sum in parallel with the carry when he designed such logic (now called carry-lookahead) into his Analytical Engine in the 1820's. In 1947, Stibbitz and Williams proposed the use of multiple processors to construct a reliable self-checking computer for the Bell Laboratories' relay computer. (Williams, 1947). However, it was not until the late fifties that true parallel processing appeared. For the first time, multiple computer systems, which were faster than the fastest uniprocessor that could be built with the available technology, were constructed. Such machines as the **NBS PILOT** (Leiner *et al.*, 1959) and the Burroughs D825 (Anderson *et al.*, 1962) were *multiprocessors*.

Multiprocessors consist of several autonomous processors which can each execute separate programs. These autonomous processors are coupled by hardware (in the form of dedicated channels or in the form of a common memory) and by software (in the form of synchronization points) to attain the performance needed to master applications unreachable by contemporaneous uniprocessors.

In the years from 1964 to 1972, the complexity of parallel computer architecture increased dramatically. Prototypes of all of today's parallel processor types were constructed in this period except, of course, for multiprocessors for which prototypes already existed. In 1964, the CDC 6600 (Thornton, 1964), the first widely accepted *multifunction processor,* was introduced. In this architecture several independent processing units, each one designed to perform only a few specific functions, are controlled by a single instruction stream. In 1967, the IBM 360/91 (Anderson *et al.*, 1967) advanced multifunction architecture by dispatching several of the instructions in the stream into queues of waiting instructions. Each instruction waited until its data or a functional unit was available. The 360/91 was the prototype of current *dataflow processors.*

Toward the end of this period, extremely fast (even by today's standards) parallel processors were not only conceived but also actually built. The ILLIAC IV (Barnes *et al.*, 1968), for example, was a 64-element array processor. An *array processor* consists of many functionally equivalent processing units under the control of a single control unit. The TI ASC (Watson, 1972) is another example. It is a *pipelined processor* which attains speed by dividing each processing unit into several stages. In this way, all of the stages can operate on different data simultaneously. Neither of these processors were true prototypes of an architecture. For example, the SOLOMON I was an array processor that was designed, but not built, before ILLIAC IV. And the IBM STRETCH and the 360/91 did incorporate pipelining before the TI ASC. But the ILLIAC IV and the TI ASC capped off the terrific progress that was made in less than a decade of exciting developments in computer architecture.

A summary of the progress that has been made in parallel processing is included from Enslow's article, "Multiprocessor Organization-A survey" (Enslow, 1977). This information was updated in 1977 and serves as a prologue for the architectures that are contained in the subsequent chapters of this tutorial.

Parallel Processor Taxonomies

Noting the many parallel processing systems that have been designed, it is natural for us to seek a taxonomy which would permit us to grasp this diversity in simple terms. Thus, let us review some of the taxonomies that have been proposed for paralled processors.

Flynn appears to be one of the original parallel processing taxonomists. He proposed a taxonomy in 1966 (Flynn, 1966) based on two orthogonal classifications, which has persisted until today. These two classifications are based on the number of instruction and data streams. He proposed four types of computer architectures:

SISD—single instruction stream, single data stream;

SIMD—single instruction stream, multiple data stream;

MISD—multiple instruction stream, single data stream; and

MIMD—multiple instruction stream, multiple data stream.

These four taxonomic types illustrate, at least intuitively, what a reasonable taxonomy should be. For example, a uniprocessor is an SISD computer, a multiprocessor is an MIMD computer, and an array processor is an SIMD computer. Unfortunately, however, some architectures can be placed in either of two classes depending upon one's concept of instruction and data stream. For example, Flynn originally considered pipelined processors to be confluent SISD computers. Later, when the concept and limitations of pipelining were better understood, Flynn considered pipeline processors to be SIMD (Flynn, 1972). However, other taxonomists, Händler (1975) and Thurber (1976), for example, felt that pipelined processors were actually MISD computers. Despite these differences of opinion, Flynn's taxonomy has persisted and, in fact, has been elaborated on. For example, Händler (1975) breaks Flynn's taxonomy into eight types by distinguishing between bit and word parallel data. Kuck (1978) goes even farther by expanding Flynn's basic orthogonal concepts into no less than 16 taxonomic types, and he shows that examples of each type have been designed.

By 1973, a less conceptual and more practical *common taxonomy* seems to have evolved. It is exemplified by the Appendix to a survey by Baer (1973), where we find the following types:

Type	Example	Also known as
Homogeneous Multi-processors	D825	Multiprocessors
Nonhomogeneous Multi-processors	CDC6400	Multifunction Processors
Array Processors	ILLIAC IV	Parallel Processors
Pipeline Processors	TI ASC	Pipeline Processors

Flynn recognized these common types and attempted to incorporate them in his taxonomy (Flynn, 1972). The roots of another taxonomy were also pointed out in Baer's paper (1973). Baer observed that homogeneous multiprocessors can be further classified according to their interconnection scheme, such as:

Crossbar Switch Systems,

Multiple-Bus Connected Systems, and

Time-Shared Bus Systems.

This sort of interconnection taxonomy has been developed further by others, notably by Anderson and Jensen (1975).

Although the common taxonomy of the previous paragraph evolved spontaneously, it still seems to apply to contemporary parallel processors. Consider, for example, Kuck's paper (in press) in which he points out that these four common types represent the most prominent alternatives for a parallel processor design. Although a few of the most recently proposed designs fall precisely into these types, most current designs are hybrids which combine concepts from two or more of these types. We have included Fig. 1 (Kuck, in press) to illustrate this point. Dataflow processing, for example, is seen as a hybrid design—borrowing some ideas from multifunction processors and some ideas from multiprocessors. Again, the CRAY-1 is a hybrid design, since it has multiple functional units and thus is a multifunction processor. But its functional units are pipelined; so it is also a pipeline processor.

In this tutorial, we use primarily the common taxonomy; not only because it is less ambiguous, but also because it divides a representative set of contemporary parallel architectures into (more or less) equal subsets. In a practical sense, we note that although many architectures are a combination of the four common types, as Kuck (in press) claims, for ourpurposes any such architectures can be described under any of the constituent types.

Theoretical Arguments

From the historical successes of parallel processing and the decreasing costs of hardware, one must inevitably ask what the limits of parallel processing are. Several theoreticians have attempted to extrapolate our current knowledge of computer applications and computer architecture to some arbitrary future date when massively parallel computers can be built. We will briefly discuss these limits and will note some detailed arguments that have been raised. Before beginning, note that we have included in this chapter a paper by Flynn which discusses some of the arguments that were prevalent circa 1972. For the most part, the arguments Flynn describes are still being heard today. Several papers have appeared on the arguments posed in Flynn's paper, some *pro* parallel processing but many *con*.

Against pipeline and array processors, two venerable arguments have come to be known as "Amdahl's argument" and "Minsky's conjecture." Amdahl's argument (Amdahl, 1967) is that the limiting factor to increasing the speed of a parallel algorithm is the reciprocal of the fraction of the computation that the parallel algorithm must do sequentially. For example, if 5 percent of the parallel algorithm uses one processor, then the best possible speed up is only 20. Or, to put it another way, the parallel computation is at most 20 times faster than the original sequential algorithm. As we can see, this argument is based entirely on the structure of the algorithm; hardware can be assumed to be unlimited. No one denies the argument as stated. There is, however, a hidden premise that makes it look impressive. Most people perceive 5 percent as being a small percentage—perhaps because they relate it to the scale of everyday objects. Science, however, has shown many instances in which human perception of scale is inadequate. For example, what if the percentage of sequential time is actually only .1 percent or .01 percent, the speedup will be large.

Minsky's conjecture on the limits of array and pipeline processors (Minsky and Papert, 1971) is parametrically quite different. It assumes that a fixed amount of hardware, say P processors, is available, and asks how well can such a parallel processor perform. The conjecture is that the limit of the speedup is $\log_2 P$ for large P. This pessimistic bound was observed empirically, but it can be argued theoretically if we make some general assumptions about the structure of algorithms. For example, Flynn (in the paper included in this chapter) assumes that programs contain many nested branches. He shows that if the nest depth is deep enough and there is an equal number of statements at each nest depth, then indeed the limit of the speedup will be $\log_2 P$. To refute Minsky's conjecture, Flynn then assumes that the number of statements on each nest depth decreases exponentially and shows that the same analysis gives a speedup limit of $P/\log_2 P$. This speedup is considered to be relatively acceptable compared to the best possible speedup, P. It turns out that there are many ways to refute Minsky's conjecture besides Flynn's branching argument. Lee (1977) and Banerjee (1979) attempt to refute Minsky's conjecture based on their own conjectures about the degree of parallelism in algorithms. On the other hand, in Chapter 8 of this tutorial, Kuck *et al.* have claimed that purely empirical data shows that the limit on speedup is nearly linear within a reasonable range of P values. On the whole, however, both Amdahl's argument and Minsky's conjecture are based on extrapolations of current data which is relatively meager.

The two arguments reviewed above are representative of many of the arguments describing the limits of parallel processing. We will mention a few other arguments. For example, pipeline processors are sensitive to interruptions in the flow of control or data which force the pipeline to drain. This is true especially when instruction processing is pipelined and a branch instruction is encountered. A famous study (Foster and Riseman, 1972) purports to show empirically that the limit on speedup is small due to program branching. One possible counter argument to this study is that flow of control frequently goes in one direction most of the time. Control units have actually been built which effectively predict which direction flow of control will go. Multiprocessors have engendered their own set of arguments. The two most frequent are that (1) multiprocessors, accessing a common memory composed of multiple modules, will frequently try to access the same module, and that (2) parallel tasks running on a multiprocessor will frequently need to have exclusive access to at least part of the data. The first argument is called the "memory conflict problem," and it is the subject of a paper by Chang *et al.* in Chapter 4. The second argument is called the "lockout problem." The prevalent conjecture by those involved in multiprocessing is that the amount of data requiring exclusive access can be made very small in most applications. See, for example, the paper by Fennell and Lesser in Chapter 4 and the paper by Bayer and Schkolnick in Chapter 10.

Organization of the Tutorial

The rest of this tutorial is organized into two parts. Part I on parallel architectures consists of five chapters. The next four chapters follow the four common taxonomic types: Chapter 2 is on pipeline processors; Chapter 3 is on array processors; while Chapter 4 is on multiprocessors; Chapter 5 is on dataflow processors, which (as we have seen) can be viewed as an extension of the fourth common taxonomic type, multifunction processors. There is also a chapter in Part I on special-purpose parallel processors to give the reader some feeling for how parallel processors can be "tuned" to particular applications. Each chapter is organized into two sections, one section on example architectures, and the other on papers discussing how the chapter's architecture type has been or could be profitably used to solve real world problems. Part II is on software. It includes the following: languages for parallel programming (Chapter 7); compilers for the translation of sequential programs into parallel ones (Chapter 8); operating systems for parallel computers (Chapter 9); and algorithms for parallel computers (Chapter 10). Each chapter starts with a brief introduction that summarizes the contents of the chapter and gives some suggestions for further reading.

Multiprocessor Organization—A Survey

PHILIP H. ENSLOW JR.

CHART 1. A Brief Chronology of Multiprocessor and Parallel Systems (updated from [9])

Date	System Manufacturer and Model Number	Remarks
1958	National Bureau of Standards Pilot	Three independently operating computers that could work in cooperation.
1958 (circa)	IBM AN/FSQ-31 and 32	Solid-state Sage computer; not multiprocessors; merely duplexed systems.
1960	Burroughs D-825 (This system carried various military model designations depending on the major system of which it was part.)	First modular system with identical processors. Total memory shared by all processors. Up to four processors, 16 memory modules, 10 I/O controllers, and 64 devices. Important feature was one of the earliest examples of a modern operating system—the Automatic Operating and Scheduling Program (ASOP).
1960	Ramo Wooldridge TRW-400	"Polymorphic system"; for USAF command and control. Some construction done, not completed. Important for early concepts.
May 1960	Univac Larc	One I/O processor and one computational processor capable of operating in parallel. One delivered to Livermore AEC Laboratories. Not a "true" multiprocessor.
May 1961	IBM Stretch (7030)	Original design called for separate character-oriented processor and binary arithmetic processor. These were dropped from final design; therefore, final product was not a multiprocessor. It did contain look-ahead. Only seven delivered.
Feb. 1963	Burroughs B-5000	One or two processors. Up to eight memory modules. Programs independent of addresses. Supervisor was the Master Control Program (MCP). Utilized virtual memory concepts and hardware. Machine code based on Polish notation. Users programmed only in ALGO or COBOL. Became the B-5500 in Nov. 1964.
1963	IBM 704X/709X (7040 or 44 and 7090 or 94)	"Direct Coupled System"
1963	Bendix G-21 (later CDC)	A multiprocessor version of the G-20 developed for Carnegie Institute of Technology. A crossbar system.
1963	IBM, MSC	A custom multiprocessor system to support Manned Space Center. Originally 7090s sharing large core; later 360/75s.
Sep. 1964	CDC 6600	Contained multiple arithmetic and logic units each of which could execute only a small fraction of the total instruction repertoire. Ten peripheral processors were an integral part of the system. (Number of PPUs increased to 20 in 1969.) The PPUs constitute a multiprocessor system. Overall system an example of an asymmetric multiprocessor.
Nov. 1964	Burroughs B-5500	An upgrade of the B-5000 (see Feb. 1963).
1964	GE 645 (now Honeywell)	Ordered by Project MAC at MIT.
May 1965	GE 645 (now HIS-645)	Delivered to Project MAC at MIT. Hardware not a standard product; however Multics operating system is being released.
Nov. 1965	Univac 1108	
1965	Solomon I	Design only. First large-scale array processor.

Excerpted from and reprinted with permission from "Multiprocessor Organization—A Survey" by P.H. Enslow, Jr., from *Computing Surveys*, Volume 9, Number 1, March 1977, pages 122-126. Copyright © 1977 by the Association for Computing Machinery, Inc.

CHART 1—*Continued*

Date	System Manufacturer and Model Number	Remarks
Mar. 1966	IBM S/360 Model 67	Special dual-processor time-sharing system.
Apr. 1966	CDC 6500	Dual 6400s
Dec. 1966	XDS Sigma 7	
1966	Solomon II	Design only.
Jun. 1967	CDC 6700	Dual CDC 6600s
Aug. 1967	XDS Sigma 5	
1968	CDC 7600	Very similar to 6600, but higher speed and included hierarchy of main memory as standard feature.
Apr. 1969	IBM S/360 Model 65 MP	Dual-processor version of standard Model 65.
Jun. 1970	XDS Sigma 6	
Oct. 1970	Burroughs B-5700	Similar to B-5500 with capability for increased memory. Capability for four B-5700 systems to share disk storage.
1970	CII Iris 80	True multiprocessor; processors considered as anonymous resources; virtual memory.
Feb. 1971	Honeywell 6050, 6060, 6080	
Jun. 1971	Burroughs B-6700	
Sep. 1971	DEC System 10/1055, 10/1077	
Sep. 1971	XDS Sigma 8, 9	
Nov. 1971	Univac 1110	
1971	SDC Pepe (Parallel Element Processing Ensemble)	Prototype for processing of radar data for ballistic missile defense system.
1971	Fairchild Symbol 2R	Seven processors dedicated to separate functions
Jan. 1972	Univac 1106	
Jan. 1972	Honeywell 2088	
Sep. 1972	Illiac IV	Array processor. 64 processor elements. Driven by a conventional multiprocessor used as a front-end control processor.
Feb. 1972	Burroughs B-7700	
1972	CDC, Cyber 72, 73, 74, 76	
1972	Goodyear Staran S	Parallel associative system.
1972	Texas Instruments ASC (Advanced Scientific Computer)	Embodies both multiprocessing and pipelining.
Jun. 1973	Bolt Beranek and Newman, Pluribus	Multi-minicomputer stressing reliability.
1973	CDC Star-100	Pipeline system.
1974	IBM S/370, Models 158 MP & 168 MP	Shared real and virtual storage.
1974	CDC Cyber 175	Similar to CDC 6000 and Cyber 70 series; memory capacity extensions.
1974	Carnegie-Mellon Univ. C.mmp	Multiprocessor with 16 PDP-11s sharing memory through a crossbar.
Mar. 1975	Univac 1100/20, 1100/40	
Oct. 1975	Univac 1100/10	
1975	Tandem, T16	Fault-tolerant multiprocessor
1976	DEC System 10/1088	Dual-processor
1976	Cray-1	Pipeline system
1976	IBM S/370, Models 158 AP & 168 AP	Asymmetric multiprocessors
Nov. 1976	Univac 1100/80	
1977	Goodyear Staran E	Parallel associative system.

Philip H. Enslow Jr.

TABLE 1. CHARACTERISTICS OF MULTIPROCESSOR AND PARALLEL PROCESSING SYSTEMS
(UPDATED FROM [9])

Name	System Organization[a]		Maximum Number of Functional Units		Memory[c]
	Proc	I/O	Proc	I/O[b]	
Minicomputers					
Microdata MICRO 1600D	TS	TS (separate)	2	—/One TS bus per CPU and one DMA per system/—	$\{ \begin{smallmatrix} 16 \times 4K \\ 8 \times 8K \end{smallmatrix} \} \times 8b$ (max 64K)
Small					
Xerox SIGMA—5[e]	MP	MP	5[f]	5[f]/8 per IOP/32 per chnl	$\{ \begin{smallmatrix} 32 \times 4K \\ 16 \times 8K \end{smallmatrix} \} \times 32b$ (max 131K)
Medium					
DEC System-10/1055	MP	TS	2	—/ff/ii	$16 \times 16K \times 36b$
Honeywell HIS 2088	MP	MP	2	—/16[d]/96[d]	$4 \times 131K \times 8b$
Memorex MRX/40 & 50	TS	TS (common)	7[h]	7[h]/—/—	(max 64K bytes)
RCA model 215	CB	CB	4	4/1 mux or 2 selec. per IOC/—	$8 \times 32K \times 36b$
Systems Engineering Labs SEL 88	MP	MP	3[i]	3[i]/—/—	$16 \times 8K \times 32b$
Tandem T16	MP	MP	16	—/16/256	$128 \times 32K \times 16b$
Xerox SIGMA—6 and 7[e]	MP	MP	7[j]	7[j]/8 per IOP/32 per chnl	$8 \times 16K \times 32b$
Medium-to-large					
Bolt Beranek and Newman PLURIBUS	TS[k]	TS[k]	56	—[k]/—/768	$4 \times 128K \times 16b$ $1 \times 8K \times 16b^d$
Burroughs B-5700 (B-5500)[l]	CB	CB (common)	2	4/4/—	$8 \times 4K \times 48b$
CII, IRIS 80	MP	MP	4	7/16/1768	$8 \times 128K \times 32b$
DEC System-10/1077	MP	TS	2	—/ff/ii	$64 \times 64K \times 36b$
Hitachi, 8700 8800	MP	MP	3	1/12/—	
	MP	MP	4	1/12/—	
Xerox SIGMA—8[e]	MP	MP	11[m]	11[m]/8 per IOP/32 per chnl	$8 \times 16K \times 32b$
Xerox SIGMA—9[e]	MP	MP	11[m]	11[m]/8 per IOP/32 per chnl	$32 \times 16K \times 32b$
Large					
Burroughs B-6700 (B-6500)	CB	CB (common)	3	3/36[n]/128	$\{ \begin{smallmatrix} 64 \times 16K \\ 16 \times 64K \end{smallmatrix} \} \times 48b$ (max 1048K)
CDC CYBER 72 (equivalent to CDC 6200)	CB	TS	2	20/20/160	$32 \times 4K \times 60b$
CDC CYBER 73 (equivalent to CDC 6400 & 6500)	CB	TS	2	20/20/160	$32 \times 4K \times 60b$
DEC System 10/1088	MP	TS	2	—/12/126	$32 \times 128K \times 36b$ or $16 \times 256K \times 36b$
Honeywell HIS 6050/ 6060	MP	MP	4	4/96/—	$16 \times 32K \times 36b$
Honeywell HIS 6070/ 6080	MP	MP	4	4/96/—	$16 \times 64K \times 36b$
Honeywell HIS 6180	MP	MP	4	4/96/—	$32 \times 64K \times 36b$
Honeywell HIS 635	MP	MP	4	4/64/—	$8 \times 32K \times 36b$
Honeywell HIS 645 (MULTICS)	MP	MP	4	4/64/—	$8 \times 32K \times 36b$
IBM S/360, Model 65 MP	MP	MP	2[o]	—/12 (selec) 2 (mux)/—	$8 \times 256K \times 8b$
IBM S/360, Model 67	MP	MP	2	2/12 (selec) 2 (mux)/—	$8 \times 256K \times 8b$
Manchester Univ. MU5	TS	TS			$4 \times 8K \times 32b$
UNIVAC 1106	MP	MP	2	—/32/—	$4 \times 128K \times 36b$
UNIVAC 1100/12	MP	MP	2	—/32/—	$4 \times 128K \times 36b$
Large-to-extra large					
Burroughs B-7700	CB	CB	7[h]	7[h]/224/255	$\{ \begin{smallmatrix} 8 \times 131K \\ 4 \times 262K \end{smallmatrix} \} \times 48b$ (max 1048K)
CDC 6500	CB	TS	2	20/24/—	$32 \times 4K \times 60b$
CDC 6600	CB	TS	1	20/24/—	$32 \times 4K \times 60b$
CDC 6700	CB	TS	2	20/24/—	$32 \times 4K \times 60b$
CDC CYBER—74 (equivalent to CDC 6600 and 6700)	CB	TS	2	20/20/160	$32 \times 4K \times 60b$

TABLE 1—*Continued*

Name	System Organization[a]		Maximum Number of Functional Units		Memory[c]
	Proc	I/O	Proc	I/O[b]	
IBM S/370 model 158 MP	MP	MP	2	—/10 blk mux 4 mux/—	8 × 1024K × 8b
Univac 1108	MP	MP	3	2/32/—	4 × 65K × 36b
Univac 1100/22	MP	MP	2	—/32/—	8 × 64K × 36b
Extra large					
CDC 7600	CB	TS	1	13/15/—	SCM[p] 32 × 2K × 60b / LCM 8 × 64K × 60b
CDC Cyber—76 (equivalent to CDC 7600)	CB	TS	1	13/15/—	SCM 32 × 4K × 60b / LCM 8 × 64K × 60b
CDC Cyber 175	CB	TS	1	20/24/—	16 × 16K × 60b
IBM S/370 model 168 MP	MP	MP	2	—/24 (max 22 blk mux)/—	16 × 1024K × 8b
Univac 1110	MP	MP	6[q]	4/96/—	8 × 32K × 36b / 8 × 128K × 36b[r]
Univac 1100/40	MP	MP	6[q]	4/96/—	8 × 64K × 36b / 8 × 128K × 36b[r]
Univac 1100/82	MP	MP	2	2/58/—	16 × 256K × 36b
Giant and special systems					
U.S. Army Adv. Ballistic Missile Defense Agency Pepe)[s]	AV	MP	288[t]	3[u]/—/—	Data memories { PE 1 × 1K × 32b / ACU 1 × 4K × 32b / CCU 1 × 2K × 32b / AOCU 1 × 2K × 32b } Program memories { ACU 2 × 32K × 32b / CCU 1 × 2K × 32b / AOCU 1 × 2K × 32b }
Bell Labs CLC (Safeguard)	MP	MP	10	5/80/80	63 × 4K × 64b[v] / 32 × 4K × 64b[w]
Burroughs D 825	CB	CB	4	2/20/128	16 × 4K × 48b
Carnegie-Mellon C.mmp	CB	TS[x]	16	x	16 × 1M × 16b / 1 × 4K × 16b[d]
Goodyear Aerospace Staran "S"	AV	AV	8192	—/2[y]/—	1 × 64K × 32b[v] / 32 × 256K × 256b[w]
Staran "E"	AV	AV	2048	—/—/—	1 × 64K × 32b[v] / 8 × 256K × 64Kb[w]
Burroughs Illiac IV	AV	TS	64		1 × 2K × 64b[d]
Fairchild Symbol 2R	TS	TS	7[aa]	1/31/—	1 × 8K × 64b
Hughes H-4400	CB (common)	CB	7[bb]	7[bb]/8 per IOP/—	16 × 16K × 32b
IBM 9020A (360/50) (special FAA system)	MP	MP	4	3/—/—	24 × 32K × 32b
IBM 9020D (360/65) (special FAA system)	MP	MP	4	3/—/—	40 × 32K × 32b
IBM 4-pi, EP/MP	MP	MP	3	2/(na)/(na)	8 × 16K × 32b
IBM 4-pi, CC-1 (Awacs)	MP	MP	2	2/2 per IOU[cc]/(na)	11 × 16K × 32b
Plessy 250	MP	MP	16	2/—/—	20 × 32K × 24b
Texas Instruments ASC (Advanced Scientific Computer)	PL	TS	2[dd]	8[ee]/—[ff]/—[ff]	8 × 512K × 32b[gg] / 8 × 256K × 32b[hh]
Ramo-Wooldridge RW-400	CB	CB	—	—	—
Univac ARTS III (Air Traffic Control)	MP	MP	8	—/128/—	16 × 16K × 30b
Univac AN/UYK-7	MP	MP	3	2/32/	16 × 16K × 32b
Univac Model 1832 (avionics computer)	MP	MP	2	2/18/—	3 × 32K × 32b

[a] Abbreviations used:
  TS: time-shared/common-bus
  CB: crossbar
  MP: multiport
  AV: array/vector
  PL: pipeline
[b] Expressed as (I/O Processors)/(I/O Channels)/(I/O Devices) Dashes have two meanings:
  In the IOP position: System does not utilize separately identifiable I/O Processors. The channels communicate directly with memory.

In the channel or

device position: The maximum number is not firmly established or limited by the basic system design.

[c] Expressed as: (number of modules) × (size of module) × (size of memory word).

[d] Per processor system.

[e] The Sigma-5 and larger models are designed to permit the attachment of multiple CPU's and I/O processor up to the capacity of the memory ports available; however, the standard Xerox software supports only the uniprocessor configuration.

[f] Sum of number of CPUs and IOPs cannot exceed six due to memory port limitations.

[g] Plus a dedicated data communications channel and a low-speed channel connected directly to one of the processors.

[h] Total number of CPUs plus IOPs must not exceed eight.

[i] Any combination of CPUs and DMAs up to total of four.

[j] Sum of number of CPUs and IOPs cannot exceed eight due to memory port limitations.

[k] One processor bus for each two processors. One or two I/O busses per system.

[l] The B-5700 is an upgrade of the B-5500 with a shared disk available.

[m] Sum of number of CPUs and IOPs cannot exceed 12 due to memory port limitations.

[n] Floating data switching channels.

[o] "Because of the design of the 360 I/O control units, connection to more than two processors is not feasible. Also, because of the nature of the direct control feature for communications between processors, the system is limited to two processors. Thus the system is restricted by its hardware design from expansion beyond a two-CPU configuration, although the principles upon which the system is based are not as restricted." [Miller]

[p] Main memory is divided into two parts: small core memory (SCM), which is executable, and large core memory (LCM), which is used as bulk core storage for very high speed on-line operations such as swapping.

[q] Only four being supported at this time.

[r] Executable magnetic core high-speed extended storage.

[s] Pepe is an architecture to augment a host general purpose computer such as the CDC 7600.

[t] The MSI Model Pepe is designed for 288 processing elements. The architecture does not limit the number of processing elements.

[u] Pepe attaches to a host computer via three control units. No peripherals are directly attached to the Pepe computer system.

[v] Program store.

[w] Variable store.

[x] One PDP-11 UNIBUS associated with each processor.

[y] One 1-Gbit channel and one 1-Mbit channel.

[z] For present implementation of one quadrant.

[aa] Each dedicated to a special function (i.e. CPU, translation, system supervision I/O, etc.).

[bb] Total number of CPUs plus IOPs must not exceed eight.

[cc] One high-speed channel and one low-speed channel.

[dd] One central processor can have one, two, three, or four arithmetic units all controlled by a single instruction processing unit. Two central processors can each have one or two arithmetic units.

[ee] The peripheral processors are virtual processors. (The operating system executes entirely in a peripheral processor.)

[ff] Not set by system design but rather by memory port transfer capacities.

[gg] Central memory.

[hh] Central memory extension (directly executable).

[ii] Not set by system design but rather by physical length of channel bus.

High-Speed Machines and Their Compilers

D.J. Kuck

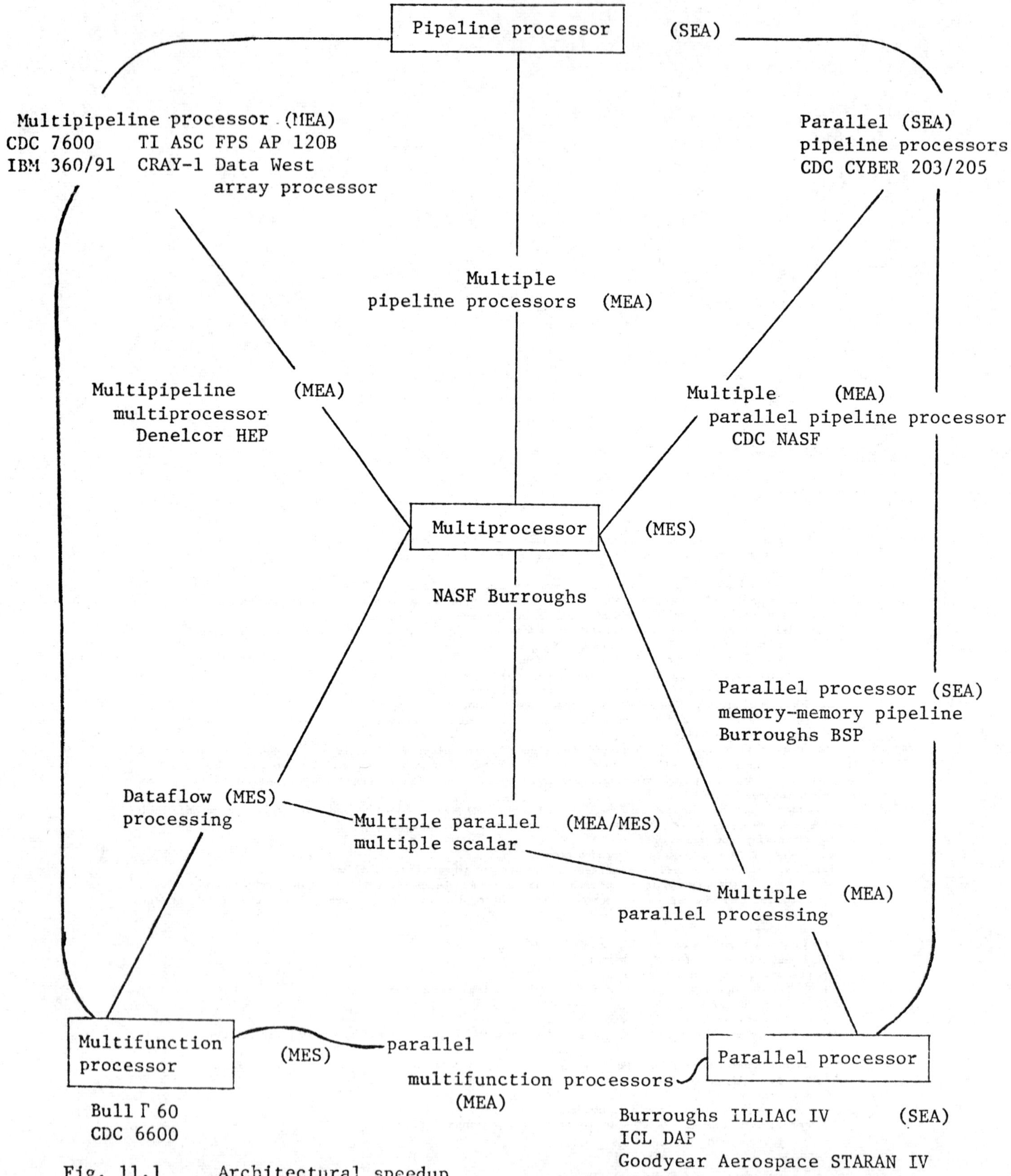

Fig. 11.1   Architectural speedup
                   techniques

Excerpted from and reprinted with permission from "High-Speed Machines and Their Compilers" by D.J. Kuck, from *Proceedings of the CREST Parallel Processing Systems Course*, September 1980. Copyright © 1980 by Cambridge University Press.

IEEE TRANSACTIONS ON COMPUTERS, VOL. C-21, NO. 9, SEPTEMBER 1972

Some Computer Organizations and Their Effectiveness

MICHAEL J. FLYNN, MEMBER, IEEE

Abstract—A hierarchical model of computer organizations is developed, based on a tree model using request/service type resources as nodes. Two aspects of the model are distinguished: logical and physical.

General parallel- or multiple-stream organizations are examined as to type and effectiveness—especially regarding intrinsic logical difficulties.

The overlapped simplex processor (SISD) is limited by data dependencies. Branching has a particularly degenerative effect.

The parallel processors [single-instruction stream–multiple-data stream (SIMD)] are analyzed. In particular, a nesting type explanation is offered for Minsky's conjecture—the performance of a parallel processor increases as log M instead of M (the number of data stream processors).

Multiprocessors (MIMD) are subjected to a saturation syndrome based on general communications lockout. Simplified queuing models indicate that saturation develops when the fraction of task time spent locked out (L/E) approaches $1/n$, where n is the number of processors. Resources sharing in multiprocessors can be used to avoid several other classic organizational problems.

Index Terms—Computer organization, instruction stream, overlapped, parallel processors, resource hierarchy.

INTRODUCTION

ATTEMPTS to codify the structure of a computer have generally been from one of three points of view: 1) automata theoretic or microscopic; 2) individual problem oriented; or 3) global or statistical.

In the microscopic view of computer structure, relationships are described exhaustively. All possible interactions and parameters are considered without respect to their relative importance in a problem environment.

Measurements made by using individual problem yardsticks compare organizations on the basis of their relative performances in a peculiar environment. Such comparisons are usually limited because of their ad hoc nature.

Global comparisons are usually made on the basis of elaborate statistical tabulations of relative performances on various jobs or mixtures of jobs. The difficulty here lies in the fact that the analysis is *ex post facto* and usually of little consequence in the architecture of the system since the premises on which they were based (the particular computer analyzed) have been changed.

The object of this paper is to reexamine the principal interactions within a processor system so as to generate a more "macroscopic" view, yet without reference to a particular user environment. Clearly, any such effort must be sharply limited in many aspects; some of the more significant are as follows.

1) There is no treatment of I/O problems or I/O as a limiting resource. We assume that all programs of interest will either not be limited by I/O, or the I/O limitations will apply equally to all computer memory configurations. That is, the I/O device sees a "black box" computer with a certain performance. We shall be concerned with *how* the computer attained a performance potential, while it may never be realized due to I/O considerations.

2) We make no assessment of particular instruction sets. It is assumed that there exists a (more or less) ideal set of instructions with a basically uniform execution time—except for data conditional branch instructions whose effects will be discussed.

3) We will emphasize the notion of effectiveness (or efficiency) in the use of internal resources as a criterion for comparing organizations, despite the fact that either condition 1) or 2) may dominate a total performance assessment.

Within these limitations, we will first attempt to classify the forms or gross structures of computer systems by observing the possible interaction patterns between instructions and data. Then we will examine physical and logical attributes that seem fundamental to achieving efficient use of internal resources (execution facilities, memory, etc.) of the system.

CLASSIFICATION: FORMS OF COMPUTING SYSTEMS

Gross Structures

In order to describe a machine structure from a macroscopic point of view, on the one hand, and yet avoid the pitfalls of relating such descriptions to a particular problem, the stream concept will be used [1]. Stream in this context simply means a sequence of items (instructions or data) as executed or operated on by a processor. The notion of "instruction" or "datum" is defined with respect to a reference machine. To avoid trivial cases of parallelism, the reader should consider a reference instruction or datum as similar to those used by familiar machines (e.g., IBM 7090). In this description, organizations are categorized by the magnitude (either in space or time multiplex) of interactions of their instruction and data streams. This immediately gives rise to four broad classifications of machine organizations.

Manuscript received February 26, 1970; revised May 25, 1971, and January 21, 1972. This work was supported by the U. S. Atomic Energy Commission under Contract AT (11-1) 3288.

The author is with the Department of Computer Science, The Johns Hopkins University, Baltimore, Md. 21218.

EHO182-6/81/0000/0011 © 1972 IEEE

Reprinted from *IEEE Transactions on Computers*, Volume C-21, Number 9, September 1972, pages 948-960. Copyright © 1972 by The Institute of Electrical and Electronics Engineers, Inc.

1) The single-instruction stream–single-data stream organization (SISD), which represents most conventional computing equipment available today.

2) The single-instruction stream–multiple-data stream (SIMD), which includes most array processes, including Solomon [2] (Illiac IV).

3) Multiple-instruction stream–single-data stream type organizations (MISD), which include specialized streaming organizations using multiple-instruction streams on a single sequence of data and the derivatives thereof. The plug-board machines of a bygone era were a degenerate form of MISD wherein the instruction streams were single instructions, and a derived datum (SD) passed from program step i to program step $i+1$ (MI).

4) Multiple-instruction stream–multiple-data stream (MIMD), which include organizations referred to as "multiprocessor." Univac [3], among other corporations, has proposed various MIMD structures.

These are qualitative notations. They could be quantified somewhat by specifying the number of streams of each type in the organization or the number of instruction streams per data stream, or vice versa. But in order to attain a better insight into the notions of organization, let us formalize the stream view of computing. Consider a generalized system model consisting of a *requestor* and a *server*. For our purposes we will consider the requestor as synonymous with a program (or user) and the server as synonymous with the resources, both physical and logical, which process the elements of the program. Note that, for now, the distinction between a program and a resource is not precise; indeed, under certain conditions a resource may be a program and vice versa. Then a *problem* can be defined as a stream (or sequence) of requests for service (or resources). Since each request is, in general, a program and can also specify a sequence of requests, we have a request hierarchy.

Let P be a program. A program is defined simply as a request for service by a structured set of resources. P specifies a sequence of other (sub) requests: $R_1, R_2, R_3, R_4, \cdots, R_n$, called tasks. While the tasks appear here as a strictly ordered set, in general the tasks will have a more complex control structure associated with them.

Each request, again, consists of a sequence of subrequests (the process terminates only at the combinational circuit level). Regardless of level, any request R_i is a bifurcated function having two roles:

$$R = \{f_i{}^l, f_i{}^p\}$$

the logical role of the requestor $f_i{}^l$ and the combined logical and physical role of a server $f_i{}^p$.

1) Logical Role of Requestor: The logical role of the requestor is to define a result given an argument and to define a control structure or precedence among the other tasks directly defined by the initiating program P. We

anticipate a hierarchy of requests, where the transition between the initiating level P and the next level tasks $\{R_i\}$ is viewed as the logical role of each of the R_i, while actual service is through a combination of a tree of lower level logical requests and eventual physical service at the leaves of the tree.

Thus consider

$$f_i{}^l(x, \tau) \rightarrow (y, \tau^*)$$

where $f_i{}^l$ is a functional mapping (in a mathematical sense) of argument x into result y. Here, $x, y \in B$, where B is the set of values defined by the modulo class of the arithmetic (logical and physical notions of arithmetic should be identical). The τ and τ^* indicate logical time or precedence; τ is a Boolean control variable whose validity is established by one or more predecessor logical functions $\{f_i{}^l\}$.

The requirement for a τ control variable stems from the need for specification of the validity of $f_i{}^l$ and its argument x. Notice that two tasks $f_i{}^l, f_j{}^l$ are directly dependent if either $\tau_i = 1$ implies $\tau_j{}^* = 1$ or $\tau_j = 1$ implies $\tau_i{}^* = 1$. This precedence specification may be performed implicitly by use of a restrictive convention (e.g., by strict sequence)—that the physical time t at which the ith task control variable τ_i becomes valid, $t(\tau_i = 1)$, has $t(\tau_i = 1) \geq t(\tau_{i-1}{}^* = 1)$, for all i—or by explicit control of τ and τ^*.

That there can be no general way of rearranging the request sequence $f_i{}^l$ (or finding an alternate sequence $g_i{}^l$) such that the precedence requirement vanishes, is a consequence of the composition requirement $f(g(x))$, intrinsic to the definition of a computable function. That is, f cannot be applied to an argument until $g(x)$ has been completed.

The notion of an explicit precedence control has been formalized by Leiner [16] and others by use of a precedence matrix.

Given an unordered set of requests (tasks) $\{f_j{}^l \mid 1 \leq j \leq n\}$, an $n \times n$ matrix is defined so that: $a_{ij} = 1$ if we require $t(\tau_j = 1) \geq t(\tau_i{}^* = 1)$, i.e., task f_i must be completed before f_j can be begun. Otherwise, $a_{ij} = 0$.

The matrix M so defined identifies the initial priority. By determining M^2 (in the conventional matrix product sense), secondary implicit precedence is determined. This process is continued until

$$M^{P+1} = 0.$$

The fully determined precedence matrix H is defined as

$$H = M + M^2 + M^3 + \cdots + M^P, \qquad P \leq n$$

where $+$ is the Boolean union operation: $(a+b)_{ij} = a_{ij} + b_{ij}$.

Thus H defines a scheduling of precedence among the n tasks. At any moment of logical time (τ_i), perhaps a set of tasks $\{f_k; k \mid$ either $a_{jk} = 0$, for all j, or if $a_{jk} = 1$, then $\tau_j{}^* = 1\}$ are independently executable.

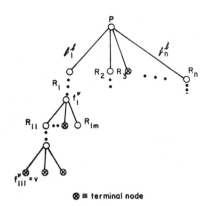

⊗ ≡ terminal node

Fig. 1. Service hierarchy.

Since "task" and "instruction" are logically equivalent requests for service, the preceding also applies to the problem of detecting independent instructions in a sequence. In practice, tasks are conditionally issued. This limits the use of the precedence computation to the "while running" or dynamic environment.

2) Service Role of Request: Thus far we have been concerned with precedence or task control at a single level. The service for node R_i is defined by f_i^v, which is a subtree structure (see Fig. 1) terminating in the physical resources of the system, i.e., the physically executable primitives of the system. Thus f_i^l defines the transition from P to R_i and among R_i, $(i=1, \cdots, n)$, at a given level, while f_i^v defines the substructure under node R_i. Thus f_i^v is actually a hierarchy of subrequests terminating in a primitive physical service resource.

These terminal nodes are defined as a request for service lying within the physical resource vocabulary of the system, i.e.,

$$f_{ijk \ldots}^v \equiv v \mid v \in V$$

where V is the set of available physical resources. Note that the request is generally for any element in a particular resource class rather than a specific resource v. The elements $\{v\}$ are usually of two types: operational or storage. A storage resource is a device capable of retaining a representation of a datum after the initial excitation is removed. The specification of a device is usually performed by coordinate location, contents, or implication. An operational resource is a combinational circuit primitive (e.g., add, shift, transfer, ...) that performs a (usually) binary mapping $S \times S \rightarrow S$; S the set storage (space) resource.

Strictly speaking, since a request for a physical resource v is a request for accessing that resource, there is no "request for storage resource" but rather a request to an allocation algorithm to access or modify the memory map. Thus a storage resource has operational characteristics if we include the accessing mechanism in the storage resource partition.

Partitions are defined on physical resources which define a memory hierarchy (space) or a set of primitive operations. Note that since partitions may not be unique, resulting tree structures may also differ. Also note that while leaves of the tree must be requests for physical resources, higher level nodes may also be if all inferior nodes are physical.

Since physical time is associated with a physical activity, at the terminal nodes we have

$$f_{ijk'}^v \ldots (S \times S, t_b) \rightarrow S, t_f$$

where t_b is the initiation time and t_f is the completion time. Initiation is conditioned on the availability of operational resource v and the validity of both source operands ($\tau = 1$). When the operation is complete, the result is placed in a specified sink location, and the control variable τ^* is set to "1."

The advantage of this model is that it allows a perspective of a system at a consistent hierarchical level of control structure. One may replace the subtree with its equivalent physical execution time (actual or mean value) and mean operational and spatial resource requirements if task contention is a factor. The net effect is to establish a vector space with a basis defined by the reference of the observer. The vector of operations O_k may appear as physical resources at a particular level k in the tree, but actually may represent a subtree of requests—similarly with the storage vector S_k. The control structure defined by the set of request functions $\{f_{ki}^l \mid 1 \leq i \leq n\}$ will determine the program structure as an interaction of resources on $O_k \times S_k$. The reader may note the similarity, in hierarchy treatment at least, between the preceding model and the general model of Bell and Newell [28].

Implicit in the foregoing statement is the notion that a physical resource exists in space–time, not space or time alone. For example, N requests may be made for an "add" operational resource—these may be served by N servers each completing its operation in time T or equivalently by one resource that operates in time T/N. Two parameters are useful in characterizing physical resources [1]—latency and bandwidth. *Latency* is the total time associated with the processing (from excitation to response) of a particular data unit at a phase in the computing process. *Bandwidth* is an expression of time-rate of occurrence. In particular, operational bandwidth would be the number of operand pairs processed per unit time.

If, as a hierarchical reference point, we choose operations and operands as used by, for example, an IBM 7090, we can explore arrangements of, and interactions between, familiar physical resources. The IBM 7090 itself has a trivial control tree. In particular, we have the SISD—single operational resource operating on a single pair of storage resources. The multiple-stream organizations are more interesting, however, as well as two considerations: 1) the latency for interstream communication; and 2) the possibilities for high computational bandwidth within a stream.

Interstream Communications

There are two aspects of communications: operational resource accessing of a storage item $(\overline{O} \times \overline{S})$ and storage to storage transfer $(\overline{S} \times \overline{S})$. Both aspects can be represented by communications matrices each of whose entry t_{ij} is the time to transfer a datum in the jth storage resource to the ith resource (operational or storage). The operational communication matrix is quite useful for MIMD organizations, while the storage communications matrix is usually more interesting for SIMD organizations. An $(\overline{O} \times \overline{O})$ matrix can also be defined for describing MISD organizations.

An alternate form of the communications matrix, called the connection matrix, can also be developed for the square matrix cases. This avoids possibly large or infinite entries possible in the communications matrix (when interstream communications fail to exist). The reciprocal of the normalized access time t_{ii}/t_{ij} (assuming t_{ii} is the minimum entry for a row) is entered for the access time of an element of the ith data storage resource by the jth operational or storage resource d_{ij}. The minimum access time (resolution) is 1. If a particular item were inaccessible, there would be a zero entry. Notice that in comparing parallel organizations to the serial organization, the latter has immediate access to corresponding data. While it appears that under certain conditions an element expression can be zero due to lack of communication between resources, in practice this does not occur since data can be transferred from one stream to another in finite time, however slow. Usually such transfers occur in a common storage hierarchy.

Stream Inertia

It is well known that the action of a single-instruction stream may be telescoped for maximum performance by overlapping the various constituents of the execution of an individual instruction [4]. Such overlapping usually does not exceed the issuing of one instruction per instruction decode resolution time Δt. This avoids the possibly exponentially increasing number of decision elements required in such a decoder [1], [5]. A recent study [13] provides an analysis of the multiple-instruction issuing problem in a single-overlapped instruction stream. In any event, a certain number of instructions in a single-instruction stream are being processed during the latency time for one instruction execution. This number may be referred to as the confluence factor or inertia factor J of the processor per individual instruction stream. Thus the maximum performance per instruction stream can be enhanced by a factor J. If the average instruction execution time is $L \cdot \Delta t$ time units, the maximum performance per stream would be

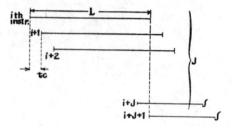

Fig. 2.   Stream inertia.

$$\text{perf.}_{\max} = \frac{J}{L \cdot \Delta t}$$

This is illustrated in Fig. 2. Successive instructions are offset in this example by Δt time units.

System Classification

Then to summarize, a technology independent macroscopic specification of a large computing system would include: 1) the number of instruction streams and the number of data streams—the "instruction" and "data" unit should be taken with respect to a convenient reference; 2) the appropriate communications (or connection) matrices; and 3) the stream inertia factor J and the number of time units of instruction execution latency L.

EFFECTIVENESS IN PERFORMING THE COMPUTING PROCESS

Resolution of Entropy

Measures of the effectiveness are necessarily problem based. Therefore, comparisons between parallel and simplex organizations frequently are misleading since such comparisons can be based on different problem environments. The historic view of parallelism in problems is probably represented best by Amdahl [6] and is shown in Fig. 3. This viewpoint is developed by the observation that certain operations in a problem environment must be done in an absolutely sequential basis. These operations include, for example, the ordinary housekeeping operations in a program. In order to achieve any effectiveness at all, from this point of view, parallel organizations processing N streams must have substantially less than $1/N \times 100$ percent of absolutely sequential instruction segments. One can then proceed to show that typically for large N this does not exist in conventional programs. A major difficulty with this analysis lies in the concept of "conventional programs" since this implies that what exists today in the way of programming procedures and algorithms must also exist in the future. Another difficulty is that it ignores the possibility of overlapping some of this sequential processing with the execution of "parallel" tasks.

To review this problem from a general perspective, consider a problem in which N_1 words each of p bits

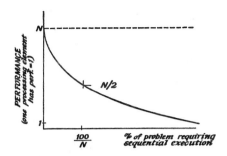

Fig. 3. "Parallelism" in problems.

serve as input data. The program or algorithm operates on this input data and produces output results corresponding to N_2 words each of p bits. If we presume that as a maximum each of the input bits could affect each of the bits in the output, then there are $N_1 \times p$ bits of uncertainty or entropy which specify an output bit. Thus a table-oriented solution algorithm (i.e., generate a table of solutions—one solution for each input combination) requires 2^{pN_1} entries and uses pN_2 bits per entry. The total number of bits required is $pN_2 2^{pN_1}$.

We could generalize this for variable length input and output by treating N_2 and N_1 as the maximum number of words required to specify output or input information. Note that this imposes a limit on the size of output strings, and hence the table algorithm is too restrictive for generalized computable functions. However, within this restricted class the entropy Q to be resolved by an algorithm is

$$pN_2 \le Q \le pN_2 \cdot 2^{pN_1}.$$

The lower bound also needs special interpretation for trivial algorithms (e.g., strings of identical ones); the pN_2 bits were assumed to be independently derived. Hence the pN_2 bits must be reduced by their dependency. (See Kolmogarov [10] for an alternate notion on the specification of Q.)

In any event, Q bits of uncertainty must be resolved. This resolution may be performed in space or time. Typically it is resolved in space by combinatorial logic. Each decision element may resolve between zero and one bit of information depending upon the associated probabilities of the binary outcomes. Usually a useful repertoire or vocabulary of logical decisions is available to an instruction stream. Let an element of the vocabulary consist of M decisions. Depending upon the type of operation to be performed, these execution unit decision elements resolve less than M bits of information; thus

$$Q \le m'MN_t$$

where m' is the number of data stream execution units and N_t is the number of time operations that were used (i.e., number of sequential instructions). In order to retire the complete algorithm, of course, a sequence of operations is performed to execute the instruction stream; each operation in the sequence resolves or exceeds the required amount of entropy for a solution.

Thus from this most general point of view there is little difference in the resolution of entropy in space or time. The reader will note, however, that space resolution is not necessarily as efficient as time sequences. In fact, the number of time sequence operations N_t is a linear function of input size n:

$$N_t = k \cdot n$$

while Muller [32] has shown that for combinational circuits of arbitrary functional basis a measure for the number of circuits required N_s is

$$k_1 \cdot \frac{2^n}{n} \le N_s \le k_2 \frac{2^n}{n}$$

where n is the number of input lines. See Cook [33] and Cook and Flynn [34] for a more general and complete treatment of space–time functional measures. Later in this paper we will discuss similar inefficiencies in parallel SIMD processors.

Recursive Functions

Substantial difficulties arise when the preceding "general point of view" is reduced to the specific. In particular, the class of functions for which arbitrary "space–time" transformations can be developed is not equivalent to the class of all recursive (computable) functions. Recursion (in Kleene's sense [7]) is based on the application of the composition operation on a finite set of initial functions. This composition operation [8] is the association of functions $h(X_1, X_2, \cdots, X_n)$ with $F(X_1, \cdots, X_n)$, $g_1(X_1, \cdots, X_n)$, $g_2(X_1, \cdots, X_n)$, $\cdots$, $g_n(X_1, \cdots, X_n)$, so that $h(X_1, \cdots, X_n) = F(g_1(X_1, \cdots, X_n), \cdots, g_n(X_1, \cdots, X_n))$. Clearly, the application of F on the results of g_i is a sequential operation. Any general attempts to resolve the functional entropy without such sequential (time) dependence leads to "recursion" based on infinite sets of initial functions.

Bernstein [9] has developed three (rather strong) sufficient conditions for two programs to operate in parallel based on the referencing of partitions of storage. As in the preceding discussion, these conditions specify limitations on the interactions between programs.

Notice that none of the foregoing serves to limit the *capability* of a processor organized in a parallel fashion to perform computation, but rather serves as a limit on the efficiency of such an operation. Also note that the composing function F may induce similar inefficiencies in a confluent simplex processor (depending on the nature of F and the last g_i to be evaluated). Such performance degradation will be discussed later. The composition mechanism that causes a problem here is an interprogram action, while the stream inertia difficulty occurs more prominently in purely intraprogram conditional actions. Indeed, there are techniques for the elimination of branches in simple programs by use of Boolean test variables (0 or 1) operating multiplicatively on each of two alternate task paths [14]. This is a direct "branch" to "composition" transformation.

System Organizations and Their Effectiveness in Resource Use

SISD and Stream Inertia

Serious inefficiencies may arise in confluent SISD organizations due to turbulence when data interacts with the instruction stream. Thus an instruction may require an argument that is not yet available from a preceding instruction (direct composition), or (more seriously) an address calculation is incomplete (indirect composition). Alternately, when a data conditional branch is issued, testable data must be available before the branch can be fully executed (although both paths can be prepared). In conventional programs delays due to branching usually dominate the other considerations; then in the following we make the simplified assumption that inertia delay is due exclusively to branching. In addition to providing a simple model of performance degradation, we can relate it to certain test data derived from a recent study. The reader should beware, however, that elimination of branching by the introduction of composition delay will not alter the turbulence situation. For a machine issuing an instruction per Δt, if the data interaction with the stream is determined by the ith instruction and the usage of such data is required by the $(i+1)$th instruction, a condition of maximum turbulence is encountered, and this generates the maximum serial latency time $(L-1)\Delta t$ which must be inserted into the stream until the overlapped issuing conditions can be reestablished.

If we treat the expected serial latency time of an instruction $L \cdot \Delta t$ as being equivalent to the total execution time for the average instruction (from initiation to completion), we must also consider an anticipation factor N as the average number of instructions between (inclusively) the instruction stating a condition and the instruction which tests or uses this result. Clearly, for $N \geq J/L$ instructions no turbulence (or delay) will result.

Thus under ideal conditions one instruction each $L \cdot \Delta t/J$ (time units) would be executed. Turbulence adds a delay:

$$\text{delay} = \left(L - \frac{NL}{J}\right)\Delta t, \quad \text{for } N < \frac{J}{L}$$

$$= 0, \quad \text{for } N \geq \frac{J}{L}.$$

Given a block of M instructions with a probability of encountering a turbulence causing instruction p the total time to execute these instructions would be

$$T = \left[\frac{L}{J}[M(1-p)] + 1 + pM\left(L - \frac{NL}{J}\right)\right]\Delta t.$$

The additional "1" in the expression is due to the

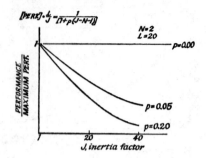

Fig. 4. Stream inertia and effects of branch.

startup of the instruction overlapping. If we define performance as the number of instructions executed per unit time, then

$$\text{perf.} = \frac{M}{T} = \frac{M}{\left[\frac{L}{J}[M(1-p)] + pM\left(L - \frac{NL}{J}\right) + 1\right]\Delta t}$$

$$= \frac{1}{\frac{L \cdot \Delta t}{J}\left[(1-p) + p(J-N) + \frac{J}{L \cdot M}\right]}.$$

The last term in the denominator drops out as M becomes large. Then

$$\text{perf.} = \frac{J}{L\Delta t} \cdot \frac{1}{[1 + p(J - N - 1)]}.$$

Fig. 4 shows the effect of turbulence probability p for various J and L. In particular, if $J = 20$ and L were 20 time units, $N = 2$ instructions and a turbulence probability of 10 percent, the performance of a system would degrade from a maximum possible of 1 (instructions/time unit) to 1/2.7 or about 30 percent of its potential.

A major cause of turbulence in conventional programs is the conditional branch; typically the output of a computer would include 10–20-percent conditional branches. A study by O'Regan [12] on the branch problem was made using the foregoing type of analysis. For a typically scientific problem mix (five problems: root finding; ordinary differential equation; partial differential equations; matrix inversion; and Polish string manipulation), O'Regan attempted to eliminate as many data conditional branches as possible using a variety of processor architectures (single and multiple accumulators, etc.). O'Regan did not resort to extreme tactics, however, such as multiplying loop sizes or transformations to a Boolean test (mentioned earlier). For four of the problems selected the best (i.e., minimum) conditional branch probability attainable varied from $p = 0.02$ to $p = 0.10$. The partial differential equation results depend on grid size, but $p = 0.001$ seems attainable. The best (largest) attainable N (the set-test offset) average was less than 3. No attempt was made in the study to evaluate degradation due to other than branch dependent turbulence.

16

SIMD and Its Effectiveness

There are three basic types of SIMD processors, that is, processors characterized by a master instruction applied over a vector of related operands. These include (Fig. 5) the following types.

1) The Array Processor: One control unit and m directly connected processing elements. Each processing element is independent, i.e., has its own registers and storage, but only operates on command from the control unit.

2) The Pipelined Processor: A time-multiplexed version of the array processor, that is, a number of functional execution units, each tailored to a particular function. The units are arranged in a production line fashion, staged to accept a pair of operands every Δt time units. The control unit issues a vector operation to memory. Memory is arranged so that it is suitable to a high-speed data transfer and produces the source operands which are entered a pair every Δt time units into the designated function. The result stream returns to memory.

3) The Associative Processor: This is a variation of the array processor. Processing elements are not directly addressed. The processing elements of the associative processor are activated when a generalized match relation is satisfied between an input register and characteristic data contained in each of the processing elements. For those designated elements the control unit instruction is carried out. The other units remain idle.

A number of difficulties can be anticipated for the SIMD organization. These would include the following problems.

1) Communications between processing elements.

2) Vector Fitting: This is the matching of size between the logical vector to be performed and the size of the physical array which will process the vector.

3) Sequential Code (Nonvector): This includes housekeeping and bookkeeping operations associated with the preparation of a vector instruction. This corresponds to the Amdahl effect. Degradation due to this effect can be masked out by overlapping the sequential instructions with the execution of vector type instructions.

4) Degradation Due to Branching: When a branch point occurs, several of the executing elements will be in one state, and the remainder will be in another. The master controller can essentially control only one of the two states; thus the other goes idle.

5) Empirically, Minsky and Papert [29] have observed that the SIMD organization has performance portional to the $\log_2 m$ (m, the number of data streams per instruction stream) rather than linear. If this is generally true, it is undoubtedly due to all of the preceding effects (and perhaps others). We will demonstrate an interpretation of it based upon branching degradation.

Communication in SIMD organizations has been

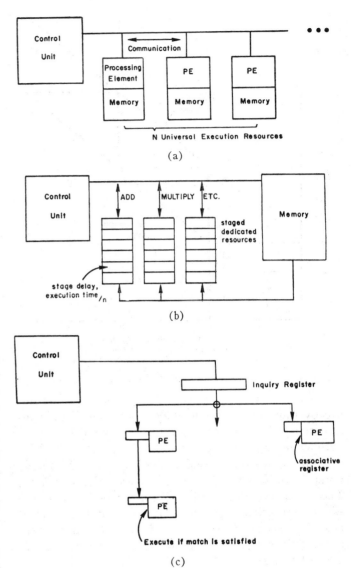

Fig. 5. SIMD processors. (a) Array processor. (b) Pipelined processor. (c) Associative processor.

widely studied [17]–[20]. Results to date, however, indicate that it is not as significant a problem as was earlier anticipated. Neuhauser [17], in an analysis of several classical SIMD programs, noted that communications time for an array-type organization rarely exceeded 40 percent of total job time and for the matrix inversion case was about 15 percent.

The fitting problem is illustrated in Fig. 6. Given a source vector of size m, performance is effected in an array processor when the M physical processing elements do not divide m [21]. However, so long as m is substantially larger than M, this effect will not contribute significant performance degradation. The pipeline processor exhibits similar behavior, as will be discussed later.

The Amdahl effect is caused by a lack of "parallelism" in the source program; this can be troublesome in any multistream organization. Several SIMD organizations

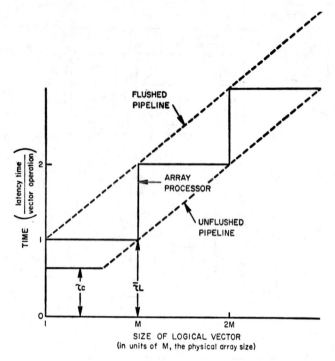

Fig. 6.   Fitting problem.

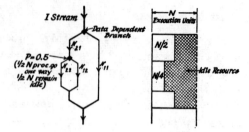

Fig. 7.   SIMD branching.

use overlapping of "sequential type" control unit instructions with "vector operations" to avoid this effect, with some apparent success.

Multiple-execution organizations such as SIMD have potential difficulty in the use of the execution resources. The reason for this is that all units must process the, same instruction at a particular unit of time. When nested decisions are considered (Fig. 7), difficulty arises because the execution units are not available to work on any other task.

Consider an SIMD system with M data streams and an average instruction execution time (per data stream) of $L \cdot \Delta t$ time units. Now a single instruction will act uniformly on M pairs of operands. With respect to our reference instruction I (which operates on only a pair of operands) the SIMD instruction, designated I^*, has M times the effect. Ignoring possible overlap, a single I^* instruction will be executed in a least time $L \cdot \Delta t$, while the conventional unoverlapped SISD system would execute in $M \cdot L \cdot \Delta t$.

To achieve close to the $1/M$ bound, the problem must be partitionable in M identical code segments. When a conditional branch is encountered if at least one of the M data differs in its condition, the alternate path instructions must be fully executed. We now make a simplifying assumption: the number of *source* instructions are the same for the primary branch path and the alternate. Since the number of data items required to be processed by a branch stream is M, only the fraction available will be executed initially and the task will be reexecuted for the remainder. Thus a branch identifying

two separate tasks, each of length N, will take twice the amount of time as their unconditional expectation. Thus the time to execute a block of N^* source instructions (each operating on M data streams) with equal probability on primary and alternate branch paths is

$$T = L \cdot \sum_i N_{i,0} + L \cdot \sum_i N_{i,1} \cdot 2 + L \cdot \sum_i N_{i,2} \cdot 4 + \cdots$$
$$+ L \cdot \sum_i N_{i,j} \cdot 2^j$$
$$T = L \cdot \sum_j \sum_i N_{i,j} 2^j$$

where j is the level of nesting of a branch and $N_{i,j}$ is the number of source instructions in the primary (or alternate) branch path for the ith branch at level j. As the level of nesting increases, fewer resources are available to execute the M data streams, and the time required increases—the situation would be similar if we had used other branch probabilities ($p \neq 0.5$). Thus the performance is

$$\text{perf.} = \frac{I}{T} = \frac{N^*}{L \cdot \sum_j \sum_i N_{i,j} 2^j} \cdot$$

The factor $\sum_i N_{i,j}/N^*$ is the probability of encountering a source instruction:

$$P_j = \sum N_{i,j}/N^* \leq 1.$$

This analysis assumed that the overhead for reassigning execution elements to alternate paths tasks is prohibitive. This is usually true when the task sire N_{ij} is small or when the swapping overhead is large (an array processor, each of whose data streams has a private data storage). Based on empirical evaluation of program performance in a general scientific environment (i.e., not the well-known "parallel type" programs such as matrix inversion, etc.) it has been suggested [29] that the actual performance of the SIMD processor is proportional to the $\log_2$ of the number of slave processing elements rather than the hoped for linear relation. This has been called Minsky's conjecture:

$$\text{perf.}_{\text{SIMD}} \approx \log_2 M.$$

While this degradation is undoubtedly due to many causes, it is interesting to interpret it as a branching degradation. Assume that the probability of being at one of the lower levels of nesting is uniform. That is, it is equally likely to be at level 1, 2, $\cdots$, $[\log_2 M]$. Since beyond this level of nesting no further degradation occurs, assume $P_1 = P_2 = \cdots = P_j = P_{[\log M]-1}$ and $P_1 = \sum_{k=[\log_2 M]}^{\infty} Pk$. Now

$$P_j = \frac{1}{[\log_2 M]} \Big|_{j=0}^{j=[\log_2 M]-1}$$

and the earlier performance relation can be restated:

$$\text{perf.} = \frac{1}{L} \cdot \frac{1}{\sum_j p_j 2^j}.$$

This was derived for an absolute model, i.e., number of SIMD instructions per unit time. If we wish to discuss performance *relative* to an SISD unoverlapped processor with equivalent latency characteristics, then

$$\text{perf. relative} = \frac{M}{\sum_j P_j 2^j}.$$

Thus the SIMD organization is M times faster if we have no degradation. Now

$$\text{perf. relative} = \frac{M}{\sum_j \frac{2^j}{[\log_2 M]}}$$

or, ignoring the effect of nonintegral values of $\log_2 M$

$$\text{perf. relative} = \frac{M}{\frac{2M-1}{\log_2 M}}$$

for M large:

$$\text{perf. relative} \approx \frac{\log_2 M}{2}.$$

Note that if we had made the less restrictive assumption that

$$P_j = 2^{-j}$$

then

$$\text{perf. relative} \approx \frac{M}{\log_2 M}.$$

Thus we have two plausible performance relations based on alternate nesting assumptions. Of course this degradation is not due to idle resources alone; in fact, programs can be restructured to keep processing elements busy. The important open question is whether these restructured programs truly enhance the performance of the program as distinct from just keeping the resource busy. Empirical evidence suggests that the most effi-

cient single-stream program organization for this larger class of problems is presently substantially more efficient than an equivalent program organization suited to the SIMD processors. Undoubtedly this degradation is a combination of effects; however, branching seems to be an important contributor—or rather the ability to efficiently branch in a simple SISD organization substantially enhances its performance.

Certain SIMD configurations, e.g., pipelined processors, which use a common data storage may appear to suffer less from the nested branch degradation, but actually the pipelined processor should exhibit an equivalent behavior. In a system with source operand vector $A = \{a_s, a_1, \cdots, a_i, \cdots, a_n\}$ and $B = \{b_0, b_1, \cdots, b_i, \cdots, b_n\}$, a sink vector $C = \{c_0, c_1, \cdots, c_i, \cdots, c_n\}$ is the resultant. Several members of C will satisfy a certain criterion for a type of future processing, and others will not. Elements failing this criterion are tagged and not processed further, but the vector C is usually left unaltered. If one rearranges C, filters the dissenting elements, and compresses the vector, then an overhead akin to task swapping the array processor is introduced. Notice that the automatic hardware generation of the compressed vector is not practical at the high data rates required by the pipeline.

If the pipelined processor is logically equivalent to other forms of SIMD, how does one interpret the number of data streams? This question is related to the vector fitting problem. Fig. 6 illustrates the equivalence of an array processor to the two main categories of pipeline processors.

1) Flushed: The control unit does not issue the next vector instruction until the last elements of the present vector operation have completed their functional processing (gone through the last stage of the functional pipeline).

2) Unflushed: The next vector instruction is issued as soon as the last elements of the present vector operation have been initiated (entered the first state of the pipeline).

Assuming that the minimum time for the control unit to prepare a vector instruction τ_c is less than the average functional unit latency $\bar{\tau}_L$, for the flushed case the equivalent number of data streams per instruction stream m is

$$m = \frac{\bar{\tau}_L}{\Delta t} \text{ flushed pipeline}$$

where Δt is the average stage time in the pipeline.

With the unflushed case, again assuming the $\bar{\tau}_L > \tau_c$, the equivalent m is

$$m = \frac{\tau_c}{\Delta t} \text{ unflushed pipeline.}$$

Notice that when $\tau_c = \Delta t$, $m = 1$, and we no longer have

SIMD. In fact, we have returned to the overlapped SISD.

MIMD and Its Effectiveness

The multiple-instruction stream organizations (the "multiprocessors") include at least two types.

1) True Multiprocessors: Configurations in which several physically complete and independent SI processors share storage at some level for the coopertive execution of a multitask program.

2) Shared Resource Multiprocessor: As the name implies, skeleton processors are arranged to share the system resources. These arrangements will be discussed later.

Traditional MIMD organizational problems include: 1) communications/composition overhead; 2) cost increases linearly with additional processors, while performance increases at a lesser rate (due to interference); and 3) providing a method for dynamic reconfiguration of resources to match changing program environment, (critical tasks)—this is related to 1).

Shared resource organization may provide limited answers to these problems, as we will discuss later.

Communications and composition is a primary source of degradation in MI systems. When several instruction streams are processing their respective data streams on a common problem set, passing of data points is inevitable. Even if there is naturally a favorable precedence relationship among parallel instruction streams insofar as use of the data is concerned, composition delays may ensue, especially if the task execution time is variable. The time one instruction stream spends waiting for data to be passed to it from another is a macroscopic form of the strictly sequential problem of one instruction waiting for a condition to be established by its immediate predecessor.

Even if the precedence problem (which is quite program dependent) is ignored, the "lockout" problem associated with multiple-instruction streams sharing common data may cause serious degradation. Note that multiple-instruction stream programs without data sharing are certainly as sterile as a single-instruction stream program without branches.

Madnick [11] provides an interesting model of software lockout in the MIMD environment. Assume that an individual processor (instruction stream control unit) has expected task execution time (without conflicts) of E time units. Suppose a processor is "locked out" from accessing needed data for L time units. This locking out may be due to interstream communications (or accessing) problems (especially if the shared storage is an I/O device). Then the lockout time for the jth processor (or instruction stream) is

$$L_j = \sum_i p_{ij} T_{ij}$$

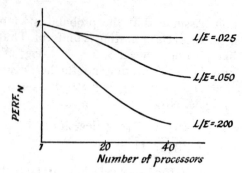

Fig. 8.   MIMD lockout.

where T_{ij} is the communications time discussed earlier and p_{ij} is the probability of task j accessing data from data stream i. Note that the lockout here may be due to the broader communications problem of the jth processor requesting a logical data stream i. This includes the physical data stream accessing problem as well as additional sources of lockout due to control, allocation, etc.

In any event, Madnick [11] used a Markov model to derive the following relationship:

$$\varepsilon \text{ (idle)} = \sum_{i=2}^{n} \frac{(i-1)}{\left(\dfrac{E}{L}\right)^i (n-i)!} \Bigg/ \sum_{i=0}^{n} \frac{1}{\left(\dfrac{E}{L}\right)^i (n-i)!}$$

where ε (idle) is the expected number of locked-out processors and n is the total number of processors. If a single processor has unit performance, then for n processors

$$\text{perf.} = n - \varepsilon \text{ (idle)}$$

and normalized performance (max $= 1$) is given by

$$\text{perf.}_N = \frac{n - \varepsilon \text{ (idle)}}{n}.$$

Fig. 8 is an evaluation of the normalized performance as the number of processors (instruction stream–data stream pairs) are increased for various interaction activity ratios L/E.

Regis [15] has recently completed a study substantially extending the simple Markovian model previously described (homogeneous resources, identical processors, etc.) by developing a queuing model that allows for vectors of requests to a vector of service resources. Lehman [30] presents some interesting simulation results related to the communications interference problem.

Since shared resource MIMD structures provide some promising (though perhaps limited) answers to the MI problems, we will outline these arrangements. The execution resources of an SISD overlapped computer (adders, multiplier, etc.—most of the system exclusive of registers and minimal control) are rarely efficiently used, as discussed in the next section.

In order to effectively use this execution potential,

consider the use of multiple-skeleton processors sharing the execution resources. A "skeleton" processor consists of only the basic registers of a system and a minimum of control (enough to execute a load or store type instruction). From a program point of view, however, the skeleton processor is a complete and independent logical computer.

These processors may share the resources in space [22], or time [23]–[25]. If we completely rely on space sharing, we have a "cross-bar" type switch of processors —each trying to access one of n resources. This is usually unsatisfactory since the cross-bar switching time overhead can be formidable. On the other hand, time-phased sharing (or time-multiplexing) of the resources can be attractive in that no switching overhead is involved and control is quite simple if the number of multiplexed processors are suitably related to each of the pipelining factors. The limitation here is that again only one of the m available resources is used at any one moment.

A possible optimal arrangement is a combination of space–time switching (Fig. 9). The time factor is the number of skeleton processors multiplexed on a time-phase ring, while the space factor is the number of multiplexed processor "rings" K which simultaneously request resources. Note that K processors will contend for the resources and, up to $K-1$, may be denied service at that moment. Thus a rotating priority among the rings is suggested to guarantee a minimum performance. The partitioning of the resources should be determined by the expected request statistics.

When the amount of "parallelism" (or number of identifiable tasks) is less than the available processors, we are faced with the problem of accelerating these tasks. This can be accomplished by designing certain of the processors in each ring with additional staging and interlock [13] (the ability to issue multiple instructions simultaneously) facilities. The processor could issue multiple-instruction execution requests in a single-ring revolution. For example, in a ring $N=16$, 8 processors could issue 2 request/revolutions, or 4 processors could issue 4 request/revolutions; or 2 processors could issue 8 request/revolutions; or 1 processor could issue 16 request/revolutions. This partition is illustrated in Fig. 10. Of course mixed strategies are possible. For a more detailed discussion the reader is referred to [25], [26], and [31].

SOME CONSIDERATIONS ON SYSTEMS RESOURCES

The gross resources of a system consist of execution, instruction control, primary storage, and secondary storage.

Execution Resources

The execution resources of a large system include the decision elements which actually perform the operations

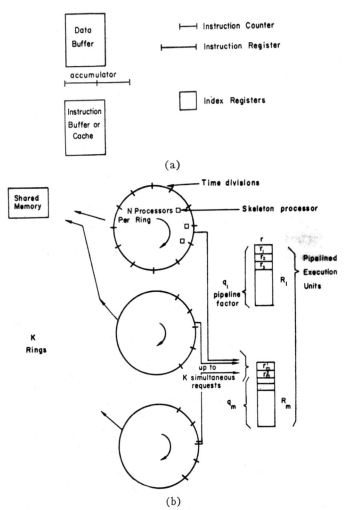

Fig. 9.   (a) Skeleton processor. (b) Time-multiplexed multiprocessing.

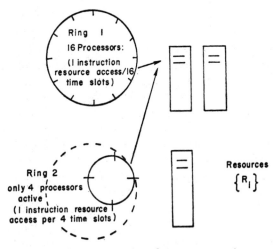

Fig. 10.   Subcommutation of processors on ring.

implied in the instruction upon the specified operands. The execution bandwidth of a system is usually referred to as being the maximum number of operations that can be performed per unit time by the execution area. Notice that due to bottlenecks in issuing instructions, for example, the execution bandwidth is usually substantially in excess of the maximum performance of a system. This overabundance of execution bandwidth has become a major characteristic of large modern systems.

In highly confluent SISD organizations specific execution units are made independently and designed for maximum performance. The autonomy is required for ease of implementation since from topological considerations an individual independent unit executing a particular class of operands gives much better performance on the class than an integrated universal type of unit [1]. The other notable characteristic of the SISD organization is that each of these independent subunits must in itself be capable of large or high bandwidths since the class of operations which successive instructions perform are not statistically independent, and in fact they are usually closely correlated; thus, for example, systems like the CDC 6600 and the IBM 360/91 both have execution facilities almost an order of magnitude in excess of the average overall instruction retirement rate. Fig. 11 illustrates the bandwidth concept. Given N specialized execution units, with execution pipelining factor P_i for the ith unit (the pipelining factor is the number of different operations being performed by one unit at one time—it is the execution analog of confluence), then if t_i is the time required to fully execute the ith type of operation, the execution bandwidth is

$$\text{execution bandwidth} = \sum_{i=1}^{N} \frac{P_i}{t_i}.$$

Note the bandwidth is in reality a vector partitioned by the resource class i. We sum the components as a scalar to assess gross capability. Notice that the shared resource MI organizations are, by definition, optimized for the efficient use of the execution resources.

Instruction Control

The control area is responsible for communications in addition to operational control. The communication function is essentially a process of identification of operand sink and source positions. The control area of a system is proportionally much larger in number of decision elements when confluence is introduced in the instruction stream since additional entropy must be resolved due to possible interactions between successive instructions. These precedence decisions must be made to assure normal sequential operation of the system. The analog situation is present in many parallel systems. For example, in SIMD those data streams which are activated by a particular instruction stream must be identified as well as those which do not participate. Notice that elaborations for controls, whether be it due to confluence or parallelism, basically resolve no entropy with respect to the original absolutely sequential instruction stream (and hence none with respect to the problem).

The necessary hardware to establish these sophistications is strictly in the nature of an overhead for the premium performance. From an instruction unit or con-

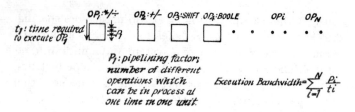

Fig. 11.   Execution bandwidth.

trol unit point of view, the maximum decision efficiency is generated when the control unit has relatively simple proportions (i.e., handles a minimum number of interlocks or exceptional conditions—as when J is small per instruction stream) and when it is being continually utilized (a minimum idle time due to interstream or intrastream turbulence or lockout). While shared resource MI organizations have an advantage over the confluent SISD and the SIMD arrangements insofar as complexity of control, the control must be repeated M times. An overlapped SIMD processor would probably have the simplest control structure of the three.

Primary and Secondary Storage

The optimization of storage as a resource is a relatively simple matter to express. The task, both program and data, must move through the storage as expeditiously as possible; thus the less time a particular task spends in primary storage, the more efficiently the storage has been used with respect to this particular resource.,

In essence we have storage efficiency measured by the space–time product of problem usage at each level of the storage hierarchy. The "cost" of storage for a particular program can be defined as

$$\text{storage cost} = \sum_{i} c_i \cdot s_i \cdot t_i$$

where i is the level of storage hierarchy, c_i is the cost per word at that level, s_i is the average number of words the program used, and t_i is time spent at that level.

While the preceding overly simplifies the situation by ignoring the dynamic nature of storage requirements, some observations can be made. The MI organizational structure, by nature, will require both task program and data sets for each of the instruction units to be simultaneously available at low levels of the hierarchy. The SIMD arrangement requires only simultaneous access to the M data sets, while the SISD has the least intrinsic storage demands. Thus in general

$$s_1 \big|_{\text{MIMD}} \geq s_1 \big|_{\text{SIMD}} \geq s_1 \big|_{\text{SISD}}.$$

Thus the MIMD and SIMD must be, respectively, more efficient in program execution t_i to have optimized the use of the storage resource.

ACKNOWLEDGMENT

The author is particularly indebted to C. Neuhauser, R. Regis, and G. Tjaden, students at The Johns Hopkins

University, for many interesting discussions on this subject. In particular, the hierarchical model presented here contains many thoughtful suggestions of R. Regis. The analysis of SIMD organizations was substantially assisted by C. Neuhauser. The author would also like to thank Prof. M. Halstead and Dr. R. Noonan of Purdue University for introducing him to the work of Aiken [14].

REFERENCES

[1] M. J. Flynn, "Very high-speed computing systems," *Proc. IEEE*, vol. 54, pp. 1901–1909, Dec. 1966.
[2] D. L. Slotnick, W. C. Borch, and R. C. McReynolds, "The Soloman computer—a preliminary report," in *Proc. 1962 Workshop on Computer Organization*. Washington, D. C.: Spartan, 1963, p. 66.
[3] D. R. Lewis and G. E. Mellen, "Stretching LARC's, capability by 100—a new multiprocessor system," presented at the 1964 Symp. Microelectronics and Large Systems, Washington, D. C.
[4] W. Buchholz, Ed., *Planning a Computer System*. New York: McGraw-Hill, 1962.
[5] D. N. Senzig, "Observations on high performance machines," in *1967 Fall Joint Comput. Conf., AFIPS Conf. Proc.*, vol. 31. Washington, D. C.: Thompson, 1967.
[6] G. M. Amdahl, "Validity of the single processor approach to achieving large scale computing capabilities," in *1967 Spring Joint Comput. Conf., AFIPS Conf. Proc.*, vol. 30. Washington, D. C.: Thompson, 1967, p. 483.
[7] Kleene, "A note on recursive functions," *Bull. Amer. Math. Soc.*, vol. 42, p. 544, 1936.
[8] M. Davis, *Computability and Unsolvability*. New York: McGraw-Hill, 1958, p. 36.
[9] A. J. Bernstein, "Analysis of programs for parallel processing," *IEEE Trans. Electron. Comput.*, vol. EC-15, pp. 757–763, Oct. 1966.
[10] A. N. Kolmogarov, "Logical basis for information theory and probability theory," *IEEE Trans. Inform. Theory*, vol. IT-14, pp. 662–664, Sept. 1968.
[11] S. E. Madnick, "Multi-processor software lockout," in *Proc. 1968 Ass. Comput. Mach. Nat. Conf.*, pp. 19–24.
[12] M. E. O'Regan, "A study on the effect of the data dependent branch on high speed computing systems," M.S. thesis, Dep. Ind. Eng., Northwestern Univ., Evanston, Ill., 1969.
[13] G. S. Tjaden and M. J. Flynn, "Detection and parallel execution of independent instructions," *IEEE Trans. Comput.*, vol. C-19, pp. 889–895, Oct. 1970.
[14] Aiken, *Dynamic Algebra*, see R. Noonan, "Computer programming with a dynamic algebra," Ph.D. dissertation, Dep. Comput. Sci., Purdue Univ., Lafayette, Ind., 1971.
[15] R. Regis, "Models of computer organizations," The Johns Hopkins Univ., Baltimore, Md., Comput. Res. Rep. 8, May 1971.
[16] A. L. Leiner, W. A. Notz, J. L. Smith, and R. B. Marimont, "Concurrently operating computer systems," *IFIPS Proc.*, UNESCO, 1959, pp. 353–361.
[17] C. Neuhauser, "Communications in parallel processors," The Johns Hopkins Univ., Baltimore, Md., Comput. Res. Rep. 18, Dec. 1971.
[18] H. S. Stone, "The organization of high-speed memory for parallel block transfer of data," *IEEE Trans. Comput.*, vol. C-19, pp. 47–53, Jan. 1970.
[19] M. C. Pease, "An adaptation of the fast Fourier transform for parallel processing," *J. Ass. Comput. Mach.*, vol. 15, pp. 252–264, Apr. 1968.
[20] ——, "Matrix inversion using parallel processing," *J. Ass. Comput. Mach.*, vol. 14, pp. 757–764, Oct. 1967.
[21] T. C. Chen, "Parallelism, pipelining and computer efficiency," *Comput. Des.*, vol. 10, pp. 69–74, 1971.
[22] P. Dreyfus, "Programming design features of the Gamma 60 computer," in *Proc. 1958 Eastern Joint Comput. Conf.*, pp. 174–181.
[23] J. E. Thornton, "Parallel operation in control data 6600," in *1964 Fall Joint Comput. Conf., AFIPS Conf. Proc.*, vol. 26. Washington, D. C.: Spartan, 1964, pp. 33–41.
[24] R. A. Ashenbrenner, M. J. Flynn, and G. A. Robinson, "Intrinsic multiprocessing," in *1967 Spring Joint Comput. Conf., AFIPS Conf. Proc.*, vol. 30. Washington, D. C.: Thompson, 1967, pp. 81–86.
[25] M. J. Flynn, A. Podvin, and K. Shimizu, "A multiple instruction stream processor with shared resources," in *Parallel Processor Systems*, C. Hobbs, Ed. Washington, D. C.: Spartan, 1970.
[26] M. J. Flynn, "Shared internal resources in a multiprocessor." in *1971 IFIPS Congr. Proc.*
[27] G. S. Tjaden and M. J. Flynn, "Detection and parallel execution of independent instructions," *IEEE Trans. Comput.*, vol. C-19, pp. 889–895, Oct. 1970.
[28] C. G. Bell and A. Newell, *Computer Structures: Readings and Examples*. New York: McGraw-Hill, 1971.
[29] M. Minsky and S. Papert, "On some associative, parallel, and analog computations," in *Associative Information Techniques*, E. J. Jacks, Ed. New York: Elsevier, 1971.
[30] M. Lehman, "A survey of problems and preliminary results concerning parallel processing and parallel processors," *Proc. IEEE*, vol. 54, pp. 1889–1901, Dec. 1966.
[31] C. C. Foster, "Uncoupling central processor and storage device speeds," *Comput. J.*, vol. 14, pp. 45–48, Feb. 1971.
[32] D. E. Muller, "Complexity in electronic switching circuits," *IEEE Trans. Electron. Comput.*, vol. EC-5, pp. 15–19, Mar. 1956.
[33] R. Cook, "Algorithmic measures," Ph.D. dissertation, Dep. Elec. Eng., Northwestern Univ., Evanston, Ill., 1970.
[34] R. Cook and M. J. Flynn, "Time and space measures of finite functions," Dep. Comput. Sci., The Johns Hopkins Univ., Baltimore, Md., Comput. Res. Rep. 6, 1971.

2. Pipeline Processors

Pipelining is one of the most widespread techniques for achieving parallelism. An analogy for a pipelined processor is the assembly line. Each of the many stations is finely tuned to efficiently perform one function on the object being assembled. Parallelism and cost-effectiveness are obtained by having each station work on a different object simultaneously.

Four commercially available pipelined processors are presented in the papers in this section. The first two, the CRAY-1 and the CDC STAR 100, are well-known, stand-alone pipelined processors; whereas the third is the recently introduced CYBER 205. It is described in the *Computerworld* article by Rita Shoor. The fourth pipelined processor, the Floating Point Systems' AP 120B pipelined processor, is an add-on processor described in excerpts from the FPS processor handbook. The advantages of add-on processors are that they are relatively inexpensive for the arithmetic processing power they add to the system (compared to the CRAY or the CDC 100), and that they can be microprogrammed to enhance their performance on specific application algorithms.

The reader may be interested in survey papers on pipelining by Ramamoorthy and Li (1977) and Chen (1975). The four pipelined processors covered by the papers in this chapter have pipelined arithmetic units.

As in Amdahl machines, pipelining is frequently used to overlap the various stages of instruction decoding and operand fetching as well as instruction execution. Pipelined processing can also be made transparent to the user by executing multiple, independent instruction streams in the pipe, as in the processor described by Smith in Chapter 5 or by Kaminsky and Davidson (1979).

The applications of pipelined processors such as the CRAY-1, the STAR, and the FPS AP120B are primarily numerical. The two papers in the applications section, one by Nolen, Kuba, and Kascic, and the other by Dawson, Huff, and Wu, describe pipeline processor performance solving partial differential equations. Signal processing is another application area requiring large "number-crunching" capabilities, although fixed-point formats are often acceptable in such applications. Several other papers on pipelined processor applications can be found in the book by Kuck *et al.* (1977) and a short course by Calahan (1979–80). Experts unanimously agree that the demand for high-speed numeric processing is considerably greater than the performance available on current machines. Watch for the development of pipelined processors in the area of fusion research and wind tunnel simulation (CDC, 1979).

Reprinted with permission from *Communications of the ACM*,
Volume 21, Number 1, January 1978, pages 63-72. Copyright
© 1978 by the Association for Computing Machinery, Inc.

Computer   G. Bell, S. H. Fuller, and
Systems   D. Siewiorek, Editors

The CRAY-1 Computer System

Richard M. Russell
Cray Research, Inc.

This paper describes the CRAY-1, discusses the
evolution of its architecture, and gives an account of
some of the problems that were overcome during its
manufacture.

The CRAY-1 is the only computer to have been
built to date that satisfies ERDA's Class VI
requirement (a computer capable of processing from
20 to 60 million floating point operations per second)
[1].

The CRAY-1's Fortran compiler (CFT) is designed
to give the scientific user immediate access to the
benefits of the CRAY-1's vector processing
architecture. An optimizing compiler, CFT,
"vectorizes" innermost DO loops. Compatible with
the ANSI 1966 Fortran Standard and with many
commonly supported Fortran extensions, CFT does not
require any source program modifications or the use
of additional nonstandard Fortran statements to
achieve vectorization. Thus the user's investment of
hundreds of man months of effort to develop Fortran
programs for other contemporary computers is
protected.

Key Words and Phrases: architecture, computer
systems

CR Categories: 1.2, 6.2, 6.3

Introduction

Vector processors are not yet commonplace machines in the larger-scale computer market. At the
time of this writing we know of only 12 non-CRAY-1
vector processor installations worldwide. Of these 12,
the most powerful processor is the ILLIAC IV (1
installation), the most populous is the Texas Instruments Advanced Scientific Computer (7 installations)
and the most publicized is Control Data's STAR 100

Copyright © 1977, Association for Computing Machinery, Inc.
General permission to republish, but not for profit, all or part of
this material is granted provided that ACM's copyright notice is
given and that reference is made to the publication, to its date of
issue, and to the fact that reprinting privileges were granted by
permission of the Association for Computing Machinery.

Author's address: Cray Research Inc., Suite 213, 7850 Metro
Parkway, Minneapolis, MN 55420.

(4 installations). In its report on the CRAY-1, Auerbach Computer Technology Reports published a comparison of the CRAY-1, the ASC, and the STAR 100
[2]. The CRAY-1 is shown to be a more powerful
computer than any of its main competitors and is
estimated to be the equivalent of five IBM 370/195s.

Independent benchmark studies have shown the
CRAY-1 fully capable of supporting computational
rates of 138 million floating-point operations per second (MFLOPS) for sustained periods and even higher
rates of 250 MFLOPS in short bursts [3, 4]. Such
comparatively high performance results from the
CRAY-1 internal architecture, which is designed to
accommodate the computational needs of carrying out
many calculations in discrete steps, with each step
producing interim results used in subsequent steps.
Through a technique called "chaining," the CRAY-1
vector functional units, in combination with scalar and
vector registers, generate interim results and use them
again immediately without additional memory references, which slow down the computational process in
other contemporary computer systems.

Other features enhancing the CRAY-1's computational capabilities are: its small size, which reduces
distances electrical signals must travel within the computer's framework and allows a 12.5 nanosecond clock
period (the CRAY-1 is the world's fastest scalar processor); a one million word semiconductor memory
equipped with error detection and correction logic
(SECDED); its 64-bit word size; and its optimizing
Fortran compiler.

Architecture

The CRAY-1 has been called "the world's most
expensive love-seat" [5]. Certainly, most people's first
reaction to the CRAY-1 is that it is so small. But in
computer design it is a truism that smaller means
faster. The greater the separation of components, the
longer the time taken for a signal to pass between
them. A cylindrical shape was chosen for the CRAY-1
in order to keep wiring distances small.

Figure 1 shows the physical dimensions of the
machine. The mainframe is composed of 12 wedge-
like columns arranged in a 270° arc. This leaves room
for a reasonably trim individual to gain access to the
interior of the machine. Note that the love-seat dis-
guises the power supplies and some plumbing for the
Freon cooling system. The photographs (Figure 2 and
3) show the interior of a working CRAY-1 and an
exterior view of a column with one module in place.
Figure 4 is a photograph of the interior of a single
module.

An Analysis of the Architecture

Table I details important characteristics of the
CRAY-1 Computer System. The CRAY-1 is equipped
with 12 i/o channels, 16 memory banks, 12 functional

Fig. 1. Physical organization of mainframe.

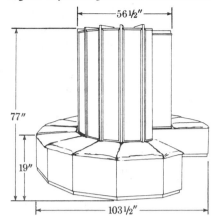

- Dimensions
    Base–103½ inches diameter by 19 inches high
    Columns–56½ inches diameter by 77 inches high including
        height of base
- 24 chassis
- 1662 modules; 113 module types
- Each module contains up to 288 IC packages per module
- Power consumption approximately 115 kw input for maximum
    memory size
- Freon cooled with Freon/water heat exchange
- Three memory options
- Weight 10,500 lbs (maximum memory size)
- Three basic chip types
    5/4 NAND gates
    Memory chips
    Register chips

Fig. 2. The CRAY-1 Computer.

Fig. 3. CRAY-1 modules in place.

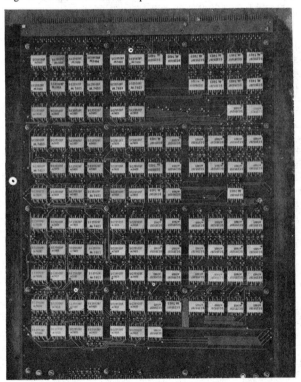

units, and more than 4k bytes of register storage. Access to memory is shared by the i/o channels and high-speed registers. The most striking features of the CRAY-1 are: only four chip types, main memory speed, cooling system, and computation section.

Four Chip Types

Only four chip types are used to build the CRAY-1. These are 16×4 bit bipolar register chips (6 nanosecond cycle time), 1024×1 bit bipolar memory chips (50 nanosecond cycle time), and bipolar logic chips with subnanosecond propagation times. The logic chips are all simple low- or high-speed gates with both a 5 wide and a 4 wide gate (5/4 NAND). Emitter-coupled logic circuit (ECL) technology is used throughout the CRAY-1.

The printed circuit board used in the CRAY-1 is a 5-layer board with the two outer surfaces used for signal runs and the three inner layers for −5.2V, −2.0V, and ground power supplies. The boards are six inches wide, 8 inches long, and fit into the chassis as shown in Figure 3.

All integrated circuit devices used in the CRAY-1 are packaged in 16-pin hermetically sealed flat packs supplied by both Fairchild and Motorola. This type of package was chosen for its reliability and compactness. Compactness is of special importance; as many as 288 packages may be added to a board to fabricate a module (there are 113 module types), and as many as 72 modules may be inserted into a 28-inch-high chassis.

Such component densities evitably lead to a mammoth cooling problem (to be described).

Main Memory Speed

CRAY-1 memory is organized in 16 banks, 72 modules per bank. Each module contributes 1 bit to a 64-bit word. The other 8 bits are used to store an 8-bit check byte required for single-bit error correction, double-bit error detection (SECDED). Data words are stored in 1-bank increments throughout memory. This organization allows 16-way interleaving of memory accesses and prevents bank conflicts except in the case

Fig. 4. A single module.

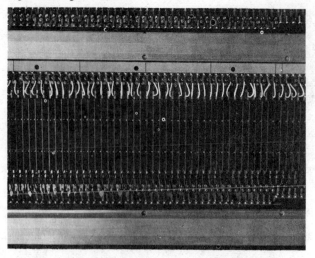

Table I. CRAY-1 CPU characteristics summary

Computation Section
  Scalar and vector processing modes
  12.5 nanosecond clock period operation
  64-bit word size
  Integer and floating-point arithmetic
  Twelve fully segmented functional units
  Eight 24-bit address (A) registers
  Sixty-four 24-bit intermediate address (B) registers
  Eight 64-bit scalar (S) registers
  Sixty-four 64-bit intermediate scalar (T) registers
  Eight 64-element vector (V) registers (64-bits per element)
  Vector length and vector mask registers
  One 64-bit real time clock (RT) register
  Four instruction buffers of sixty-four 16-bit parcels each
  128 basic instructions
  Prioritized interrupt control
Memory Section
  1,048,576 64-bit words (plus 8 check bits per word)
  16 independent banks of 65,536 words each
  4 clock period bank cycle time
  1 word per clock period transfer rate for B, T, and V registers
  1 word per 2 clock periods transfer rate for A and S registers
  4 words per clock period transfer rate to instruction buffers (up to
    16 instructions per clock period)
i/o Section
  24 i/o channels organized into four 6-channel groups
  Each channel group contains either 6 input or 6 output channels
  Each channel group served by memory every 4 clock periods
  Channel priority within each channel group
  16 data bits, 3 control bits per channel, and 4 parity bits
  Maximum channel rate of one 64-bit word every 100 nanoseconds
  Maximum data streaming rate of 500,000 64-bit words/second
  Channel error detection

of memory accesses that step through memory with either an 8 or 16-word increment.

Cooling System

The CRAY-1 generates about four times as much heat per cubic inch as the 7600. To cool the CRAY-1 a new cooling technology was developed, also based on Freon, but employing available metal conductors in a new way. Within each chassis vertical aluminum/stainless steel cooling bars line each column wall. The

Freon refrigerant is passed through a stainless steel tube within the aluminum casing. When modules are in place, heat is dissipated through the inner copper heat transfer plate in the module to the column walls and thence into the cooling bars. The modules are mated with the cold bar by using stainless steel pins to pinch the copper plate against the aluminum outer casing of the bar.

To assure component reliability, the cooling system was designed to provide a maximum case temperature of 130°F (54°C). To meet this goal, the following temperature differentials are observed:

Temperature at center of module	130°F (54°C)
Temperature at edge of module	118°F (48°C)
Cold plate temperature at wedge	78°F (25°C)
Cold bar temperature	70°F (21°C)
Refrigerant tube temperature	70°F (21°C)

Functional Units

There are 12 functional units, organized in four groups: address, scalar, vector, and floating point. Each functional unit is pipelined into single clock segments. Functional unit time is shown in Table II. Note that all of the functional units can operate concurrently so that in addition to the benefits of pipelining (each functional unit can be driven at a result rate of 1 per clock period) we also have parallelism across the units too. Note the absence of a divide unit in the CRAY-1. In order to have a completely segmented divide operation the CRAY-1 performs floating-point division by the method of reciprocal approximation. This technique has been used before (e.g. IBM System/360 Model 91).

Registers

Figure 5 shows the CRAY-1 registers in relationship to the functional units, instruction buffers, i/o channel control registers, and memory. The basic set of programmable registers are as follows:

  8 24-bit address (A) registers
  64 24-bit address-save (B) registers
  8 64-bit scalar (S) registers
  64 64-bit scalar-save (T) registers
  8 64-word (4096-bit) vector (V) registers

Expressed in 8-bit bytes rather than 64-bit words, that's a total of 4,888 bytes of high-speed (6ns) register storage.

The functional units take input operands from and store result operands only to A, S, and V registers. Thus the large amount of register storage is a crucial factor in the CRAY-1's architecture. Chaining could not take place if vector register space were not available for the storage of final or intermediate results. The B and T registers greatly assist scalar performance. Temporary scalar values can be stored from and reloaded to the A and S register in two clock periods. Figure 5 shows the CRAY-1's register paths in detail. The speed of the cft Fortran IV compiler would be

28   Communications
     of
     the ACM

January 1978
Volume 21
Number 1

Fig. 5. Block diagram of registers.

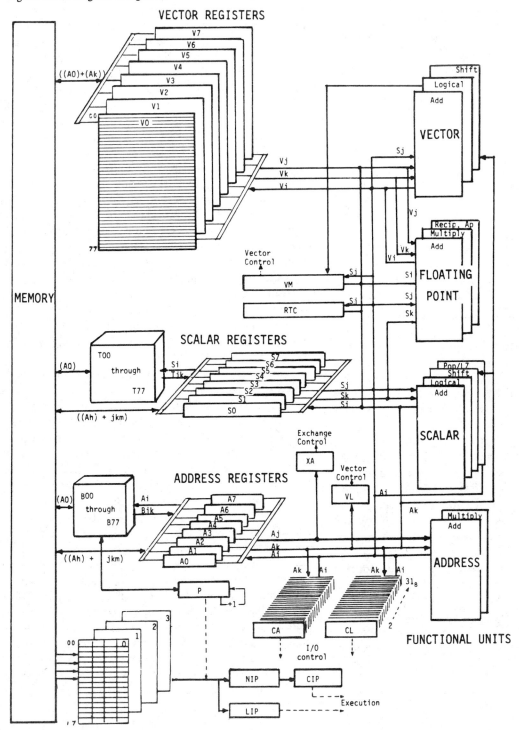

seriously impaired if it were unable to keep the many Pass 1 and Pass 2 tables it needs in register space. Without the register storage provided by the B, T, and V registers, the CRAY-1's bandwidth of only 80 million words/second would be a serious impediment to performance.

Instruction Formats

Instructions are expressed in either one or two 16-bit parcels. Below is the general form of a CRAY-1 instruction. Two-parcel instructions may overlap memory-word boundaries, as follows:

Fields	g	h	i	j	k	m
	0–3	4–6	7–9	10–12	13–15	16–31
Bit positions	(4)	(3)	(3)	(3)	(3)	(16)
					Parcel 1	Parcel 2

The computation section processes instructions at a maximum rate of one parcel per clock period.

Table II. CRAY-1 functional units

	Register usage	Functional unit time (clock periods)
Address function units		
address add unit	A	2
address multiply unit	A	6
Scalar functional units		
scalar add unit	S	3
scalar shift unit	S	2 or 3 if double-word shift
scalar logical unit	S	1
population/leading zero count unit	S	3
Vector functional units		
vector add unit	V	3
vector shift unit	V	4
vector logical unit	V	2
Floating-point functional units		
floating-point add unit	S and V	6
floating-point multiply unit	S and V	7
reciprocal approximation unit	S and V	14

For arithmetic and logical instructions, a 7-bit operation code (gh) is followed by three 3-bit register designators. The first field, i, designates the result register. The j and k fields designate the two operand registers or are combined to designate a B or T register.

The shift and mask instructions consist of a 7-bit operation code (gh) followed by a 3-bit i field and a 6-bit jk field. The i field designates the operand register. The jk combined field specifies a shift or mask count.

Immediate operand, read and store memory, and branch instructions require the two-parcel instruction word format. The immediate operand and the read and store memory instructions combine the j, k, and m fields to define a 22-bit quantity or memory address. In addition, the read and store memory instructions use the h field to specify an operating register for indexing. The branch instructions combine the i, j, k, and m fields into a 24-bit memory address field. This allows branching to any one of the four parcel positions in any 64-bit word, whether in memory or in an instruction buffer.

Operating Registers

Five types of registers—three primary (A, S, and V) and two intermediate (B and T)—are provided in the CRAY-1.

A *registers*—eight 24-bit A registers serve a variety of applications. They are primarily used as address registers for memory references and as index registers, but also are used to provide values for shift counts, loop control, and channel i/o operations. In address applications, they are used to index the base address for scalar memory references and for providing both a base address and an index address for vector memory references.

The 24-bit integer functional units modify values (such as program addresses) by adding, subtracting, and multiplying A register quantities. The results of these operations are returned to A registers.

Data can be transferred directly from memory to A registers or can be placed in B registers as an intermediate step. This allows buffering of the data between A registers and memory. Data can also be transferred between A and S registers and from an A register to the vector length registers. The eight A registers are individually designated by the symbols A0, A1, A2, A3, A4, A5, A6, and A7.

B *registers*—there are sixty-four 24-bit B registers, which are used as auxiliary storage for the A registers. The transfer of an operand between an A and a B register requires only one clock period. Typically, B registers contain addresses and counters that are referenced over a longer period than would permit their being retained in A registers. A block of data in B registers may be transferred to or from memory at the rate of one clock period per register. Thus, it is feasible to store the contents of these registers in memory prior to calling a subroutine requiring their use. The sixty-four B registers are individually designated by the symbols B0, B1, B2, . . . , and $B77_8$.

S *registers*—eight 64-bit S registers are the principle data handling registers for scalar operations. The S registers serve as both source and destination registers for scalar arithmetic and logical instructions. Scalar quantities involved in vector operations are held in S registers. Logical, shift, fixed-point, and floating-point operations may be performed on S register data. The eight S registers are individually designated by the symbols S0, S1, S2, S3, S4, S5, S6, and S7.

T *registers*—sixty-four 64-bit T registers are used as auxiliary storage for the S registers. The transfer of an operand between S and T registers requires one clock period. Typically, T registers contain operands that are referenced over a longer period than would permit their being retained in S registers. T registers allow intermediate results of complex computations to be held in intermediate access storage rather than in memory. A block of data in T registers may be transferred to or from memory at the rate of one word per clock period. The sixty-four T registers are individually designated by the symbols T0, T1, T2, . . . , and $T77_8$.

V *registers*—eight 64-element V registers provide operands to and receive results from the functional units at a one clock period rate. Each element of a V register holds a 64-bit quantity. When associated data is grouped into successive elements of a V register, the register may be considered to contain a vector. Examples of vector quantities are rows and columns of a matrix, or similarly related elements of a table. Computational efficiency is achieved by processing each element of the vector identically. Vector merge and test instructions are provided in the CRAY-1 to allow operations to be performed on individual elements designated by the content of the vector mask (VM) register. The number of vector register elements to be processed is contained in the vector length (VL) register. The eight V registers are individually designated by the symbols V0, V1, V2, V3, V4, V5, B6, and V7.

Supporting Registers

The CPU contains a variety of additional registers that support the control of program execution. These are the vector length (VL) and vector mask (VM) registers, the program counter (P), the base address (BA) and limit address (LA) registers, the exchange address (XA) register, the flag (F) register, and the mode (M) register.

VL *register* — the 64-bit vector mask (VM) register controls vector element designation in vector merge and test instructions. Each bit of the VM register corresponds to a vector register element. In the vector test instruction, the VM register content is defined by testing each element of a V register for a specific condition.

P *register* — the 24-bit P register specifies the memory register parcel address of the current program instruction. The high order 22 bits specify a memory address and the low order two bits indicate a parcel number. This parcel address is advanced by one as each instruction parcel in a nonbranching sequence is executed and is replaced whenever program branching occurs.

BA *registers* — the 18-bit base address (BA) register contains the upper 18 bits of a 22-bit memory address. The lower four bits of this address are considered zeros. Just prior to initial or continued execution of a program, a process known as the "exchange sequence" stores into the BA register the upper 18 bits of the lowest memory address to be referenced during program execution. As the program executes, the address portion of each instruction referencing memory has its content added to that of the BA register. The sum then serves as the absolute address used for the memory reference and ensures that memory addresses lower than the contents of the BA register are not accessed. Programs must, therefore, have all instructions referencing memory do so with their address portions containing relative addresses. This process supports program loading and memory protection operations and does not, in producing an absolute address, affect the content of the instruction buffer, BA, or memory.

LA *register* — the 18-bit limit address (LA) register contains the upper 18 bits of a 22-bit memory address. The lower 4 bits of this address are considered zeros. Just prior to initial or continued execution of a program, the "exchange sequence" process stores into the LA register the upper 18 bits of that absolute address one greater than allowed to be referenced by the program. When program execution begins, each instruction referencing a memory location has the absolute address for that reference (determined by summing its address portion with the BA register contents) checked against the LA register content. If the absolute address equals or exceeds the LA register content, an out-of-range error condition is flagged and program execution terminates. This process supports the memory protection operation.

XA *register* — the 8-bit exchange address (XA) register contains the upper eight bits of a 12-bit memory address. The lower four bits of the address are considered zeros. Because only twelve bits are used, with the lower four bits always being zeros, exchange addresses can reference only every 16th memory address beginning with address 0000 and concluding with address 4080. Each of these addresses designates the first word of a 16-word set. Thus, 256 sets (of 16 memory words each) can be specified. Prior to initiation or continuation of a program's execution, the XA register contains the first memory address of a particular 16-word set or exchange package. The exchange package contains certain operating and support registers' contents as required for operations following an interrupt. The XA register supports the exchange sequence operation and the contents of XA are stored in an exchange package whenever an exchange sequence occurs.

F *register* — the 9-bit F register contains flags that, whenever set, indicate interrupt conditions causing initiation of an exchange sequence. The interrupt conditions are: normal exit, error exit, i/o interrupt, uncorrected memory error, program range error, operand range error, floating-point overflow, real-time clock interrupt, and console interrupt.

M *register* — the M (mode) register is a three-bit register that contains part of the exchange package for a currently active program. The three bits are selectively set during an exchange sequence. Bit 37, the floating-point error mode flag, can be set or cleared during the execution interval for a program through use of the 0021 and 0022 instructions. The other two bits (bits 38 and 39) are not altered during the execution interval for the exchange package and can only be altered when the exchange package is inactive in storage. Bits are assigned as follows in word two of the exchange package.

Bit 37 — Floating-point error mode flag. When this bit is set, interrupts on floating-point errors are enabled.

Bit 38 — Uncorrectable memory error mode flag. When this bit is set, interrupts on uncorrectable memory parity errors are enabled.

Bit 39 — Monitor mode flag. When this bit is set, all interrupts other than parity errors are inhibited.

Integer Arithmetic

All integer arithmetic is performed in 24-bit or 64-bit 2's complement form.

Floating-Point Arithmetic

Floating-point numbers are represented in signed magnitude form. The format is a packed signed binary fraction and a biased binary integer exponent. The fraction is a 49-bit signed magnitude value. The exponent is 15-bit biased. The unbiased exponent range is:

$$2^{-20000_8} \text{ to } 2^{+17777_8},$$

or approximately

$$10^{-2500} \text{ to } 10^{+2500}$$

An exponent equal to or greater than 2^{+20000_8} is recognized by the floating-point functional units as an overflow condition, and causes an interrupt if floating point interrupts are enabled.

Chaining

The chaining technique takes advantage of the parallel operation of functional units. Parallel vector operations may be processed in two ways: (a) using different functional units and V registers, and (b) chaining; that is, using the result stream to one vector register simultaneously as the operand set for another operation in a different functional unit.

Parallel operations on vectors allow the generation of two or more results per clock period. A vector operation either uses two vector registers as sources of operands or uses one scalar register and one vector register as sources of operands. Vectors exceeding 64 elements are processed in 64-element segments.

Basically, chaining is a phenomenon that occurs when results issuing from one functional unit (at a rate of one/clock period) are immediately fed into another functional unit and so on. In other words, intermediate results do not have to be stored to memory and can be used even before the vector operation that created them runs to completion.

Chaining has been compared to the technique of "data forwarding" used in the IBM 360/195. Like data forwarding, chaining takes place automatically. Data forwarding consists of hardware facilities within the 195 floating-point processor communicating automatically by transferring "name tags," or internal codes between themselves [6]. Unlike the CRAY-1, the user has no access to the 195's data-forwarding buffers. And, of course, the 195 can only forward scalar values, not entire vectors.

Interrupts and Exchange Sequence

Interrupts are handled cleanly by the CRAY-1 hardware. Instruction issue is terminated by the hardware upon detection of an interrupt condition. All memory bank activity is allowed to complete as are any vector instructions that are in execution, and then an exchange sequence is activated. The Cray Operating System (COS) is always one partner of any exchange sequence. The cause of an interrupt is analyzed during an exchange sequence and all interrupts are processed until none remain.

Only the address and scalar registers are maintained in a program's exchange package (Fig. 6). The user's B, T, and V registers are saved by the operating system in the user's Job Table Area.

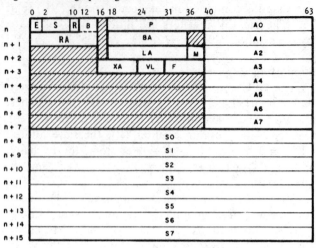

Fig. 6. Exchange package.

M - Modes†	
36	Interrupt on correctable memory error
37	Interrupt on floating point
38	Interrupt on uncorrectable memory error
39	Monitor mode

F - Flags†	
31	Console interrupt
32	RTC interrupt
33	Floating point error
34	Operand range
35	Program range
36	Memory error
37	I/O interrupt
38	Error exit
39	Normal exit

Registers	
S	Syndrome bits
RAB	Read address for error (where B is bank)
P	Program address
BA	Base address
LA	Limit address
XA	Exchange address
VL	Vector length

E - Error type (bits 0,1)	
10	Uncorrectable memory
01	Correctable memory

R - Read mode (bits 10,11)	
00	Scalar
01	I/O
10	Vector
11	Fetch

†Bit position from left of word

The CRAY-1's exchange sequence will be familiar to those who have had experience with the CDC 7600 and Cyber machines. One major benefit of the exchange sequence is the ease with which user jobs can be relocated in memory by the operating system. On the CRAY-1, dynamic relocation of a user job is facilitated by a base register that is transparent to the user.

Evolution of the CRAY-1

The CRAY-1 stems from a highly successful line of computers which S. Cray either designed or was associated with. Mr. Cray was one of the founders of Control Data Corporation. While at CDC, Mr. Cray was the principal architect of the CDC 1604, 6600, and 7600 computer systems. While there are many similarities with these earlier machines, two things stand out about the CRAY-1; first it is a vector machine, secondly, it utilizes semiconductor memories and integrated circuits rather than magnetic cores and discrete components. We classify the CRAY-1 as a second generation vector processor. The CDC STAR 100A and the Texas Instruments ASC are first-generation vector processors.

Both the STAR 100 and the ASC are designed to handle long vectors. Because of the startup time associated with data streaming, vector length is of critical importance. Vectors have to be long if the STAR 100 and the ASC vector processors are to be at all competitive with a scalar processor [3]. Another disadvantage of the STAR 100 architecture is that elements of a "vector" are required to be in consecutive addresses.

In contrast with these earlier designs, the CRAY-1 can be termed a short vector machine. Whereas the others require vector lengths of a 100 or more to be competitive with scalar processors, the cross-over point between choosing scalar rather than vector mode on the CRAY-1 is between 2 and 4 elements. This is demonstrated by a comparison of scalar/vector timings for some mathematical library routines shown in Figure 1 [7].

Also, the CRAY-1's addressing scheme allows complete flexibility. When accessing a vector, the user simply specifies the starting location and an increment. Arrays can be accessed by column, row, or diagonal; they can be stepped through with nonunary increments; and, there are no restrictions on addressing, except that the increment must be a constant.

Vector Startup Times

To be efficient at processing short vectors, vector startup times must be small. On the CRAY-1, vector instructions may issue at a rate of one instruction parcel per clock period. All vector instructions are one parcel instructions (parcel size = 16 bits). Vector instructions place a reservation on whichever functional unit they use, including memory, and on the input operand registers. In some cases, issue of a vector instruction may be delayed by a time (in clock periods) equal to vector length of the preceding vector operation + 4.

Functional unit times are shown in Table II. Vector operations that depend on the result of a previous vector operation can usually "chain" with them and are delayed for a maximum "chain slot" time in clock periods of functional unit time + 2.

Once issued, a vector instruction produces its first result after a delay in clock periods equal to functional unit time. Subsequent results continue to be produced at a rate of 1 per clock period. Results must be stored in a vector register. A separate instruction is required to store the final result vector to memory. Vector register capacity is 64-elements. Vectors longer than 64 are processed in 64-element segments.

Some sample timings for both scalar and vector are shown in Table III [8]. Note that there is no vector ASIN routine and so a reference to ASIN within a vectorized loop generates repetitive calls to the scalar ASIN routine. This involves a performance degradation but does allow the rest of the loop to vectorize (in a case where there are more statements than in this example). Simple loops 14, 15, and 16 show the

Table III.

Execution time in clock periods per result for various simple DO loops of the form
DO 10 I = 1,N
10 A(I) = B(I)

Loop Body	$N = 1$	10	100	1000	1000 Scalar
1. $A(I) = 1.$	41.0	5.5	2.6	2.5	22.5
2. $A(I) = B(I)$	44.0	5.8	2.7	2.5	31.0
3. $A(I) = B(I) + 10.$	55.0	6.9	2.9	2.6	37.0
4. $A(I) = B(I) + C(I)$	59.0	8.2	3.9	3.7	41.0
5. $A(I) = B(I)*10.$	56.0	7.0	2.9	2.6	38.0
6. $A(I) = B(I)*C(I)$	60.0	8.3	4.0	3.7	42.0
7. $A(I) = B(I)/10.$	94.0	10.8	4.1	3.7	52.0
8. $A(I) = B(I)/C(I)$	89.0	13.3	7.6	7.2	60.0
9. $A(I) = SIN(B(I))$	462.0	61.0	33.3	31.4	198.1
10. $A(I) = ASIN(B(I))$	430.0	209.5	189.5	188.3	169.1
11. $A(I) = ABS(B(I))$	61.0	7.5	2.9	2.6	
12. $A(I) = AMAX1(B(I), C(I))$	80.0	11.2	5.2	4.8	
13. $\begin{cases} C(I) = A(I) \\ A(I) = B(I) \\ B(I) = CCI \end{cases}$	90.0	12.7	6.3	5.8	47.0
14. $A(I) = B(I)*C(I) + D(I)*E(I)$	110.0	16.0	7.7	7.1	57.0
15. $A(I) = B(I)*C(I) + (D(I)*E(I))$	113.0	14.7	6.6	6.0	63.0
16. $A(I) = B(I)*C(I) + D(I)$	95.0	12.7	5.5	5.0	52.0

Fig. 7. Scalar/vector timing.

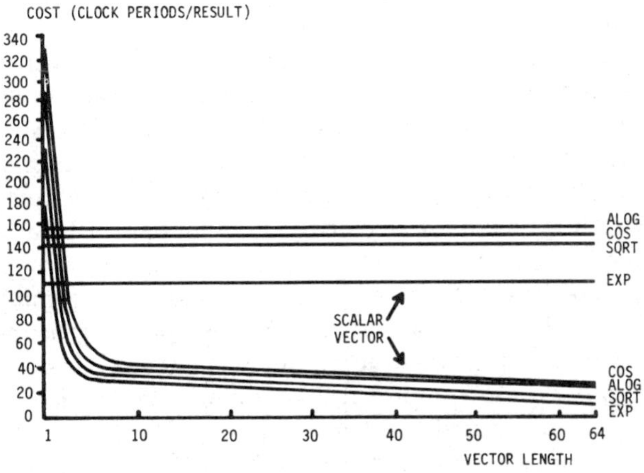

influence of chaining. For a long vector, the number of clock periods per result is approximately the number of memory references + 1. In loop 14, an extra clock period is consumed because the present CFT compiler will load all four operands before doing computation. This problem is overcome in loop 15 by helping the compiler with an extra set of parentheses.

Software

At the time of this writing, first releases of the CRAY Operating System (COS) and CRAY Fortran Compiler (CFT) have been delivered to user sites. COS is a batch operating system capable of supporting up to 63 jobs in a multiprogramming environment. COS is designed to be the recipient of job requests and data files from front-end computers. Output from jobs is normally staged back to the front-ends upon job completion.

CFT is an optimizing Fortran compiler designed to compile ANSI 66 Fortran IV to take best advantage of the CRAY-1's vector processing architecture. In its present form, CFT will not attempt to vectorize certain

Fig. 8. Front-end system interface.

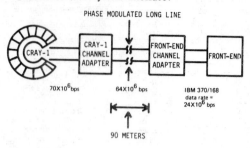

loops which, due to dependence conditions, appear at first sight, unvectorizable.

However, future versions of CFT will be designed to eliminate as many dependency conditions as possible increasing the amount of vectorizable code. Basically, to be vectorizable, a DO loop should manipulate arrays and store the results of computations in arrays. Loops that contain branches such as GO TO's, IF's, or CALL statements are not currently vectorized. Loops may contain function references if the function is known to the compiler to have a vector version. Most of the mathematical functions in the CRAY library are vectorizable. By using the vector mask and vector merge features of the CRAY-1, future versions of the compiler will be able to vectorize loops containing IF and GO TO statements.

Early experience with CFT has shown that most Fortran loops will not run as fast as optimally hand-coded machine language equivalents. Future versions of CFT will show improved loop timings due mainly to improved instruction scheduling.

Other CRAY-1 software includes Cray Assembler Language (CAL) which is a powerful macro assembler, an overlay loader, a full range of utilities including a text editor, and some debug aids.

Front-End Computer Interface

The CRAY-1 was not designed for stand-alone operation. At the very minimum a minicomputer is required to act as a conduit between the CRAY-1 and the everyday world. Cray Research software development is currently being done using a Data General Eclipse computer in this category. The Cray Research "A" processor, a 16-bit, 80 MIPS minicomputer is scheduled to replace the Eclipse in early 1978. Front-end computers can be attached to any of the CRAY-1's 12 i/o channels.

The physical connection between a front-end computer and the CRAY-1 is shown in Figure 8. In this example an IBM 370/168 is assumed in the front-end role. Note that each computer requires a channel adapter between its own channel and a Cray Research phase-modulated long line. The link can only be driven at the speed of its slowest component. In this example it is the IBM block multiplexer channel speed of 3 megabytes/second. The discipline of the link is governed by the Cray Link Interface Protocol.

CRAY-1 Development Problems

Two of the most significant problems [9] encountered on the way to the CRAY-1 were building the first cold bar and designing circuits with a completely balanced dynamic load.

Building the Cold Bar

It took a year and a half of trial and error before the first good cold bar was built. The work was done by a small Minnesota company. A major problem was the discovery, quite early, that aluminum castings are porous. If there is a crack in the stainless steel tubing at the bond between the tubing and the elbow then the Freon leaks through the aluminum casing. The loss of the Freon is not itself a problem, but mixed with the Freon is a little oil, and the oil can cause problems if it is deposited on the modules. Aluminum also tends to get bubbles in it when it is cast, requiring a long process of temperature cycling, preheating of the stainless steel tube, and so on.

Designing the Circuits

CRAY-1 modules are 6 inches wide. The distance across the board is about a nanosecond which is just about the edge time of the electrical signals. Unless due precautions are taken, when electric signals run around a board, standing waves can be induced in the ground plane. Part of the solution is to make all signal paths in the machine the same length. This is done by padding out paths with foil runs and integrated circuit packages. All told, between 10 and 20 per cent of the IC packages in the machine are there simply to pad out a signal line. The other part of the solution was to use only simple gates and make sure that both sides of every gate are always terminated. This means that there is no dynamic component presented to the power supply. This is the principal reason why simple gates are used in the CRAY-1. If a more complex integrated circuit package is used, it is impossible to terminate both sides of every gate. So all of the CRAY-1's circuits are perfectly balanced. Five layer boards have one ground layer, two voltage layers, and then the two logic layers on the outside. Twisted pairs which interconnect the modules are balanced and there are equal and opposite signals on both sides of the pairs. The final result is that there is just a purely resistive load to the power supply!

Summary

The design of the CRAY-1 stems from user experience with first generation vector processors and is to some extent, evolved from the 7600 [2]. The CRAY-1 is particularly effective at processing short vectors. Its architecture exhibits a balanced approach to both scalar and vector processing. In [1], the conclusion is drawn that the CRAY-1 in scalar mode is more than twice as fast as the CDC 7600. Such good scalar performance is required in what is often an unvectorizable world.

At the time of this writing, Cray Research has shipped CRAY-1 systems to three customers (Los Alamos Scientific Laboratory, National Center for Atmospheric Research, and the European Center for Medium Range Weather Forecasts) and has contracts to supply three more systems, two to the Department of Defense, and one to United Computing Systems (UCS). Production plans already anticipate shipping one CRAY-1 per quarter. As the population of CRAY-1 computers expands, it will become clear that the CRAY-1 has made a significant step on the way to the general-purpose computers in the future.

Received February 1977; revised September 1977

Acknowledgments. Acknowledgments are due to my colleagues at Cray Research. G. Grenander, R. Hendrickson, M. Huber, C. Jewett, P. Johnson, A. La Bounty, and J. Robidoux, without whose contributions, this paper could not have been written.

References
1. CRAY-1 Final Evaluation by T. W. Keller, LASL, LA-6456-MS.
2. CRAY-1 Report, Auerbach Computer Technology Report, Auerbach Publisher's, 6560 North Park Drive, Pennsauken, N. J. 08109.
3. Preliminary Report on Results of Matrix Benchmarks on Vector Processors: Calahan, Joy, Orbits, System Engineering Laboratory, University of Michigan, Ann Arbor, Michigan 48109.
4. Computer Architecture Issues in Large-Scale Systems, 9th Asilomar Conference, Naval Postgraduate School, Monterey, California.
5. Computer World, August 1976.
6. The IBM 360/195 by Jesse O'Murphy and Robert M. Wade, Datamation, April 1970.
7. Work done by Paul Johnson, Cray Research.
8. Work done by Richard Hendrickson, Cray Research.
9. The section on CRAY-1 development problems is based on remarks made by Seymour Cray in a speech to prospective CRAY-1 users in 1975.

CONTROL DATA® STAR-100 PROCESSOR DESIGN

R. G. Hintz and D. P. Tate
Control Data Corporation, Advanced Design Laboratory
St. Paul, Minnesota 55112

Summary

The Control Data STAR-100 computer is a pipeline processor structured around a 4-million byte (8 million byte optional) high-bandwidth memory. Instructions in the CDC STAR-100 specify operations on variable length streams of data thereby allowing full use of the memory bandwidth and the arithmetic pipelines. In streaming mode, the system has the capability of producing 100 million 32-bit floating point results per second. Design aspects of the pipeline processors and the associated memory bus are discussed.

A block diagram of the CDC STAR-100 memory-pipeline data paths is shown in Figure 1. The core memory and the data bus configuration has been designed to support a pipeline rate of 100 million operations per second. The core memory has 32 interleaved banks, with each bank containing 2048 512-bit words. The cycle time of the memory is 1.28 microseconds (32 minor cycles). The minor cycle rate in the STAR machine is 40 nanoseconds. Therefore, the memory system of 32 banks can support a total bandwidth of 512 bits of data per minor cycle.

As shown in Figure 1, the width of the memory data bus for each group of four banks is 128 bits. The data bus transfer rate is 128 bits per minor cycle. During streaming operations, four buses will be active with each bus transferring data at a rate of 128 bits per minor cycle. Two of the buses are used for transferring operand streams to the pipeline processors. The third bus is used for storing the result stream elements and the fourth bus is shared between input/output storage requests and control vector references. This data bus configuration allows the pipelines to operate at their maximum rate of 100 million results per second.

The read and write buffers shown in Figure 1 are used to synchronize the four active buses. The memory requests are buffered to space them eight banks

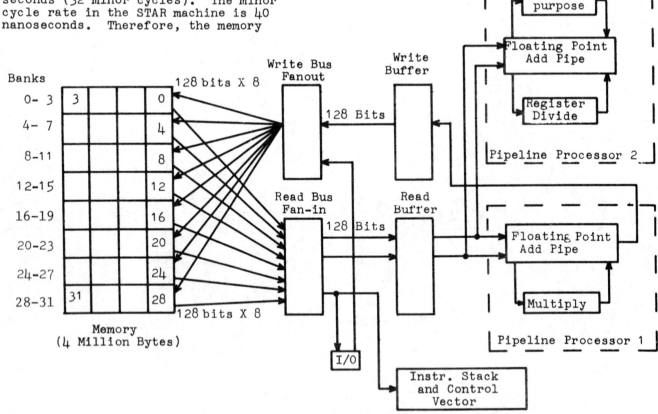

STAR-100 MEMORY-PIPELINE DATA PATHS

Figure 1

EHO182-6/81/0000/0036 © 1972 IEEE

Reprinted from *Proceedings, COMPCON Fall 1972,* September 1972, pages 1-4. Copyright © 1972 by The Institute of Electrical and Electronics Engineers, Inc.

apart, eliminating memory conflict situations. Therefore, the maximum pipeline rate can be sustained regardless of the distribution of addresses between the four active buses.

The floating point arithmetic section of the CDC STAR-100 consists of two independent pipeline processors. In a pipeline processor, operands flow through the processor much like water flowing through a pipeline, hence the name pipeline processor.

Processor 1 consists of a pipelined floating point addition unit and a pipelined floating point multiplication unit. Processor 2 consists of a pipelined floating point addition unit, a non-pipelined floating point divide unit, and a pipelined multipurpose unit which is capable of performing a floating point multiplication, divide, or square root operation. Using both pipeline processors for an addition or multiplication operation provides the CDC STAR-100 with its maximum capability of 100 million 32-bit floating point results per second. The floating point addition and multiplication units are typical pipelined units. This paper will describe them in some detail.

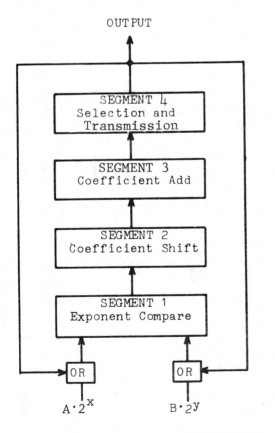

OUTPUT

SEGMENT 4
Selection and
Transmission

SEGMENT 3
Coefficient Add

SEGMENT 2
Coefficient Shift

SEGMENT 1
Exponent Compare

OR   OR

$A \cdot 2^x$ $B \cdot 2^y$

FLOATING POINT ADDITION PIPELINE

Figure 2

Figure 2 shows a typical pipeline processor. It consists of a group of networks (segments 1, 2, 3 and 4) connected serially. At regular time intervals the output of a given network is gated to the input of the next network. A new input operand enters network 1 at the beginning of every time interval. An output element flows from network 4 during every time interval.

The difference between the maximum and minimum delay in the networks in a pipeline processor necessitates the deskewing or clocking of the data in the processor. The duration and position of the time period during which this clocking may occur is determined by the output rate at which the pipeline is to operate, the difference between the maximum and minimum delay for the networks in the pipeline, and the minimum width of the pulse necessary to activate a deskewing element in the pipeline.

In the CDC STAR-100 it is possible to maintain a 40 nanosecond output rate from the pipelines and still maintain a reasonable number of logic levels between deskewing elements.

The input-to-output time of the pipeline can be as important as the output rate of the pipeline. If we wish to do conventional, single, non-streaming operations as well as streaming operations in the pipeline, then input-to-output time becomes critically important. Input-to-output time in the pipeline also directly influences the start-up and unloading time for the pipeline when the pipeline is doing streaming operations. The input-to-output time for the basic floating point addition pipeline in the CDC STAR-100 computer is 160 nanosecond. The input-to-output time for the floating point multiply unit is 320 nanoseconds.

Certain basic operations are necessary to form the sum of two floating point numbers. The exponents of the two numbers must be compared. The coefficient of the number having the smaller exponent must be right-shifted by the difference between the two exponents before it is added to the other coefficient. The coefficients are then added and the appropriate upper or lower result, as specified by the operation code, must be selected.

Figure 2 is a simplified diagram of a pipeline capable of performing a floating point addition operation. The two inputs to the pipeline are expressed in conventional floating point notation such that one of the inputs equals $A \cdot 2^x$ and the other input equals $B \cdot 2^y$. The x will be referred to as the exponent of coefficient A and the y will be referred to as the exponent of coefficient B. The logic between the deskewing elements in the pipeline will be referred to as a segment of logic.

The first segment of logic in the floating addition pipeline compares exponents x and y and saves the larger. The difference between the exponents is produced and saved as a shift count for the coefficient alignment shift. If a subtraction operation is being performed the B coefficient is complemented. The shift count, larger exponent, and the two coefficients are gated to segment two.

In segment two the coefficient with the smaller exponent is right-shifted by the shift count. The shifted and unshifted coefficients and the larger exponent are gated to segment three.

In segment three the shifted and unshifted coefficients are added and the sum and larger exponent are gated to segment four.

Segment four selects the desired upper or lower half of the sum, corrects the result for any coefficient overflow, and transmits the result coefficient and the larger exponent to the result trunk.

A path exists which allows the output of segment four to be gated directly back to either input of the pipeline. This feature is useful when performing conventional, non-streaming type operations. It can decrease the execution time for these operations by fifty percent when the output of an operation is needed as an operand for a subsequent operation.

It is possible to split the floating point addition pipeline into two independent 32-bit pipelines. Little additional hardware is necessary to accomplish this pipeline splitting. The concept of pipeline splitting is used extensively in the CDC STAR-100 to give the machine an increased performance capability for half-width (32-bit) arithmetic.

Figure 3 shows the basic high speed multiplication pipeline used by the CDC STAR-100 computer. The two operands, A and B, are gated into the multiplier decode and multiplicand gating network. The multiplier is decoded into twelve two-bit groups. Multiples of a multiplicand are gated to the first rank of partial addition networks under control of the multiplier decode groups. Each multiplier decode group controls one input to the first rank of partial addition networks. The multiplication operation is performed in the multiplier decode and multiplicand gating network and the first rank of partial addition networks. The remaining hardware in the multiplication pipeline merges the partial sums and partial carries from the first rank of partial addition networks down to two numbers. These two numbers, when added together, are the product of the input numbers A and B.

Figure 4 shows how these basic multiplication pipelines are used to form a multiplication pipeline unit. The unit

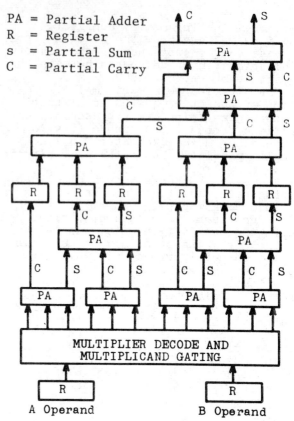

PA = Partial Adder
R = Register
s = Partial Sum
C = Partial Carry

32-BIT MULTIPLICATION PIPELINE

Figure 3

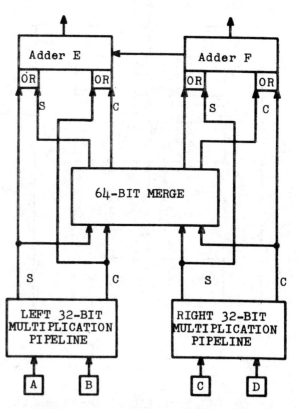

PIPELINE MULTIPLICATION UNIT

Figure 4

is capable of simultaneously performing
two independent 32-bit multiplication
operations or of performing one 64-bit
multiplication operation. When the unit
is performing the 32-bit operations, the
left multiplication pipeline multiplies
inputs A and B together. The partial
sums and partial carries from this pipeline are merged together in Adder E.
The right multiplication pipeline
multiplies together inputs C and D.
The partial sums and partial carries
from this multiplication are merged
together in Adder F.

To perform 64-bit multiplication,
we split the multiplier and multiplicand
into two pieces such that the multiplier
$A = A_0 + A_1 2^W$ and the multiplicand
$B = B_0 + B_1 2^W$, where W is the width of
the basic pipeline multiplier. Then
$A \cdot B = A_0 \cdot B_0 + (A_0 \cdot B_1 + A_1 \cdot B_0) 2^W + (A_1 \cdot B_1) 2^{2W}$. The 64-bit multiplication
is performed by doing the 32-bit
multiplications $A_0 \cdot B_0$ and $A_0 \cdot B_1$ during
one cycle and $A_1 \cdot B_0$ and $A_1 \cdot B_1$ on the next
cycle. The partial sums and partial
carries from these multiplications are
then merged into one partial sum and
one partial carry in the 64-bit merge
pipeline. The partial sum and the
partial carry from a 64-bit merge pipeline are then added together in the final
adders. The output of these adders is
the desired 64-bit product.

References

1. L. W. Cotten, "Circuit Implementation
   of High-Speed Pipeline Systems",
   AFIPS Conference Proceedings, Vol. 27,
   Part 1, 1965 Fall Joint Computer
   Conference, Spartan Books, Washington,
   D.C., pp. 489-532.

2. L. W. Cotten, "Maximum-Rate Pipeline
   Systems", AFIPS Conference Proceedings,
   Vol. 34, 1969 Spring Joint Computer
   Conference, AFIPS Press, Montvale,
   New Jersey, pp. 581-586.

3. W. R. Graham, "The Parallel and the
   Pipeline Computers", Datamation,
   Vol. 16, No. 4, April 1970,
   pp. 68-71.

4. T. C. Chen, "Parallelism, Pipelining,
   and Computer Efficiency", Computer
   Design, Vol. 10, No. 1, January 1971,
   pp. 69-74.

5. R. L. Curtis, "Management of High
   Speed Memory in the STAR-100 Computer",
   Proceedings of the 1971 IEEE Inter-
   national Computer Society Conference,
   September, Boston, pp. 131-132.

CDC 205 Runs 800 Million Operation/Sec

By Rita Shoor
CW Staff

MINNEAPOLIS — In the world of supercomputers, where 16M bytes of main memory is considered a nice round number and vendors speak casually of hundreds of millions of operations per second (Mops), Control Data Corp. has announced the Cyber 205 — a system capable in its maximum configuration of performing 800 Mops, according to the company.

The new system competes directly with Cray Research, Inc.'s Cray-1S machine, a CDC spokesman said. However, he described the 205 as "Cray-independent .... It's a pure CDC machine." (Seymour Cray, who formed Cray Research, was formerly employed by CDC as a designer of its 6000 and 7000 series.) .

The Cyber 205 is the second member in the Cyber 200 series and, like its predecessor, the model 203, large-scale integrated (LSI) bipolar circuitry is utilized in the unit's scalar processor.

However, logic boards from CDC's Star-100 used in the earlier model's vector processor have been replaced with 168 gate/chip LSI circuitry in the Cyber 205 vector unit.

This architectural modification was predicted about six months ago [CW, Jan. 7].

The Cyber 205 processor consists of a scalar and a vector unit (see architecture diagram). The scalar (serial) unit performs a single operation or instruction up to a maximum of 50 Mops. It operates with a 64-word instruction stack and a 256-word register file.

The vector (parallel) unit performs arithmetic operations on arrays or streams of data and consists of one, two or four segmented pipelines, allowing for a new set of 32- or 64-bit operands to be streamed directly to and from central memory into each pipeline every 20 nsec, according to the company.

A maximum of four million 64-bit words comprise the 205's central memory, and CDC maintained that data is transferred between central memory and the central processor at speeds up to "25.6 billion bit/sec for each million-word increment of central memory."

A basic Cyber 205 system features eight I/O ports expandable to 16, and each of them has a maximum transfer rate of 200 million bit/sec, CDC said. Up to two trillion words of virtual memory are offered to each user.

The Cyber 205 runs under Cyber 200-OS software, which allows users to access the system from remote batch or interactive terminals or through local devices via front-end processors.

The Cyber 205 systems are priced from $7.9 million to $16.5 million in "typical configuration" and will be available for shipment in January 1981, according to the company.

Target Applications

Who needs it?

"Ten years ago," the spokesman said, "applications which fell into the supercomputer spectrum were essentially either nuclear or high-energy physics problem solving."

Additional target applications which require number-crunching capabilities involve search for new and alternate energy sources, the production of long-range weather forecasts and the design and manufacture of aircraft.

The petroleum industry requires "huge computing power" to process seismic data form exploration activities and to simulate reservoirs for maximum oil produciton — one possible application for the 205, the spokesman said.

"The [supercomputer] market is growing at a faster rate than any other [computer market] is absolute terms," the spokesman said. He acknowledged that he was comparing an increase from "perhaps five to 50 supercomputer installations" to something like the minicomputer market "where you might go from 1.5 million to 2 million [machines sold]."

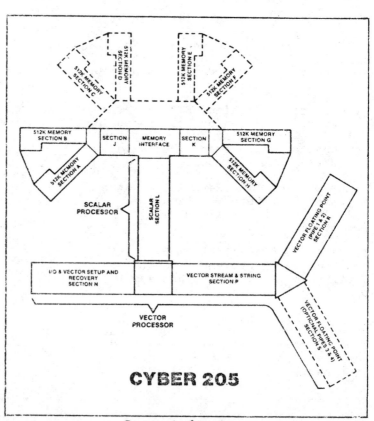

CYBER 205

System Architecture

Reprinted with permission from Computerworld, Volume 14, Number 23, June 9, 1980, pages 1-2. Copyright © 1980 by CW Communications/Inc., Framingham, MA 01701.

Processor Handbook
860-7259-003B

CHAPTER 1
GENERAL INFORMATION

1.1 INTRODUCTION

The AP is a high-speed (167ns cycle time) peripheral floating-point arithmetic array processor (AP), which is intended to work in parallel with a host computer.

The AP's internal organization is particularly well suited to performing the large numbers of reiterative multiplications and additions required in digital signal processing, matrix arithmetic, statistical analysis, and numerical simulation.

The highly-parallel structure of the AP allows the overhead of array indexing, loop counting, and data fetching from memory to be performed simultaneously with arithmetic operations on the data. This allows much faster execution than on a typical general-purpose computer where each of the above operations must occur sequentially.

The AP achieves its high speed through the use of fast commercial integrated circuit elements and an architecture that permits each logical unit of the machine to operate independently and at maximum speed.

Specifically:

- Programs, constants, and data each reside in separate, independent memories to eliminate memory accessing conflicts.

- Independent floating-point multiply and adder units allow both arithmetic operations to be initiated every 167ns.

- Two large (32 locations each) blocks of floating-point accumulators are available for temporary storage of intermediate results from the multiplier, adder, or memory.

- Address indexing and counting functions are performed by an independent integer arithmetic unit that includes 16-integer accumulators.

In a typical application, such as a fast fourier transform (FFT), the above features allow nearly the entire computation to be overlapped with data memory access time.

Effective processing precision is enhanced by 38-bit internal data words, an internal floating-point format with optimum numerical properties, and a convergent rounding algorithm.

FPS 860-7259-003   41

Excerpted from and reprinted with permission from "Processor Handbook 860-7259-003B" by FPS Technical Publications Staff, from *AP-120B Processor Handbook*, February 1979, pages 1-1, 1-3-1-5, 1-12-1-13, 1-23. Copyright © 1979 by Floating Point Systems, Inc.

1.2 SYSTEM OVERVIEW

A general block diagram of AP arithmetic paths appears in Figure 1-1.

Connection is made to the host in a manner that permits data transfers to occur under control of either the host computer or the AP. For most host computers, this means that the AP is interfaced to both the programmed I/O and DMA channels.

The system elements are interconnected with multiple parallel paths so that transfers can occur in parallel. All internal floating-point data paths are 38 bits wide (10-bit biased binary exponent and 28-bit 2's complement mantissa).

Main data memory (MD) is organized in 8K-word modules of 38-bit words expandable up to 64K words in the main chassis. The effective memory cycle time (interleaved) is 333ns.

Table memory (TM) is used for storage of constants (FFT constants) and is tied to a separate data path so as not to interfere with data memory. It is bi-polar 167ns read-only memory and is organized in 512-word, 38-bit increments.

Data pad X (DPX) and data pad Y (DPY) are two blocks of 32 floating accumulators. Each is a two-part register block, wherein one register may be read and another written from each block in one instruction cycle.

The floating adder (FA) consists of two input registers (A1 and A2) and a two-stage pipeline which performs the operations and convergently rounds the normalized result.

The floating multiplier (FM) consists of input registers (M1 and M2) and a three-stage pipeline which performs the multiply operation. Products are normalized and convergently rounded 38-bit numbers.

The s-pad consists of 16 integer registers and an integer arithmetic unit which is used to form operand addresses and to perform integer arithmetic.

Chapter 2 contains a more detailed description of each of the functional elements. Chapter 3 describes programming considerations.

Chapter 4 describes in detail the host computer interface, which Floating Point Systems, Inc., supplies. A number of off-the-shelf interfaces are available.

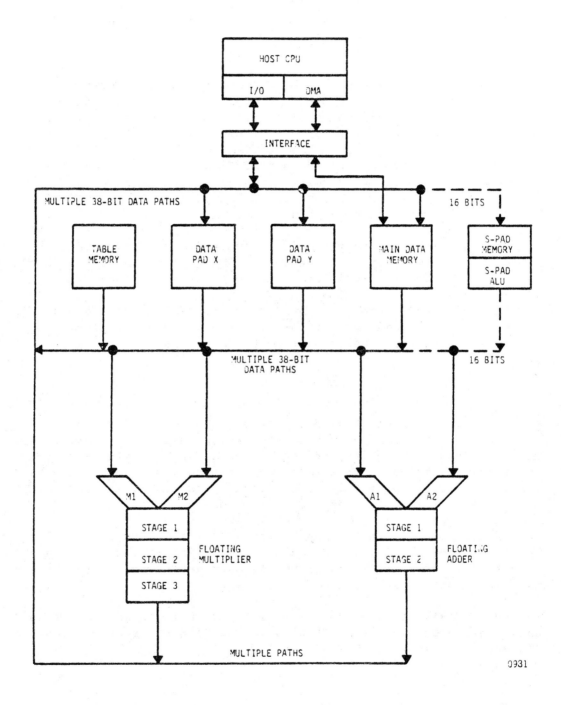

Figure 1-1 General AP Block Diagram

1.3 EXAMPLE AP APPLICATION

A simple FFT processing sequence goes as follows:

Initial conditions are that the FFT program is resident in program source memory internal to the AP, the array to be transformed is resident in host memory, and the host CPU has initiated the AP processor with an I/O instruction.

1. The AP requests host DMA cycles to transfer the array from host memory to internal data memory. Data is converted from host floating-point format to internal AP floating-point format on-the-fly.

2. The FFT algorithm is performed with data remaining in internal AP format. This yields the benefit of 38-bit precision and convergent rounding during the critical phases of processing.

3. The frequency domain array is transferred back to host memory by requesting host DMA cycles. Data is converted from internal format to host format on-the-fly.

4. The AP proceeds to another process or stops executing, depending on previously established conditions. An interrupt to the host can be issued.

The AP is most efficiently used when a sequence of operations is performed on one or more sets of data which reside in internal data memory. This reduces data transfer overhead and retains maximum numerical precision. For example, a reasonable sequence would be to transfer a trace and a filter, FFT both, array multiply, inverse FFT, and transfer the result back to host memory.

The AP data memory has DMA capability. That is to say, MD cycles can be stolen from the AP microprocessor by the interface. This capability allows host computer DMA to AP DMA data transfers to occur, thereby minimizing both host CPU and AP overhead.

The AP is designed with enough flexibility built in so that its power can be harnessed in a variety of ways. Subsequent sections describe its use in detail.

Table 1-1   Floating-Point Arithmetic Times

OPERATION	TRAVEL TIME	PIPELINE INTERVAL
Add/Subtract	0.333 us	0.167 us
Multiply	0.500 us	0.167 us
Multiply-Add	0.833 us	0.167 us
Complex Add/Subtract	0.500 us	0.333 us
Complex Multiply	1.333 us	0.667 us
Complex Multiply-Add	1.667 us	0.667 us

0983

Travel time is the total time required to get from the data source to
the destination including the full transport through the arithmetic
units. Pipeline interval is the time between successively available
resultants. The former is important when the successive arguments of a
computation depend on previous calculations. The latter is indicative
of the maximum throughput rate available for successively independent
calculators.

Table 1-2 Basic Scalar Functions

OPERATION	TYPICAL EXECUTION TIME/LOOP (us)		PROGRAM SIZE (AP PS WORDS)	
	167 ns	333 ns	167 ns	333 ns
Divide	3.8	3.8	28	28
Square Root	3.8	3.8	28	28
Exponential	4.2	4.2	28	28
Natural Logarithm	4.0	4.0	37	37
Base 1Ø Logarithm	4.7	4.7	37	37
Sine	4.9	4.9	35	35
Cosine	5.4	5.4	35	35
Arctangent	8.7	8.7	74	74
Arctangent of (Y/X)	13.8	13.8	74	74

0984

These functions take arguments from data pad and return full-word
accuracy results to data pad. Full-precision polynomial coefficients
for these functions are contained on the standard 512 words of table
memory.

Table 1-4 Convolution (Correlation)

ELEMENT COUNTS		TYPICAL EXECUTION TIME/LOOP (us)	
M	N	167ns	333ns
8	128	0.28	0.28
32	128	0.83	0.83
128	128	3.0	3.0
8	1024	2.3	2.3
32	1024	6.6	6.6
128	1024	24.0	24.0
1024	1024	186.2	186.2

0985

Table 1-5 Fast Fourier Transforms

POINTS	RFFT		RFFTB		CFFT		CFFTB	
	167ns	333ns	167ns	333ns	167ns	333ns	167ns	333ns
64	0.18	0.27	0.14	0.20	0.28	0.40	0.20	0.28
128	0.35	0.50	0.27	0.38	0.62	0.95	0.47	0.72
256	0.74	1.13	0.58	0.90	1.28	1.86	0.97	1.41
512	1.50	2.22	1.20	1.76	2.86	4.38	2.26	3.48
1024	3.30	5.08	2.70	4.18	5.95	8.73	4.75	6.93
2048	6.81	10.12	5.61	8.32	13.32	20.10	10.83	16.60
4096	14.95	22.96	12.56	19.37	27.44	40.33	22.66	33.16
8192	30.88	45.86	26.09	38.69	60.33	91.66	50.76	77.31
16384	67.19	102.70	57.63	88.36	124.70	183.27	105.58	154.59
32768	138.42	205.35	119.30	176.68	--	--	--	--

0986

SPE 7675

Society of Petroleum Engineers of AIME

APPLICATION OF VECTOR PROCESSORS TO THE SOLUTION OF FINITE DIFFERENCE EQUATIONS

Reprinted with permission from *1979 Society of Petroleum Engineers of AIME 5th Symposium on Reservoir Simulation,* February 1979, pages 37-44. Copyright © 1979 by the Society of Petroleum Engineers of AIME.

by James S. Nolen, Member SPE-AIME, INTERCOMP; D. W. Kuba, and M. J. Kascic, Jr., Control Data Corporation

Copyright 1979, American Institute of Mining, Metallurgical, and Petroleum Engineers, Inc.

This paper was presented at the 1979 Society of Petroleum Engineers of AIME Fifth Symposium on Reservoir Simulation held in Denver, Colorado, February 1-2, 1979. The material is subject to correction by the author. Permission to copy is restricted to an abstract of not more than 300 words. Write: 6200 N. Central Expy., Dallas, Tx. 75206.

ABSTRACT

With computer technology drawing close to limitations imposed by the speed of light increased emphasis has been placed on vector processors, which have the ability to greatly increase the speed of arithmetic even without improvements in such basic computer characteristics as memory cycle time. This paper deals with the solution of systems of finite difference equations on the STAR 100 and the CYBER 203, two Control Data Corporation computers with built in vector processors.

Systems of three-dimensional finite difference equations having from 2000 to 8000 unknowns were solved by means of Gaussian elimination and line successive overrelaxation (LSOR). On these machines the D4 Gaussian elimination technique reduced computer time by factors as large as 4.6 relative to standard Gaussian elimination. Vectorization of the D4 code reduced computer times relative to scalar results by factors as large as 26, despite nonoptimal coding.

LSOR was successfully vectorized with attendant computer time reduction factors of 35-43 on the STAR 100. On the CYBER 203 run times were reduced by factors of 45-54 relative to the scalar performance of the STAR 100. On an 8000 block problem average processing speed for a complete LSOR solution was approximately 25 megaflops.

INTRODUCTION

Large computers with hardware specifically designed for vector processing offer the potential for solving large systems of finite difference equations with exceptional speed. This work was intended to test certain solution algorithms and determine which perform best on two such computers, the Control Data Corporation STAR 100 and the CYBER 203 (previously called the STAR 100 A). The algorithms discussed in this work are all well known, (1) Gaussian elimination, (2) successive overrelaxation [SOR], and (3) the strongly implicit procedure [SIP].

The STAR 100 is a most unusual computer. It comes with as much as 1024 K words of 64 bit core memory and has a virtual operating system that will address storage locations in excess of 10^{12}. Its most unusual characteristic, however, is the tremendous range of speeds that it can exhibit, depending upon the structure of the computer code being processed. The speed of 64 bit arithmetic ranges from about 0.5 to 50 million floating operations per second (megaflops). (A floating operation is an add, multiply, divide, etc.)

At the low end of the speed range it performs about like a CDC 6600, a 1960's technology computer. At the high end it will challenge any commercial machine in the world. This large speed variation results from the fact that the STAR 100's core memory has a destructive read characteristic that prevents the same core area from being referenced for 31 machine cycles following a prior read. (This results in a "memory cycle time" of 1280 nsec.) Coupled with this slow (by modern standards) core memory is a vector arithmetic unit that can produce two 64 bit adds or one 64 bit multiply during every 40 nsec. clock cycle, once the arithmetic unit reaches steady state. (See the Appendix for details.)

All vector operations (adds, multiplies, etc.) have a linear performance characteristic of the form

$$C = S + RN \qquad (1)$$

where C is the number of machine cycles required to complete the operation and N is vector length.

For example, a floating point vector multiply requires 159 + N clock cycles. This means that very long vectors must be processed before the full potential of the computer can be realized, or that scalar arithmetic is extremely slow relative to long-vector arithmetic.

References and illustrations at end of paper.

The CYBER 203 is similar in concept to the STAR 100, but it contains a modern semiconductor memory having an 80 nsec. memory cycle time and an independent scalar unit. The vector arithmetic unit is identical to that in the STAR 100. The net result is to increase the speed of the machine at the low end by a factor of about 5 while maintaining the 50 megaflop maximum rate.

In order to make best use of either of these computers it is necessary to organize storage and structure algorithms to facilitate long vector operations. A vector consists of contiguous, logical storage locations and is characterized by a starting location and a length. (Logical storage locations are distinguished from physical storage locations since the memory is interleaved to put contiguous logical locations in separate memory banks.)

GAUSSIAN ELIMINATION

In 1973 Price and Coats described how the computer time required to solve systems of finite difference equations by Gaussian elimination could be reduced by a factor ranging from 2 to nearly 6 simply by renumbering grid blocks to change the matrix structure.[1] Their D4 method effectively reduces the number of equations requiring elimination by a factor of 2 and then reduces the work still further by taking advantage of a variable band width.

With the D4 method there is a certain amount of overhead associated with the generation of the matrix to which Gaussian elimination is ultimately applied. Therefore, it is not obvious that the D4 algorithm will achieve theoretical improvement factors relative to standard Gaussian elimination on vector hardware.

In this work an existing scalar subroutine for D4 Gaussian elimination was directly vectorized in FORTRAN using the CDC vector compiler. The code was made as efficient as possible without changing its basic structure. It is significant that in the scalar routine the forward and back substitutions following factorization are performed with inner products (dot products). It is possible to code these portions of the solution as vector multiplies rather than inner products, but this requires that the coefficient matrix be stored by columns rather than rows and would have necessitated a complete rewrite of the existing subroutine.

The use of inner products in vector mode slows those portions of the code by roughly a factor of 6 relative to vector products, since the inner product work estimate is $130 + 6N$ cycles compared to $159 + N$ cycles for the vector product. Thus, in at least this respect the vector D4 elimination routine was non-optimal.

A collection of six test problems was constructed using the following finite difference equation:

$$TX_{i-\frac{1}{2}}(P_{i-1} - P_i)^{n+1} - TX_{i+\frac{1}{2}}(P_i - P_{i+1})^{n+1}$$
$$+ TY_{j-\frac{1}{2}}(P_{j-1} - P_j)^{n+1} - TY_{j+\frac{1}{2}}(P_j - P_{j+1})^{n+1}$$
$$+ TZ_{k-\frac{1}{2}}(P_{k-1} - P_k)^{n+1} - TZ_{k+\frac{1}{2}}(P_k - P_{k+1})^{n+1}$$

$$- q = \frac{PV \cdot CR}{\Delta t} (p^{n+1} - p^n) \qquad (2)$$

$$TX = TY = 10 \qquad \text{(zero on the boundaries)}$$
$$TZ = 100 \qquad \text{(zero on the boundaries)}$$
$$PV = 1.0 \times 10^5$$
$$CR = 5.0 \times 10^{-6}$$
$$\Delta t = 1 \text{ day}$$

Sources and sinks were defined as follows:

$$q(1,1,1) = q(1,10,1) = q(20,1,1) = -100$$
$$q(20,10,1) = 300$$

The problems differed only in the number of grid blocks, with six different grids being used: 40x10x5, 40x20x5, 40x40x5, 20x20x5, 20x20x10, and 20x20x20.

Each problem was solved for one time step using D4 Gaussian elimination on both the STAR 100 and the CYBER 203 in both scalar and vector modes. (One exception to this was the 20x20x20 problem which was not run in scalar mode on the STAR 100.) In addition each problem was solved in vector mode on the STAR 100 using a standard Gaussian elimination routine. These results are summarized in Tables 1 and 2.

First, comparing the CDC 6600 time to the scalar time on the STAR 100, we verify that the STAR 100 runs in scalar mode about like a 6600. Next, it is clear from the increase in efficiency factor that in vector mode both the STAR 100 and the CYBER 203 gain efficiency as vector length increases. (The vector length for this algorithm is the half band width, or NY·NZ.) In particular note that on each machine the efficiency factor is almost identical for the 40x40x5 and the 20x20x10 cases, which both have a half band of 200, but different numbers of grid blocks. The CYBER 203 runs consistently 4.4 times faster than the STAR 100 in scalar mode and 1.1 to 1.5 times faster in vector mode. The CYBER 203 runs 15-31 times faster in vector mode than the STAR 100 in scalar mode (CDC 6600 equivalent).

Table 2 compares run times on the STAR 100 of the vectorized D4 Gaussian elimination routine with a vectorized version of standard Gaussian elimination. Also included in the table are theoretical estimates of the work reduction achieved by the D4 routine. Obviously, the D4 algorithm tested in this work failed to achieve all of its theoretical advantage; however, performance improved with band width and computer run time was reduced by a factor of 4.61 compared to the theoretical estimate of 5.00 on the 20x20x20 problem.

The D4 algorithm was broken into 4 pieces for an analysis of its efficiency on the STAR 100, (1) band construction, (2) factorization, (3) forward and back solution, and (4) solution storage (moving the solution from D4 ordering to standard ordering). The results of timing breakdowns for the 40x10x5 and 20x20x10 cases, presented in Table 3, demonstrate that the overhead of the D4 algorithm (band construction plus solution storage) was significant (27.67%) for the relatively small half band of 50 in the 40x10x5 problem, but as the half band increased to 200 in the 20x20x10 the overhead dropped to 10.23% of total time.

Although we do not have comparable breakdowns for the CYBER 203 (the timing routine is not available), it is apparent from a comparison of the vector run times of the two machines on the 40x10x5 problem that the algorithm's overhead has been substantially reduced by the new machine. (The run time was reduced by a factor of 1.57.)

SUCCESSIVE OVERRELAXATION (SOR)

Successive overrelaxation encompasses a family of matrix solution techniques.[2] These differ only in the grouping of grid blocks for simultaneous solution within each stage of a single iteration. The method is point SOR if grid blocks are treated individually, line SOR (LSOR) if complete lines of grid blocks are coupled for simultaneous solution, 2-line SOR if pairs of lines are treated, plane SOR if entire planes are solved simultaneously, etc.

At first glance it appears that any SOR method not encompassing groups of planes is doomed to a future of short vectors. Examine for example the matrix structures of line, 2-line, and plane SOR in Figs. 3 and 7. Line SOR is completely recursive (vector length is 1), 2-line has a vector length of 2, and plane SOR has a vector length of NZ.

As the clever reader has already guessed, there is a trick that dramatically improves the situation. As with D4 Gaussian elimination, the key is a renumbering of the grid blocks. This is illustrated in Figs. 1, 2, 5, 6, and 9. These numbering schemes produce matrices like those illustrated in Figs. 4, 8, and 10.

It can be shown that line SOR applied to any matrix derived from the numbering system of Fig. 2 will have a maximum vector length of $NX \cdot NY/2$. (Either NX or NY must be an even number, or the LSOR algorithm becomes rather complicated.) Similarly, 2-line SOR applied to the numbering system of Fig. 6 produces a maximum vector length of $NX \cdot NY/4$, and plane SOR yields vectors of length $NX/2$. (In the 2-line case NX should be even.)

Line SOR was coded in accordance with the numbering system of Fig. 2 and was then converted to vector form with CDC vector FORTRAN. All six test problems previously described were then solved on both the STAR 100 and the CYBER 203. In addition the 40x10x5 and the 20x20x5 were run on the CDC 6600. The results are summarized in Table 4.

As in the case of Gaussian elimination it is found that the CDC 6600 run times are nearly identical to the STAR 100 in scalar mode. The vector runs on the first three problems show that computer time on a basis of microseconds/iteration/grid block declines with vector length, but the vectors are so long in all cases (200-800) that the effect is not dramatic. The scalar performance of the CYBER 203 exceeds that of the STAR 100 by a factor of about 4.95 in all cases.

The most dramatic result, however, is that the vector efficiency factor for the STAR 100 ranges from 35 to 43 and that of the CYBER 203 from 44 to 54. Remember, these are effectively speed factors rela-

tive to the CDC 6600, a very respectable piece of hardware, even in 1979. Conversion of the best results (the 40x40x5 problem) to floating point operation counts, ignoring overhead, yields the following:

$$((25 \text{ iter.}) \ (9 \text{ adds} + 9 \text{ mults.})$$

$$+ 10 \text{ adds} + 11 \text{ mults.} + 1 \text{ divide}) \times 8000 \text{ grid blocks}$$

$$\div 0.1542 \text{ sec.} = 24.5 \text{ megaflops}$$

This compares to a hardware design maximum for the same mix of operations of approximately 37. It is therefore clear that LSOR is an extremely effective algorithm on these machines.

It is also impressive that an 8000 grid block finite difference network can be solved in 0.15 sec. (0.75 microseconds/grid block/iteration) Furthermore, LSOR beat D4 Gaussian elimination in these tests by factors ranging from 15 to 141.

STRONGLY IMPLICIT PROCEDURE (SIP)

The strongly implicit procedure (SIP) has been demonstrated to be an effective solution technique for many systems of finite difference equations;[3,4] however, it appears to be very poorly suited for use on a vector computer. The algorithm is highly recursive and apparently cannot benefit from a renumbering of equations such as succeeded for SOR.

The best use of SIP on a vector computer may prove to be as an approximate solution technique applied to planes within the context of a plane SOR algorithm. Vectors of length NX/2 would be generated with the numbering system of Fig. 9. This combination of SIP and plane SOR could exhibit rapid convergence for systems that trouble LSOR, such as 3-D cylindrical coordinates.

To date no attempt has been made to test the performance of SIP in view of its lack of promise.

DISCUSSION OF RESULTS

The advantages of vectorizing Gaussian elimination and SOR subroutines are obvious from the results presented above. On the STAR 100, efficiency factors ranging from 9 to 25 were achieved with D4 Gaussian elimination and 35 to 43 with LSOR. Since the scalar performance of the CYBER 203 has been improved relative to the STAR 100 and vector performance is relatively unchanged, the benefits of vectorization on the CYBER 203 are less dramatic. Nevertheless, vectorization improves D4 elimination by a factor of 3-9.5 while LSOR improves by a factor of approximately 10 in all 6 examples.

The benefits realized by vectorizing matrix solution algorithms should extend to a complete reservoir simulator. After the one time cost of input and output each time step of a reservoir simulator can be broken up into four calculation phases (1) well calculations, (2) coefficient generation, (3) matrix solution, and (4) overhead. Overhead typically should be less than 1% of the time step computing time.

Now that this work has demonstrated the dramatic computer savings possible in the matrix solution, the next step will be to vectorize the coefficient generation and well calculations. It should be possible to vectorize both of these reasonably well, particularly the coefficient generation. It is unlikely, however, that a simulator developed for use on a scalar computer will be structured for optimum vector performance; therefore, extensive modification of code will generally be required to take maximum advantage of vector capabilities.

Even if nothing more than the matrix solution algorithms are vectorized, overall simulator performance will improve as the work done by the solution algorithm becomes an increasingly large portion of the total work. The work done by Gaussian elimination per grid block increases as the square of band width, so any program relying on Gauss will quickly be dominated by the elimination work as problem size increases. This dominance will occur with reasonably small grids if the elimination routine must simultaneously determine multiple unknowns for each grid block.

For example, in INTERCOMP's Combustion Model over 90% of the work per time step is in the matrix solution phase of the calculation. Since this program typically solves simultaneously for 6 (m) or more unknowns per grid block the half band for a problem would be m·NY·NZ. Therefore, using an m of 6, Table 1 indicates that significant efficiency factors will be achieved, even for very small problems.

Theoretically, vectorization of the D4 elimination routine would reduce the total run time for a 6x6x3 combustion problem by a factor of 6.4 on the STAR 100 and 3.6 on the CYBER 203. (The CYBER 203 vectorization would come on top of its 5 fold computer time reduction in scalar mode relative to the STAR 100 for a total computer time reduction of about 18 relative to STAR 100 scalar performance.) Moreover, since efficiency factors seem to increase almost linearly with increases in half band width up to widths of about 400, the run time for the Combustion Model also should increase only linearly with increasing band width, rather than as the square.

Again a theoretical projection of the work for the Combustion Model would say that on the STAR 100 a (15x15x4) grid with 6 unknowns per point would run only about 9 times longer than a (6x6x3) grid with 6 unknowns. The run time increase on a scalar machine would be nearly 100. These projections indicate that it is practical to run 1000 grid block combustion studies on the STAR 100 or the CYBER 203.

Successive overrelaxation also tends to consume an increasing fraction of the total run time as problem size increases. This follows from the expected increase in the number of iterations required to obtain convergence.

In transient problems the accumulation term added to the matrix diagonal makes the matrix diagonally dominant[2]. If this term is large relative to the matrix coefficients, then the number of LSOR iterations will not change dramatically with problem size. This seems to be the case for the examples presented in this work.

CONCLUSIONS

On the basis of the work described here the following conclusions have been reached:

1. The D4 Gaussian elimination method can be coded on a vector computer to yield computer time reductions relative to standard Gaussian elimination that approach theoretical values.

2. Successive overrelaxation (SOR) methods vectorize very successfully if grid blocks are properly ordered prior to solution.

3. Vectorization of D4 Gaussian elimination on a CDC STAR 100 computer can reduce scalar run times by factors as large as 26. On the CDC CYBER 203 vectorization of this algorithm can reduce scalar run times by a factor approaching 10. (Relative to the scalar performance of the STAR 100, vectorization on the CYBER 203 reduces run times by factors as large as 32.)

4. Vectorization of line successive overrelaxation (LSOR) can reduce scalar run times by factors in excess of 43 on the STAR 100. Scalar run times on the CYBER 203 can be reduced by factors exceeding 10. (Relative to the scalar performance of the STAR 100, vectorization on the CYBER 203 can cut run times by factors as large as 54.)

NOMENCLATURE

C - Clock cycles required for a vector operation

CR - Compressibility, $psia^{-1}$

N - Vector length

P - Pressure, psia

PV - Pore volume, bbls.

q - Production rate, bbls./day

R - Proportionality factor

S - Vector startup time, clock cycles

TX - x-direction flow coefficient, bbls./day-psi

TY - y-direction flow coefficient, bbls./day-psi

TZ - z-direction flow coefficient, bbls./day-psi

Δt - Time step size, days

Subscripts and superscripts

i - x-direction index
j - y-direction index   missing subscripts imply (i,j,k)
k - z-direction index

n - Old time level

n+1- New time level

REFERENCES

1.   Price, H. S., and Coats, K. H.,: "Direct Methods in Reservoir Simulation," *J. Soc. Petr. Eng.* (1974) Vol. 14, No. 3, pp 295-308.

2.   Varga, R. S., *Matrix Iterative Analysis*, Prentice-Hall, Inc. (1962).

3.   Stone, H. L., *SIAM J. Numerical Anal.* Vol. 5, No. 3, (Sept. 1968).

4.   Weinstein, H. G., Stone, H. L. and Kwan, T. V., "Iterative Procedure for Solution of Systems of Parabolic and Elliptic Equations in Three Dimensions," *I&EC Fundamentals*, Vol. 8, No. 2, (May, 1969).

APPENDIX

CDC STAR Floating Point Hardware. The vector hardware in a CDC STAR 100 or CYBER 203 consists of 2 units called pipe 1 and pipe 2. The "pipe" terminology is appropriate since operands "flow" through these units passing from segment to segment.

Both pipe 1 and pipe 2 have the ability to do vector addition and multiplication, while pipe 2 alone does vector division and square root.

It is possible to procure 2 pairs of 64 bit operands from memory per cycle (40 nsec.); however, it takes 6 cycles to perform a normalized addition. If only one operand pair could be processed at a time, it would not be possible to use the full memory band-width. However, since the pipes are segmented, i.e., they can process a different pair of operands at each segment of the pipe, each pipe can have six operand pairs present at various stages of addition. Hence, once the pipes are full, each can accept a pair of addends each cycle and produce one result.

The production of two 64 bit additions each 40 nsec. means 50 million results per second, i.e., 50 megaflops. If 32 bit operands were used, conceptually each pipe could be thought of as two pipes, producing 2 results per 40 nsec., or 100 megaflops.

Vector multiplication of 64 bit operands requires each pair of operands to pass through the pipes twice. Hence, the pipes accept operand pairs for vector multiplication every *other* cycle, with a resultant rate of 25 megaflops. For 32 bit operands the pipes are wide enough to accommodate one pair each cycle, resulting in a vector multiplication rate of 100 megaflops. Significant multiplication (64-bit) is divided into 10 segments; hence, it takes a little longer to fill and empty the pipes than for addition.

Since only pipe 2 does division and square roots, the result rate for these operations is half that for multiplication, i.e., 12.5 megaflops for 64 bit operands and 50 megaflops for 32 bit operands. The length of pipe 2 for these operations is 24 segments.

The vector operations that have been discussed can be broken into two phases. The first is a transient phase during which the pipe(s) are filling. The number of machine cycles spent in this phase, which is independent of vector length, is "lumped" together into what is called startup time. This includes those cycles when the microcode unit is busy setting up the stream buffers and other ancillary operations to facilitate vector operations.

The second phase, or steady-state phase, begins when the pipe(s) are full. Its length is directly proportional to the length of the vectors being processed, the constant of proportionality being the number of cycles required to process a pair of operands.

Hence, the time to execute vector instructions of the above types is S+RN where

S = startup time

R = steady state result rate

N = length of the vector.

For 64 bit operands the timings for vector arithmetic are as follows:

Normalized vector addition $71 + N/2$

Significant vector multiplication $159 + N$ cycles

Significant vector division $163 + 2N$.

The difference in startups reflects, among other things, the fact that the number of segments differs for each operation.

TABLE 1
PERFORMANCE OF D4 GAUSSIAN ELIMINATION

Problem	CDC 6600	STAR 100			CYBER 203		
		Scalar	Vector	EFF	Scalar	Vector	EFF
40x10x5	10.81 (5.405)	11.04 (5.520)	1.183 (.5915)	9.33	2.47 (1.235)	0.754 (.377)	14.64
40x20x5	* *	70.34 (17.58)	4.116 (1.029)	17.09	15.98 (3.995)	3.040 (.760)	23.14
40x40x5	* *	366.26 (45.78)	14.239 (1.780)	25.72	83.63 (10.45)	11.435 (1.429)	32.03
20x20x5	* *	24.01 (12.01)	1.660 (0.8300)	14.46	5.43 (2.717)	1.173 (.587)	20.46
20x20x10	* *	170.82 (42.71)	6.828 (1.707)	25.02	39.03 (9.758)	5.453 (1.363)	31.33
20x20x20	* *	* *	29.345 (3.668)	*	241.42 (30.18)	25.200 (3.150)	*

Elapsed computer time is tabulated in seconds.

( ) indicates elapsed time in milliseconds per grid block.

EFF is efficiency factor (STAR 100 scalar time divided by STAR 100 or CYBER 203 vector time.)

* indicates that the run was not made.

TABLE 2
COMPARISON OF D4 WITH STANDARD GAUSSIAN ELIMINATION

STAR 100 Vector Timing, Sec.

Problem	Standard	D4	Standard/D4 Actual	Standard/D4 Theoretical[1]
40x10x5	2.024	1.183	1.71	2.32
40x20x5	9.219	4.116	2.24	2.69
40x40x5	46.728	14.239	3.28	*
20x20x5	4.511	1.660	2.72	*
20x20x10	22.837	6.828	3.34	*
20x20x20	135.135	29.345	4.61	5.00

*Not calculated due to the complexity of the theoretical work estimate.

TABLE 3
COMPUTER TIME DISTRIBUTION WITHIN THE D4 GAUSSIAN ELIMINATION ROUTINE

Code Segment	40x10x5		20x20x10	
	Scalar	Vector	Scalar	Vector
Band construction	2.95	21.09	0.71	7.98
Factorization	93.88	66.21	98.47	87.05
Forward and Back Solutions	1.70	6.12	0.51	2.71
Solution Storage	1.47	5.58	0.31	2.25
	100.00	100.00	100.00	100.00

TABLE 4
VECTOR PERFORMANCE OF LSOR

Problem	ITER	CDC 6600	STAR 100			CYBER 203		
			Scalar	Vector	EFF	Scalar	Vector	EFF
40x10x5	29	2.392 (41.24)	2.315 (39.91)	0.0636 (1.097)	36.4	0.4671 (8.053)	0.0507 (0.874)	45.6
40x20x5	27	*	4.321 (40.01)	0.1064 (0.985)	40.6	0.3731 (8.084)	0.0848 (0.785)	51.0
40x40x5	26	*	8.322 (40.01)	0.1924 (0.925)	43.3	1.6757 (8.056)	0.1542 (0.741)	54.0
20x20x5	27	2.212 (40.96)	2.157 (39.94)	0.0612 (1.133)	35.3	0.4346 (8.048)	0.0490 (0.907)	44.0
20x20x10	26	*	4.249 (40.86)	0.1165 (1.120)	36.5	0.3520 (8.192)	0.0933 (0.897)	45.5
20x20x20	25	*	8.233 (41.17)	0.2241 (1.121)	36.7	1.6632 (8.316)	0.1791 (0.896)	46.0

TABLE 5
COMPUTER TIME DISTRIBUTION WITHIN THE VECTORIZED LSOR ROUTINE STAR 100

Code Segment	40x10x5
Initialization	13
Residual calculation	36
Factorization	2
Forward solution	17
Back solution	10
Relaxation	9
Convergence test	2
Solution storage	11
	100

Elapsed computer time is tabulated in seconds.

( ) indicates elapsed time in microseconds per grid block per iteration.

ITER is total iterations

EFF is efficiency factor (scalar STAR 100 time divided by vector STAR 100 or CYBER 203 time)

* indicates that the run was not made.

53

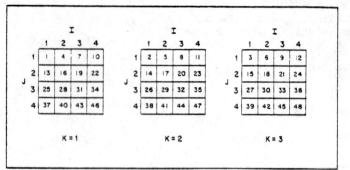

Fig. 1 - Grid block order for normal z-direction LSOR or Gaussian elimination. (4x4x3)

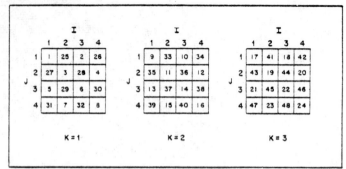

Fig. 2 - Grid block order for vectorized z-direction LSOR. (4x4x3 grid)

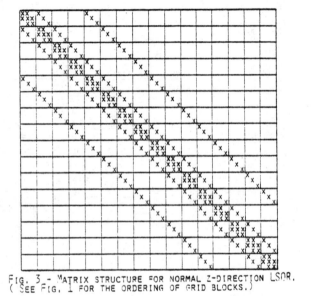

Fig. 3 - Matrix structure for normal z-direction LSOR. (See Fig. 1 for the ordering of grid blocks.)

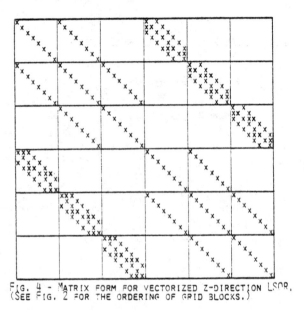

Fig. 4 - Matrix form for vectorized z-direction LSOR. (See Fig. 2 for the ordering of grid blocks.)

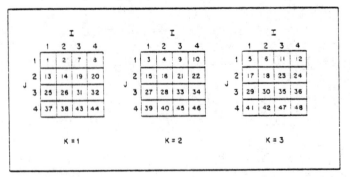

Fig. 5 - Grid block order for normal 2-line SOR. (z-direction lines)

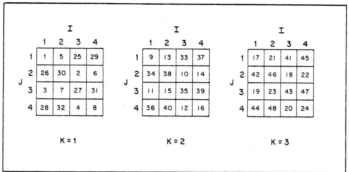

FIG. 6 - GRID BLOCK ORDER FOR A VECTORIZED 2-LINE SOR.
(Z-DIRECTION LINES)

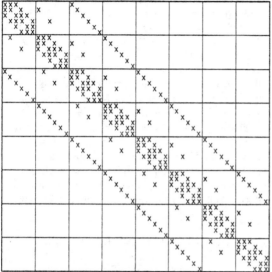

FIG. 7 - MATRIX STRUCTURE FOR NORMAL 2-LINE SOR.
(SEE FIG. 5 FOR THE ORDERING OF GRID BLOCKS.)

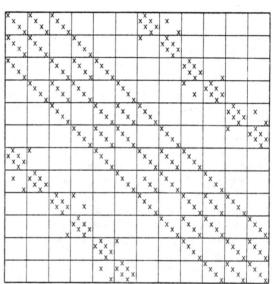

FIG. 8 - MATRIX STRUCTURE FOR VECTORIZED 2-LINE SOR.
(SEE FIG. 6 FOR THE ORDERING OF GRID BLOCKS.)

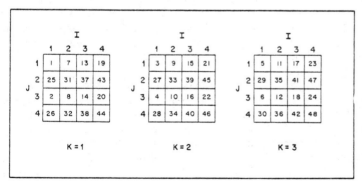

FIG. 9 - GRID BLOCK ORDER FOR VECTORIZED XZ-PLANE SOR.
(4x4x3 GRID)

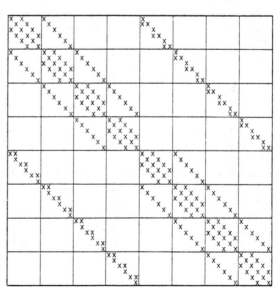

FIG. 10 - MATRIX STRUCTURE FOR VECTORIZED XZ-PLANE SOR.
(SEE FIG. 9 FOR THE ORDERING OF GRID BLOCKS.)

Reprinted with permission from *Proceedings of the National Computer Conference*, Volume 47, 1978, pages 395–407. Copyright © 1978 by AFIPS Press.

Plasma simulation on the UCLA CHI computer system

by JOHN M. DAWSON, ROBERT W. HUFF and CHENG-CHIN WU

University of California
Los Angeles, California

INTRODUCTION

Computer simulations have played an important role in fusion energy research. Although the basic physical principles of plasma physics are well understood, the coupled physical phenomena are so complex that analytical analyses cannot be easily carried out. Moreover, laboratory experiments are costly. With the enormous power of modern computers, one naturally resorts to computer simulations to gain insights into physical phenomena, as well as to guide the design and planning of experiments.

In order to cope with the rich and disparate phenomena occurring in a plasma, a wide variety of simulation models are required.[1] The models may generally be classified as: particle models, which treat the plasma at the microscopic level by following the motion of a large number of particles; fluid models, which treat plasma on a more macroscopic level; and also hybrid models which are a mixture of the first two models.

It is obvious that one cannot do plasma experiments in a computer with the 10^{12} to 10^{19} particles involved in physical problems of interest. Still, one would hope to have as many as 1 million particles on a mesh system of 64^3 for particle codes. For fluid codes, one may want a system of 64^3 to have better resolution, especially when local structure is present.

This shows that plasma simulations require a large computing capability and therefore have only been carried out on large computers, such as the IBM360/91 or CDC7600. Nevertheless, few attempts have been made for systems as large as mentioned above, for they need several megawords of storage and a considerable amount of computer time for a significant run.

Lately, with the development of computer technology, microprogrammable specialized minicomputers appear to provide the possibility of doing some of the jobs effectively and economically. Because of a successful pilot study[2] initiated by John M. Dawson and Burton D. Fried of the UCLA Plasma Physics Group and Glen J. Culler of Culler/Harrison, Inc. (CHI), a CHI plasma simulation computer system is being installed at UCLA. Our preliminary results indicate that the system offers a significant improvement in performance and, most importantly, it reduces cost by about two orders of magnitude from the IBM360/91.

The CHI plasma simulation system consists of six micro-processors: one array processor (AP-120B, manufactured by Floating Point Systems, Inc.),[3] one macro-processor (MP-32 made by CHI)[4] and four I/O processors (IOP made by CHI). The AP does most of the calculations, the IOP moves data around, and the MP does scheduling and control. Mass data are stored on disk. The parallel processing among and within these processors accounts for most of the performance advantage of the system. Further details of the system are given in the third section of this paper.

Three plasma simulation codes have been tested on the system: a 2-½ dimensional electrostatic particle simulation code,[2] and both 2-½ and 3 dimensional ideal MHD fluid codes.[5] The basic structure of these codes is described in the third section, together with comparative performance data. Conclusions are presented in last section.

THE UCLA CHI COMPUTER SYSTEM

General description of the system

The configuration of the UCLA CHI computer system is shown in Figure 1. It includes a macro-processor (MP-32), an array processor (AP-120B) and four input/output processors (IOP). Data Throughput and capacity of each processor is summarized in Table I. The AP does high speed floating point arithmetic operations. Further descriptions of the AP are given later.

The MP is used for control, I/O, bookkeeping calculations, and integer arithmetic operations, and serves as the host computer for the AP. In the present system it supports an interactive mathematical system (Math System),[7] provides a text editor, file facilities, the necessary assemblers and linkers.

The IOP's are fixed program micro-processors with access to both AP and MP main data memories and the UNIBUS. Their primary function is to provide high level control over access to the disk drives. Each IOP functions as a disk formatter supporting any of the four disk drives. This allows the configuration of individual drive capacities from 5 million to over 60 million 38 bit words. Transfer time per word is under 4 μs. In addition to transferring data between the AP main data memory and disk, the IOP can also transfer data

Macro Processor (MP-32A)

(a)   A 16-bit fixed point processor with a 1/6 μs machine cycle.

(b)   Memories:

> 64 words scratch pad data memory
>
> 512 words fixed instruction memory
>
> 64 words writeable instruction memory
>
> 65,536 words of 1/3 μs instruction and data memory (CD).

(c)   Integer multiplication of two 16-bit words in 1/3 μs.

(d)   Functions:

> (i)   Controls high-speed local station displays.
> Display rate: 2 μs/point
>> < 2 ms for longest line
>>
>> > 4000 characters/second.
>
> (ii) Schedules IOPs and Array Processor.
>
> (iii) Controls data transfer to modems (1200-9600 baud) and
> other PDP-11 compatible I/O devices over Universal I/O bus.

Disk-IOPs

(a)   Disk capacity: 4 Trident T80 drives - over 16 million 38-bit words each.

(b)   IOPs are fixed program micro-processors.

(c)   Data transfer rate: Data on all four disks can be simultaneously
transferred to/from AP-MD or MP-CD, each at 250,000 words/second.
Any IOP can be used for memory transfer between AP-MD and MP-CD at
1,000,000 words/second.

Array Processor (AP-120B)

(a)   A 38-bit floating point arithmetic unit with maximum speed of 12 megaflops.

(b)   Memories:

> (i)   Two 32-word data pad memories
> 2560 words 1/3 μs fixed table memory
> 65536 words 1/3 μs data memory (MD)
> 512 words instruction memory
>
> (ii) Data pad access is immediate. Table memory may be referenced
> every cycle, with an access delay of two cycles. Data memory
> may be referenced every other cycle, with an access delay of
> three cycles.

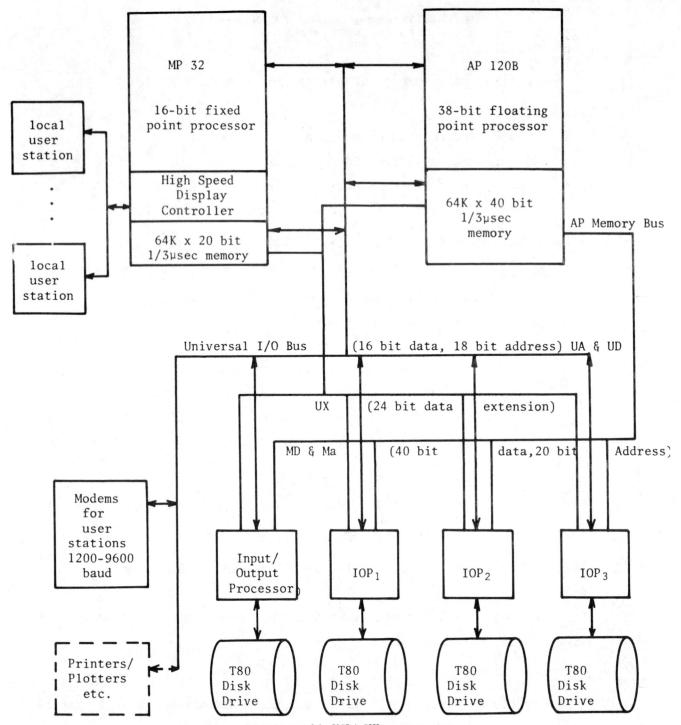

Figure 1—Block diagram of the UCLA CHI computer system

between the MP memory and disk or perform memory to memory transfers between or within either memory.

Each processor can process independently while the whole system is controlled by the MP (host processor). Each processor is scheduled to perform a specific process. It interrupts the host when it completes each process, then begins immediately, without having to wait for service from the MP, on its next process if one has been scheduled for it. This parallel logic computing capability is one of the main features of the system and makes possible the handling of large scale computing problems. An illustration is given in the third section.

AP-120B processor

Since all floating point calculations (therefore most of model calculations) are performed in the AP, it is of importance to explore the structure of the AP.[3] The architecture of the machine is shown in Figure 2; and its features are summarized in Table I.

Special features are noted as follows: (1) Programs, constants, and data each reside in separate, independent memories: program source memory, table memory and main data memory, respectively. Thus, it eliminates memory accessing conflicts. (2) Independent pipelining floating-point multiplier and adder units allow multiply and add operations to each be initiated every $1/6$ μs. (3) Two blocks of fast access floating-point accumulators, DPX and DPY with 32 locations each, are available for temporary storage of intermediate results from the multiplier, adder, or memory. (4) Address indexing and counting functions are performed by an inde-

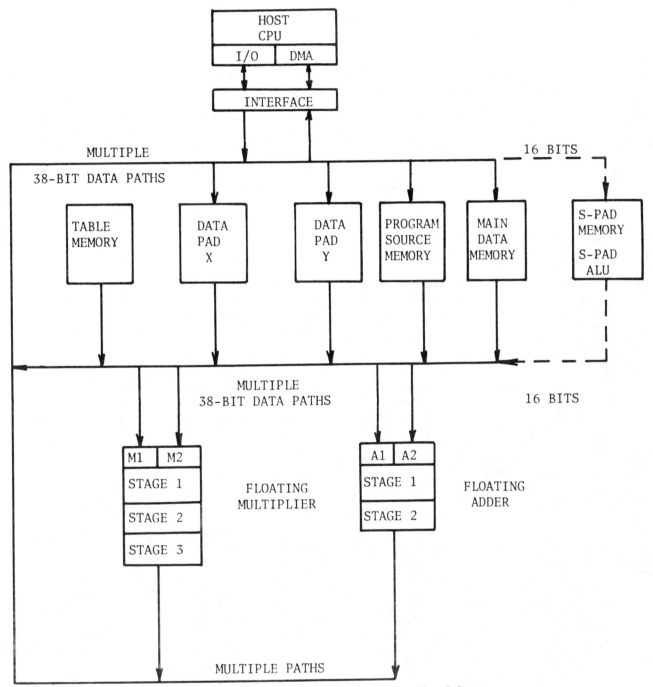

Figure 2—Block diagram of the AP-120B micro-processor (From Reference 3)

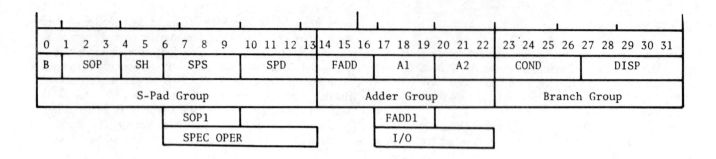

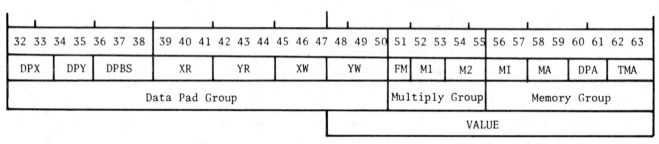

Figure 3—AP-120B Instruction Field Layout (From Reference 3)

pendent integer arithmetic unit (S-Pad and ALU). (5) Floating-point data is represented by 38-bit words which gives a precision of 8.1 decimal digits.

Each instruction word has 64 bits so that many different operations may be performed concurrently during each cycle. The instruction field layout is shown in Figure 3. It is separated into five general areas: program control, address control, arithmetic, memory and I/O. The highly parallel and pipeline structure of the AP-120B make it possible to achieve fast execution with lower speed logic and thus with lower cost. It requires $1/2$ μs for a single multiplication and $1/3$ μs for a single addition in the AP. But with adder and multiplier units working in parallel and with their pipeline structure, the AP allows multiply and add operations to each be initiated every $1/6$ μs. This gives a maximum speed of 12 megaflops comparable with a large general purpose computer. In the three test plasma simulation problems the speed achieved is about 4 megaflops for the fluid codes and 6 megaflops for the particle code.

In order to achieve this high speed capability, each instruction of a micro-coded program should use as many fields as possible. For this reason, our experience in coding plasma simulation codes suggests that calculations done in the manner of particle by particle, or grid-point by grid-point may be more efficient than trying to vectorize the code. Besides, vectorization usually requires several additional arrays for intermediate results. In contrast, vector operations are useful in applications such as digital signal processing, where the AP is called upon to perform vector operations at high speed. The Math System is designed for efficient support of these AP vector operations.

The basic arithmetic operations in the AP are addition and

multiplication. The divide operation is carried out in software with speed of 3.83 μs. Hence, it is essential in the programming to use as few divide operations as possible. For instance, there is no divide operation in the $2^1/2$D particle code; however, one such operation is required in the MHD codes. In the $2^1/2$D MHD code, the divide operation uses 7 percent of the total processing time of 50 μs per grid point.

As previously mentioned, in the CHI system, the IOP's have a separate data bus into the AP main memory from that used by the AP processor. Thus the CHI system eliminates the bottleneck problem[8] which may exist in other host setups where all data must enter and leave the AP through the interface module and the host computer.

Programming languages

Programming can be carried out in four languages, which include two machine languages, the AP- and the MP- micro languages; and two high level languages, the MP-macro language[6] and the Math System language.[7] The AP micro-instructions have just been mentioned. The MP micro-instruction consists of 28 bits and provides for parallel operations. The MP macro-language is a set of macro-instructions which are pre-programmed in both the AP and the MP micro-languages and is used for system programming.

The Math System language, programmed in the MP micro- and macro-language is an interactive interpreter, and supports operations of mathematical functions applied to real or complex vector data as well as useful graphics. It can execute either interactively or from a program consisting of

```
(+) A, B → C          "C(i): = A(i) + B(i) for all i


(SIN) C               "C(i): = sin C(i) for all i


(DISPLAY)             "plot C(i) vs. i
```

Figure 4—A Math System program for the calculation, $C_i = \sin(A_i + B_i)$,
with three vectors A, B and C

these mathematical operations. Since the Math System uses vector data which are entities usually occurring in physical problems, programming in this language is more concise and less error-prone than in the standard Fortran language.

A Math System program is shown in Figure 4 for the calculation of $C_i = \sin(A_i + B_i)$ with three vectors A, B and C. The operation $\oplus A, B \to C$ calculates $C_i = A_i + B_i$ for all i, so does the operation SIN C for $C_i = \sin(C_i)$. The program therefore saves an explicit loop that is required in a Fortran program. The statement DISPLAY will plot C_i against i in terms of its natural units.

In plasma simulation codes, we anticipate using only the Math System language and the AP micro-language. AP micro-programming is done only where the development of maximally efficient routines is warranted, as the particle push routines for particle simulations. The remaining routines, such as initialization, control, and force-calculation routines in the particle codes, which require only a small fraction of total processing time, are easily coded in the Math System language.

The operating system supports both batch and on-line usage. Thus, it allows old production or test runs of a code simultaneous with code development, editing or on-line Math System usage.

PLASMA SIMULATION MODELS AND THEIR TEST RESULTS ON THE CHI SYSTEM

A particle code and a fluid code, which together represent a wide spectrum of plasma simulation models, have been adapted to the CHI computer system. The particle code is the standard $2\frac{1}{2}$ dimensional electrostatic model with a constant magnetic field plus mirroring.[2] The fluid code is an ideal magnetohydrodynamics (MHD) code,[5] which is being implemented in both $2\frac{1}{2}$ and 3-dimensional versions. These are very basic models that include the most important general features of plasma simulations.

In this section, we present basic structures of these codes, the utilization of the resources of the CHI system and their test results. Details of the models and their numerical method aspects will not be discussed here.

A $2\frac{1}{2}$ dimensional electrostatic model with a constant magnetic field

In a particle model, the trajectories of a large number of charged particles (electrons and ions) under the influence of self-consistent fields are followed in time. The particular model considered consists of a large number of charged rods parallel to the z-axis which are allowed to have velocity components in the x, y, and z directions as shown in Figure 5. It allows spatial variation in the x and y directions. The system is periodic in both x and y directions such that particles that leave one side of the system are re-entered at the opposite side. A uniform static magnetic field is permitted to point in an arbitrary direction. The charged rods move under the influence of their self-consistent electric fields and the given magnetic field. In addition, the rods may be reflected at the y-boundaries if a mirroring condition is satisfied by the velocity components parallel and perpendicular to the magnetic field.

The motion of the system is generated in the computer by a leap-frog time difference scheme, using a standard finite-size particle model, in which the charge of a particle is distributed over a finite region about the center of mass, and also using a dipole expansion technique. The finite-size particle model effectively reduces undesirable collisions and also numerical noise from the discrete nature of the spatial grid. However, in the following discussions, only the basics of the model are presented.

Mathematically, the simulation model solves the following equations self-consistently:

$$\vec{\nabla} \cdot \vec{E}(\vec{r}) = \rho(\vec{r}), \tag{1}$$

$$\frac{d\vec{v}_i}{dt} = \frac{q_i}{m_i}(\vec{E}(\vec{r}_i) + \vec{v}_i \times \vec{B}(\vec{r}_i)), \tag{2}$$

$$\frac{d\vec{r}_i}{dt} = \vec{v}_i. \tag{3}$$

$\vec{E}$ and $\vec{B}$ are the electric and magnetic fields, respectively; $\vec{B}$ is assumed to be a constant vector. ρ is the charge density distribution and $\vec{r}_i$, $\vec{v}_i$ stand for the position and velocity of the ith particle with charge q_i and mass m_i.

In the $2\frac{1}{2}$D model, a spatial grid mesh in the x-y plane

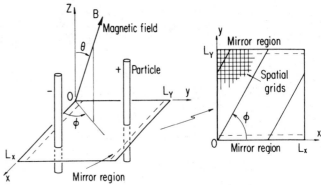

Figure 5—2-½ D Plasma particle model with mirror

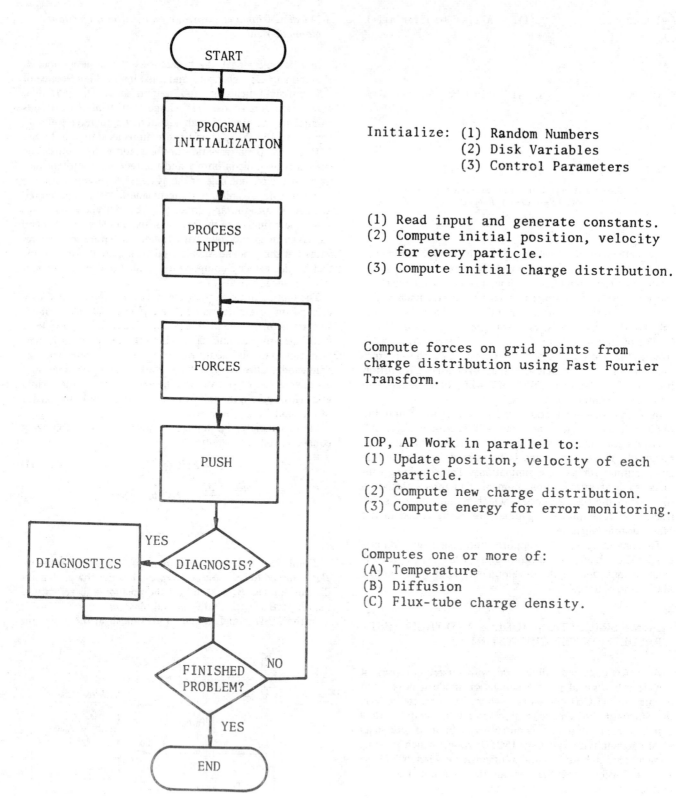

Initialize: (1) Random Numbers
            (2) Disk Variables
            (3) Control Parameters

(1) Read input and generate constants.
(2) Compute initial position, velocity
    for every particle.
(3) Compute initial charge distribution.

Compute forces on grid points from
charge distribution using Fast Fourier
Transform.

IOP, AP Work in parallel to:
(1) Update position, velocity of each
    particle.
(2) Compute new charge distribution.
(3) Compute energy for error monitoring.

Computes one or more of:
(A) Temperature
(B) Diffusion
(C) Flux-tube charge density.

Figure 6—Program flow of the particle model

is introduced. All macroscopic quantities, such as $\vec{E}$ and ρ are calculated on the grid points. The basic flow of the program is shown in Figure 6. It starts with setting up initial configuration of the system by assigning $\vec{v}_i$ and $\vec{r}_i$ and q_i for each particle and specifying the $\vec{B}$ field.

Inside the loop, calculations are performed in two stages: (a) Force calculation: $\rho(\vec{r})$ is used to solve Eq. (1) for the electric field $\vec{E}$. Eq. (1) is solved efficiently by fast Fourier transforms. (This technique is especially useful when finite-size particle model is used.) (b) Particle push: After $\vec{E}$ is obtained, the particle positions and velocities are advanced in time by means of Eqs. (2) and (3), using the leap-frog method with a dipole expansion of the force. As each particle position is updated, its contribution to $\rho(\vec{r})$, including dipole terms, is calculated. We are now ready to start the next time step.

In the actual code with the finite size particle model and dipole expansion technique, the data required are 6 words per particle, i.e., $\vec{r}$ and $\vec{v}$ with three components each, 9 words per grid points which include E_x, E_y, ρ, D_x, D_y, E_{xx}, E_{xy}, E_{yx}, and E_{yy}. (The last six variables are dipole terms.) Since particles are grouped according to species, it is not necessary to specify charge and mass for each particle individually.

For a 10^6 particle and 64^2 grid-point system, more than 90 percent of the computer time is used in the particle PUSH routine. Therefore the PUSH routine is coded in the AP micro-language with maximal optimization, whereas other routines are efficiently programmed in the Math System. The PUSH routine takes 13 μs per particle which is four times the speed of the corresponding IBM360/91 assembly-language code. The AP PUSH routine is not a direct translation of the corresponding Fortran code, but a new design for an efficient usage of the AP. There are 33 multiplications and 45 additions in the routine, and therefore an effective speed of 6 megaflops is achieved.

The data storage requirement as well as processing timing are given in Table II. To handle the large quantity of data the technique of parallel processing among the AP, the MP and the IOP's is used. To further explain this parallelism, a section of the Math System program is shown in Figure 7. The section is essentially the control program for pushing particles. The actual code, however, is a simple three-statement loop program for this two-disk system.

The instruction, OP PUSH BUFFI causes the AP to initiate or schedule an AP micro-program named PUSH for advancing particles whose descriptors are in the array BUFFI of AP main memory. The execution will begin as soon as the AP has completed all its previously scheduled processes and data BUFF1 is free from operations associated with other processors. If the AP is ready but data block BUFF1 is still being loaded with data by the IOP, the AP will wait until the latter action is completed. The instruction, MOVE INDISK→BUFF1, will instruct an IOP to move data from disk that is used for input to the location BUFF1 in AP main memory. An IOP will perform the operation once it comes to the instruction and neither block of data is being used by other processors. Similar operation is defined for the instruction MOVE BUFF1→OUTDISK.

Math System Program			Processor
. . .			
MOVE	INDISK → BUFF3		IOP1
MOVE	BUFF1 → OUTDISK		IOP2
OP	PUSH	BUFF2	AP
MOVE	INDISK → BUFF1		IOP1
MOVE	BUFF2 → OUTDISK		IOP2
OP	PUSH	BUFF3	AP
MOVE	INDISK → BUFF2		IOP1
MOVE	BUFF3 → OUTDISK		IOP2
OP	PUSH	BUFF1	AP
. . .			

Figure 7—A section of a Math System program for controlling the AP and the IOP's in particle push

Therefore, in executing the program shown in Figure 7, two IOP's and the AP are operating simultaneously: One IOP loads into one block of AP main memory a block of old particle data from one disk, the AP executes PUSH routine in advancing particle data stored in the second block of AP memory, while the other IOP stores a third block of updated particle data from AP memory into the second disk. By choosing adequate blocksize and using enough number of IOP's, it is possible to eliminate restrictions on over-all processing time imposed by I/O.

To handle 10^6 particles, four disks are used with two disks for input, and two disks for output. The two pair of disks are interchanged with respect to I/O at each time step. The size of block is chosen to be 4K words (a track or 680 particle descriptors). It takes 17.7 ms for the AP to update two blocks of data and 20 ms for each IOP to transfer one track of data between disk and AP memory. (The transfer rate of 20 ms per track includes a 20 percent allowance for the loss of one rotation at the cylinder boundary). The over-all processing time is then slightly limited by I/O to 14.7 μs per particle.

Magnetohydrodynamic codes

The set of magnetohydrodynamic equations includes:

$$\frac{\partial \rho}{\partial t} = -\vec{\nabla}\cdot(\rho\vec{v}) + \epsilon\nabla^2\rho, \tag{4}$$

$$\frac{\partial}{\partial t}(\rho v_i) = -\frac{\partial}{\partial x_j}\left(\rho v_i v_j + \left(\rho T + \frac{B^2}{2}\right)\delta_{ij} - B_i B_j\right) + \nu\nabla^2\rho v_i - \lambda\rho v_i - \rho\vec{g}, \tag{5}$$

$$\frac{\partial \vec{B}}{\partial t} = \vec{\nabla}\times(\vec{v}\times\vec{B}) + \eta\nabla^2\vec{B}, \tag{6}$$

Data:

6 Words/particle x, y, z, v_x, v_y, v_z

9 Words/gridpoint: E_x, E_y, E_{xx}, E_{xy}, E_{yx}, E_{yy}, C, D_x, D_y

The particle descriptors are on disk, 680 particles/track, 1472 tracks, or 736 tracks on each of two disks for input, and the same for output, with the two pairs of disks being interchanged with respect to I/O at each timestep.

AP-Memory Allocation:

Electric Field arrays (6):	24k
Charge and dipole arrays (3):	12K
Particle buffers (5):	20k
Total	56k

Data Transfer Timing:

60 disk rotations/second or 16.7 ms/track, for a transfer rate of 24.5 μs/particle for each of two disks, or an overall rate of 12.2 μs/particle on a track-by-track basis. Loss of one rotation at the cylinder boundary (5 tracks/cylinder) increases this by 20%, giving 15 μs/particle on a cylinder-by-cylinder basis.

Processing Time:

Dominated by the particle-push AP routine for this system size.
Present AP code estimated at 13 μs/particle.
Thus the AP processing is slower than the I/O on a track-by-track basis, but is faster than the I/O on an overall basis.

Overall Timing:

15 μs/particle overall, or 15 seconds/timestep.
16 hours for a run of 4000 timesteps (to $\omega_p t = 1000$ @ $\Delta t = 0.25/\omega_p$)

Data:

7 variables: $V_x, V_y, V_z, B_x, B_y, B_z, \rho$.

Each variable occupies an array of dimension $(N + 3)*(N_y + 2)$, where N_x and N_y are the numbers of grids in x- and y-direction, respectively.

The system is periodic in y and bounded in x. Temperature is assumed to be constant.

AP-Memory Allocation:

$7*(N_x + 3)*(N_y + 2) + 30$ words.

With 45K memory, the system can be as large as 80 x 80.

AP-Program Memory:

445 program words.

Processing Time:

55 µsec/grid for a 20 x 20 system.

50 µsec/grid for a 40 x 40 system.

There are $1/2*(N_x + 1)*N_y$ grid calculations per time step in the leap-frog scheme.

$$\frac{\partial T}{\partial t} = -\vec{\nabla}\cdot(T\vec{v}) + (2-\gamma)T\vec{\nabla}\cdot\vec{v} + \frac{\eta(\gamma-1)}{\rho}(\vec{\nabla}\times\vec{B})^2$$

$$+ (\gamma-1)\nu\left(\frac{\partial v_i}{\partial x_j} + \frac{\partial v_j}{\partial x_i} - \delta_{ij}\vec{\nabla}\cdot\vec{v}\right)\frac{\partial v_i}{\partial x_j}$$

$$+ (\gamma-1)\kappa\nabla^2 T. \qquad (7)$$

Here, the mass density is denoted by ρ, the velocity by $\vec{v}$, the temperature by T, the magnetic field by $\vec{B}$ and the gravitational acceleration by $\vec{g}$. γ is the ratio of specific heats. The transport coefficients ϵ, ν, λ, η and κ are assumed to be constants.

The computer code solves the equations as an initial-value problem, by integrating them in time using an Eulerian grid and an explicit, conservative, leap-frog finite-difference scheme. The details of the numerical procedures can be found elsewhere.[1,5]

All variables are macroscopic and are defined at grid points. In a three-dimensional code, a three dimensional grid is introduced. For the case of $2^1/_2$ dimensional code, a two dimensional grid is used, with $\vec{v}$ and $\vec{B}$ still having three components.

The basic flow of the program as shown in Figure 8 is a loop over timestep, similar to that of particle model, except here the routine STEP performs one timestep integration of the MHD equations for all grid points. The routine STEP is coded in the AP micro-language, whereas other routines including initialization and control are in the Math System.

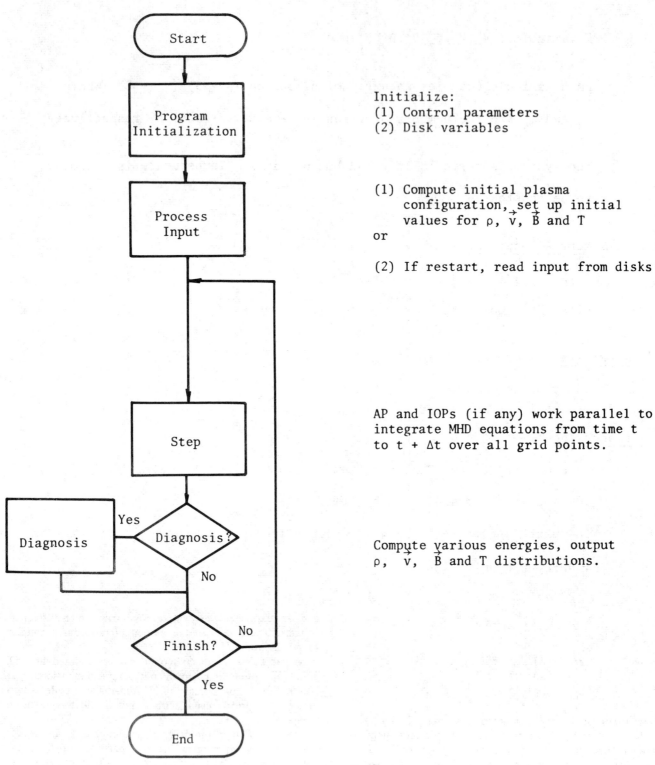

Initialize:
(1) Control parameters
(2) Disk variables

(1) Compute initial plasma
    configuration, set up initial
    values for ρ, $\vec{v}$, $\vec{B}$ and T
or

(2) If restart, read input from disks

AP and IOPs (if any) work parallel to
integrate MHD equations from time t
to t + Δt over all grid points.

Compute various energies, output
ρ, $\vec{v}$, $\vec{B}$ and T distributions.

Figure 8—Program flow of the MHD fluid codes

	IBM360/91	CHI SYSTEM
PARTICLE CODE		
Time/Particle Push	Assembly Code	
CPU	55 μs	13 μs
I/O	- -	0.6 × 24 μs
Overall	55 μs	14 μs
10^6 Particles, 4000 Timesteps		
Time	61 hr	16 hr
CPU Cost	32 k$	- -
I/O Cost	18 k$	- -
Total Cost	50 k$	0.3 k$
2-1/2D MHD CODE	Fortran Code (H-Compiler)	
Time/Gridpoint	130 μs	50 μs
3D MHD CODE	Fortran (H-Compiler)	
Time/Gridpoint	230 μs	90 μs
64^3 System, 4000 Timesteps		
Time	33 hr	13 hr
CPU Cost	17 k$	- -
I/O Cost	10 k$	- -
Total Cost	27 k$	0.24 k$

The routine STEP is coded in such a way that calculations are done grid-point by grid-point, which seems to be the most efficient method in utilizing parallel operations in the AP. The processing time for the 2½D code is 50 μs per grid as compared with 130 μs for a corresponding Fortran code on IBM360/91. For the 3D code, it is 90 μs on the CHI computer, while a Fortran code requires 230 μs on the IBM360/91. The number of floating point operations is 101 multiplications, 92 additions and 1 division for the 2½ code and 184 multiplications, 174 additions and 1 division for the 3D code. Both codes reach an effective speed of about 4 megaflops.

The storage requirement, processing timing and other statistics of the $2\frac{1}{2}$D code is given in Table III. This code is an isothermal one, in which temperature is a constant, so there are seven equations instead of eight. The AP main memory is big enough to store data for a system as large as 80^2.

In case of the 3D code, disks must be used; for instance, it requires two megawords of data in a 64^3 system. In each grid point calculation, eight variables defined on the grid point and its six nearest neighbor points, or a total of 56 numbers are used. However, some of these data can be saved for calculations at the next grid point in the column or adjacent grid point in the next column, so the need of data transfer is reduced. The technique of parallel processing between the IOP's and the AP is used.

Comparison with results on the IBM360/91

The comparison of these plasma simulation codes on the CHI system and the corresponding Fortran (or Assembly) codes on the IBM360/91 are given in Table IV. For executing a one-million-particle simulation or a 64^3 3D MHD code on the IBM360/91, we assume disks are used for storage. The I/O charges are based on this assumption.

The speed of the particle code is four times faster than the IBM assembly-language code. For the MHD codes, the speed advantage is not as good. Nevertheless, all codes attain an effective speed of 4 to 6 megaflops. Most importantly, the CHI system shows a tremendous savings in total cost, with better than a two-order-of-magnitude decrease in cost from the IBM360/91. The figures for the IBM360/91 are actual costs if the programs were run at UCLA. For the CHI computer system, estimates are based on the assumption that computer time charge is directly proportional to the price of the computer system.

In addition, we should point out that the CHI system achieves better accuracy than the IBM360/91 in single precision. One example is that the kinetic energy calculated in the $2\frac{1}{2}$D MHD code on the CHI machine is two digits more accurate than on the IBM360/91 in single precision.

CONCLUSION

We have presented a general description of the UCLA CHI computer system and have emphasized its special features, namely, two levels of parallelism in the system. Parallel processing among the AP, the MP, and the IOP's allows execution of large-scale problems, and a high degree of internal parallelism within each processor allows fast operations at very moderate cost. In addition the CHI system provides a time sharing operating system and supports a high level language, the Math System, which is particularly useful in solving physics related problems.

The test results for three plasma simulation models clearly show the capabilities of the system. It performs high speed execution of large problems at relatively low cost. Since the plasma simulation models are similar in structure to many simulation models in other research fields, the CHI computer system is expected to have a wide range of applications.[8]

ACKNOWLEDGMENTS

The authors gratefully acknowledge discussions with our colleagues at UCLA and CHI: G. Ball, G. J. Culler, M. Curtis, B. Fried, P. Kokelaar, M. McCammon, and P. L. Pritchett.

This work was supported by ERDA, Contract No. EY-76-C-03-0010 PA26, Task III.

REFERENCES

1. For a general discussion of plasma simulation models, refer to "Methods in Computational Physics," edited by B. Adler, S. Fernbach, and M. Rotenberg, Vol. 16, Academic, New York, 1976.
2. Kamimura, T., J. M. Dawson, B. Rosen, G. J. Culler, R. D. Levee and G. Ball, Plasma Simulation on the CHI Micro-processor System," UCLA Report, p. 248, 1975.
3. AP-120B Processor Handbook, Floating Point Systems, Inc., Portland, Oregon, Form #7259, 1976.
4. MP-32A Micro-Programming Manual, Culler-Harrison, Inc., Goleta, CA., Publication 29107, 1973.
5. Pritchett, P. L., K. V. Roberts, and J. M. Dawson, *Bull. Am. Phys. Soc.*, 21, p. 1045, 1976. K. V. Roberts and D. E. Potter, in "Methods in Computational Physics," edited by B. Adler, S. Fernbach, and M. Rotenberg, Academic, New York, 1970, Vol. 9, p. 339.
6. MP-32A Macro-Programming Manual, Culler-Harrison, Inc., Goleta, CA., Publication 29106, 1973.
7. The Math System is an extensive generalization of earlier systems developed at UCLA, UCSB and TRW by G. Culler and B. Fried. User's Manual, Culler-Harrison, Inc., Goleta, CA., 1977.
8. Karplus, W. J., "Peripheral Processors for High-Speed Simulation," *Simulation* 29, p. 143, 1977.

3. Array Processors

The first computers to use extensive parallelism were array processors. SOLOMON (Slotnick *et al.*, 1962) and ILLIAC IV (Barnes *et al.*, 1968) had a tremendous impact on parallel processing, but not all of it was positive (Falk, 1976).

Three commercially designed array processors are presented in this chapter. First, the BSP is an example of an array processor in which each processing element has the arithmetic performance of a large general-purpose processor (i.e., single and double precision floating-point). The second and third array processors, the STARAN and the MPP, represent the opposite extreme in which each processing element performs bit-level operations. One major distinction between these two array processors is in the interconnection networks. In all of these processors, the control unit, the support processor, the array memory, and the interconnection network play crucial roles in the performance of the system.

One element of array processor architecture that has engendered a large amount of research is interconnection network design. Feng's paper exemplifies a coherent approach to interconnection network design. Before designing the interconnection network, the data manipulation functions needed by the proposed applications should be ascertained. Although Lawrie's paper is similar in approach, it is more complex in that Lawrie develops an elegant abstraction for an interconnection network's capabilities. In addition, he considers array-memory indexing for conflict-free access as an integral part of the problem. To pursue this point, the reader should read the papers by Lawrie and Vora (1980) and Batcher (1977), who describe the interconnection networks and memory indexing hardware used in the BSP and the STARAN, respectively.

The two papers in the applications section consider applications of the STARAN array processor. Rohrbacher and Potter's paper is on digital image processing which is one of the original applications of STARAN. The paper by Berra and Oliver shows that the associative memory capability of STARAN can be used for general database processing as well. See also the paper by Sameh in Chapter 10 for algorithms suitable for numeric array processors, and the paper by Jordan *et al.* in Chapter 6, on special-purpose array processors.

EHO182-6/81/0000/0069 © 1981 IEEE

BURROUGHS SCIENTIFIC PROCESSOR

Richard A. Stokes
Burroughs Corporation

I. INTRODUCTION

The Burroughs Scientific Processor is designed to provide
very high speed execution of algorithms used to help solve
complex scientific and engineering problems in such fields
as meteorology, nuclear energy, seismic data analysis, structure analysis, and econometric modelling.

The BSP is capable of performing 50 million floating
point operations per second. This speed is achieved primarily
through the utilization of 16 arithmetic units that operate
in parallel. Other significant features that contribute to
the high computation rate are:

- conflict-free memory that allows access to vectors of
  arbitrary length and skip distance at full bandwidth

- a pipeline that allows overlapping of array operations

- overlapped array and scalar operations

- a charge coupled device auxiliary memory

- in-line processing of input and output

II. SYSTEM MANAGER

The Burroughs Scientific Processor (BSP) is intended to
be used in conjunction with a sophisticated system manager,
such as the Burroughs B 7800 or B 7700 computer system. This
allows the BSP to execute scientific and engineering programs
at high speed with a minimum of interruption to perform
ancillary tasks.

On the other hand, the user is provided with a complete
sophisticated computing facility that is easy to use because
the management processor provides:

- time sharing

- data and program file editing

- data communications to remote job entry stations,
  terminals, and networks

- compiling and linking of BSP programs

- long-term data storage and data base management

- general purpose data processing utilizing languages
  such as COBOL, BASIC, APL, ALGOL, PL/I, and FORTRAN

Reprinted with permission from *High Speed Computer and
Algorithm Organization*, 1977, pages 85-89. Copyright © 1977
by Academic Press.

III. SYSTEM COMPONENTS

The Burroughs Scientific Processor consists of a control processor (CP), 16 arithmetic elements (AE), an array memory (AM) consisting of 17 memory units, an alignment network to interface the AE's and AM, a file memory (FM), and a file memory control unit. The components are shown in Figure 1.

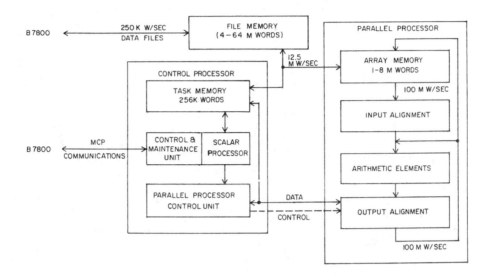

Fig. 1. Burroughs Scientific Processor Block Diagram

A. Control Processor

The control processor (CP) is a high-speed asynchronous element of the BSP that provides the supervisory interface to the system manager in addition to controlling the parallel processor and the file memory. The CP consists of a scalar processor unit (SPU), a parallel processor control unit (PPCU), a task memory (TM), and a control and maintenance unit (CMU).

The control processor executes some serial or scalar portions of user programs utilizing an arithmetic element similar to one of the 16 arithmetic elements in the array processor, but containing additional capabilities to perform integer arithmetic and indexing operations. The CP also performs task scheduling, file memory allocation, and I/O management under control of the BSP operating system.

1. Scalar Processor Unit

The scalar processor unit processes all operating system and user program instructions, which are stored in task memory. It has a clock frequency of 12M Hz and is able to perform up to 3 million floating point operations per second. All array instructions and certain scalar operations are passed to the parallel processor control unit, which queues them for execution on the parallel processor.

2. Parallel Processor Control Unit

The parallel processor control unit receives array operations from the scalar processor unit. The instructions are validated and transformed into microsequences that control the operation of the 16 arithmetic elements in the parallel processor.

3. Task Memory

The task memory is used to store portions of the operating system and user programs as they are being executed. It is also used to store program data values that are operands for those instructions executed by the scalar processor unit.

The task memory is a 4K-bit bipolar memory with a 160 ns cycle time. Four words are accessed simultaneously. Capacity of the memory is 256K words; each word consists of 48 data bits and 8 bits for error detection and correction.

4. Control and Maintenance Unit

The control and maintenance unit (CMU) serves as the direct interface between the system manager and the rest of the control processor for initialization, communication of supervisory commands, and maintenance. It communicates with the input/output processor of the system manager.

The CMU has access to critical data paths and registers of the BSP, so that it can perform state analysis and circuit diagnostics under control of maintenance software running on the system manager.

B. Parallel Processor

The parallel processor performs array oriented computations at high speeds by executing 16 floating point operations simultaneously in its 16 arithmetic elements. Data for the array operations are stored in an array memory (AM) consisting of 17 memory modules. Array memory is accessed by the arithmetic elements through an array memory alignment network (AN).

1. Arithmetic Element

At any time, all of the arithmetic elements are executing the same instruction on different data values. The arithmetic elements operate at a clock frequency of 6.25M Hz and are able to complete the most common arithmetic operations in two clock periods. Each arithmetic element can perform a floating point add, subtract, or multiply in 320 nanoseconds, so the BSP is capable of executing up to 50 million floating point operations per second. Each arithmetic element can perform a floating point divide in 1280 ns and extract a square root in 2080 ns.

2. Array Memory

The array memory consists of 17 memory units, each of which may contain from 32K to 512K words, making a total of from .5 to 8 million words. Like the control processor memory, it is a 4K bit bipolar memory. Each word contains 48 data bits and 8 bits for error detection and correction. The rate of data transfer between the array memory and the arithmetic elements is 100M words/second.

The organization of the array memory is unique in that it permits simultaneous access to almost any consecutive 16 elements of the commonly referenced components of an array, such as rows, columns, and diagonals.

3. *The Alignment Networks*

The Alignment Network is functionally divided into two parts: The Input Alignment network for data fetching and the Output Alignment network for data stores. Both units are full crossbar switching networks, which permit general purpose interconnectivity between the arithmetic array and the memory storage modules. It is the combined function of the memory storage scheme and the alignment networks which support the "conflict-free" capabilities of the Array Memory.

Other inter-arithmetic element switching is provided to support special functions such as the data COMPRESS and EXPAND operations and Fast Fourier Transform algorithm.

C. File Memory

The file memory (FM) is a high-speed secondary storage device. The FM is loaded by the system manager with BSP tasks and task files. These tasks are then queued for execution by the control processor. The FM is also used to store scratch files and output files produced during execution of a BSP program. It is the only peripheral device under the direct control of the BSP; all other peripheral devices are controlled by the system manager.

The FM utilizes high-speed charge coupled devices (CCD) as its storage media. The CCD memory combines a one millisecond access time with a 12.5M word/second transfer rate. Since it is entirely electronic, the reliability of the file memory is much greater than that of conventional rotating storage devices.

Reprinted with permission from *Proceedings of the National Computer Conference*, Volume 43, 1974, pages 405-410. Copyright © 1974 by AFIPS Press.

STARAN parallel processor system hardware

by KENNETH E. BATCHER

Goodyear Aerospace Corporation
Akron, Ohio

INTRODUCTION

The parallel processing capability of STARAN* resides in n array modules ($n \leq 32$). Each array module contains 256 small processing elements (PE's). They communicate with a multi-dimensional access (MDA) memory through a "flip" network, which can permute a set of operands to allow inter-PE communication. This gives the programmer a great deal of freedom in using the processing capability of the PE's. At one stage of a program, he may apply this capability to many bits of one or a few items of data; at another stage, he may apply it to one or a few bits of many items of data.

The remainder of this paper deals with the MDA memories, the STARAN array modules, the other elements of STARAN, and the results of certain application studies.

MULTI-DIMENSIONAL ACCESS (MDA) MEMORIES

A common implementation of associative processing is to treat data in a bit-sequential manner. A small one-bit PE (processing element) is associated with each item or word of data in the store, and the set of PE's accesses the data store in bit-slices; a typical operation is to read Bit i of each data word into its associated PE or to write Bit i from its associated PE.

The memory for such an associative processor could be a simple random-access memory with the data rotated 90 deg, so that it is accessed by bit-slices instead of by words. Unfortunately, in most applications, data come in and leave the processor as items or words instead of as bit-slices. Hence, rotating the data in a random-access memory complicates data input and output.

To accommodate both bit-slice accesses for associative processing and word-slice accesses for STARAN input/output (I/O), the data are stored in a multi-dimensional access (MDA) memory (Figure 1). It has wide read and write busses for parallel access to a large number (256) of memory bits. The write mask bus allows selective writing of memory bits. Memory accesses (both read and write accesses) are controlled by the address and access mode control inputs; the access mode selects a stencil pattern of 256 bits, while the address positions the stencil in memory.

For many applications, the MDA memory is treated as a square array of bits, 256 words with 256 bits in each word. The bit-slice access mode (Figure 2A) is used in the associative operations to access one bit of all words in parallel, while the word access mode (Figure 2B) is used in the I/O operations to access several or all bits of one word in parallel.

The MDA memory structure is not limited to a square array of 256 by 256. For example, the data may be formatted as records with 256 8-bit bytes in each record. Thirty-two such records can be stored in an MDA memory and accessed several ways. To input and output records, one can access 32 consecutive bytes of a record in parallel (Figure 3A). To search key fields of the data, one can access the corresponding bytes of all records in parallel (Figure 3B). To search a whole record for the presence of a particular byte, one can access a bit from each byte in parallel (Figure 3C).

The MDA memories in the STARAN array modules are bipolar. They exhibit read cycle times of less than 150 nsec and write cycle times of less than 250 nsec.

STARAN ARRAY MODULES

A STARAN array module (Figure 4) contains an MDA memory communicating with three 256-bit registers (M, X, and Y) through a flip (permutation) network. One may think of an array module as having 256 small processing elements (PE's), where a PE contains one bit of the M register, one bit of the X register, and one bit of the Y register.

The M register drives the write mask bus of the MDA memory to select which of the MDA memory bits are modified in a masked-write operation. The MDA memory also has an unmasked-write operation that ignores M and modifies all 256 accessed bits. The M register can be loaded from the other components of the array module.

In general, the logic associated with the X register can perform any of the 16 Boolean functions of two variables;

---

* TM, Goodyear Aerospace Corporation, Akron, Ohio.

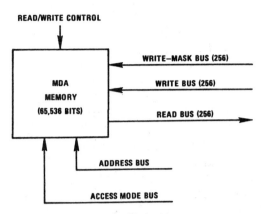

Figure 1—Multi-dimensional access memory

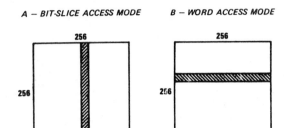

Figure 2—Bit-slice and word access modes

that is, if x_i is the state of the ith X-register bit, and f_i is the state of the ith flip network output, then:

$$x_i \leftarrow \phi(x_i, f_i) \quad (i = 0, 1, \ldots, 255)$$

where ϕ is any Boolean function of two variables. Similarly, the logic associated with the Y-register can perform any Boolean function:

$$y_i \leftarrow \phi (y_i, f_i) \quad (i = 0, 1, \ldots, 255)$$

where y_i is the state of the ith Y-register bit. The programmer is given the choice of operating X alone, Y alone, or X and Y together.

If X and Y are operated together, the same Boolean function, ϕ, is appled to both registers:

$$x_i \leftarrow \phi (x_i, f_i)$$
$$y_i \leftarrow \phi (y_i, f_i)$$

The programmer also can choose to operate on X selectively, using Y as a mask:

$$x_i \leftarrow \phi (x_i, f_i) \quad \text{(where } y_i = 1)$$
$$x_i \leftarrow x_i \quad \text{(where } y_i = 0)$$

Another choice is to operate on X selectively while operating on Y:

$$x_i \leftarrow \phi (x_i, f_i) \quad \text{(where } y_i = 1)$$
$$x_i \leftarrow x_i \quad \text{(where } y_i = 0)$$
$$y_i \leftarrow \phi (y_i, f_i)$$

In this case, the old state of Y (before modification by ϕ) is used as the mask for the X operation.

For a programming example, the basic loop of an unmasked add fields operation is selected. This operation adds the contents of a Field A of all memory words to the contents of a Field B of the words and stores the sum in a Field S of the words. For n-bit fields, the operation executes the basic loop n times. During each execution of the loop, a bit-slice (a) of Field A is ready from memory, a bit-slice (b) of Field B is read, and a bit-slice (s) of Field S is written

into memory. The operation starts at the least significant bits of the fields and steps through the fields to the most significant bits. At the beginning of each loop execution, the carry (c) from the previous bits is stored in Y, and X contains zeroes:

$$x_i = 0$$
$$y_i = c_i$$

The loop has four steps:

Step 1: Read Bit-slice a and exclusive-or ($\oplus$) it to X selec-

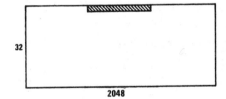

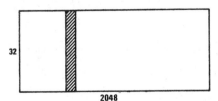

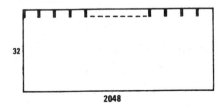

Figure 3—Accessing 256-byte records

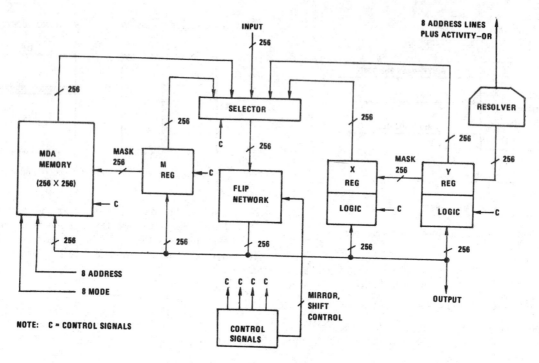

Figure 4—STARAN array module

tively and also to Y:

$$x_i \leftarrow x_i \oplus y_i a_i$$

$$y_i \leftarrow y_i \oplus a_i$$

The states of X and Y are now:

$$x_i = a_i c_i$$

$$y_i = a_i \oplus c_i$$

Step 2: Read Bit-slice b and exclusive-or it to X selectively and also to Y:

$$x_i \leftarrow x_i \oplus y_i b_i$$

$$y_i \leftarrow y_i \oplus b_i$$

Registers X and Y now contain the carry and sum bits:

$$x_i = a_i c_i \oplus a_i b_i \oplus b_i c_i = c'_i$$

$$y_i = a_i \oplus b_i \oplus c_i = s_i$$

Step 3: Write the sum bit from Y into Bit-slice s and also complement X selectively:

$$s_i \leftarrow y_i$$

$$x_i \leftarrow x_i \oplus y_i$$

The states of X and Y are now.

$$x_i = c'_i \oplus s_i$$

$$y_i = s_i$$

Step 4: Read the X-register and exclusive-or it into both

X and Y:

$$x_i \leftarrow x_i \oplus x_i$$

$$y_i \leftarrow y_i \oplus x_i$$

This clears X and stores the carry bit into Y to prepare the registers for the next execution of the loop:

$$x_i = 0$$

$$y_i = c'_i$$

Step 3 takes less than 250 nsec, while Steps 1, 2, and 4 each take less than 150 nsec. Hence, the time to execute the basic loop once is less than 700 nsec. If the field length is 32 bits, the add operation takes less than 22.4 microsec plus a small amount of setup time. The operation performs 256 additions in each array module. This amounts to 1024 additions, if four array modules are enabled, to achieve a processing power of approximately 40 MIPS (million-instructions-per-second).

The array module components communicate through a network called the flip network. A selector chooses a 256-bit source item from the MDA memory read bus, the M register, the X register, the Y register, or an outside source. The bits of the source item travel through the flip network, which may shift and permute the bits in various ways. The permuted source item is presented to the MDA memory write bus, M register, X register, Y register, and an outside destination.

The permutations of the flip network allow inter-PE communication, A PE can read data from another PE either directly from its registers or indirectly from the MDA memory. One can permute the 256-bit data item as a whole or divide it into groups of 2, 4, 8, 16, 32, 64, or 128 bits and permute within groups.

The permutations allowed include shifts of 1, 2, 4, 8, 16, 32, 64, or 128 places. One also can mirror the bits of a group (invert the left-right order) while shifting it. A positive shift of mirrored data is equivalent to a negative shift of the unmirrored data. To shift data a number of places, multiple passes through the flip network may be required. Mirroring can be used to reduce the number of passes. For example, a shift of 31 places can be done in two passes: mirror and shift 1 place on the first pass, and then remirror and shift 32 places on the second pass.

The flip network permutations are particularly useful for fast-fourier transforms (FFT's). A 2^n point FFT requires n steps, where each step pairs the 2^n points in a certain way and operates on the two points of each pair arithmetically to form two new points. The flip network can be used to rearrange the pairings between steps. Bitonic sorting (2) and other algorithms (3) also find the permutations of the flip network useful.

Each array module contains a resolver reading the state of the Y register. One output of the resolver (activity-or) indicates if any Y bit is set. If some Y bits are set, the other output of the resolver indicates the index (address) of the first such bit. Since the result of an associative search is marked in the Y register, the resolver indicates which if any words respond to the search.

OTHER STARAN ELEMENTS

Figure 5 is a block diagram of a typical STARAN system with four array modules. Each array module contains an assignment switch that connects its control inputs and data inputs and outputs to AP (associative processor) control or the PIO (parallel input/output) module.

The AP control unit contains the registers and logic necessary to exercise control over the array modules assigned to it. It receives instructions from the control memory and can transfer 32-bit data items to and from the control memory. Data busses communicate with the assigned array modules. The busses connect only to 32-bits of the 256-bit-wide input and output ports of the array modules (Figure 4), but the permutations of the array module flip networks allow communication with any part of the array. The AP control sends control signals and MDA memory addresses and access modes to the array modules and receives the resolver outputs from the array modules.

Registers in the AP control include:

1. An instruction register to hold the 32-bit instruction being executed.
2. A program status word to hold the control memory address of the next instruction to be executed and the program priority level.
3. A common register to hold a 32-bit search comparand, an operand to be broadcast to the array modules, or an operand output from an array module.

4. An array select register to select a subset of the assigned array modules to be operated on.
5. Four field pointers to hold MDA memory addresses and allow them to be incremented or decremented for stepping through the bit-slices of a field, the words of a group, etc.
6. Three counters to keep track of the number of executions of loops, etc.
7. A data pointer to allow stepping through a set of operands in control memory.
8. Two access mode registers to hold the MDA memory access modes.

The parallel input/output (PIO) module contains a PIO flip network and PIO control unit (Figure 5). It is used for high bandwidth I/O and inter-array transfers.

The PIO flip network permutes data between eight 256-bit ports. Ports 0 through 3 connect to the four array modules through buffer registers. Port 7 connects to a 32-bit data bus in the PIO control through a fan-in, fan-out switch. Ports 4, 5, and 6 are spare ports for connections to high bandwidth peripherals, such as parallel-head disk stores, sophisticated displays, and radar video channels. The spare ports also could be used to handle additional array modules. High bandwidth inter-array data transfers up to 1024 bits in parallel are handled by permuting data between Ports 0, 1, 2 and 3. Array I/O is handled by permuting data between an array module port and an I/O port. The PIO flip network is controlled by the PIO control unit.

The PIO control unit controls the PIO flip network and the array modules assigned to it. While AP control is processing data in some array modules the PIO control can input and output data in the other array modules. Since most of the registers in the AP control are duplicated in PIO control, it can address the array modules associatively.

The control memory holds AP control programs, PIO control programs, and microprogram subroutines. To satisfy the high instruction fetch rate of the control units (up to 7.7 million instructions per second), the control

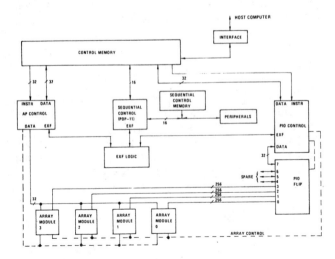

Figure 5—Typical STARAN block diagram

memory has five banks of bipolar memory with 512 32-bit words in each bank. Each bank is expandable to 1024 words. To allow for storage of large programs, the control memory also has a 16K-word core memory with a cycle time of 1 microsec. The core memory can be expanded to 32K words. Usually the main program resides in the core memory, and the system microprogram subroutines reside in bipolar storage. For flexibility, users are given the option of changing the storage allocation and dynamically paging parts of the program into bipolar storage.

A Digital Equipment Corporation (DEC) PDP-11 minicomputer is included to handle the peripherals, control the system from console commands, and perform diagnostic functions. It is called sequential control to differentiate it from the STARAN parallel processing control units. The sequential control memory of 16K 16-bit words is augmented by a 8K×16-bit "window" into the main control memory. By moving the window, sequential control can access any part of control memory. The window is moved by changing the contents of an addressable register.

The STARAN peripherals include a disk, card reader, line printer, paper-tape reader/punch, console typewriter, and a graphics console.

Synchronization of the three control units (AP control, sequential control, and PIO control) is maintained by the external function (EXF) logic. Control units issue commands to the EXF logic to cause system actions and read system states. Some of the system actions are: AP control start/stop/reset, PIO control start/stop/reset, AP control interrupts, sequential control interrupts, and array module assignment.

The design of STARAN allows it to be connected to other computers (host computers) as a special-purpose peripheral. The interface can take many different forms. One could connect to an I/O channel of the host. Alternately, one could connect to the memory bus of the host so that it can address STARAN memory directly and/or allow STARAN to address its memory directly. For example, the STARAN at Rome Air Development Center (4) is connected to an I/O channel of a Honeywell HIS-645 computer. At Goodyear Aerospace, another STARAN is interfaced to the direct memory access port of an XDS Σ 5 computer.

APPLICATIONS

Several representative application areas—fast Fourier transforming, sonar post-processing, string search, file processing, and air traffic control—are discussed below. Other application-oriented work which has been performed under contract to various government agencies, include image processing, data management, position locating and reporting, bulk filtering and radar processing.

Fast fourier transform

The Fast Fourier Transform (FFT) is a basic operation in digital signal processing which is being widely used in the real-time processing of radar and sonar signals. The structure of the FFT algorithm is such that it can be segmented into many similar concurrent operations. Parallel implementation of the FFT can provide orders of magnitude speed increases over sequential computer execution times. The organization of STARAN lends itself to efficient manipulation of data in the FFT.

The Air Force supplied real radar data (on tapes) to GAC to be transformed by the STARAN system. A 512-point, 16-bit FFT was performed on this real data in 2.7 milliseconds using only two MDA arrays. A 1024-point transform on real input data could be performed in about 3.0 milliseconds using all four arrays available at GAC's STARAN evaluation and training facility. For comparison purposes, the following is a list of reported execution times for a 1024-point, real input, FFT:

Sequential Computers	
XDS Sigma 5	660 msec
IBM 360/67	446 msec
UNIVAC 1108	190 msec (complex)
UNIVAC 1108 (with array processor attachment)	29.2 msec (complex)

Special Purpose FFT Systems	
Time/Data 90 System	28 msec
ELSYTEC 306/HFFT	18 msec
SPECTRA SYSTEM '900'	9.2 msec

Sonar post-processing

Sensor data processing can be split into two major categories—signal processing and post-processing. Signal processing is the area of the system where operations such as the FFT are performed; post-processing involves the sorting and editing of the signal processor output data to determine tactical information such as whether a real target is in the coverage area and where the target is.

The job of sorting the spectral lines that result from the FFT operations is a formidable task, especially in a multi-sensor case. The trend has been for increasing the sensitivity of signal processing systems. The acoustic signal line sorting task that accompanies any increased sensitivity can be staggering. For instance, a 6 db improvement in sensitivity, in a classified Navy sonar system, would result in increasing the target load by a factor of 16 and the computer processing load by a factor of 250 or more.

A digital sonar signal processing system, under development at the Naval Air Development Center (NADC), requires that subroutines operate on the target spectral lines (outputs from an FFT) and other input data to form outputs suitable for later use in classification algorithms. Since the system is a multi-sensor system, these subroutines must process a very large volume of data in real-time. The content addressability feature of STARAN provides the potential for significant performance gains due to the

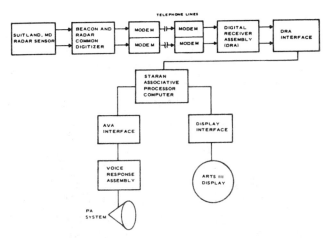

Figure 6—TRANSPO '72 demonstration system

requirement for many searches in these post-processing subroutines.

As a consequence of this potential improvement, NADC issued a contract to GAC to assess the comparative run times for the STARAN versus a large-scale conventional computer (the CDC-6600). NADC-developed algorithms for the most time consuming operations in the post-processor system were programmed on the STARAN computer. Real data was then processed on both the STARAN and, by NADC, on a CDC-6600.

The STARAN executed the programs, using the real data, 200 times faster than the CDC-6600.

String search

A processing function used by several agencies for locating specific character strings (such as place names) in textual information, was developed for STARAN and tested on a sample data base. The same function was executed on a conventional computer (Sigma 5) for a timing comparison. The STARAN solution ran 100 times faster. This function is also applicable to nondefense applications such as patent, legal, and chemical information searches where cost of search may be a limiting parameter.

File processing

A personnel record file was used as a sample data base for demonstrating multiple-key searches. STARAN and a parallel-head disk were used for the demonstration. This work demonstrated that a query, simple or complex, can be processed in less than 120 milliseconds and that several queries may be batched and processed in the same processing time period. The simplicity of the software for retrieval and update was also demonstrated.

Air traffic control

In May 1972 a complete terminal automation system was demonstrated at the TRANSPO '72 exhibit at Dulles International Airport and later at private showings in Washington and Boston. Live radar and beacon sensor data were provided from the FAA site at Suitland, Maryland. The complete system is shown in Figure 6. The following ATC functions were demonstrated: beacon tracking, radar tracking, conflict prediction, conflict resolution, display processing, automatic voice advisory (AVA), and terrain avoidance.

The TRANSPO demonstration illustrated the use of STARAN in a full repertoire of terminal automation functions including advanced features such as automatic track initiation of all the aircraft, automatic tag placement on the display, and automatic handoff from sector to sector. The live targets were supplemented with 256 simulated targets so that up to 400 targets (representative of larger terminal densities) could be provided.

Average execution times for the most important functions were:

conflict prediction	90 msec
conflict resolution	25 msec
tracking	100 msec
display processing	160 msec

The entire ATC program executed in less than 5 percent of real-time.

REFERENCES

1. Batcher, K. E., "Flexible Parallel Processing and STARAN," *1972 WESCON Technical Papers*, Session 1.
2. Batcher, K. E., "Sorting Networks and Their Applications," 1968 Spring Joint Computer Conference, *AFIPS Proceedings*, Vol. 32, pp. 307-314.
3. Stone, H. S., "Parallel Processing with the Perfect Shuffle," *IEEE Transactions on Computers*, Vol. C-20, No. 2, February 1971, pp. 153-161.
4. Feldman, J. D., *RADCAP: An Operational Parallel Processing Facility*, Goodyear Aerospace Corporation.

DESIGN OF A MASSIVELY PARALLEL PROCESSOR

Kenneth E. Batcher
Goodyear Aerospace Corporation, Akron, Ohio

Abstract -The massively parallel processor (MPP) system is designed to process satellite imagery at high rates. A large number (16,384) of processing elements (PE's) are configured in a square array. For optimum performance on operands of arbitrary length, processing is performed in a bit-serial manner. On 8-bit integer data, addition can occur at 6553 million operations per second (MOPS) and multiplication at 1861 MOPS. On 32-bit floating-point data, addition can occur at 430 MOPS and multiplication at 216 MOPS.

Index Terms -Array processing, bit-slice processing, computer architecture, image processing, parallel processing, satellite imagery.

INTRODUCTION

In this decade, NASA will orbit imaging sensors that can generate data at rates up to 10^{13} bits per day. A variety of image processing tasks such as geometric correction, correlation, image registration, feature selection, multispectral classification, and area measurement are required to extract useful information from this mass of data. The expected workload is between 10^9 and 10^{10} operations per second.

In 1971 NASA Goddard Space Flight Center initiated a program to develop ultra high-speed image processing systems capable of processing this workload. These systems use thousands of processing elements (PE's) operating simultaneously (massive parallelism) to achieve their speed. They exploit the fact that the typical satellite image contains millions of picture elements (pixels) that can generally be processed at the same time.

In December 1979 NASA Goddard awarded a contract to Goodyear Aerospace to construct a massively parallel processor (MPP) to be delivered in the first quarter of 1982. The basic elements of the MPP architecture were developed at NASA Goddard. This correspondence presents the design of the MPP system. The major components are shown in Fig. 1. The array unit (ARU) processes arrays of data at high speed and is controlled by the array control unit (ACU), which also performs scalar arithmetic. The program and data management unit (PDMU) controls the overall flow of data and programs through the system and handles certain ancillary tasks such as program development and diagnostics. The staging memories buffer and reorder data between the ARU, PDMU, and external (host) computer.

ARRAY UNIT

Logically, the array unit (ARU) contains 16,384 processing elements (PE's) organized as a 128 by 128 square. Physically, the ARU has an extra 128 by 4 rectangle of PE's that is used to reconfigure the ARU when a PE fault is detected. The PE's are bit-serial processors for efficiently processing operands of any length. The basic clock rate is 10 MHz. With 16,384 PE's operating in parallel, the ARU has a very high processing speed (see Table 1). Despite the bit-serial nature of the PE's, even the floating-point speeds compare favorably with several fast number crunchers.

TABLE I - SPEED OF TYPICAL OPERATIONS

Operations	Execution Speed*
Addition of Arrays	
8-bit integers (9-bit sum)	6553
12-bit integers (13-bit sum)	4428
32-bit floating-point numbers	430
Multiplication of Arrays (Element-by-Element)	
8-bit integers (16-bit product)	1861
12-bit integers (24-bit product)	910
32-bit floating-point numbers	216
Multiplication of Array by Scalar	
8-bit integers (16-bit product)	2340
12-bit integers (24-bit product)	1260
32-bit floating-point numbers	373

*Million operations per second

Reprinted from *IEEE Transactions on Computers*, September 1980, pages 1-9. Copyright © 1980 by The Institute of Electrical and Electronics Engineers, Inc.

EHO182-6/81/0000/0080 © 1980 IEEE

Routing Topology

Each PE in the 128 by 128 square communicates with its nearest neighbor; up, down, right, and left—a topology similar to Illiac IV and some other array processors. Alternative routing topologies such as the flip network (1) or one of its equivalents (2) were investigated. They have the ability to shift data over many PE's in one step and allow data to be accessed in many different directions (3). Certain paths in the alternative topologies have long runs that complicate their layout and limit their cycle rate. When the number of PE's interconnected is only 256 as in the STARAN® computer, this is no problem; when 16,384 PE's are interconnected, it is a severe problem.

Most of the expected workload does not use the routing flexibility of the alternative topologies. The ability to access data in different directions is important when arrays of data are input and output; it can be used to reorient the arrays between the bit-plane format of the ARU and the pixel format of the outside world.

These considerations lead to the conclusion that the ARU should have a two-dimensional nearest neighbor routing topology such as Illiac IV since it is easy to implement and matches the two-dimensional nature of satellite imagery. The problem of reformatting I/O data is best handled in a staging memory between the ARU and the outside world.

Around the edges of the 128 by 128 array of PE's the edges can be left open (e.g., a row of zeros can be entered along the left edge when routing data to the right) or the opposite edges can be connected. Cases were found where open edges were preferred and other cases where connected edges were preferred. It was decided to make edge-connectivity a programmable function. A topology-register in the array control unit defines the connections between opposite edges of the PE array. The top and bottom edges can either be connected or left open. The connectivity between the left and right edges has four states: open (no connection), cylindrical (connect the left PE of each row to the right PE of the same row), open spiral (for $1 \leq n \leq 127$, connect the left PE of row n to the right PE of row n-1), and closed spiral (like the open spiral, but also connect the left PE of row 0 to the right PE of row 127).

The spiral modes connect the 16,384 PE's together in one long linear array. One can pack several linear arrays of odd sizes (e.g., lines with thousands of image pixels per line) in the ARU and process them in parallel.

Redundancy

The ARU includes some redundancy so that a faulty PE can be bypassed. Redundancy can be added to a two-dimensional array of PE's by adding an extra column (or row) of PE's and inserting bypass gates in the routing network. When a faulty PE is discovered, one disables the whole column containing the faulty PE and joins the columns on either side of it with the bypass gates.

The PE's in the ARU are implemented with two-row by four-column VLSI chips; thus, it is more convenient to add four redundant columns of PE's and bypass four columns at a time. The PE array has 128 rows and 132 columns. It is divided into 33 groups, with each group containing 128 rows and four columns of PE's. Each group has an independent group-disable control line from the ACU. When a group is disabled, all its outputs are disabled and the groups on either side of it are joined together with 128 bypass gates in the routing network.

When there is no faulty PE, an arbitrary group is disabled so that the size of the logical array is always 128 by 128. Application programs are not aware of which group is disabled and need not be modified when the disabled group is changed. They always use the logical address of a PE to access PE dependent data. The logical address of a PE is a pair of 7-bit numbers X and Y showing its position in the logical array of enabled PE's. A simple routine executed in 27 μs will load the memory of each PE with its logical address.

When a faulty PE is discovered, its data cannot be trusted so the normal error recovery procedure is to reconfigure the ARU to disable the column containing the fault and then to restart the application program from the last checkpoint or from the beginning.

Bit-Serial Processing

The data arrays being processed have a wide range of element lengths. A spectral band of an input pixel may have a resolution of 6 to 12 bits. Intermediate results can have any length from 6 to more than 30 bits. Single-bit flag arrays are generated when pixels are classified. Some computations may be performed in floating point. Thus, the PE's should be able to process operands of any length efficiently.

Conventional computers typically use bit-parallel arithmetic units with certain fixed-word lengths such as 8, 16, or 32 bits. Operands of odd lengths are extended to fit the standard word sizes of the machine. Some of the hardware in the memory and the arithmetic unit is wasted storing and processing the extensions.

Bit-serial processors process operands bit by bit and can handle operands of any length without any wasted hardware. Their slower speed can be counteracted by using a multitude of them and processing many operands in parallel.

There is a wide variety of operand lengths and a prevalence of low-precision operands in the expected workload. Thus, bit-serial processors are more efficient in the use of hardware than bit-parallel processors.

Processing Elements

The initial MPP design had PE's using downshifting binary counters for arithmetic (4), (6), (7). The PE design was modified to use a full adder and shift register combination for arithmetic. The modified design performs the basic arithmetic operations faster. Each of the PE's has six 1-bit registers (A, B, C, G, P, and S), a shift register with a programmable length, a random-access memory, a data bus (D), a full adder, and some combinatorial logic (see Fig. 2). The basic cycle time of the PE is 100 ns.

Logic and Routing: The P-register is used for logic and routing operations. A logic operation combines the state of the P-register and the state of the data bus (D) to form the new state of the P-register. All 16 Boolean functions of the two variables P and D are implemented. A routing operation shifts the state of the P-register into the P-register of a neighboring PE (up, down, right, or left).

Arithmetic: The full adder, shift register, and registers A, B, and C are used for bit-serial arithmetic operations. To add two operands, the bits of one operand are put into the A-register, one at a time, least significant bit (LSB) first; corresponding bits of the other operand are put into the P-register; the full adder adds the bits in A and P to the carry bits in the C-register to form the sum and carry bits; each carry bit is stored in C to be added in the next cycle; and each sum bit is stored in B. The sum formed in B can be stored in the random-access memory and/or in the shift register. Two's complement subtraction is performed by adding the one's complement of the operand in P to the operand in A and setting the initial carry bit in C to 1 instead of 0.

Multiplication is a series of addition steps where the partial product is recirculated through the shift register and registers A and B. Appropriate multiples of the multiplicand are formed in P and added to the partial product as it recirculates. Division is performed with a nonrestoring division algorithm. The partial dividend is recirculated through the shift register and registers A and B while the divisor or its complement is formed in P and added to it.

Floating-point addition compares exponents; places the fraction of the operand with the least exponent in the shift register; shifts it to the right to align it with the other fraction; adds the other fraction to the shift register; and normalizes the sum. Floating-point multiplication is a multiplication of the fractions, a normalization of the product, and an addition of the exponents.

Masking: The G-register can hold a mask bit that can control the activity of the PE. Unmasked logic, routing, and arithmetic operations are performed in all PE's. Masked operations are only performed in those PE's where the G-register equals 1.

Several operations may be combined in one 100 ns instruction. Logic and routing operations are masked independently of arithmetic operations so one can combine a masked routing operation with an unmasked arithmetic operation or vice versa. This feature proves to be quite useful in a number of algorithms.

Storage: The random-access memory stores 1024 bits per PE. Standard RAM integrated circuits are used to make it easy to expand storage as advances occur in solid-state memory technology. The ACU generates 16-bit addresses so ARU storage can be expanded to 65,536 bits per PE. Thus, the initial complement of 2 Mbytes of ARU storage can be expanded sixty-fourfold if technology allows it.

Parity error detection is used to find memory faults. A parity bit is added to the eight data bits of each 2 by 4 subarray of PE's. Parity bits are generated and stored for each memory write cycle and checked when the memories are read. A parity error sets an error flip-flop associated with the 2 by 4 subarray. A tree of logic element gives the ACU an inclusive-or of all error flip-flops (after some delay). By operating the group-disable control lines, the ACU can locate the group containing the error and disable it.

Sum-Or Tree: The data bus states of all enabled PE's are combined in a tree of inclusive-or elements called the sum-or tree. The output of this tree is fed to the ACU and used in certain operations such as finding the maximum or minimum value of an array in the ARU.

Input/Output: The S-register is used to input and output ARU data. While the PE's are processing data in the random-access memories, columns of input data are shifted into the left side of the ARU (Fig. 1) and through the S-registers (Fig. 2) until a plane of 16,384 bits is loaded. The input plane is then stored in the random-access memories in one 100 ns cycle by interrupting the processing momentarily in all PE's and moving the S-register values to the memory elements. Planes of data are output by moving them from the memory elements to the S-registers and then shifting them out column by column through the right side of the ARU. The shift rate is 10 MHz; thus, up to 160 Mbytes/s can be transferred through the ARU I/O ports. Processing is interrupted for 100 ns for each bit plane of 16,384 bits transferred—less than 1 percent of the time.

Packaging

Standard 4 by 1024-bit RAM elements are used for the PE memories. All other components of a 2 by 4 subarray of PE's are packaged on a custom VLSI CMOS/SOS chip. The VLSI chip also contains the parity tree and the bypass gates for the subarray.

Each 8-1/2 in. by 14 in. printed circuit board contains 192 PE's in a 16 by 12 array. A board contains 24 VLSI chips, 54 memory elements, and some support circuitry. Eleven boards make up an array slice of 16 by 132 PE's.

Eight array slices (88 boards) make up the ARU. Eight other boards contain the topology switches, control fan out, and other support circuitry. The 96 boards of the ARU are packaged in one cabinet (the leftmost cabinet in Fig. 3). Forced-air cooling is used.

ARRAY CONTROL UNIT

Like the control units of other parallel processors, the array control unit (ACU) performs scalar arithmetic and controls the PE's. It has three sections that operate in parallel (see Fig. 4): PE control, I/O control, and main control. PE control performs all array arithmetic of the application program. I/O control manages the flow of data in and out of the ARU. Main control performs all scalar arithmetic of the application program. This arrangement allows array arithmetic, scalar arithmetic, and input/output to be overlapped for minimum execution time.

PE Control

PE control generates all ARU control signals except those associated with I/O. It contains a 64-bit common register to hold scalars and eight 16-bit index registers to hold the addresses of bit planes in the PE memory elements, to count loop executions, and to hold the index of a bit in the common register. PE control

reads 64-bit-wide microinstructions from PE control memory. Most instructions are read and executed in 100 ns. One instruction can perform several PE operations, manipulate any number of index registers, and branch conditionally. This reduces overhead significantly so that little, if any, PE processing power is wasted.

PE control memory contains a number of system routines and user-written routines to operate on arrays of data in the ARU. The routines include both array-to-array and scalar-to-array arithmetic operations. A queue between PE control and main control queues up to 7 calls to the PE control routines. Each call contains up to 8 initial index-register values and up to 64 bits of scalar information. Some routines extract scalar information from the ARU (such as a maximum value) and return it to main control.

I/O Control

I/O control shifts the ARU S-registers, manages the flow of information in and out of the ARU ports, and interrupts PE control momentarily to transfer data between the S-registers and buffer areas in the PE memory elements. Once initiated by main control or the PDMU, I/O control can chain through a number of I/O commands. It reads the commands from main control memory.

Main Control

Main control is a fast scalar processor. It reads and executes the application program in the main control memory. It performs all scalar arithmetic itself and places all array arithmetic operations on the PE control call queue. It contains 16 general purpose registers, three registers to control the ARU group-disable lines, 13 registers associated with the call queue, 12 registers to receive scalars from PE control, and six registers to monitor and control the status of PE control, I/O control, and the ARU.

PROGRAM AND DATA MANAGEMENT UNIT

The program and data management unit (PDMU) controls the overall flow of programs and data in the system (Fig. 1). Control is from an alphanumeric terminal. The PDMU is a minicomputer (DFC PDP-11) with custom interfaces to the ACU control memories and registers and to the staging memories. The operating system is DEC's RSX-11M real-time multiprogramming system.

The PDMU also executes the MPP program-development software package. The package includes a PE control assembler to develop array processing routines for PE control, a main assembler to develop application programs executing in main control, a linker to form load modules for the ACU, and a control and debug module that loads programs into the ACU, controls their execution, and facilitates debugging. This package is written in Fortran for easy movement to the host computer.

STAGING MEMORIES

The staging memories reside between the wide I/O ports of the ARU and the PDMU. They also have a port to an external (host) computer. Besides acting as buffers for ARU data being input and output, the memories reorder arrays of data.

Satellite imagery is normally stored in pixel order in the PDMU and other conventional computers. That is, line 1 pixel 1 followed by line 1 pixel 2, etc., followed by the pixels of line 2, line 3, etc. The imagery might be band-interleaved (all spectral bands of a pixel stored together) or band-sequential (band 1 of all pixels followed by band 2 of all pixels, etc.).

Arrays of data are transferred through the ARU ports in bit-sequential order. That is, the most (or least) significant bit of 16,384 elements followed by the next bit of 16,384 elements, etc. Reordering is required to fit the normal order of satellite imagery in the PDMU or the host. Thus the staging memories are given a reordering capability.

The staging memories are packaged together in a large multidimensional-access (MDA) or corner-turning memory. Items of data flow through a substager which is a smaller MDA memory. Input data items from the ARU, PDMU, or host are reformatted in the substager into patches which are sent to the large staging memory. Output data patches from the large staging memory are reformatted in the substager for transmission to the ARU, PDMU, or host.

The large staging memory uses 1280 dynamic RAM integrated circuits for data storage and 384 RAM's for error-correcting-code (ECC) storage. (A 6-bit ECC is added to each 20-bit word.) Initially, the boards will be populated with 16K bit RAM's for a capacity of 2.5 Mbytes. Later, as memory technology advances, the 16K bit RAM's can be replaced with 64K bit RAM's or 256K bit RAM's to increase the capacity of 10 Mbytes or 40 Mbytes.

The substager can access the main stager at a 320 Mbyte per second rate (thirty-two 20-bit words every 250 ns). The accesses can be spread across the main stager in a variety of ways. Patches of data in various orientations can be read or written conveniently.

The substager has a smaller memory with 1-bit words. It assembles input data into patches for the main staging memory and disassembles patches of data from the main staging memory for output.

The main staging memory and the substager are controlled by a control unit that can be programmed to input and output imagery in a wide variety of formats.

HOST INTERFACE

The MPP to be delivered to NASA will use a DEC VAX-11/780 for a host computer. The staging memories of the MPP are connected to a DR-780 high-speed user interface of the VAX-11/780. Imagery can be transferred over this path at the rate of the DR-780 (at least 6 Mbytes/s). To allow control of the MPP by the host, the custom interface of the MPP is switched from the PDMU to the host. The switching is simplified by the fact that both the PDMU (a DEC PDP-11) and the host (a DEC VAX-11/780) have a DEC UNIBUS. The transfer of system software to the host is simplified by writing much of it in Fortran and using the compatibility mode of VAX to execute those portions written in PDP-11 code.

CONCLUSIONS

The massively parallel processor is designed to process satellite imagery at high rates. Its high-processing speed, large memory capacity, and I/O re-formatting capabilities should make it useful in other applications. Preliminary studies indicate that the MPP can support such diverse application areas as general image processing, weather simulation, aerodynamic studies, radar processing, reactor diffusion analysis, and computer-image generation.

The modular structure of the MPP allows it to be scaled up or down for different applications. The number of processing elements in the ARU can be adjusted to support different processing rates. The sizes of the ARU and staging memories are also adjustable. Host computers other than the VAX-11/780 can be accommodated. The PDMU functions can be absorbed by the host or alternatively, the PDMU can act as the host (since the PDMU is in the PDP-11 and VAX family, a wide variety of PDMU capacities and configurations is feasible).

As part of its ongoing program to develop space-borne image processors, NASA-Goddard is pursuing the design of a miniaturized version of the MPP (5).

REFERENCES

(1) K. E. Batcher, "The Flip Network in STARAN," in *1976 Proc. Int. Conf. Parallel Processing*, pp. 65-71.

(2) H. J. Siegel and S.D. Smith, "Study of Multistage SIMD Interconnection Networks," in *Proc. 5th Annual Symp. Computer Architecture*, April 1978, pp. 223-229.

(3) K. E. Batcher, "The Multi-dimensional-access Memory in STARAN," *IEEE Trans. Computer*, vol. C-26, pp. 174-177, Feb. 1977.

(4) L.W. Fung, *A Massively Parallel Processing Computer: High-Speed Computer and Algorithm Organization*, D. J. Kuck *et al*, Ed. New York: Academic, 1977, pp. 203-204.

(5) D. H. Schaefer, "Massively Parallel Information Processing Systems for Space Applications," presented at AIAA Computer Aerospace Conf. II, Oct. 1979.

(6) L. W. Fung, "MPPC: A Massively Parallel Processing Computer," Goddard Space Flight Center, Greenbelt, MD, GSFC Image Systems Section Report, Sept. 1976.

(7) Request for Proposal, RFP GSFC-5-45191/254 (Appendix A).

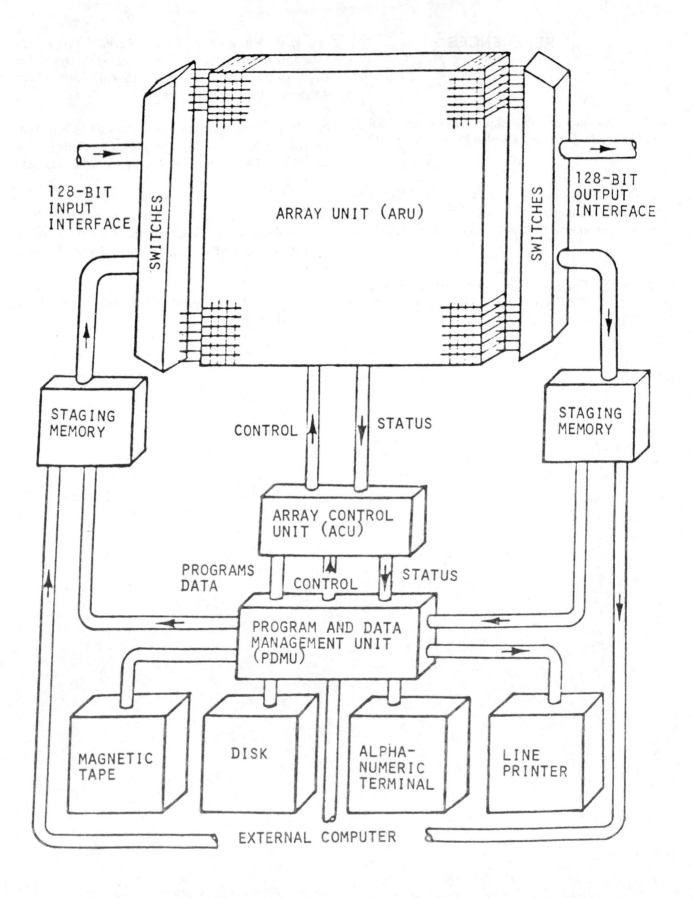

Figure 1 - Block Diagram of the Massively Parallel Processor (MPP)

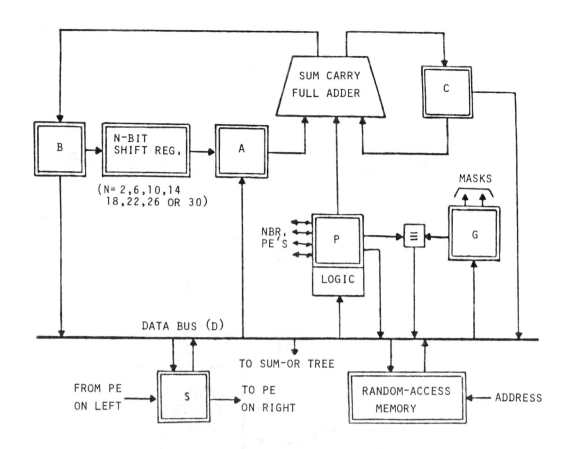

Figure 2 - One Processing Element

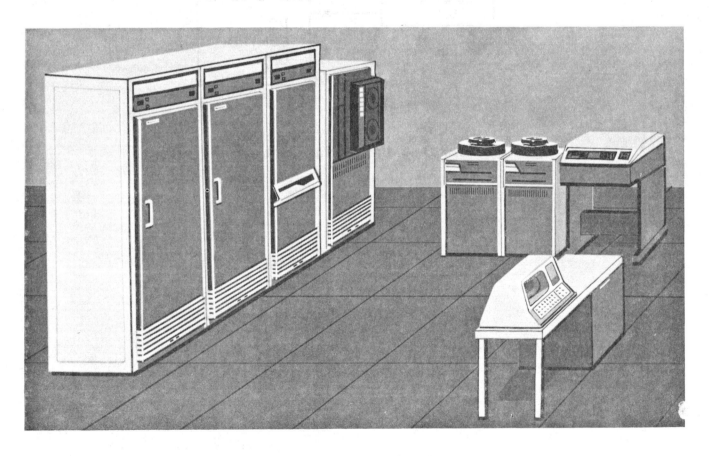

Figure 3 - MPP Physical Configuration

87

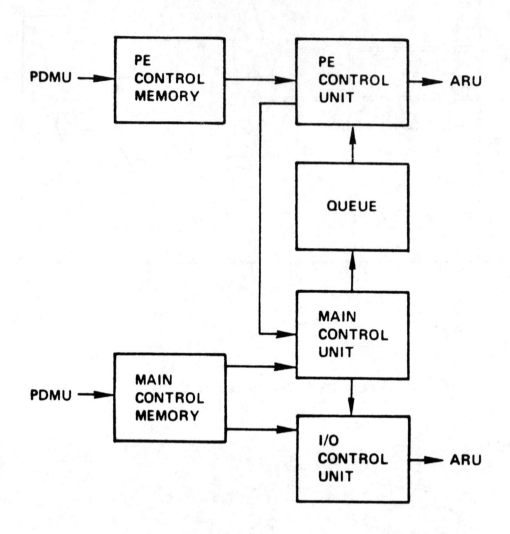

Figure 4 - Block Diagram of Array Control Unit (ACU)

Reprinted from *IEEE Transactions on Computers*, Volume
C-23, Number 3, March 1974, pages 309–318. Copyright © 1974
by The Institute of Electrical and Electronics Engineers, Inc.

Data Manipulating Functions in Parallel Processors and Their Implementations

TSE-YUN FENG

Abstract—This paper shows that there exists a class of functions
called data manipulating functions (DMF's), in sequential as well as
parallel processors. The circuits used to achieve these functions can be
considered to form an independent functional block, called a data
manipulator. A basic organization applicable to both sequential and
parallel processors is then suggested. The main deviation of a parallel
processor organization from the conventional Von Neumann
organization is seen to be in the bit-slice (bis) manipulating functions. A
comprehensive set of bis manipulating functions from the categories of
permuting, replicating, spacing and masking is given. Implementation of
the last category, the masking functions, is usually through a mask
register by defining its content (mask pattern). It is found that for
many operations the required mask patterns are periodic and/or
monotonic. The upper bounds of generating these patterns are found.
The techniques and designs of two data manipulators for the first three
categories of DMF's (permuting, replicating, spacing) are given. Periodic
and monotonic mask patterns are also used to help in implementing
some of these functions. In addition, it is shown that the data
manipulator designs presented in this paper are extremely flexible to
suit the requirements of various parallel processors.

Index Terms—Cell communications, data manipulating functions,
data manipulator, logic design, parallel processing, parallel processor
organization, processing characteristics.

INTRODUCTION

IT is well known that as the switching speeds of computer
devices approach a limit, any further improvement in
computer throughput has to be in increasing the number of
bits which can be processed simultaneously. Thus, given the
same cycle time the slowest method of processing is by
bit-serial (one bit at a time). The processing speed is increased
by an order of magnitude or more when a number of bits,
called a word, can be processed simultaneously. This

Manuscript received August 20, 1972; revised May 24, 1973. This
work was supported by the Rome Air Development Center under
Contract F30602-72-C-0281.
The author is with the Department of Electrical and Computer
Engineering, Syracuse University, Syracuse, N.Y.

word-sequential processing technique is employed by most conventional computers. Since the word widths are limited by application requirements, further increase in throughput can be obtained only by concurrent, overlapping, or parallel processing a number of words. Each of these processing techniques has its merits as well as limitations; an ultimate computer system may very well possess all these techniques. In this paper we limit ourselves to the parallel processing characteristics, even though some of the discussions are applicable to other processing techniques as well.

To parallel process a number of words under single-instruction control, a set of processing elements (PE's) are used [1], [2]. Depending on the design, a PE may contain either a serial or a parallel arithmetic-logic unit. In the former case, the operations are performed in a *bis-sequential*[1] manner. If, as in the latter case, each PE is capable of performing bit-parallel operations, the processor is called a *fully parallel* processor, or simply parallel processor.[2] In sequential processors, the storage unit is a register (whether it is a word register, or a bis register) but in a (fully) parallel processor a number of registers are involved.

PROCESSING CHARACTERISTICS

In this section we discuss some processing characteristics and suggest that there exists a class of functions in sequential as well as parallel processors.

Before an operation is applied on a pair of operands, one operand may need to be manipulated in some way so that appropriate bit-pairs can be formed for execution. As an example, consider a conventional word-sequential processor performing multiplication. One technique is by repeated shifts and additions. We may say that while the addition is an arithmetic operation, the shift is actually a *data manipulating function* (DMF) which is defined to be *a function required for preparing appropriate operands for fetching, execution, and storing*. The data manipulating functions for a word-sequential processor is called the *word manipulating functions*. Since a word operand represents a meaningful entity which has definite positional relations among its bits, the required word manipulating functions are usually limited to shift[3] and mask operations. In some cases, it may also involve other functions such as flip.

A bis operand, on the other hand, does not have any fixed positional relations among its bits which implies that the interbit manipulation in a bis processor is much more complicated than that in a word processor. Usually a bis processor requires a proper alignment in sizes as well as locations of two operand sets, so that appropriate operand pairs (bit pairs) can be formed. Such complicated *bis manipulating functions* are characteristic of most bis-sequential processors. Without any aid of special circuitry, the time

required for implementing the bis manipulating functions could be intolerably long particularly when sequential manipulations cannot be avoided.

A fully parallel processor has a combination of the processing characteristics possessed by the word and the bis processors. Along the word direction a parallel processor should be capable of performing horizontal shifts and masks. Vertically (bis-wise), it should also be able to prepare appropriate operand pairs for fetching, execution, and storing.

PARALLEL PROCESSOR ORGANIZATION

The relations between processor organizations and DMF's are discussed in this section. It is suggested that not only similarities and differences between sequential and parallel processors can be seen in terms of the data manipulating capabilities, but also the use of DMF's provides a means of more precisely specifying the users' requirements on the system design. A basic organization that is applicable to both sequential and parallel processors is then given.

A conventional Von Neumann-type computer organization consists of five basic functional units: control, arithmetic, memory, input, and output. Since the hardware used in implementing the word manipulating functions is usually simple, there is no special classification for it.

For parallel processors it has been recognized that there should be some structural changes from the word-sequential organization. The required change is loosely identified as in the communications among PE's. In ILLIAC IV [3], for example, a fixed toroidal communication pattern is provided. On the other hand, depending on applications other communication patterns may be needed for efficient performance. Perfect shuffle [4], [5] is one example. Replication [6] is another. Generally, the more applications intended for a parallel processor, the more flexible communications among PE's (or the more bis manipulating functions) are needed. The structural deviation of a parallel processor from the Von Neumann organization is thus seen to be in the circuits required for achieving the bis manipulating functions.

A basic organization for the sequential and parallel processors is suggested in Fig. 1(a). The data manipulator achieves the bis and/or word manipulating functions depending on the type of processors under consideration. The two data manipulator designs described in this paper can be considered to be the module data manipulator of Fig. 1(b). All module broadcasting registers (MBR's) in that figure form a module of Q words for $Q \leqslant N$ or a number of modules for $Q > N$, where N is the number of PE's in a PE module. The content of each MBR module may be manipulated by the module data manipulator.

In a conventional word-sequential computer each machine instruction involves three classes of operations: 1) instruction and operand fetch, 2) decode and address generation, and 3) execution. The word manipulating functions are included in the execution. In a parallel processor, the instructions and the operands are usually fetched from different memories, and the operands usually require some manipulation before execution.

---

[1] All *i*th bits of a given set of operands (or word registers) form the *i*th bit-slice, or *bis*, of the set.

[2] Conventionally bis-sequential processors are also called parallel processors.

[3] Carry handling involves shift operations, usually a special circuitry is built into the arithmetic unit to achieve carry propagation (shift) functions.

Thus, for each machine instruction there can be four classes of operations: 1) instruction fetch, 2) decode and address generation, 3) operand fetch and data manipulation, and 4) execution.

It is also noted that in a sequential processor, one word or one bis is fetched at a time, while in a parallel processor, one page (a fixed number of words) is fetched. In a word-sequential processor it is sometimes desirable to address a half-word or a byte. Similarly, in a parallel processor it is often desirable to address a subpage of desired size or a word.

DMF's

In the previous sections it is pointed out that the word manipulating functions are more limited than the bis manipulating functions. Thus, our discussions on the complexity of the DMF's can be in terms of the bis manipulating functions. In this section we suggest a comprehensive set of the bis manipulating functions. Such a set of functions is evidently helpful to the development of parallel-processing languages. Considerations and techniques of implementing the DMF's are also discussed.

The word manipulating functions are usually limited to shifts and masks, but the bis manipulating functions involve a variety of operations which may be classified under the following four categories:

1) permuting (shift, flip, shuffle, transpose, merge, mix, bit-reverse sort, sort);
2) replicating (multiplicate, duplicate),
3) spacing (spread, compress, transfer), and
4) masking.

The major bis manipulating functions are listed in Fig. 2.[4] These manipulating functions are defined in Appendix A. Since the number and the types of DMF's needed vary with the intended applications, the complexity of the data manipulator design also varies. A good parallel processor design is highly dependent on how efficiently the DMF's required by the intended applications are implemented. There are two approaches[5]: the circuit may be scattered among the PE's such as the routing circuit and the barrel switches in ILLIAC IV, or may be concentrated to form a separate functional unit within the organization.[6] The latter approach seems to have several distinct advantages. One is that the design of a separate unit is easier to be tailored to the user's specifications. Another advantage is in the overall system reliability. It is not only easier to isolate any data manipulator fault in a concentrated design,[7] but also for a data manipulator capable of performing the "spacing" functions to

<hr/>

[4] Some of the functions suggested here are being implemented in the Texas Instrument SIMDA processor [7]. A recent version of STARAN by Goodyear Aerospace also has a permutation network for data manipulation [8].

[5] A combination of these two approaches also exists.

[6] In analogy, it is noted that in some word-sequential processors the data manipulator circuit is embedded in the arithmetic-logic unit, while the design of most high-speed word-sequential processors favors a separate unit.

[7] In case of data manipulator fault, the processor may work as an ensemble system (Fig. 1).

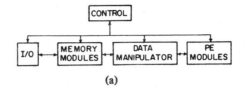

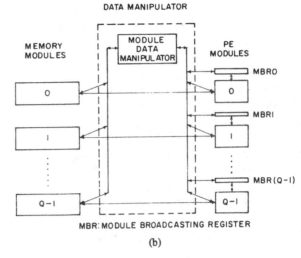

Fig. 1. Basic parallel processor organization. (a) Block diagram. (b) Data manipulator.

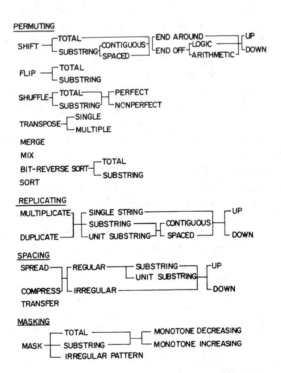

NOTE THAT COMPLEMENTING FUNCTIONS CAN BE INCLUDED AS ANOTHER CATEGORY OF DATA MANIPULATING FUNCTIONS WHICH USUALLY REQUIRE UNARY OPERATIONS ONLY.

Fig. 2. Bis manipulating functions.

provide graceful degradation by isolating the faulty PE's, or even to provide a "self-repairing" capability. Also, it should be noted that in a concentrated design appropriate logic partitions are possible [9]. Thus, the total number of pins could be drastically reduced which again improves the system reliability. The fourth advantage is that there could be a tremendous amount of hardware sharing in achieving the bis and/or word manipulating functions. The design of a basic data manipulator is then to find the common characteristics among the bis and word manipulating functions, and to construct a circuit such that the required hardware components are minimized, yet the circuitry design should have the flexibility of being alterable as needs vary. This is demonstrated by the two data manipulator designs described in this paper. The line manipulator which operates one word or one bis at a time, has a two-dimensional circuit configuration. The page manipulator may be considered as a three-dimensional extension of the line manipulator. It is capable of manipulating a set of words as well as a set of bises.

In implementing the DMF's a data manipulator circuit, whether distributed or concentrated, usually uses one or more mask registers to achieve the masking functions. Since the generation of mask patterns is usually independent of the data manipulator design, we discuss it in a separate section followed by the designs of two data manipulators.

In the following discussions and designs we assume that there are $N = 2^n$ processing elements in a parallel processor module and the word width is $M = 2^m$ bits.

MASK PATTERN GENERATION

The mask patterns of a data manipulator circuit are specified either by results of search and other operations, or by a user. In the former case, the mask pattern are generated by the problem itself. In this section we discuss some characteristics of mask generation by a user. It is found that for most applications the required mask patterns possess certain common characteristics, viz., periodic and monotonic. We then show that the upper bounds of generating these patterns grow as the logarithm of the bis lengths or word widths.

Definition 1: A *(2^i)-periodic string* is a bit string consisting of a number of contiguous, identical substrings of length 2^i.

Definition 2: A *monotonic string* is a bit string of i variables satisfying: either $p(x) \leqslant p(y)$ wherever $x \leqslant y$ (monotone increasing) or $p(x) \geqslant p(y)$ wherever $x \leqslant y$ (monotone decreasing) where x, y are the binary values of addresses $(x_{i-1} x_{i-2} \cdots x_0)$ and $(y_{i-1} y_{i-2} \cdots y_0)$, respectively, and $p(x)$, $p(y)$ are the bit values in the string at addresses x, y. (The special cases of all-0 and all-1 strings are excluded.)

Definition 3: A *(2^i)-periodic, monotonic string* is a (2^i)-periodic string consisting of a number of contiguous identical monotonic substrings.

Definition 4: The *complement* of a string is accomplished by complementing every bit in the string.

Definition 5: A *logic operation* between two strings of the same length is the logic operation between every two corresponding bit pairs.

The following notations are used in our discussion.

$S(k)$ A string consists of k contiguous bits where k is an arbitrary integer and $k \leqslant 2^n$. A string may consist of a number of contiguous substrings, $S(k_1)$, $S(k_2)$, $\cdots$, $S(k_j)$ and is denoted by concatenation, i.e., $S(k) = S(k_1)S(k_2) \cdots S(k_j)$ where $k = k_1 + k_2 + \cdots + k_j$. It

is noted that concatenation of strings or substrings takes precedence over union and intersection operations.

$0(k)$ An all-0 string of length k.

$I(k)$ An all-1 string of length k.

$\beta_i(j \times 2^{i+1})$ A $(j \times 2^{i+1})$-bit string consists of j contiguous (2^{i+1})-bit substrings, each of which starts with 2^i 0's followed by 2^i 1's, where $0 \leqslant i \leqslant n - 1, 1 \leqslant j \leqslant 2^{n-i-1}$ and $2 \leqslant (j \times 2^{i+1}) \leqslant 2^n$. Thus, $\beta_i(j \times 2^{i+1})$ is a (2^{i+1})-periodic and monotone increasing string. For the special case of $j \times 2^{i+1} = 2^n$, $\beta_i(2^n)$ is written in its abbreviated form β_i.

$\overline{\beta_i(j \times 2^{i+1})}$ The complement of $\beta_i(j \times 2^{i+1})$, a (2^{i+1})-periodic and monotone decreasing string. It is assumed that both β_i's and $\bar{\beta}_i$'s are readily available for mask pattern generation.

$B_A(2^k)$ A monotone increasing 2^k-bit string generated by a number of logic (union or intersection) operations on β_i's. The string starts with A 0's, $1 \leqslant A \leqslant 2^k - 1$ and followed by $(2^k - A)$ 1's, i.e., $B_A(2^k) = 0(A) I(2^k - A)$.

$\bar{B}_{\bar{A}}(2^k)$ The complement of $B_A(2^k) = \overline{B_A(2^k)} = \bar{B}_{\bar{A}}(2^k) = \bar{B}_{(2^k-A)}(2^k) = I(A) 0(2^k - A)$. It is a monotone decreasing 2^k-bit string.

Note that

$$B_A(2^k) = 0(A) I(2^k - A)$$
$$B_{\bar{A}}(2^k) = 0(2^k - A) I(A)$$
$$\bar{B}_A(2^k) = I(2^k - A) 0(A)$$
$$\bar{B}_{\bar{A}}(2^k) = I(A) 0(2^k - A).$$

In the following theorems and their proofs, whenever a union, intersection, or multiplication operation is involved, the symbol $\cup$, $\cap$, or $\times$ is always, respectively, used, while a concatenation is always used to denote two contiguous strings or substrings.

Lemma 1: For any positive integer i

$$B_A(2^i) = \beta_{i-1}(2^i) \cup B_A(2^{i-1}) B_A(2^{i-1}) \qquad 1 \leqslant A < 2^{i-1},$$
$$B_A(2^i) = \beta_{i-1}(2^i) \qquad\qquad\qquad\qquad A = 2^{i-1},$$
$$B_A(2^i) = \beta_{i-1}(2^i) \cap B_{(A-2^{i-1})}(2^{i-1}) B_{(A-2^{i-1})}(2^{i-1})$$
$$2^{i-1} < A < 2^i.$$

Proof:

$$\beta_{i-1}(2^i) \cup B_A(2^{i-1}) B_A(2^{i-1}) = 0(2^{i-1}) I(2^{i-1})$$
$$\cup B_A(2^{i-1}) B_A(2^{i-1})$$
$$= [0(2^{i-1}) \cup B_A(2^{i-1})] [I(2^{i-1}) \cup B_A(2^{i-1})]$$
$$= B_A(2^{i-1}) I(2^{i-1}) = B_A(2^i).$$

$$\beta_{i-1}(2^i) = 0(2^{i-1})I(2^{i-1}) = B_A(2^i).$$

$$\beta_{i-1}(2^i) \cap B_{(A-2^{i-1})}(2^{i-1})B_{(A-2^{i-1})}(2^{i-1}) = 0(2^{i-1})I(2^{i-1})$$

$$\cap B_{(A-2^{i-1})}(2^{i-1})B_{(A-2^{i-1})}(2^{i-1})$$

$$= 0(2^{i-1})B_{(A-2^{i-1})}(2^{i-1}) = B_A(2^i).$$

Theorem 1: $B_A(2^n)$, for $1 \leqslant A \leqslant 2^n$, can be generated in, at most, $(n-1)$ Boolean operations with each β_i used at most once.

Proof: For $n = 1, B_A(2^1) = \beta_0(2^1)$, a trivial case. For $n = 2$, there are three cases. 1) $A = 1, B_1(2^2) = \beta_1(2^2) \cup \beta_0(2^2)$. 2) $A = 2, B_2(2^2) = \beta_1(2^2)$. 3) $A = 3, B_3(2^2) = \beta_1(2^2) \cap \beta_0(2^2)$.

By induction assume that it is true for $n = k - 1$, i.e., $B_A(2^{k-1})$ can be generated in, at most, $(k-2)$ Boolean operations. For $n = k$ we apply Lemma 1 and find that $B_A(2^k)$ can be generated in, at most, $(k-1)$ operations.

Theorem 2: It takes at most $(n-s-1)$ operations on β_i's, $0 \leqslant i \leqslant n-1$, to generate a monotone increasing 2^n-bit string starting with $j \times 2^s$ 0's, for $1 \leqslant j < 2^{n-s}$ and $0 \leqslant s \leqslant n-1$.

Theorem 1 may be viewed as a special case of Theorem 2 by setting $j = A$ and $s = 0$.

Theorem 3: It takes exactly $(n-s-1)$ union (or intersection) operations on β_i's, $0 \leqslant i \leqslant n-1$, to generate a monotone increasing 2^n-bit string starting with 2^s (or $2^n - 2^s$) 0's.

In particular,

1) $B_{2^s}(2^n) = \beta_{n-1} \cup \beta_{n-2} \cup \cdots \cup \beta_s,$

2) $B_{(2^n-2^s)}(2^n) = \beta_{n-1} \cap \beta_{n-2} \cap \cdots \cap \beta_s.$

Proof: 1) For $s = n-1, B_{2^{n-1}}(2^n) = 0(2^{n-1})$ $I(2^{n-1}) = \beta_{n-1}$. For $s = n-2,$

$$B_{2^{n-2}}(2^n) = 0(2^{n-2})I(2^{n-2})I(2^{n-1})$$

$$= 0(2^{n-2})0(2^{n-2})I(2^{n-1}) \cup 0(2^{n-2})I(2^{n-2})\beta_{n-2}(2^{n-1})$$

$$= \beta_{n-1} \cup \beta_{n-2}.$$

Suppose that it is true for $s = k+1$, i.e.,

$$B_{2^{k+1}}(2^n) = \beta_{n-1} \cup \beta_{n-2} \cup \cdots \cup \beta_{k+1}.$$

For $s = k$, we have

$$B_{2^k}(2^n) = 0(2^k)I(2^k)I(2^n - 2^{k+1})$$

$$= 0(2^k)0(2^k)I(2^n - 2^{k+1}) \cup 0(2^k)I(2^k)\beta_k(2^n - 2^{k+1})$$

$$= B_{2^{k+1}}(2^n) \cup \beta_k$$

$$= \beta_{n-1} \cup \beta_{n-2} \cup \cdots \cup \beta_{k+1} \cup \beta_k.$$

2) This can be proved similarly.

Theorem 4: It takes at most $(s-1)$ operations on β_i's, $0 \leqslant i \leqslant n-1$, to generate any (2^s)-periodic, monotone increasing 2^n-bit string for $0 \leqslant s \leqslant n-1$. The proof of this theorem is similar to that of Theorem 1.

Theorem 5: It takes at most $(n-1)$ operations on β_i's and/or $\bar{\beta_i}$'s, $0 \leqslant i \leqslant n-1$, to generate j contiguous $B_A(2^s)$-substrings for $1 \leqslant j < 2^{n-s}$ and $0 \leqslant s \leqslant n-1$. Theorem 5 is a direct consequence of Theorems 2 and 4.

The previous discussions involve mainly the monotone increasing strings. It is obvious that they also hold for the monotone decreasing strings by applying the DeMorgan's theorems and the definitions given in this paper.

For any arbitrary mask patterns which are not monotonic, Karnaugh maps and other minimization techniques can be used to aid the implementation. Since in the mask pattern generation β_i-sequential operations are assumed, the aim of minimization is in the reduction of total count of literals (β_i's) or operations on β_i's. The multilevel minimization techniques, instead of Quine-McCluskey method, should be used.

A LINE MANIPULATOR

The merits of implementing the DMF's within a separate functional unit are discussed in a previous section. In this section a basic data-manipulator design is described and illustrated. Possible design variations are discussed. It can be seen that such a design is flexible enough to be considered as one basic approach that can be tailored to suit various users' requirements.

A. Design

The basic line-manipulator circuit for $n = 3$ is shown in Fig. 3 (the circuit within the dash-lined box). There are $n + 1$ columns of logic cells. Except the last column, all other column having control lines are labeled by numbers, 2^{n-1}, $2^{n-2}, \cdots, 2^1, 2^0$, as shown. Each logic cell in the intermediate columns consists of four logic gates (Fig. 4). The logic cell of the first column (Column 2^{n-1}) has the construction of the right half of the intermediate cell and that of the last column, the left half. Referring to Fig. 4, whenever $u2^i(k)$ [or $d2^i(k)$] is activated, the data input from the left side of the cell may pass through the cell and move up [or down] 2^i positions to the input of Cell $(k - 2^i)$, mod 2^n, [or Cell $(k + 2^i)$, mod 2^n] of the next column, Column 2^{i-1}. If $h2^i(k)$ is activated, the input passes horizontally to Cell k of Column 2^{i-1}. Since there are $N = 2^n$ logic cells in each column, there are three sets, denoted by $U2^i, H2^i$, and $D2^i$, of N control lines each for Column 2^i. In other words, $U2^i, H2^i$, and $D2^i$ represent, respectively, all $u2^i, h2^i$, and $d2^i$ control lines of Column 2^i. Each set of N control lines is then subdivided into two groups (indicated by adding a subscript 1 or 2 to the set symbol). Thus, all the control lines for each Column 2^i are connected in six groups, $U_1^{2^i}, U_2^{2^i}, H_1^{2^i}, H_2^{2^i}, D_1^{2^i}, D_2^{2^i}$. This is illustrated in Fig. 5[8] where, for clarity, only the interconnection lines are shown. It is noted that Groups $U_1^{2^{n-1}}$ and $U_2^{2^{n-1}}$ are functionally identical to Groups $D_1^{2^{n-1}}$ and $D_2^{2^{n-1}}$, respectively, but inclusion of these redundant groups simplifies implementation.

[8] Superimposing the interconnections of (a)-(c) in Fig. 5 gives the interconnections of the basic line-manipulator circuit of Fig. 3.

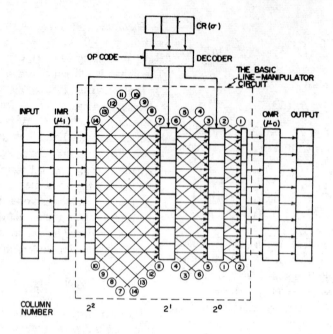

CR   CONTROL REGISTER (σ)
IMR   INPUT MASK REGISTER (μ_I)
OMR   OUTPUT MASK REGISTER (μ_0)

Fig. 3. Structure of a line manipulator.

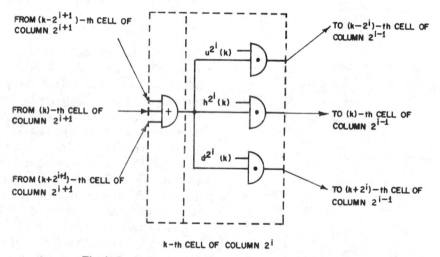

Fig. 4. Logic circuit of a line-manipulator intermediate cell.

B. Implementation

Most of the DMF's given in Fig. 2 can be achieved by the line manipulator described previously. A detailed description of the implementation can be found in [9]. In the following, three examples are provided in Figs. 6-8 illustrating the implementation of each of the permuting, replicating, and spacing functions. A heavy interconnection line in these figures indicates that its control line is energized for the operation. The use of a periodic, monotone decreasing mask pattern (a masking function) is also illustrated in Fig. 6.

Fig. 6 shows the implementation of "contiguous substrings shift up (by 1 position), end off," with 2 substrings of length 4 each. To achieve this function either the control line groups

$U_1 2^i$ and $U_2 2^i$ or groups $H_1 2^i$ and $H_2 2^i$ are energized depending on whether the corresponding bit in the control register CR, where the binary shift value is stored, is 1 or 0. Thus, for this operation, 001 is stored in CR and the control lines belonging to groups $H_1 2^2$, $H_2 2^2$, $H_1 2^1$, $H_2 2^1$, $U_1 2^0$, and $U_2 2^0$ are energized. With appropriate output mask pattern[9] the specified function is achieved. The required mask pattern is a (2^s)-periodic, monotone decreasing 2^n-bit string (Fig. 6). Since the substring length is 4 or $s = 2$ according to Theorem 4 and its subsequent discussion, only $s - 1 = 1$ operation on $\bar{\beta}_i$'s is needed. It is also noted that for this

_____

[9] Without masking the operation is a "total shift up (by 1 position), end around."

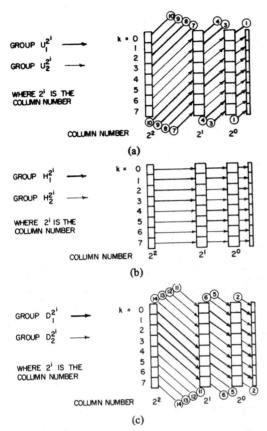

Fig. 5. Interconnection groups in the line manipulator. (a) Interconnections controlled by U control-line groups. (b) Interconnections controlled by H control-line groups. (c) Interconnections controlled by D control-line groups.

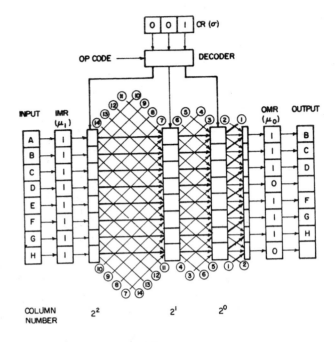

CR CONTROL REGISTER (σ)
IMR INPUT MASK REGISTER (μ_1)
OMR OUTPUT MASK REGISTER (μ_0)

Fig. 6. Contiguous substrings shift up, end off.

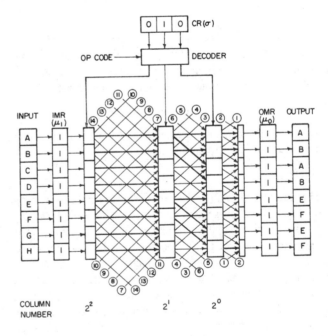

CR CONTROL REGISTER (σ)
IMR INPUT MASK REGISTER (μ_1)
OMR OUTPUT MASK REGISTER (μ_0)

Fig. 7. Duplicate spaced substrings down.

operation, the value of A (the number of zeros in the substring) is the same as the shift value, i.e., 1.

A "duplicate spaced substrings down" operation is illustrated in Fig. 7. The two substrings to be duplicated are AB and EF. For this operation the control line groups $D_1 2^i$ and $H_1 2^i$ or $H_1 2^i$ and $H_2 2^i$ are activated depending on whether the control bit is 1 or 0 which is determined by the substring length. In this example, the substring length is 2 or $s = 1$, thus, only the control bit for Column 2^1 has a value of 1, all others are 0's.

Fig. 8 illustrates the "spread substrings with 2^s (for $s = 1$) spacing down" operation. The control lines to be energized for Column 2^{n-1} are fixed, i.e., it is always those in group $H_1 2^i$ irrespective of the control bit value. The control lines for other columns are either $H_1 2^i$ and $D_2 2^i$ or $H_1 2^i$ and $H_2 2^i$ dependent on their control bit values which are assigned as follows: the control bits for Columns 2^s to 2^{n-2} are 1's and all others (for Columns 2^{s-1} to 2^0) are 0's.

C. Discussion

The line-manipulator circuit described here requires a relatively small amount of hardware, yet the data manipulating capability provided by this circuit satisfies many application needs. The total number of logic gates in the circuit is proportional to $N\log_2 N$ without counting the control and masks. The design is quite flexible. By properly combing or dividing the control lines in the circuit the basic line manipulator instruction repertoire can be expanded or contracted to some extent. Also, compress with regular spacing may be implemented in the line-manipulator circuit if the logic gates are made bidirectional or if the number of inputs as well as outputs of each logic cell is increased to 5 from the present 3.

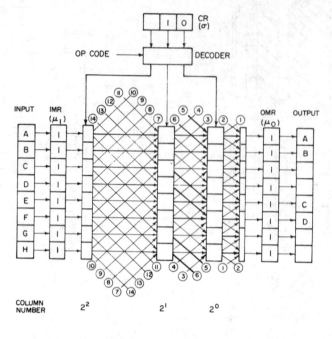

CR CONTROL REGISTER(σ)
IMR INPUT MASK REGISTER (μ_I)
OMR OUTPUT MASK REGISTER (μ_O)

Fig. 8. Spread substrings with 2^s spacing down.

It may also be pointed out that with appropriate logic partitioning this circuit can be implemented with only one circuit type and with much reduced interconnections [9].

A PAGE MANIPULATOR

This section shows how the design of a line manipulator can be extended to a page manipulator.

A. Design

The line manipulator described previously executes the DMF's in either bis-sequential or word-sequential fashion. Since the bis manipulating functions (Fig. 2) are much more complex than the word manipulating functions which usually involve shift operations only and since the bis length and the word width of a parallel processor may not be equal it is usually not efficient to use one of these circuits to perform both the bis and the word manipulating functions. In addition, in many applications it is desirable that the DMF's are executed in fully parallel fashion (rather than bis-sequential or word-sequential) to reduce the manipulation time.

The line manipulator design can be extended to satisfy the above requirements. The basic page manipulator is thus similar to that of Fig. 3 except that there are $M = 2^m$ such circuits interconnected together. The cell interconnection is shown in Fig. 9. The control lines are similarly grouped as those shown in Fig. 5 except that additional R and L groups are added [9].

B. Implementation

The implementation of the bis manipulating functions is the same as those described under the line manipulator. The

word manipulating functions are expressed in terms of R, L, and H control-line groups [9].

The bis and word manipulating functions are usually not executed simultaneously in the page manipulator.

C. Discussion

The implication resulting from the fully parallel data manipulator is that the data transfer between parallel processor modules and their memories should be in blocks (pages) of $N \times M$ bits.

The cell complexity of the page manipulator is somewhat increased from that of the line manipulator. However, there does exist a large amount of hardware sharing between bis and word manipulations.

CONCLUSION

When a group of bits (an operand or a number of operands) are to be processed, some manipulations on these bits, either before or after execution, are often needed. This is particularly true for parallel processors including bis-sequential processors. Thus, a set of DMF's derived from the user's intended applications characterize part of the users' specifications and should provide a guide for the parallel processor design. The DMF's also serve as a bridge between the hardware implementations and the language development for parallel processors.

The four classes of DMF's[10] suggested in this paper are

[10]It should be noted that some of the DMF's are also needed in applications other than parallel processing [10].

96

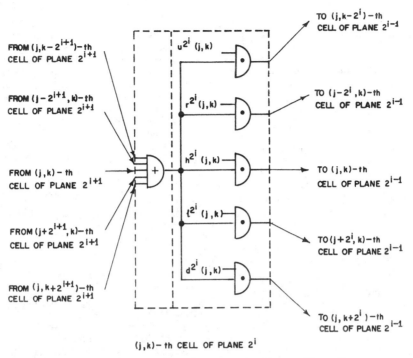

Fig. 9. Logic circuit of a page-manipulator intermediate cell.

found to be essential in such important mathematical computations as matrix operations, fast Fourier transform (FFT), solution to differential equations, etc., and nonnumerical data processing as in searches and sorting. For example, shift functions are needed for solving partial differential equations, and for matrix operations, particularly for square matrices. Flip is an operation required for parallel divisions, and memory operations. Shuffle and bit-reverse sort are both used for FFT processing. Shuffle can also be used for parallel sorting. Replications are required for matrix operations in general, and other applications such as signal processing, solution to differential equations. In many memory operations and sparse matrix operations spread and compress are essential. Compress function is also useful for counting, multiple additions, multiple responses resolving, etc.

These applications have been studied and some of them were reported [4]-[6], [11]. The need and the effectiveness of a data manipulator for parallel processing are supported by these studies. Its use would help to

1) reduce the number of sequential operations during processing so that both the throughput and the hardware utilization are improved,
2) reduce the memory storage spaces,
3) increase the system capability.

Since the DMF's vary widely depending upon the intended applications, it is important that a basic data manipulator design should not only be cost-effective, but also possess a great amount of flexibility so that the design can be easily tailored according to the users' needs. The basic design reported here seems to fulfill these requirements. There are four variable parameters in this design:

1) the number of output gates (or communication paths) of each cell;

2) the number of control line groups;
3) the number of manipulator columns (or planes); and
4) the interconnection paths between cells.

Appropriate control of these parameters could produce a suitable data manipulator in accordance with the specifications.

APPENDIX A

DMF GLOSSARY

PERMUTING Rearranging a group of elements.[11]

SHIFT Displacing a group of elements by a number of positions.

FLIP Interchanging a group of elements, end for end. For example, for a group of 2^i elements the kth element is interchanged with the $(2^i - k + 1)$th element.

SHUFFLE Dividing a group of elements into two subgroups and interleaving the elements of the two subgroups such that the output is formed by taking the first k elements from the first subgroup followed by k elements from the other group, etc.

TRANSPOSE Dividing a group of elements into a number of subgroups and interleaving the elements of these subgroups such that the output is formed by taking the first element from each subgroup in succession, then the second element, etc.

MERGE Interleaving two or more ordered subgroups of elements into one ordered group.

MIX Rearranging a group of elements in any desired pattern.

[11] An element may be a bit, a word, or a bis.

BIT-REVERSE SORT Rearranging a group of elements in bit-reverse order.

SORT Rearranging a group of elements in a desired numerical order.

REPLICATING Reproducing a group of elements.

MULTIPLICATE Producing more than two copies of a group of elements.

DUPLICATE Producing two copies of a group of elements.

SPACING Inserting or dropping spaces in a group of elements without altering their original order.

SPREAD Stretching a group of contiguous elements to form a group of elements with regular or irregular spacing among elements.

COMPRESS Contracting a group of spaced elements to form a group of contiguous elements.

TRANSFER Repositioning a group of regularly or irregularly spaced elements to another group of regularly or irregularly spaced elements.

MASKING Inhibiting or truncating some elements from a group of elements.

REFERENCES

[1] T. Feng, "An overview of parallel processing systems," in *1972 Westcon Tech. Papers, Sess. 1–Parallel Processing Systems*, pp. 1-2, Sept. 1972.

[2] ——, "Some characteristics of associative/parallel processing," in *1972 Proc. Sagamore Comput. Conf.*, pp. 5-16, Aug. 1972.

[3] G.H. Barnes *et al.*, "The ILLIAC IV computer," *IEEE Trans. Comput.*, vol. C-17, pp. 746-757, Aug. 1968.

[4] M.C. Pease, "An adaption of the fast fourier transform for parallel processing," *J. Ass. Comput. Mach.*, pp. 252-264, Apr. 1968.

[5] H.S. Stone, "Parallel processing with perfect shuffle," *IEEE Trans. Comput.*, vol. C-20, pp. 153-161, Feb. 1971.

[6] RADC-SU, *Associative Processor Computing System, Parts I-III*, presented at the Air Force Scientific Advisory Board Information Processing Panel, June 25, 1971.

[7] A.H. Wester, "Special features in SIMDA," in *1972 Proc. Sagamore Comput. Conf.*, pp. 29-40, Aug. 1972.

[8] K.E. Batcher, "Flexible parallel processing and STARAN," in *1972 Westcon Tech. Papers, Session 1–Parallel Processing Systems*, pp. 1/5.1-1/5.3, Sept. 1972.

[9] T. Feng, "Parallel processor characteristics and implementation of data manipulating functions," Dep. Elec. Comput. Eng., Syracuse Univ., Syracuse, N.Y., Tech. Rep. TR-73-1, Apr. 1973.

[10] K.N. Levitt, M.W. Green, and J. Goldberg, "A study of the data communication problems in self-repairable multiprocessor," in *1968 Spring Joint Comput. Conf., AFIPS Conf. Proc.*, vol. 32. Washington, D.C.: Thompson, 1968, pp. 515-527.

[11] W.T. Cheng and T. Feng, "Associative processing of FFT," in *Proc. 6th Annu. Princeton Conf. Inform. Sciences and Syst.*, pp. 297-301, Mar. 1972.

Tse-Yun Feng received the B.S. degree from the National Taiwan University, Tapei, Taiwan, the M.S. degree from Oklahoma State University, Stillwater, and the Ph.D. degree from the University of Michigan, Ann Arbor, all in electrical engineering.

He joined the faculty of the Department of Electrical and Computer Engineering, Syracuse University, Syracuse, N.Y., in 1967. His major experience has been in the areas of associative processing, parallel processors, computer architecture, switching theory and logic design, and he has publications in these areas. He has also been an invited speaker to various organizations and served as a consultant or reviewer to several companies and publishers. He has helped in initiating the RADCAP project–an associative processor consisting of 1024 processing elements. The machine is currently in operation at the Rome Air Development Center.

Dr. Feng is presently a Distinguished Visitor of IEEE Computer Society. He is also the Conference Chairman of the 1973 Sagamore Computer Conference on Parallel Processing.

IEEE TRANSACTIONS ON COMPUTERS, VOL. C-24, NO. 12, DECEMBER 1975

Reprinted from *IEEE Transactions on Computers*, Volume C-24, Number 12, December 1975, pages 1145-1155. Copyright © 1975 by The Institute of Electrical and Electronics Engineers, Inc.

Access and Alignment of Data in an Array Processor

DUNCAN H. LAWRIE, MEMBER, IEEE

Abstract—This paper discusses the design of a primary memory system for an array processor which allows parallel, conflict-free access to various slices of data (e.g., rows, columns, diagonals, etc.), and subsequent alignment of these data for processing. Memory access requirements for an array processor are discussed in general terms and a set of common requirements are defined. The ability to meet these requirements is shown to depend on the number of independent memory units and on the mapping of the data in these memories. Next, the need to align these data for processing is demonstrated and various alignment requirements are defined. Hardware which can perform this alignment function is discussed, e.g., permutation, indexing, switching or sorting networks, and a network (the *omega* network) based on Stone's shuffle-exchange operation [1] is presented. Construction of this network is described and many of its useful properties are proven. Finally, as an example of these ideas, an array processor is shown which allows conflict-free access and alignment of rows, columns, diagonals, backward diagonals, and square blocks in row or column major order, as well as certain other special operations.

Index Terms—Alignment network, array processor, array storage, conflict-free acess, data alignment, indexing network, omega network, parallel processing, permutation network, shuffle-exchange network, storage mapping, switching network.

I. INTRODUCTION

IN THIS paper we will discuss the design of a memory system for an array processor. By an array processor we mean a collection of N arithmetic-logic units (ALU's) driven by a common instruction decoding unit (e.g., Illiac IV). We shall assume that the ALU's are connected to a collection of M memory units by some networks as illustrated in Fig. 1. In this system data come from the memory units in the form of vectors of N or fewer words, or N-vectors. The first network does the necessary rearranging or *alignment* of the elements of the N-vector so that each element can be paired in some ALU with the corresponding element of a second N-vector. This second N-vector may already be in the ALU's or it may be the next N-vector to be fetched from the memory. After some pairwise operation has been done on the two N-vectors, the resulting N-vector may be aligned for storage by the second network and stored in the memory units.

We can picture this system operating in a pipelined way: successive N-vectors being fetched, aligned, computed, aligned, and stored all at the same time. In order

Manuscript received December 12, 1973; revised June 2, 1975. This work was supported by the NSF under Grant DCR73-07980 A02.

The author is with the Department of Computer Science, University of Illinois, Urbana, Ill. 61801.

to do this, each subsystem in Fig. 1 must normally function in a constant time and each subsystem must be balanced with all other subsystems. That is, in the time required to perform a vector operation, the memory must be capable of fetching two N-vector operands and storing an N-vector result, the first switch must be capable of aligning two separate N-vectors, and the second switch must perform a result alignment. Other paths than those shown in Fig. 1 might also be desirable, e.g., a path from the output of the ALU's to the input of the first switch in order to bypass the memories for intermediate results.

Of course other arrangements are possible, and the results we present in this paper are not necessarily restricted to the arrangement shown. We feel this arrangement is of interest due to the potential for high utilization of all the hardware.

One of the most significant factors in determining the performance of an array processor (aside from the parallelism of the program) is the system's capability for providing data vectors at a rate matched to the processor rate. It is not sufficient to provide a memory whose raw bandwidth is matched to the bandwidth of the processor. We must also insure that data access normally occurs without memory conflicts and that operand pairs can be brought together in the right ALU's for processing. The primary concern of this paper is to design a memory system which can do this.

We will begin by describing a memory organization which allows conflict-free access to various kinds of N-vectors. Then we discuss the problem of data alignment and present some data alignment networks.

II. MEMORY ORGANIZATION ACCESS AND ALIGNMENT REQUIREMENTS

Memory organizations which allow conflict-free access to various slices of data have been discussed previously in the literature. For example, memories which allow access to either words or bit slices have been described for the STARAN [2] and OMEN [3] computers.

In this paper we are interested in accessing certain slices of arrays, e.g., rows and columns. One technique is to *skew* the data [4] as illustrated in Fig. 2. Here the 4×4 array a is stored in four independent memory units. By skewing the data in this fashion we can access, without conflict, any row or column of the array. But access to the main diagonal would involve a memory conflict since a_{00} and a_{22} both lie in the same memory unit (cf. Kraska [5] and Millstein [6]).

Budnik and Kuck [7] described a different scheme

EHO182-6/81/0000/0099 © 1975 IEEE

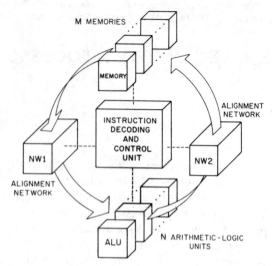

Fig. 1. An array processor.

MEMORY

	0	1	2	3
	a_{00}	a_{01}	a_{02}	a_{03}
	a_{13}	a_{10}	a_{11}	a_{12}
	a_{22}	a_{23}	a_{20}	a_{21}
	a_{31}	a_{32}	a_{33}	a_{30}

Fig. 2. 1-skew storage.

MEMORY

0	1	2	3	4
a_{00}	a_{02}	$\times$	a_{01}	a_{03}
a_{11}	a_{13}	a_{10}	a_{12}	$\times$
a_{22}	$\times$	a_{21}	a_{23}	a_{20}
a_{33}	a_{30}	a_{32}	$\times$	a_{31}

Fig. 3. Five memories with $\delta_1 = 2$ and $\delta_2 = 3$.

which used data skewing and a prime number of memories M, where $M > N = 2^n$. Their scheme allowed conflict-free access of rows, columns, diagonals, backward diagonals, and $N^{1/2} \times N^{1/2}$ blocks of $N \times N$ arrays.[1] However, their scheme has two drawbacks. First, address generation is difficult, involving modulo M arithmetic. Second, the only known data switch capable of performing the necessary alignment of data from a prime number of input ports is a full crossbar switch. (Alignment requirements will be discussed in more detail in the next section.) But for large N, crossbar switches are generally too expensive.

In this section we will present a new storage scheme which allows conflict-free access to rows, columns, forward and backward diagonals, and square blocks. In a later section we will present a data switching network which has fewer gates than a crossbar switch but which can still provide the necessary data alignment functions. We begin by generalizing the concept of skewed storage.

A. Generalized Skewing and Conflict-Free Access

Let M be the number of memories and let δ_i be the skewing distance in the ith dimension. Thus, for a two-dimensional ($N \times N$) matrix, element a_{jk} will be stored in memory $j \cdot \delta_1 + k \cdot \delta_2$, i.e., each successive element of the first dimension (column) is stored $\delta_1 \pmod{M}$ memories away from the previous element. Similarly for the second dimension (rows) and δ_2. This is called a (δ_1, δ_2) skewing scheme. Fig. 3 illustrates a system with $M = 5$, $\delta_1 = 2$,

and $\delta_2 = 3$. Clearly this generalizes to matrices with k dimensions (i.e., ($\delta_1, \delta_2, \cdots, \delta_k$) skewing) and matrices whose dimensions are larger than N.

Define a d-ordered N-vector (mod M) as a vector of N elements whose ith logical element is stored in memory unit $di + c \pmod{M}$ where c is an arbitrary constant. For example in Fig. 3, the third row, $a_{22}, X, a_{21}, a_{23}, a_{20}$ is a 3-ordered 4-vector (mod 5) since the ith element is in memory μ where $\mu = 3i + 4 \pmod 5$, $0 \leq i \leq 3$.

A sufficient condition for a d-ordered N-vector (mod M) to be accessible without conflicts is for the following condition to hold:

$$M \geq N \, gcd(d, M) \tag{1}$$

where $gcd(d, M)$ is the greatest common divisor of d and M. This follows from the fact that the set $\{\mu \mid \mu = di + c \pmod{M}, 0 \leq i \leq N - 1\}$ must contain N *distinct* elements. That is, the memories in which the N elements of the d-ordered N-vector are stored must be distinct. This will be true if Condition (1) is met.

If we use a (δ_1, δ_2) skewing scheme, then clearly columns will be δ_1-ordered, and rows will be δ_2-ordered. Similarly, diagonals will be $\delta_1 + \delta_2$-ordered. Thus, in order to access these three types of N-vectors the following conditions must hold:

$$
\begin{array}{ll}
M \geq N \, gcd(\delta_1, M) & \text{(columns)} \\
M \geq N \, gcd(\delta_2, M) & \text{(rows)} \\
M \geq N \, gcd(\delta_1 + \delta_2, M) & \text{(forward diagonals)} \\
M \geq N \, gcd(\delta_1 - \delta_2, M) & \text{(backward diagonals).}
\end{array}
$$

Clearly, if $M = N$ then $gcd(\delta_1, M)$, $gcd(\delta_2, M)$, and $gcd(\delta_1 + \delta_2, M)$ must equal 1 if these conditions are to hold. If M is even then δ_1, δ_2, and $\delta_1 + \delta_2$ must be odd for this to hold. But it is easy to show that δ_1, δ_2, and $\delta_1 + \delta_2$ cannot all be odd. Thus, we cannot have conflict-free access to rows, columns, and diagonals if $M = N$ and M is even.

Let us choose $M = 2N$ memories where N is the number of processors, N is an *even* power of two, and use ($N^{1/2} + 1, 2$) skewing. This is illustrated in Fig. 4 for $N = 4$. (Notice that storage is somewhat "sparse." However, another matrix can be stored in the "holes" created by this matrix or this matrix can be squeezed into half as many rows.)

Using this scheme we get the following results.
1) Rows are 2-ordered.
2) Columns are ($N^{1/2} + 1$)-ordered.
3) Diagonals are ($N^{1/2} + 3$)-ordered.
4) Backward diagonals are ($N^{1/2} - 1$)-ordered.

It is easy to see that $N^{1/2} + 1$, $N^{1/2} + 3$, and $N^{1/2} - 1$

---

[1] The need for backward diagonals, e.g., $a_{03}, a_{12}, a_{21}, a_{30}$, comes from the need to sweep certain meshes at a 45° angle (see Muraoka [8] and Kuck and Chen [9]). Square blocks are used to improve the "resolution" of the array processor (see Kuck [4]), as well as in certain important computations (see Kuck and Chen [9]).

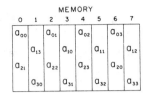

Fig. 4.   A memory system with $M = 2N = 8$, using $(N^{1/2} + 1,2)$ skewing.

are all odd and therefore are prime to M which is a power of two. Thus, $gcd(d,M) = 1$ and the condition $M \geq N \cdot gcd(d,M)$ is satisfied for columns, diagonals, and backward diagonals. For rows we see that

$$d_{\text{row}} = 2 \quad \text{and} \quad gcd(d_{\text{row}},M) = 2,$$

so the condition is again satisfied ($M \geq 2N$). Thus, we have conflict-free memory access to these N-vectors. $N^{1/2} \times N^{1/2}$ blocks are not well ordered, but nevertheless it can be shown that these can be accessed without conflict.

Theorem 1: The elements of a $N^{1/2} \times N^{1/2}$ square block lie in distinct memory modules when stored $(N^{1/2} + 1,2)$ skewed in $2N$ memories.

Proof: Since we are using $(N^{1/2} + 1,2)$ skewing, elements of the $N^{1/2} \times N^{1/2}$ block $a_{i,j}, a_{i,j+1}, \cdots, a_{i,j+N^{1/2}-1}$, $a_{i+1,j}, \cdots, a_{i+1,j+N^{1/2}-1}, \cdots, a_{i+N^{1/2}-1,j}, \cdots, a_{i+N^{1/2}-1,j+N^{1/2}-1}$ will be stored in memories numbered $\mu_{x_1,x_2} = (i + x_1) \cdot (N^{1/2} + 1) + (j + x_2) \cdot 2 \pmod{2N}$. For $0 \leq x_1, x_2 \leq N^{1/2} - 1$ we need only show that these memories are distinct, i.e., that[2] $\mu_{x_1,x_2} \not\equiv_{2N} \mu_{y_1,y_2}$ unless $x_1 = y_1$ and $x_2 = y_2$. Assume $\mu_{x_1,x_2} \equiv_{2N} \mu_{y_1,y_2}$. Then we will show that $x_1 = y_1$ and $x_2 = y_2$. Eliminate the i and j terms and we get

$$x_1(N^{1/2} + 1) + 2x_2 \underset{2N}{\equiv} y_1(N^{1/2} + 1) + 2y_2.$$

Expanding and regrouping terms we get

$$N^{1/2}(x_1 - y_1) + x_1 - y_1 \underset{2N}{\equiv} 2(y_2 - x_2). \qquad (2)$$

Without loss of generality, assume $x_1 > y_1$ so that

$$(x_1 - y_1) < N^{1/2}.$$

Then we get

$$x_1 - y_1 \underset{N^{1/2}}{\equiv} 2(y_2 - x_2). \qquad (3)$$

Also from (2) since $(x_1 - y_1) < N^{1/2}$, we get

$$(x_1 - y_1) \underset{N^{1/2}}{\equiv} 2(y_2 - x_2) \div N^{1/2}. \qquad (4)$$

From (3) and (4) we get

$$2(y_2 - x_2) \underset{N^{1/2}}{\equiv} 2(y_2 - x_2) \div N^{1/2}. \qquad (5)$$

Let

$$2(y_2 - x_2) \underset{2N}{\equiv} aN^{1/2} + b, \qquad 0 \leq a, b \leq N^{1/2} - 1;$$

[2] The notation $a \equiv_c b$ means a is congruent to b modulo c.

then from (5) we get

$$aN^{1/2} + b \underset{N^{1/2}}{\equiv} a$$

so that $a,b = 0$, i.e., $2(y_2 - x_2) \equiv_{2N} 0$ and since $x_2, y_2 < N^{1/2}$, $x_2 = y_2$. Using this and (2) again we get

$$N^{1/2}(x_1 - y_1) + (x_1 - y_1) \underset{2N}{\equiv} 0.$$

So since $x_1, y_1 < N^{1/2}$, $x_1 = y_1$.   Q.E.D.

Thus, we have shown that using $2N$ memories where N is an even power of 2 with a $(N^{1/2} + 1,2)$ skewing scheme we can provide conflict-free access to rows, columns, forward and backward diagonals, and $N^{1/2} \times N^{1/2}$ blocks. Of course this solution is not unique. But as we shall show, the data alignments required with this solution can be provided by a special switching network whose time-gate product is more attractive than a crossbar switch.

B. Alignment Requirements

Up to this point we have described various types of N-vectors which we would like to access. Now we will discuss what we want to do with these N-vectors and describe the required alignments of these N-vectors. By *alignment* of an N-vector we mean taking the N elements and placing them in some specified order. This function is performed by the networks shown in Fig. 1.

As described earlier, (δ_1,δ_2) skewing results in N-vectors which are not in logical order. Given any two N-vectors, in order to align these for operations between corresponding pairs of elements we must first shift one or both vectors so that their first elements are in the same physical location (processor). Then, if their ordering is not the same we must change the ordering of one of the vectors to the ordering of the other, or change the ordering of both vectors to a common third ordering. After the operation is performed we may have to shift and change the ordering of the vector in order to store the result appropriately. To simplify matters in this paper, we shall assume that we will always change d-ordered vectors to 1-order for processing and vice versa for storage of the result.

If we allow operations between any pair of N-vectors corresponding to rows, columns, or diagonals, then our alignment requirements thus far are that we be able to shift arbitrary distances and at the same time change d-ordered vectors to 1-ordered vectors for $d = \delta_1, \delta_2, \delta_1 + \delta_2$, $\delta_1 - \delta_2$, or change 1-ordered vectors to the above d-ordered vectors.

Several requirements for alignment of square blocks can also be identified. Two such requirements are to place the blocks in row major or column major order. Two other requirements can also be identified. Consider taking an $N^{1/2}$-vector and *expanding* it to an N-vector in two special ways as shown in Fig. 5. In one case the $N^{1/2}$-vector is duplicated $N^{1/2}$ times to make an N-vector. In the other case each element of the $N^{1/2}$-vector is fanned out $N^{1/2}$ times to make an N-vector.

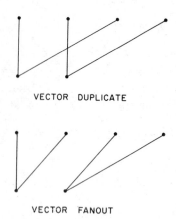

VECTOR DUPLICATE

VECTOR FANOUT

Fig. 5.   Vector duplicate and vector fanout with $N = 4$.

If the $N^{1/2}$-vector which is being expanded consists of consecutive elements of a row, then we call this *row fanout* or *row duplication*. Similarly for columns, etc. These patterns are useful, for example, when multiplying two $N^{1/2} \times N^{1/2}$ blocks using N processors in $N^{1/2}$ steps.

Thus far we have described a variety of alignment requirements. However, we make no claim that these requirements are either necessary or sufficient. We only believe that these patterns account for a vast majority of cases which would be required for an array processor intended for numerical applications. Verification of this will have to await empirical evaluation of real programs.

III. ALIGNMENT NETWORKS

As we have seen, array processing requires the capability for some complex data alignments. In order to provide these capabilities we must build some complex switches. To some it may seem unusual and unnecessary to provide expensive and complex pieces of hardware just to channel the data from one place to another. Yet when one considers the cost and complexity of the memory exchanges, buses, ports with priority resolution, etc., which are used in more conventional computer systems, this should not seem so unusual. When one further observes expensive memories and processors idling while waiting for data alignments, more expensive alignment hardware should not appear unnecessary.

In this section we will discuss some switches or *alignment networks* and we will present a network which provides the capabilities discussed in the previous section.

The traditional $N \times M$ crossbar switch is one possibility for an alignment network. This switch can perform any one-to-one mapping of inputs to outputs and with slight modification, can do any one-to-many mapping. The time required to do this mapping is[3] $0(\log N)$ or $0(\log M)$ gate delays. Unfortunately, the number of gates in an $N \times M$ crossbar is proportional to $N \cdot M$, and for large systems this may be overly expensive in terms of gates and reliability.

Another possibility is the rearrangeable switching net-

work discussed by Benes [10]. This network has the same capability as a crossbar but only $0(N \log N)$ gates for an $N \times N$ network. The time to pass through the network is $0(\log N)$. Unfortunately, it is not easy to set up this network to do a particular alignment. The best known algorithm for doing this (Opferman and Tso Wu [11]) requires $0(N \log N)$ time units. This is too long to be practical in this application.

A third possibility is the Batcher sorting network [12]. This network also has the capabilities of a crossbar switch. It requires $0(N(\log N)^2)$ gates. $0(\log N)^2$ time units to pass through the network, and can be set up "on the fly" (i.e., at approximately the same time the data are passing through the network). This network is appealing because it is cheaper than the crossbar and faster than the Benes network. Other networks proposed by Waksman [13], Thurber [14], Kautz [15], and Rohrbacher [16] might also be adapted to meet our needs. But as we shall see, another possibility exists which is relatively cheap and fast, and even though it does not have the full capabilities of a crossbar switch, it is capable of performing the desired alignment functions.

We shall now examine the construction and properties of the "omega" network. An example of an 8×8 omega network is shown in Fig. 6. For the present, we shall only consider $N \times N$ networks where N is a power of two. Other sizes can be constructed by building the next larger power of two and deleting unnecessary switching elements and interconnections, or by using a nonbinary omega network (see Lawrie [17]).

A. Construction of an Omega Network

An $N \times N$ omega network consists of $l = \log N$ identical stages. Each stage consists of a *perfect shuffle*[4] interconnection followed by $N/2$ switching elements as shown in Fig. 6.

Each switching element can have one of the four states shown in Fig. 7. That is, it may either send its inputs *straight* through, *interchange* the inputs, or *broadcast* one of the inputs to both outputs. We do not allow both inputs to be switched to the same output.

The perfect shuffle connection has the property of taking an input at a position whose binary representation is $s_1 s_2 \cdots s_l$, and moving it to position $s_2 s_3 \cdots s_l s_1$. The switch can then move the output to $s_2 s_3 \cdots s_l 0$ or $s_2 s_3 \cdots s_l 1$.

In order to switch data through the network, each element in the network is set in one of the above four states (not necessarily all the same) and then the data are allowed to pass from the network inputs to the network outputs.

[3] The notation $0(\log N)$ means "order of log N." All logarithms in this paper are base 2.

[4] The perfect shuffle connection if known to have certain special properties as described by Golomb [18], Pease [19], and Stone [1], among others. In fact, other important switching networks described by Benes [10] and Batcher [12] can be shown to consist of various stages interconnected by this same perfect shuffle. The number of stages in the omega network (log N) is one of the primary differences between the omega network, the Batcher sorting network (log N(log N + 1)/2 stages) and the binary Benes rearrangeable network (2(log N) − 1 stages). The logic of each switching element is also somewhat different in these three types of networks, but of approximately the same complexity.

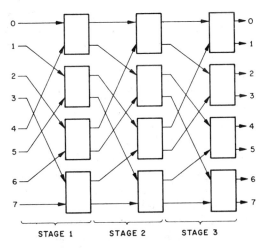

Fig. 6.   An 8 × 8 omega network.

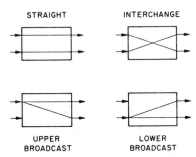

Fig. 7.   Four allowed states of the switching elements shown in
Fig. 6.

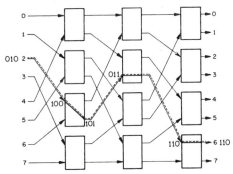

Fig. 8.   The connection (010,110).

This affects a one-to-one or one-to-many mapping of inputs to outputs.

Two questions arise at this point. First, is there an algorithm which determines the necessary states for the switching elements and can this be done in the same order of time as it takes data to pass through the network? Second, what kinds of input-output mappings are possible? This latter question will be discussed shortly. The first question concerns the existence of a rapid control algorithm for the network.

B. Controlling the Omega Network

As it turns out, there is an efficient algorithm for setting the states of the omega network. First, consider switching input number S to output number D. By examining Fig. 6, it should be easy to see that there is one and only one path between any given input, output pair. Let $D = d_1d_2\cdots d_l$ be the *destination tag*, i.e., the binary representation of the output number to which input number S is to be connected, and let $S = s_1s_2\cdots s_l$ be the *source tag*, i.e., the binary representation of the input number. Starting at input S, the first switch to which S is connected is set to switch input S to the upper output if $d_1 = 0$ or the lower output if $d_1 = 1$. This is shown in Fig. 8 for $S = 010$, $D = 110$. Following this through to a switch in the next stage, we again switch the input to the upper output if $d_2 = 0$ or to the lower output if $d_2 = 1$. We continue in this manner, switching on d_i at each stage i, until we get to the proper output. It is easy to see that during any

given stage i, an input which has been switched to position $s_is_{i+1}\cdots s_ld_1d_2\cdots d_{i-1}$ goes through the perfect shuffle and ends up in position $s_{i+1}s_{i+2}\cdots s_ld_1d_2\cdots d_{i-1}s_i$, and is then switched into position $s_{i+1}s_{i+2}\cdots s_ld_1d_2\cdots d_{i-1}d_i$. Thus, after $l = \log N$ operations, the original input must be connected to output $d_1d_2\cdots d_l$. A similar algorithm works by starting at output $d_1d_2\cdots d_l$ and working backwards through the network, switching the element at stage i according to s_i.

In order to set up a particular mapping of inputs to outputs, we simply follow the above procedure simultaneously for all inputs or all outputs. It remains for us to show that this procedure is complete in the sense that it can set up any mapping of which the network is capable. We will not prove this formally (see Lawrie [17]). Instead, notice that the algorithm always chooses one path through the network between any given input and output. Thus the algorithm will specify paths for any mapping of inputs to outputs. Since there is one and only one path between any input and output, the set of paths for a given mapping must be unique, and this must be the set determined by the algorithm. Notice, however, that the algorithm can specify path sets for mappings of which the network is not capable. For example, Fig. 9 shows the paths established for the mapping $000 \rightarrow 000$, $100 \rightarrow 010$. These paths share a common connection at the output of the first stage—a condition which we call a conflict and which by definition is not allowed since it means two different signals must share a common wire. (We assume two signals can share a common wire only if both signals have a common source, in which case we assume they are identical signals.) Thus we see that the algorithm will choose the unique set of paths in the network for any given mapping, but the paths in a set will not necessarily be disjoint, i.e., a conflict may be present.

There are many options available when it comes to actually designing an omega network. We will briefly mention some of them here. Further details can be found in Lawrie [17]. The switching elements in Fig. 6 are 2×2 exchange-broadcast units. It is possible to construct an omega network from larger elements as illustrated in Fig. 10. Here an 8×8 network is constructed from 4×4 and 2×2 elements. The 4×4 elements could be crossbar/broadcast elements in which case this network is somewhat more powerful than the network constructed

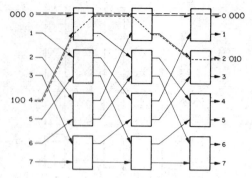

Fig. 9. Paths for (000,000), (100,010).

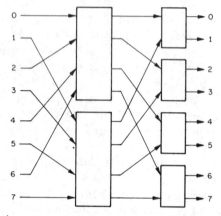

Fig. 10. An omega network using 4 × 4 and 2 × 2 elements.

solely from 2 × 2 elements. Or these 4 × 4 elements could be 4 × 4 omega networks constructed from 2 × 2 elements, in which case this network is identical to one constructed solely from 2 × 2 elements. Thus, the omega network can be *partitioned* to suit the architecture of a machine and the packaging requirements of a given circuit technology.

For example, we could connect a group of 16 processors with 16 memories using a 16 × 16 crossbar/broadcast switch, and then interconnect four such groups with two shuffle, exchange stages. This would allow complex data mapping capabilities within groups of 16 processors and provide more restricted omega-type alignments between all 64 processors.

Another option involves building only one stage of an omega network. Suppose we build a $2^l \times 2^l$ omega network from elements of a uniform size $K = 2^k$ where l is an integer multiple of k, i.e., $\sigma k = l$. Then this network will have σ stages, and each stage will be identical. It is not necessary to construct all σ stages. We only need to build one such stage and recycle this stage σ times. Of course this requires some extra registers, etc., but this solution may save a lot of gates, and it gives us the possibility of recycling other than exactly σ times which allows (us to perform some mappings which cannot be done in exactly σ stages (cf. Lang [20] and Lawrie [17]).

C. Properties of Omega Networks

It should be clear from the last section that due to conflicts, an omega network cannot produce all possible one-

to-one or one-to-many mappings of inputs to outputs. In this section we will demonstrate classes of mappings which can be produced.

Definition: Let $a = a'm + \alpha$ and $b = b'm + \beta$ where $\alpha, \beta < m$ and $a, b, \alpha, \beta, a', b'$, and m are all nonnegative integers. We say $a \equiv_m b$ if and only if $\alpha = \beta$. This is the common definition of "a is congruent to b modulo m."

Definition: Assume m is a factor of N. With a and b as above, we say $a \equiv_N^m b$ if and only if $a'm \equiv_N b'm$, i.e., $m\lfloor a/m \rfloor \bmod N = m\lfloor b/m \rfloor \bmod N$.

For example, let $a = 11010$ (binary), $b = 01010$, and $c = 10010$. Then $a \equiv_4 b \equiv_4 c$, $a \equiv_{16}^2 b$ (since $101 = 101$) and $a \not\equiv_{16}^2 c$ (since $101 \neq 001$).

Shortly we will present some proofs which will be easier to follow if at this point we present, without proof, some results from number theory. In the following, "$\rightarrow$" means logical implication and "$\leftrightarrow$" means logical equivalence.

R1) $x + a \equiv_m y + a \leftrightarrow x \equiv_m y$.

R2) $x \equiv_m y \rightarrow ax \equiv_m ay$.

R3) If a is prime to m (i.e., $gcd(a,m) = 1$), then
$$ax \equiv_m ay \rightarrow x \equiv_m y.$$

R4) $ax \equiv_{am} ay \leftrightarrow x \equiv_m y$.

R5) If $0 \leq x, y < m$, then
$$x \equiv_{am} y \leftrightarrow x \equiv_m y.$$

R6) $x \equiv_m y$ and $x \not\equiv_N y \rightarrow x \not\equiv_N^m y$.

Definition: Define P_N to be a set of integer pairs $P_N = \{(S_i, D_i) \mid 0 \leq i < N\}$ which represents a mapping of inputs to outputs.

$$S_0 \rightarrow D_0, S_1 \rightarrow D_1, \cdots, S_q \rightarrow D_q, \qquad q < N.$$

Definition: Let Ω_N be the $N \times N$ omega network as described above,[5] where $N = 2^l$. If Ω_N can produce the mapping specified by P_N then we say Ω_N passes P_N or $\Omega_N \uparrow P_N$. Otherwise, we say $\Omega_N \not\uparrow P_N$.

Recall from the previous section, that given an input-output connection represented by $(s_1 s_2 \cdots s_l, d_1 d_2 \cdots d_l)$, after k stages input $s_1 s_2 \cdots s_l$ will be connected to output $s_{k+1} s_{k+2} \cdots s_l d_1 d_2 \cdots d_k$ of stage k. Given a set

$$P_N = \{(S_i, D_i) \mid 0 \leq i < N\}$$

representing an input-output mapping, then $\Omega_N \uparrow P_N$ unless there is a conflict, i.e., unless two distinct inputs are connected to the same output of some stage. That is, for some pair of connections (S_i, D_i), $(S_j, D_j) \in P_N$ and

[5] In the discussions to follow, we will only concern ourselves with omega networks whose size is a power of two. For networks of other sizes, see Lawrie [17].

for some k, we have $s_{i,k+1}s_{i,k+2}\cdots s_{i,l} = s_{j,k+1}s_{j,k+2}\cdots s_{j,l}$ and $d_{i,1}d_{i,2}\cdots d_{i,k} = d_{j,1}d_{j,2}\cdots d_{j,k}$. This is equivalent to saying that for some $m = 2^{l-k}$, $1 \leq k \leq l$, and for some (S_i,D_i) and (S_j,D_j), we have $S_i \not\equiv_N S_j$ and $S_i \equiv_m S_j$ and $D_i \equiv_N^m D_j$. Thus we have the following theorem.

Theorem 2: Given a set of desired input-output connections $P_N = \{(S_i,D_i) \mid 0 \leq i < N\}$, then $\Omega_N \uparrow P_N$ if and only if $S_i \not\equiv_N S_j$ and $S_i \equiv_m S_j$ implies $D_i \not\equiv_N^m D_j$ for all $S - D$ pairs in P_N and for all $m = 2^k$, where $1 \leq k \leq l$.

Now we will begin to identify some of the mappings which the omega network can produce.

Theorem 3: Let

$$P_N(a,b,c,d,\xi) = \{(ax + b,cx + d) \mid 0 \leq x < \xi\}$$

where $(ax + b,cx + d)$ represents a connection from input $ax + b \pmod N$ to output $cx + d \pmod N$. If $gcd(a,N) \leq gcd(c,N)$ and $\xi \leq N/gcd(c,N)$ then $\Omega \uparrow P_N(a,b,c,d,\xi)$.

Proof: Let $\alpha = gcd(a,N)$, $\gamma = gcd(c,N)$, $a' = a/\alpha$ and $c' = c/\gamma$. We must show that if $\alpha \leq \gamma$ and $\xi \leq N/\gamma$ then Theorem 2 is satisfied, i.e., for all $0 \leq x, y < \xi$ and for all $m = 2^k$ where $1 \leq k \leq l$ and $2^l = N$, then $ax + b \not\equiv_N ay + b$ and $ax + b \equiv_m ay + b$ implies $cx + d \not\equiv_N^m cy + d$. We begin with the hypothesis $ax + b \equiv_m ay + b$ and by R1 we get $ax \equiv_m ay$ and since a' is prime to m we get $\alpha x \equiv_m \alpha y$ by R3. Now since $(\gamma/\alpha) \geq 1$ and since $c'(\gamma/\alpha)\alpha = c$, by R2 we get

$$cx \underset{m}{\equiv} cy$$

and by R1

$$cx + d \underset{m}{\equiv} cy + d. \tag{6}$$

We also have as a hypothesis that

$$ax + b \underset{N}{\not\equiv} ay + b$$

so by R1,R2 we get

$$x \underset{N}{\not\equiv} y$$

and by R4 we get

$$\gamma x \underset{\gamma N}{\not\equiv} \gamma y. \tag{7}$$

But we know $x,y < \xi \leq N/\gamma$ so $\gamma x,\gamma y < N$ and from (7) and R5 we get

$$\gamma x \underset{N}{\not\equiv} \gamma y,$$

and since c' is prime to m, by R3 we get

$$cx \underset{N}{\not\equiv} cy$$

and so

$$cx + d \underset{N}{\not\equiv} cy + d. \tag{8}$$

Now, from (6) and (8) by R6 we get

$$cx + d \underset{N}{\overset{m}{\not\equiv}} cy + d. \qquad \text{Q.E.D.}$$

Corollary 1: Define $I_N = \{(x,x) \mid 0 \leq x \leq N - 1\}$ to be the identity mapping. Then $\Omega_N \uparrow I_N$. This follows trivially by setting $a = c = 1$ and $b = d = 0$ in the previous theorem, and noting that $\alpha = \gamma = 1$ and so $\alpha \leq \gamma$ and $x < \xi \leq N/\gamma$.

Corollary 2: Let $P_N = \{(ax + b,x) \mid a \leq x < N\}$ where a is odd. Then $\alpha = 1$, $\gamma = 1$, and $\xi = N$. So $\Omega_N \uparrow P_N$ since $\alpha \leq \gamma$ and $\xi \leq N/1$. Thus, the omega network can unscramble and shift any a-ordered vector where a is odd.

Theorem 4: If $\Omega_N \uparrow P_N$ and a is odd, then $\Omega_N \uparrow P_N \cdot a$ where $P_N = \{(S_i,D_i) \mid 0 \leq i < N\}$ and $P \cdot a$ is the set $\{(a \cdot S_i(\bmod N),D_i) \mid (S_i,D_i) \in P_N\}$.

Proof: By contradiction, assume $\Omega_N \not\uparrow P_N \cdot a$. Then there exists an m and (aS_i,D_i), $(aS_j,D_j) \in P_N \cdot a$ such that $aS_i \not\equiv_N aS_j$, $aS_i \equiv_m aS_j$ and $D_i \equiv_N^m D_j$. But since a is odd, $gcd(a,m) = 1$ so $aS_i \equiv_m aS_j \rightarrow S_i \equiv_m S_j$ and thus $\Omega_N \not\uparrow P_N$. Thus, Theorem 2 must be satisfied and so $\Omega_N \uparrow P_N$. Q.E.D.

Theorem 5: If $\Omega_N \uparrow P_N$ then $\Omega_N \not\uparrow P_N + a$ where $P_N = \{(S_i,D_i) \mid 0 \leq i < N\}$, and $P_N + a$ is the set $\{(S_i + a(\bmod N),D_i) \mid (S_i,D_i) \in P_N\}$.

Proof: By contradiction, assume $\Omega_N \uparrow P_N + a$. Then there exists an m and $(S_i + a,D_i)$, $(S_j + a,D_j) \in P_N + a$ such that $S_i + a \not\equiv_N S_j + a$, $S_i + a \equiv_m S_j + a$, and $D_i \equiv_N^m D_j$. But then $S_i \not\equiv_N S_j$ and $S_i \equiv_m S_j$ so $\Omega_N \not\uparrow P_N$. So again Theorem 2 must be satisfied. Q.E.D.

The mapping $P_N + a$ is called a *uniform shift* (by a) of P_N. Theorem 5 states that if an omega network can produce the mapping P_N, then it can produce a uniform shift of this mapping.

Theorem 6: Given $P = \{(S_i,D_i)\}$ If $\Omega_N \uparrow P$ then $\Omega_{2N} \uparrow P$.

Proof: Suppose $\Omega_{2N} \not\uparrow P$. Then there exists an m and there exists (S_i,D_i), $(S_j,D_j) \in P$ such that $S_i \equiv_m S_j$, $S_i \not\equiv_{2N} S_j$, and $D_i \equiv_{2N}^m D_j$. m cannot be $2N$ as this would lead to an immediate contradiction. If $m < 2N$ then $\Omega_N \uparrow P$. Thus, Theorem 6 is true by contradiction.

Q.E.D.

Theorem 7: Let $P_N = \{(S_i,D_i) \mid 0 \leq S_i,D_i < N\}$. Define $P_{aN} * a = \{(S_i,a \cdot D_i)\}$. If a is a power of two and if $\Omega_N \uparrow P_N$ then $\Omega_{aN} \uparrow P_{aN} * a$.

Proof: From Theorem 6, $\Omega_N \uparrow P_N \rightarrow \Omega_{aN} \uparrow P_N$. Now $\Omega_{aN} \uparrow P_N$ implies that for all $m = 2,4,8,\cdots,aN$, if $S_i \not\equiv_{aN} S_j$ and $S_i \equiv_m S_j$ then $D_i \not\equiv_{aN}^m D_j$. Since $aD_i,aD_j < aN$, $D_i \not\equiv_{aN}^m D_j$ implies $aD_i \not\equiv_{aN}^m aD_j$. Q.E.D.

Theorem 8: Let $P_N = \{(S_i,D_i) \mid 0 \leq S_i,D_i < N\}$. Define $P_{aN} \cdot a * a = \{(aS_i,aD_i)\}$ and let a be a power of two. If $\Omega_N \uparrow P_N$ then $\Omega_{aN} \uparrow P_{an} \cdot a * a$.

Proof: We must show that Theorem 2 is satisfied, i.e., that for all $am = 2,4,8,\cdots,aN$, $aS_i \not\equiv_{aN} aS_j$ and $aS_i \equiv_{am} aS_j$ imply $aD_i \not\equiv_{aN}^{am} aD_j$. Assume $aS_i \not\equiv_{aN} aS_j$ and $aS_i \equiv_{am} aS_j$. Then $S_i \not\equiv_N S_j$ and $S_i \equiv_m S_j$ for all $m = 1,2,4,\cdots,N$. Since $\Omega_N \uparrow P_N$ this implies $D_i \not\equiv_N^m D_j$. This in turn implies $aD_i \not\equiv_{aN}^{am} aD_j$. Q.E.D.

For Theorem 9 we will need the following lemma.

105

Lemma 1: Let $0 \leq x_1, y_1 \leq n - 1$ and $0 \leq x_2, y_2 \leq a - 1$. Then $ax_1 + x_2 \equiv_{an} ay_1 + y_2$ implies $x_1 = y_1$ and $x_2 = y_2$.

Proof: Assume $ax_1 + x_2 \equiv_{an} ay_1 + y_2$. Then by R2 $anx_1 + nx_2 \equiv_{an} any_1 + ny_2$. Since $anx_1 \equiv_{an} 0$ we get $nx_2 \equiv_{an} ny_2$. Thus, by R4 $x_2 \equiv_a y_2$. Since $0 \leq x_2, y_2 < a$ we get $x_2 = y_2$ and so $ax_1 \equiv_{an} ay_1$. Thus, by R4, $x_1 \equiv_n y_1$ and since $0 \leq x_1, y_1 < n$ we get $x_1 = y_1$. Q.E.D.

Theorem 9: $\Omega_M \uparrow P(x_1, x_2)$ where $M = 2n^2$, n a power of two, and

$$P(x_1, x_2)$$
$$= \{(2x_1 + (n + 1)x_2, 2x_1 + 2nx_2) \mid 0 \leq x_1, x_2 \leq n - 1\}.$$

Proof: The proof will be in two parts, first for $m = 2, 4, 8, \cdots, 2n$ and then for $m = 4n, 8n, \cdots, 2n^2$. In each case we will show that $2x_1 + (n + 1)x_2 \equiv_m 2y_1 + (n + 1)y_2$ and $2x_1 + 2nx_2 \equiv_M^m 2y_1 + 2ny_2$ implies $2x_1 + (n + 1)x_2 \equiv_M 2y_1 + (n + 1)y_2$ thus satisfying Theorem 2.

Part 1: Let $x = x_1 + nx_2$, $y = y_1 + ny_2$, and let $x_1 = am/2 + \alpha$, $y_1 = bm/2 + \beta$ where $\alpha, \beta < m/2$ and assume $m \leq 2n$. If $2x \equiv_M^m 2y$ then $2nx_2 + am + 2\alpha \equiv_M^m 2ny_2 + bm + \beta$ and since $\alpha, \beta < m/2$ and $m \leq 2n$, it follows that $2nx_2 + am \equiv_M 2ny_2 + bm$.

Since $am, bm < 2n$ we have by Lemma 1 $am = bm$ or $a = b$, and so $x_2 = y_2$. Now if $2x_1 + (n + 1)x_2 \equiv_m 2y_1 + (n + 1)y_2$, then since $x_2 = y_2$ we have $2x_1 \equiv_m 2y_1$ and since $a = b$ we get $2\alpha \equiv_m 2\beta$. Now, $\alpha, \beta < m/2$ so we have $\alpha = \beta$. Thus, $2x_1 + (n + 1)x_2 \equiv_M 2y_1 + (n + 1)y_2$.

Part 2: Now consider the case where $m = 4n, 8n, \cdots, 2n^2$. Let $m = 2gn$ where $g = 2, 4, \cdots, n$, and let $x_2 = ag + \alpha, y_2 = bg + \beta$ where $\alpha, \beta \leq g - 1$. Assume $2x \equiv_M^m 2y$, i.e., $2x_1 + 2nag + 2\alpha n \equiv_M^m 2y_1 + 2nbg + 2\beta n$. Since $m = 2ng$ and $2(\alpha n + x_1)$, $2(\beta n + y_1) < 2ng$ we get $am \equiv_M bm$ and so $a = b$. Now if $2x_1 + (n + 1)x_2 \equiv_m 2y_1 + (n + 1)y_2$ then since $a = b$ we get

$$2x_1 + (n + 1)\alpha \equiv_m 2y_1 + (n + 1)\beta.$$

Since $\alpha \leq g - 1, m = 2gn$, and $x_1 \leq n - 1$ we get

$$2x_1 + (n + 1)\alpha \leq 2(n - 1) + (n + 1)(g - 1)$$
$$\leq (g + 1)n + g - 3,$$

so that

$$2x_1 + (n + 1)\alpha \leq 2gn.$$

Thus, $2x_1 + (n + 1)\alpha \equiv_M 2y_1 + (n + 1)\beta$ and since $a = b$ we get $2x_1 + (n + 1)(\alpha + ag) \equiv_M 2y_1 + (n + 1)(\beta + bg)$. Since $\alpha + ag = x_2, \beta + bg = y_2$ we have

$$2x_1 + (n + 1)x_2 \equiv_M 2y_1 + (n + 1)y_2. \text{Q.E.D.}$$

Due to limitations on space, the following three theorems are presented without proof. Proofs may be found in Lawrie [21].

Theorem 10: $\Omega_{2n^2} \uparrow Q(x_1, x_2)$ where .

$$Q(x_1, x_2)$$
$$= \{((n + 1)x_1 + 2x_2, 2x_1 + 2nx_2) \mid 0 \leq x_1, x_2 < n - 1\}.$$

Theorem 11: $\Omega_{n^2} \uparrow F(x_1, x_2)$ where

$$F(x_1, x_2) = \{(x_1, (x_1 + x_2)) \mid 0 \leq x_1, x_2 < n - 1\}.$$

Theorem 12: $\Omega_{n^2} \uparrow G(x_1, x_2)$ where

$$G(x_1, x_2) = \{(x_1, x_1 + x_2 n) \mid 0 \leq x_1, x_2 \leq n - 1\}.$$

Definition: Define an inverse omega network Ω_N' to be an omega network whose inputs and outputs are reversed and whose switching elements have the same four states shown in Fig. 7, as illustrated in Fig. 11. Further, let P_N be any one-to-one mapping in $N \times N$, and define P_N' to be the inverse of this mapping.

Theorem 13: Given P_N is a one-to-one mapping in $N \times N$, then $\Omega_N \uparrow P_N$ if and only if $\Omega_N' \uparrow P_N'$.

The proof of this should be obvious. Thus any one-to-one mapping which can be done by the omega network can be undone by the corresponding inverse omega network.

Thus, we have presented some theorems which prove that certain basic classes of permutations and one-to-many connections can be produced by the omega network. In the next section we will present some alignment connections which are desirable in an array processor. We will then use the theorems of this section to prove that the omega network can produce these connections.

D. Application of the Omega Network to an Array Processor

Let us now consider an array computer with $N = n^2$ processors (n a power of two) connected to $M = 2N$ memories by a $2N \times 2N$ omega network. This corresponds to $NW2$ in Fig. 1. The memories are connected to the network input ports in a one-to-one fashion, i.e., memory i is connected to port i. Also, processor i is connected to output port $2i$. Thus, the odd numbered outport ports will not be used, so the last column of exchange elements could be replaced by simple OR elements. A second network, an inverse Ω network, is then connected in a similar fashion between the processors and memories. This network corresponds to $NW1$ in Fig. 1.

Finally, assume a $(N^{1/2} + 1, 2)$ skewing scheme. It is easy to show that the following data mappings are needed in order to align rows, columns, etc.

$P(\text{rows}) = \{(2x + b, 2x) \mid 0 \leq x \leq N - 1\}.$
$P(\text{columns}) = \{(x(n + 1) + b, 2x) \mid 0 \leq x \leq N - 1\}.$
$P(\text{forward diagonals}) = \{(x(n + 3) + b, 2x) \mid 0 \leq x \leq N - 1\}.$
$P(\text{backward diagonals}) = \{(x(n - 1) + b, 2x) \mid 0 \leq x \leq N - 1\}.$

For $N^{1/2} \times N^{1/2}$ blocks we need the following alignments:
$P(\text{row major}) = \{(2x_1 + (n + 1)x_2 + b, 2(x_1 + nx_2)) \mid 0 \leq x_1, x_2 \leq n - 1\}.$
$P(\text{column major}) = \{(x_1(n + 1) + 2x_2 + b, 2(x_1 + x_2)) \mid 0 \leq x_1, x_2 \leq n - 1\}.$

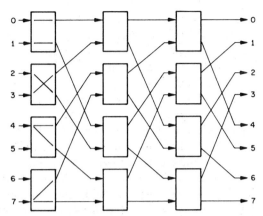

Fig. 11.   An 8 × 8 inverse omega network showing four possible states of the switching elements.

$P(\text{row fanout}) = \{(2x_1 + b, 2(x_1 n + x_2)) \mid 0 \le x_1, x_2 \le n - 1\}$.

$P(\text{column fanout}) = \{(x_1(n + 1) + b, 2(x_1 n + x_2)) \mid 0 \le x_1, x_2 \le n - 1\}$.

$P(\text{forward diagonal fanout}) = \{(x_1(n + 3) + b, 2(x_1 n + x_2)) \mid 0 \le x_1, x_2 \le n - 1\}$.

$P(\text{backward diagonal fanout}) = \{(x_1(n - 1) + b, 2(x_1 n + x_2)) \mid 0 \le x_1, x_2 \le n - 1\}$.

$P(\text{row duplicate}) = \{(2x_1 + b, 2(x_1 + x_2 n)) \mid 0 \le x_1, x_2 \le n - 1\}$.

$P(\text{column duplicate}) = \{(x_1(n + 1) + b, 2(x_1 + x_2 n)) \mid 0 \le x_1, x_2 \le n - 1\}$.

$P(\text{forward diagonal duplicate}) = \{(x_1(n + 3) + b, 2(x_1 + x_2 n)) \mid 0 \le x_1, x_2 \le n - 1\}$.

$P(\text{backward diagonal duplicate}) = \{(x_1(n - 1) + b, 2(x_1 + x_2 n)) \mid 0 \le x_1, x_2 \le n - 1\}$.

We will now show that the omega network can produce these alignments.

Theorem 14: $\Omega_{2N} \uparrow P(\text{rows})$.

Proof: By Theorem 3 where α and γ = 2 so $\alpha = \gamma$ and $\xi = N$ so $\xi \le 2N/\gamma$ is satisfied.

Theorem 15: $\Omega_{2N} \uparrow P(\text{columns})$.

Proof: By Theorem 3, since $n + 1$ is prime to 2, we have $\alpha = 1$, $a' = (n + 1)$, $\gamma = 2$, and $\xi = N$. Thus, the conditions are met.

Theorem 16: $\Omega_{2N} \uparrow P(\text{forward diagonals})$.

Proof: As in Theorem 15, since $n + 3$ is prime to two.

Theorem 17: $\Omega_{2N} \uparrow P(\text{backward diagonals})$.

Proof: Again by Theorem 3 since $(n - 1)$ is prime to two.

Theorem 18: $\Omega_{2N} \uparrow P(\text{row major})$.

Proof: Directly from Theorems 5 and 9.

Theorem 19: $\Omega_{2N} \uparrow P(\text{column major})$.

Proof: Directly from Theorems 5 and 10.

Theorem 20: $\Omega_{2N} \uparrow P(\text{row fanout})$.

Proof: Refer to Theorem 11 and note that $P(\text{row fanout}) = F(x_1, x_2) \cdot 2 * 2 + b$. Thus, by Theorem 11 $\Omega_N \uparrow F(x_1, x_2)$ and by Theorems 5 and 8 $\Omega_{2N} \uparrow F(x_1, x_2) \cdot 2 * 2 + b$.

Theorem 21: $\Omega_{2N} \uparrow P(\text{column fanout})$.

Proof: Note that $P(\text{column fanout}) = F(x_1, x_2) \cdot (n + 1) * 2 + b$. Thus the result follows from Theorems 4, 5, 7, and 11.

Theorem 22: $\Omega_{2N} \uparrow P(\text{forward diagonal fanout})$.

Proof: $P(\text{forward diagonal fanout}) = F(x_1, x_2) \cdot (n + 3) * 2 + b$. Again the result follows from Theorems 4, 5, 7, and 11.

Theorem 23: $\Omega_{2N} \uparrow P(\text{backward diagonal fanout})$.

Proof: As before by Theorems 4, 5, 7, and 11 since $P(\text{backward diagonal fanout}) = F(x_1, x_2) \cdot (n - 1) * 2 + b$.

Theorem 24: $\Omega_{2N} \uparrow P(\text{row duplicate})$.

Proof: Refer to Theorem 12 and note that $P(\text{row duplicate}) = G(x_1, x_2) \cdot 2 * 2 + b$. Thus, our result follows from Theorems 5, 8, and 12.

Theorem 25: $\Omega_{2N} \uparrow P(\text{column duplicate})$.

Proof: $P(\text{column duplicate}) = G(x_1, x_2) \cdot (n + 1) * 2 + b$. So the result follows from Theorems 4, 5, 7, and 12.

Theorem 26: $\Omega_{2N} \uparrow P(\text{forward diagonal duplicate})$.

Proof: $P(\text{forward diagonal duplicate}) = G(x_1, x_2) \cdot (n + 3) * 2 + b$. Result follows from Theorems 4, 5, 7, and 12.

Theorem 27: $\Omega_{2N} \uparrow P(\text{backward diagonal duplicate})$.

Proof: $P(\text{backward diagonal duplicate}) = G(x_1, x_2) \cdot (n - 1) * 2 + b$. Result follows from Theorems 4, 5, 7, and 12.

Thus, in Theorems 14–27 we have shown that in addition to being able to produce uniform shifts (Theorem 5) and unscrambling of p-ordered vectors where p is odd (Corollary 2), the Ω network can produce the alignments listed at the beginning of Section III-D.

IV. CONCLUSION

In order for an array process to work efficiently, the ALU's must have access to a steady stream of operand pairs. This implies the need for a large memory system capable of providing parallel access to various slices of the data, i.e., N-vectors. We have shown that in order to provide conflict-free memory access to more than a few trivial types of N-vectors, we must use more than N independent memories and/or choose a number of memories which are relatively prime to certain parameters of the data storage scheme and the memory access requirements. We have also discussed the need for some special hardware capable of placing (aligning) the data in some specific order for processing. We reviewed some networks from the literature which could provide this alignment, and we presented the omega network whose properties are shown to be particularly useful in this context. Finally, we presented a design for an array processor which uses this omega network and which provides for conflict-free memory access and alignment of rows, columns, diagonals, backward diagonals, and $N^{1/2} \times N^{1/2}$ partitions in either row or column major order, and in addition can produce $N^{1/2}$-vector fanout and duplication functions.

Another important consideration which must be mentioned concerns generating index values both for the memories and for the alignment networks. Generally, access to an N-vector in memory requires a vector of addresses specifying the address of each element of the N-vector in its memory (the *index vector*) and a similar vector of source or destination tags which will control the alignment network (the *tag vector*). For example, assume each memory in Fig. 4 has its own address register. Loading these registers with the values of 0,3,2,1,0,3,2,1, respectively, would cause access to column 0 (as well as column 2; if column 0 was desired, the alignment network would select for transmission only element of column 0). Adding 2 (mod 4) to this index vector would give us 2,1,0,3,2,1,0,3 which would provide access to column 1 (and column 3). Similarly, tag vectors are constructed to control the alignment networks. Obviously, it is desirable not to have to specify complete index and tag vectors for each memory access. Instead we would like to be able to generate a new index and tag vector from the previous index/tag vector, as for example by addition of a constant. In the case above, index vectors for successive columns were formed by adding 2 (mod 4). (A similar rule holds for tag vectors.) In general, for the N-processor, $2N$-memory system described in the last section, index/tag vectors can be generated by addition of a constant (modulo a power of two) to a *base* index/tag vector for each type of required N-vector.

However, for systems using M memories where M is relatively prime to the ordering of the desired N-vectors (cf. Section II and Budnik and Kuck [7]), generation of index/tag vectors requires addition modulo M where M is not a power of two. This requirement for "relatively prime modulus" arithmetic is one of the primary drawbacks to such a memory system. (The other drawback is the apparent lack of a cheap alignment network with the necessary capabilities.) For further discussion of index/tag vectors and their generation, see Lawrie [22].

Finally, we have not discussed the problems caused by the inability to keep the entire data set in primary memory. Large data sets stored on a secondary memory device (drum or disk) are typically stored by row or column and primary memory may only be large enough to hold a few such rows or columns. If a large matrix is stored on a disk or drum by rows and we attempt to access it by columns, we must effectively access the entire matrix in secondary memory and will spend a great deal of time waiting for disk or drum access and we will transfer many words which we will never use. This inefficiency may completely offset any improvement caused by the special primary memory organizations and alignment hardware discussed in this paper. There are two possibilities for coping with this problem. First, we might transpose the matrix when necessary. See Schumann [23] and Eklundh [24] for a further discussion of transposing large matrices. (Some form of alignment network would be particularly useful in doing the necessary row or column permutations called for in the transpose algorithms.) Second, we might take advantage of the fact that many computations, (e.g., matrix multiplication) have the property that their data can be partitioned into square blocks and the computation can be carried out on each square partition in turn. Thus, instead of storing a large matrix on disk by row or column, we might store it by square partition instead. (See also Gold and Kuck [24].) Access to various slices of these partitions then proceeds as described earlier.

ACKNOWLEDGMENT

The author remains indebted to D. Kuck for many discussions and ideas on this subject.

REFERENCES

[1] H. S. Stone, "Parallel processing with the perfect shuffle," *IEEE Trans. Comput.*, vol. C-20, pp. 153–161, Feb. 1971.
[2] K. E. Batcher, "STARAN parallel processor system hardware," in *1974 Fall Joint Comput. Conf.*, AFIPS Conf. Proc., vol. 43. Montvale, N. J.: AFIPS Press, 1974, p. 405.
[3] L. C. Higbie, "The OMEN computers: Associative array processors," in *Dig. Papers*, Compcon, p. 287, 1972.
[4] D. J. Kuck, "ILLIAC IV software and application programming," *IEEE Trans. Comput.*, vol. C-17, pp. 758–770, Aug. 1968.
[5] P. W. Kraska, "Array storage allocation," Dep. Comput. Sci., Univ. Illinois, Urbana-Champaign, Rep. 344, 1969.
[6] R. E. Millstein, "Control structures in Illiac IV Fortran," *Commun. Ass. Comput. Mach.*, vol. 16, pp. 621–627, Oct. 1973.
[7] P. Budnik and D. J. Kuck, "The organization and use of parallel memories," *IEEE Trans. Comput.* (Short Notes), vol. C-20, pp. 1566–1569, Dec. 1971.
[8] Y. Muraoka, "Parallelism exposure and exploitation in programs," Ph.D. dissertation, Univ. Illinois, Urbana-Champaign, Dep. Comput. Sci., Rep. 424, Feb. 1971.
[9] S.-C. Chen and D. J. Kuck, "Time and parallel processor bounds for linear recurrence systems," *IEEE Trans. Comput.*, vol. C-24, pp. 701–717, July 1975.
[10] V. E. Benes, *Mathematical Theory of Connecting Networks and Telephone Traffic.* New York: Academic, 1965.
[11] D. C. Opferman and N. T. Tsao-Wu, "On a class of rearrangeable switching networks," *Bell Syst. Tech. J.*, vol. 50, pp. 1579–1618, May–June 1971.
[12] K. E. Batcher, "Sorting networks and their applications," in *1968 Spring Joint Comput. Conf.*, AFIPS Conf. Proc., vol. 32. Washington, D. C.: Thompson, 1968, pp. 307–314.
[13] A. Waksman, "A permutation network," *J. Ass. Comput. Mach.*, vol. 15, pp. 159–163, Jan. 1968.
[14] K. J. Thurber, "Programmable indexing networks," in *1970 Spring Joint Comput. Conf.*, AFIPS Conf. Proc., vol. 36. Montvale, N. J.: AFIPS Press, 1970, pp. 51–58.
[15] W. H. Kauntz, K. N. Levitt, and A. Waksman, "Cellular interconnection arrays," *IEEE Trans. Comput.*, vol. C-17, pp. 443–451, May 1968.
[16] D. L. Rohrbacher, "Advanced computer organization study: Volume I—Basic report; Volume II—Appendices," Air Force Contract AF 30(602)-3550, Apr. 1966, Papers AD 631870 and AD 631871.

[17] D. H. Lawrie, "Memory-processor connection networks," Univ. Illinois, Urbana-Champaign, Dep. Comput. Sci., Rep. 557, Feb. 1973.

[18] S. W. Golomb, "Permutation by cutting and shuffling," *SIAM Rev.*, vol. 3, p. 293, Oct. 1961.

[19] M. C. Pease, "An adaption of the fast Fourier transform for parallel processing," *J. Ass. Comput. Mach.*, vol. 15, pp. 252–264, Apr. 1968.

[20] T. Lang, "Interconnection between processors and memories using the shuffle-exchange network," Stanford Univ., Stanford, Calif., Rep. R-74-19.

[21] D. H. Lawrie, "More patterns for square blocks," Dep. Comput. Sci., Univ. Illinois, Urbana-Champaign, unpublished memo 65, July 1973.

[22] ——, "Omega networks," Dep. Comput. Sci., Univ. Illinois, Urbana-Champaign, unpublished memo 64, Apr. 1973.

[23] U. Schumann, "Ein Verfahren zum Transponieren grosser, sequentiell gespeicherter Matrizen," *Angew. Inform.*, pp. 213–216, May 1972.

[24] J. O. Eklundh, "A fast computer method for matrix transposing," *IEEE Trans. Comput.* (Corresp.), vol. C-21, pp. 801–803, July 1972.

[25] D. E. Gold and D. J. Kuck, "A model for masking rotational latency by dynamic disk allocation," *Commun. Ass. Comput. Mach.*, vol. 17, pp. 278–288, May 1974.

Duncan H. Lawrie (S'66–M'73) received the B.A. degree from DePauw University, Greencastle, Ind., the B.S.E.E. degree from Purdue University, Lafayette, Ind., and the M.S. and Ph.D. degrees in computer science from the University of Illinois, Urbana-Champaign.

He is currently an Assistant Professor of Computer Science, University of Illinois. Prior to joining the faculty, he held the position of Senior Research Programmer with the Illiac IV project at the University of Illinois, where he was in charge of language development and served as manager of the computer center. His current areas of research include the design of hardware and software for high-speed computer systems, specialized architectures for information retrieval systems, and network theory.

Dr. Lawrie serves as a referee for the IEEE TRANSACTIONS ON COMPUTERS as well as several national conferences, and as a reviewer for *Computer Reviews*. He also serves as a consultant to industry and government. He is a member of the Association for Computing Machinery, the American Association for University Professors, and several honorary societies.

Reprinted from *Computer*, Volume 12, Number 6, June 1979, pages 57-65. Copyright © 1979 by The Institute of Electrical and Electronics Engineers, Inc.

Many SIMD interconnection networks have been proposed. To put the different approaches into perspective, this analysis compares a number of single- and multistage networks.

Interconnection Networks for SIMD Machines

Howard Jay Siegel
Purdue University

With the advent of microprocessors, large-scale parallel processing systems with as many as 2^{14} to 2^{16} processors have become feasible.[1,2] One multimicroprocessor structure—the SIMD (single instruction stream-multiple data stream) mode of parallel processing—is especially suitable for exploiting the parallelism inherent in certain tasks. SIMD systems are currently being used for scientific operations such as matrix calculations[3] and image processing.[4,5] In the future, their scope may be broadened to include business calculations that require the same program to be executed on many different data sets—e.g., computing bank-account interest.

Two existing SIMD machines are the Illiac IV[6] and Staran,[7] and many new ones have been proposed.[8-16] In designing SIMD systems, constructing an interconnection network for communications among the processors and memories presents a major problem. In this article, we analyze different approaches to network design, limiting our discussion to SIMD machine networks (other types are explored elsewhere[17-19]).

Interconnecting N processors and N memory modules in an SIMD system where N may be 2^6 to 2^{16} is a non-trivial task. A single shared bus is not sufficient, since in an SIMD machine it is desirable to allow many processors to send data to other processors simultaneously (e.g., from processor i to processor $i+1$, $0 \leq i < N-1$). Ideally, one would like each processor directly to every other processor, but this is highly impractical for large N, since each processor would require $N-1$ lines. An alternate network which allows all processors to communicate simultaneously is the crossbar switch.[20] The difficulty here is that network costs grow with N^2; given current technology, this makes crossbar switches infeasible for large systems.

To solve the problem of providing fast, efficient communiations at a reasonable cost, many different networks have been proposed in the literature, a number of which we discuss here. However, no single network is generally considered "best," since the cost-effectiveness of a particular design varies with such factors as the computational tasks for which it will be used, the desired speed of interprocessor data transfers, the actual hardware implementation of the network, the number of processors in the system, and the cost constraints on the construction.

SIMD machines

The acronym *SIMD* stands for *single instruction stream-multiple data stream.*[21] Typically, an *SIMD machine*[22-25] is a computer system consisting of a control unit, N processors, N memory modules, and an interconnection network. The control unit broadcasts instructions to all processors, and all active processors execute the same instruction at the same time. Thus, there is a single instruction stream. Each active processor executes the instruction on data in its own associated memory module. Thus, there is a multiple data stream. The interconnection network, sometimes referred to as an alignment or permutation network, provides a communications facility for the processors and memory modules.

Structure. The physical structure of an SIMD machine can be viewed as a set of N processing elements (PEs), where each PE consists of a processor with its own memory (e.g., Illiac IV[6]). The network connects each PE to some subset of the other PEs. A transfer instruction causes data to be moved from each PE to one of the PEs to which it is connected. To move data between two PEs that are not directly connected, the data must be passed through intermediary PEs by executing a programmed sequence of data transfers.

An alternate structure is to position the network between the processors and the memories (e.g., Staran[7]). In general, in the processor-to-memory configuration the network connects each processor to some subset of memories. A transfer instruction causes data to be moved from each processor to one of the memories to which it is connected, or from each memory to one of the processors to which it is connected. One processor can transfer data to another through any memory connected to both. To pass data between two processors, a programmed sequence of data transfers that moves the data through intermediary memories and processors must be executed. Variations on the processor-to-memory configuration include (1) using two networks, one for processor-to-memory and the other for memory-to-processor communications,[26] and (2) using the same network for processor-to-memory and processor-to-processor communications.[27]

Operation. To demonstrate how SIMD machines operate, let us consider two examples—matrix operations and image processing—using a PE-to-PE configuration of N PEs.

Assume that three N-word vectors, A, B, and C, are stored such that PE i contains $A(i)$, $B(i)$, and $C(i)$, $0 \le i < N$. To add the elements of vectors A and B and store the result in C, all PEs would execute $C = A + B$, with PE i doing the addition for elements $A(i)$ and $B(i)$. Thus, the SIMD machine does in one step a task requiring N steps on a serial processor.

As an example of why the interconnection network is needed, consider the N-step serial task:

for $i=1$ until $N-1$ do $C(i) = A(i) + B(i-1)$
$C(0) = A(0)$

An SIMD machine does this task in three steps: (1) it moves the value of $B(i-1)$ to PE i from PE $i-1$, $1 \le i < N$, via the interconnection network; (2) in PE i, it adds $A(i)$ to $B(i-1)$ and stores the result in $C(i)$, $1 \le i < N$; and (3) in PE 0, it stores $A(0)$ in $C(0)$. (At each step certain PEs will be disabled.) Assuming the appropriate interconnections are available, PE $i-1$ sends its B data to PE i for all i, $1 \le i < N$, simultaneously. Thus, Step 1 requires only one parallel data transfer. (Information about the use of SIMD machines for more complex matrix calculations can be found in Stone.[3])

As a simple example of image processing, consider smoothing, i.e., replacing point (i,j) of an image with the average value of (i,j) and its eight surrounding points: $(i-1,j)$, $(i-1,j-1)$, $(i,j-1)$, $(i+1,j)$, $(i+1,j+1)$, $(i,j+1)$, $(i-1,j+1)$, and $(i+1,j-1)$. Given a 2^k by 2^k image and a serial processor, $2^k * 2^k = 2^{2k}$ averages must be computed. Given an SIMD machine with $N = 2^n$ processors, the image can be partitioned into a $\sqrt{N}$ by $\sqrt{N}$ array of subpictures of size $2^k/\sqrt{N}$ by $2^k/\sqrt{N}$. All N subpictures can be smoothed in parallel, requiring

the calculation of $2^{2k}/N$ averages, where for each of these calculations the new values for N points are computed in parallel. In general, however, calculating the averages for the edge points in a subpicture requires obtaining data from "adjacent" subpictures stored in other PEs. This necessitates the use of the interconnection network to move data from one PE to another. (Siegel[28] mentions other image processing tasks possible with SIMD machines.)

Multistage SIMD network parameters

One type of interconnection network for SIMD machines consists of many stages of interconnected switches. Many *multistage SIMD networks* can be described by three parameters: interchange box, topology, and control structure.

Interchange box. The interchange box is a two-input two-output device used as a basic building block in many multistage networks. Let the upper input and output lines be labeled i and the lower input and output lines be labeled j. The four legitimate states of an interchange box are (1) straight—input i to output i, input j to output j; (2) exchange—input i to output j, input j to output i; (3) lower broadcast—input j to outputs i and j; and (4) upper broadcast—input i to outputs i and j.[26] A *two-function interchange box* is capable of being in either the straight or exchange states, and a *four-function interchange box* is capable of being in any of the four legitimate states.[29]

Topology. Network topology is the actual interconnection pattern used to connect a set of N input lines to N output lines. Generally, multistage networks consist of n stages, where $N = 2^n$ is the number of input and output lines. Conceptually, each stage consists of an interconnection pattern of N lines and $N/2$ interchange boxes.

One type of topology is called the cube. In the three-dimensional cube shown in Figure 1, horizontal lines connect vertices whose labels differ in the zeroth (low-order) bit position, diagonal lines connect vertices which differ in the first (middle) bit position, and vertical lines connect vertices which differ in the second (high-order) bit position. This can be generalized for an n-dimensional cube.

An example of a cube-type multistage network topology is the Staran network.[27] This network can be drawn using interchange boxes, as shown in Figure 2. For each interchange box, the upper and lower outputs are labeled with the same numbers as the upper and lower inputs, respectively. At stage i, the two input lines that differ only in their ith bit position are paired together as inputs to an interchange box, for $0 \le i < n$. The data first pass through stage 0, then 1, etc. At each stage, the interchange boxes connect their input lines to their output lines to complete the connections from one end of the network to the other.

Control structure. The control structure of a network determines how the states of the interchange boxes will be set.[29] *Individual stage control* uses the same control signal to set the state of all the interchange boxes in a stage (i.e., all the boxes in a given stage must be in the same state). Each stage has its own signal. *Individual box control* uses a separate control signal to set the state of each interchange box. *Partial stage control* uses $i+1$ control signals to control stage i, $0 \leqslant i < n$. In Staran, this is used for "shift permutations," as will be discussed later.

Multistage SIMD network comparisons

The three classifying parameters defined above will be used to analyze four multistage networks—Staran, indirect binary n-cube, omega, and data manipulator—that have appeared in the literature.

Staran. Conceptually, the Staran network[27] consists of n stages of $N/2$ two-function interchange boxes. Input lines which differ in the ith bit position are paired in the ith stage of the network (Figure 2). This network is used in the Staran SIMD machine manufactured by Goodyear Aerospace,[7] where each array module consists of 256 processors and memories (N=256). It is used in two ways: (1) to let processors communicate with other processors and (2) to let processors access memories. The network has two control mechanisms, the flip control and the shift control.

Under the flip (individual stage) control, an n-bit vector $F = f_{n-1} \ldots f_1 f_0$ determines the way stages will be set. If $f_i = 1$, stage i interchange boxes are in the exchange state, and if $f_i = 0$, they are in the straight state. For example, if N=8, and F=010, network input line $i_2 i_1 i_0$ is connected to network output line $i_2 \bar{i}_1 i_0$. The shift (partial stage) control allows shifts of data from input x to output $x + 2^m$ modulo 2^P, $0 \leqslant m \leqslant P \leqslant n$, using $i+1$ control lines at stage i, $0 \leqslant i < n$. For N=8, line $0A$ controls boxes a, b, c, and d, $1A$ controls e and g, $1B$ controls f and h, $2A$ controls i, $2B$

controls j, and $2C$ controls k and l (Figure 2). For example, to shift data from input x to output $x+1$ modulo 8, set $0A = 1A = 2A =$ exchange and $1B = 2B = 2C =$ straight. The flip control can be implemented by controlling all the shift control lines for a given stage by a single signal. The network connection capabilities are discussed by Batcher[7,27,30] and Bauer.[31]

Indirect binary n-cube. Another cube-type network that has been proposed is the indirect binary n-cube[1] network consisting of n stages of $N/2$ two-function interchange boxes under independent box control. The addresses of the two input lines to an interchange box at stage i differ only in the ith bit position, as shown in Figure 2. The stages are ordered so that data pass through stage 0, then stage 1, etc., and finally through stage $n-1$. The various connection capabilities of this network are discussed by Pease.[1]

The Staran network and the n-cube network have the same topology, and both use two-function interchange boxes. The differences in their capabilities result from their different control schemes. The individual box control of the n-cube is much more flexible than Staran's partial stage control. The n-cube can perform all of the connections that Staran can and some it cannot (e.g., connect input 0 to output 1 and input 2 to output 0). Pease gives us a theorem which may be used to determine if a particular arrangement of I/O connections can be made.[1] Not all connections are possible (e.g., input 0 to output 2 and input 1 to output 4).

Omega. Lawrie's omega network is a multistage SIMD machine network based on the perfect-shuffle interconnection pattern.[26] The perfect-shuffle connection pattern routes data from position P, whose binary representation is $p_{n-1} \ldots p_1 p_0$, to position P', whose binary representation is $p_{n-2} \ldots p_1 p_0 p_{n-1}$. Let $S(P)$ represent the "shuffle" of P. Then, the data in position P is routed to position $S(P)$, where

$$S(p_{n-1} \ldots p_1 p_0) = p_{n-2} \ldots p_1 p_0 p_{n-1}.$$

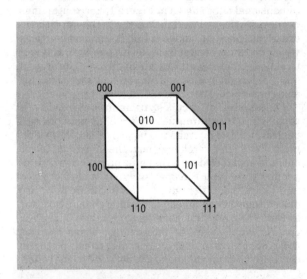

Figure 1. Three dimensional cube structure, with vertices labeled from 0 to 7 in binary.

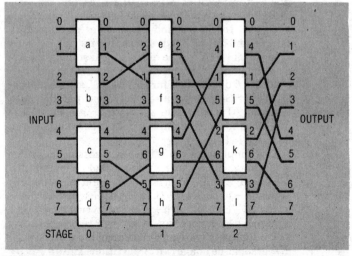

Figure 2. Staran network based on interchange boxes, for N = 8. (Also, indirect binary n-cube topology.)

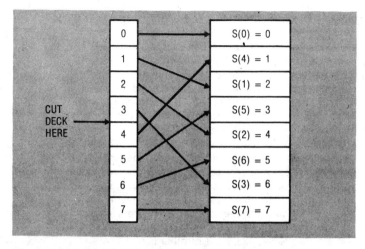

Figure 3. Perfectly shuffling a deck of eight cards.

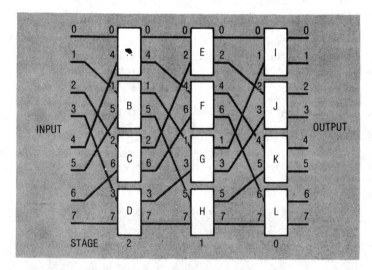

Figure 4. Omega network for $N = 8$.

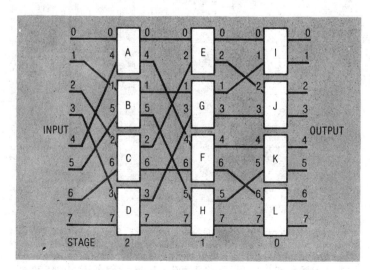

Figure 5. Omega network for $N = 8$ redrawn.

The name "perfect shuffle" has its origin in shuffling cards—i.e., perfectly intermixing two halves of a deck as shown in Figure 3. The mathematical properties of the shuffle are discussed by Golomb[32] and Johnson.[33] Its use in parallel processing has been examined by Stone.[34]

An N by N omega network consists of n identical stages, where each stage is a perfect-shuffle interconnection followed by a column of $N/2$ four-function interchange boxes under independent box control (Figure 4). The various interconnections performed by the omega network are examined by Lawrie.[26] A multistage "shuffle-exchange" network, similar to the omega network, and its capabilities are presented by Lang and Stone.[35]

The interchange boxes of the omega network can be repositioned, without modifying the interchange box interconnections, as shown in Figure 5. Thus, the networks of Figures 4 and 5 are equivalent. The Staran/n-cube topology of Figure 2 is identical to the omega topology of Figure 5 with the exception of the order of stages through which data pass. In the Staran/n-cube network, data pass through stage 0, then stage 1, etc., while in the omega network data pass through stage $n-1$, then stage $n-2$, etc. Thus, the two differences between the omega network and the n-cube network are the order in which the stages are traversed and the type of interchange box—i.e., four-function versus two-function.

The four-function interchange boxes of the omega network allow "one-to-many" connections. For example, network input 2 can be broadcast to all network outputs in one pass through the network, by setting boxes E and F to lower broadcast and $C, I, J, K,$ and L to upper broadcast. The Staran and n-cube networks are limited to one-to-one connections since they use two-function interchange boxes.

To examine the effect of the reversed stage order of the n-cube and omega networks, consider only the exchange and straight states of the four-function interchange boxes. Since the topologies of these two networks are isomorphic, the omega can be considered a cube-type network, i.e., at stage i, inputs whose labels differ in the ith bit position are compared, and to connect input I to output O, the data from input I must pass through an interchange box in the exchange state at stage i if, and only if, I and O differ in the ith bit position.

Even though the n-cube and omega have isomorphic topologies, the fact that they order their stages in an opposite manner causes their interconnection capabilities to differ. Consider the input to output connections 0 to 5 and 1 to 7. The n-cube network (Figure 2) cannot perform this task (both inputs 0 and 1 must go to output 1 at stage 0, creating a conflict). The omega network (Figure 4) can perform this task. Furthermore, the n-cube can connect 5 to 0 and 7 to 1, but the omega cannot. This occurs because, as data pass through the n-cube and omega networks, the data items that are paired in an interchange box depend on the order of the stages of the network, i.e.,

COMPUTER

stage i being encountered as the ith stage or as the $n-(i+1)$ stage, $0 \leqslant i < n$.

Consider an arbitrary set of input and output connections which the n-cube can perform. To perform these connections on the omega, it is necessary to transform the number (address) of each input and output line from $p_{n-1} \ldots p_1 p_0$ to $p_0 p_1 \ldots p_{n-1}$.[29] This implies, for example, that if the omega network is used to interconnect N PEs and one wishes to execute an SIMD machine program written for a system with the n-cube network, then PE $P = p_{n-1} \ldots p_1 p_0$ must act as if it were PE $p_0 p_1 \ldots p_{n-1}$, $0 \leqslant P < N$.

To perform the 5 to 0 and 7 to 1 connections that the n-cube can make but the omega cannot, for $N=8$, PE 4 must act as PE 1 (under the transformation, PE addresses 0, 5, and 7 are unchanged). The omega network can connect 5 to 0 and 7 to 4. Similarly, the n-cube can perform the omega connections 0 to 5 and 1 to 7 if PE 4 acts as PE 1. The correctness of this address transformation method can be proved formally by realizing that the renumbering causes the omega network first to pair data lines whose numbers differ only in the zeroth bit position, then the first bit position, etc., just the way the n-cube does.

Thus, considering only one-to-one connections, by using the relabeling technique the n-cube and omega networks are functionally equivalent. That is, by relabeling the processors and memories and loading the data into the memories based on their new labels, an SIMD progam written to run on one network can be run on the other. Since the omega network is functionally equivalent to the n-cube, it can (with relabeling) perform all the interconnections of the Staran network. Furthermore, because the omega network has four-function interchange boxes, it can perform one-to-many connections which the n-cube cannot.

Augmented data manipulator. The data manipulator network, introduced by Feng,[36] consists of n stages connecting columns of N cells, as shown in Figure 6. For $0 \leqslant j < N$ and $0 \leqslant i < n$, there are three sets of interconnections at stage i: one sends the data from input cell j to output cell $j + 2^i$ modulo N, one sends the data from input cell j to output cell $j - 2^i$ modulo N, and one sends the data from input cell j to output cell j. Stage i of the network is controlled by a pair of signals, two of H_1^i, H_2^i, U_1^i, U_2^i, D_1^i, and D_2^i, as specified in Figure 6. The topology is such that at stage i input cell j is connected to output cell j and to the output cell which differs from j in only the ith-bit position, just as the topologies of the omega and n-cube allow. In addition, the data manipulator connects j to both $j + 2^i$ modulo N and $j - 2^i$ modulo N, one of which differs from j in more than the ith bit position. The stages are ordered $n-1, n-2, \ldots 0$. as in the omega network topology.

With control structure modifications, the data manipulator is capable of all the interconnections that the omega network achieves with four-function boxes and individual box control, plus some additional ones. The augmented data manipulator, or ADM, is a data manipulator with individual cell control, i.e., each cell will get its own control signals.[29]

Specifically, each cell can get any of the signals H, U, and D.

Consider simulating the omega four-function box at stage i with upper input x and lower input y. Let the subscript x denote the ADM control for input cell x at stage i, and let the subscript y be used similarly. Then, to simulate the four possible states of an interchange box use the following control signals: straight, $H_x H_y$; exchange, $D_x U_y$; lower broadcast, $U_y H_y$; and upper broadcast, $D_x H_x$. Thus, the ADM can perform any interconnection that the omega network can. However, the omega network can perform a maximum of $2^{Nn/2}$ one-to-one connections, i.e., each box can be straight or exchange. The ADM can do all of these connections and in addition can, for example, connect 0 to 7, 7 to 0, and i to i, for $0 \leqslant i < N$, $i \neq 0,7$, when N equals 8. Thus, the number of one-to-one connections the ADM can perform exceeds the maximum physical limit for the omega. Other properties and features of the data manipulator and ADM networks are discussed by Feng[36] and Siegel and Smith.[29,37]

Network flexibility. Thus, in terms of interconnection capabilities, the four multistage networks which have been discussed can be ordered in terms of increasing flexibility as follows: Staran, indirect binary n-cube, omega, and ADM. It should be noted, however, that increased flexibility incurs increased cost, and the Staran is the only one of the four networks that has been constructed and used for a large value of N. The most cost-effective network for a particular application will depend on a variety of factors

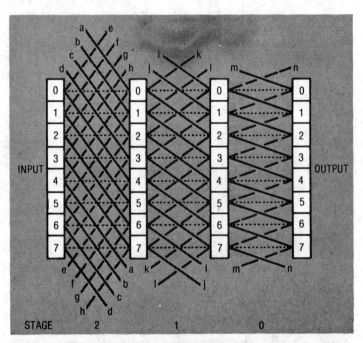

Figure 6. Data manipulator network for $N = 8$. For stage i, U_1^i, D_1^i, and H_1^i control those cells whose ith bit is 0, and U_2^i, D_2^i, and H_2^i control those cells whose ith bit is 1. U means use dashed line connection, D means use solid line connection, and H means use dotted line connection.

mentioned earlier, such as tasks to be performed and data transfer speed requirements.

The cube-type multistage network topology has also been called an SW banyan.[38] Further information about the relationships among different multistage interconnection networks can be found in Siegel and Smith[29,39] and Wu and Feng.[40]

Single-stage SIMD networks

As an alternative to multistage networks, with n or more stages of switches, a single stage of switches may be used, forming a single-stage SIMD network.

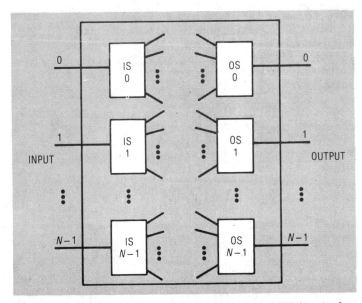

Figure 7. Conceptual view of a single-stage network. "IS" is input selector, "OS" is output selector.

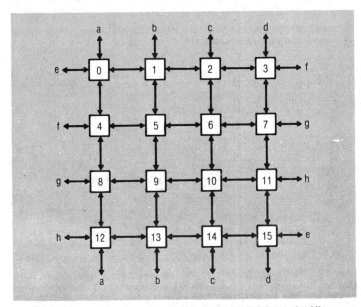

Figure 8. Illiac network for $N = 16$ (Illiac IV has $N = 64$). Vertical lines are $+\sqrt{N}$ and $-\sqrt{N}$. Horizontal lines are $+1$ and -1.

Conceptually, a *single-stage network* may be viewed as N input selectors and N output selectors, as shown in Figure 7. They way in which the input selectors are connected to the output selectors determines the allowable interconnections. Four single-stage networks will be discussed here: the Illiac, PM2I, shuffle-exchange, and cube.

Illiac. The Illiac network, used in the Illiac IV SIMD machine,[6] allows PE i to send data to any one of PE $i+1$, PE $i-1$, PE $i+\sqrt{N}$, or PE $i-\sqrt{N}$, arithmetic modulo N, as shown in Figure 8. This is often referred to as the nearest neighbor or north, south, east, and west connection pattern. Relating this to Figure 7, input selector i has lines to output selectors $i+1$, $i-1$, $i+\sqrt{N}$, and $i-\sqrt{N}$. Output selector j gets its inputs from $j-1$, $j+1$, $j-\sqrt{N}$, and $j+\sqrt{N}$. Since the Illiac is a single-instruction-stream machine, all active PEs must use the same connection at the same time. Various properties and abilities of this network are discussed in the literature.[6,41-44]

PM2I. The Plus-Minus 2^i network[42] is a generalization of the Illiac network which allows PE j to send data to any one of PE $j+2^i$ or PE $j-2^i$, $0 \le i < n$, arithmetic modulo N, as shown in Figure 9. The PM2I connection patterns form the basis for the data manipulator[36] and the ADM[29] multistage networks, i.e., stage i uses the $j+2^i$ and $j-2^i$ connections. In terms of I/O selectors, input selector j is connected to output selectors $j+2^i$ and $j-2^i$, $0 \le i < n$. Output selector j gets its inputs from input selectors $j-2^i$ and $j+2^i$, $0 \le i < n$. As with the Illiac network, all active PEs must use the same PM2I interconnection at the same time. For example, if one PE is using the $+2^0$ connection, all active PEs must use their $+2^0$ connection. The connection capabilities and other properties of the PM2I network are discussed in Siegel.[42-44]

Shuffle-exchange. The shuffle-exchange network[3,34] is based on the perfect-shuffle connection (Figure 3) defined earlier. When the perfect shuffle is used as a connection in a single-stage network, it is accompanied by an exchange connection. This is due to certain limitations of the shuffle connection, e.g., PE 0 cannot communicate with any other PE. The exchange interconnection allows each PE to send data to the PE whose address differs from it in only the low-order bit position. The shuffle-exchange connections are the basis for the omega network,[26] where the shuffle connection precedes each stage of switches and the action of the interchange boxes can implement the exchange. For the shuffle-exchange single-stage network shown in Figure 10, input selector $p_{n-1} \cdots p_1 p_0$ is connected to output selectors $p_{n-2} \cdots p_1 p_0 p_{n-1}$ and $p_{n-1} \cdots p_1 \bar{p}_0$. Output selector $g_{n-1} \cdots g_1 g_0$ gets its inputs from input selectors $g_0 g_{n-1} \cdots g_2 g_1$ and $g_{n-1} \cdots g_1 \bar{g}_0$. As with the other networks, all active PEs must use the same type of connection at the same time. For example, if one PE "shuffles," all active PEs must shuffle. The usefulness and attributes of this network are examined in Lang,[45] Siegel,[42-44] and Stone.[3,34]

Cube. The cube network is a generalization of the exchange connection, allowing each PE to communicate with any of the n PEs whose address differs from it in any one bit position.[42] Thus, PE P, whose binary representation is $p_{n-1}\ldots p_1 p_0$, can send data directly to any one of PE $p_{n-1}\ldots p_{i+1}\bar{p}_i p_{i-1}\ldots p_0$, $0 \le i < n$ (Figure 1). These cube connections are the basis of the Staran[27] and n-cube[1] multistage networks, where stage i allows PE $p_{n-1}\ldots p_1 p_0$ to send data to PE $p_{n-1}\ldots p_{i+1}\bar{p}_i p_{i-1}\ldots p_0$, $0 \le i < n$. For the cube single-stage network, shown in Figure 11, input selector $p_{n-1}\ldots p_1 p_0$ is connected to output selectors $p_{n-1}\ldots p_{i+1}\bar{p}_i p_{i-1}\ldots p_0$, $0 \le i < n$. Output selector $g_{n-1}\ldots g_1 g_0$ gets its inputs from input selectors $g_{n-1}\ldots g_{i+1}\bar{g}_i g_{i-1}\ldots g_0$, $0 \le i < n$. As with the other networks, only one type of cube connection, (i.e., a fixed value of i) can be used at a time. The features and abilities of the cube network are discussed in Siegel.[42-44]

Single-stage vs. multistage networks. Single-stage networks are also called recirculating networks because data items may have to recirculate through the single stage several times before reaching their final destinations.[37] To expand on this, consider using a single-stage network to simulate the multistage network to which it is related.

The single-stage shuffle-exchange network can be used to simulate the omega multistage network. For each stage of the omega network configuration being simulated, have all PEs use the shuffle interconnection. Then have PE j use the exchange interconnection if at that stage line j is the input to an interchange box in the exchange state or is the input being broadcast in one of the broadcast states, $0 \le j < N$. (To prevent a PE from using an interconnection, it must be turned off (disabled) for the execution of that transfer instruction.) Thus, the single-stage shuffle-exchange can simulate one pass through the omega network in at most $2n$ recirculations.

The n-cube and Staran multistage networks can be simulated by the single-stage cube network in at most n recirculations per pass. For $i = 0, 1, \ldots, n-1$, if input line j goes to an interchange box in the exchange state at stage i, PE j should use the cube interconnection that sends its data to the PE that differs from j in the ith bit position. Note that if, for example, all of the interchange boxes in the n-cube network are set to straight except for those in a single stage, then only one pass through the cube single-stage network would be required.

The PM2I network can simulate one pass through the ADM multistage network in at most $2n$ recirculations. For $i = n-1, n-2, \ldots, 0$, have PE j use the $+2^i$ PM2I interconnection if at stage i cell j in the ADM network configuration being simulated gets the D control signal. Then use the -2^i PM2I interconnection if cell j gets the U control signal. The number of recirculations needed to simulate a stage of a particular ADM configuration depends on the control signals going to its cells: (1) if there are no U or D signals, nothing needs to be transferred in the single-stage simulation; (2) if there are both Us and Ds, then

two recirculations are needed; and (3) otherwise, only one pass is needed.

Single-stage network simulations. To compare different single-stage networks with each other, upper and lower bounds on the number of parallel interprocessor data transfers needed for each network to simulate the others have been studied.[42,43] The bounds are based on the interconnection (of the network being simulated) which requires the most

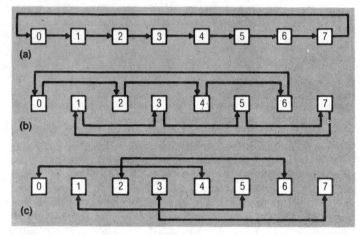

Figure 9. PM2I single stage network for $N = 8$: (a) $+2^0$ connection; (b) $+2^1$ connection; and (c) $+2^2$ connection. For the -2^i connections, reverse the directions of the arrows.

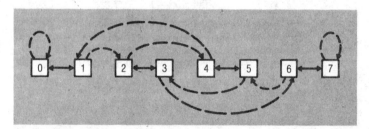

Figure 10. Shuffle-exchange single-stage network for $N = 8$. Solid line is exchange, dashed line is shuffle.

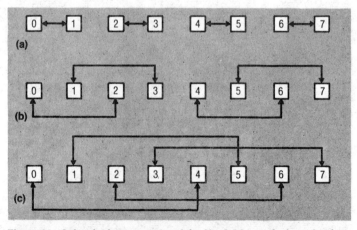

Figure 11. Cube single-stage network for $N = 8$: (a) transfer based on low-order bit, (b) transfer based on middle bit, and (c) transfer based on high-order bit.

transfers to simulate. Each upper bound is shown using an algorithm to do the simulation. To demonstrate the techniques used, the simulation of a cube interconnection by the PM2I network and a PM2I interconnection by the cube network are discussed. The "cube by PM2I" simulation is directly related to the "omega by ADM" simulation, and the "PM2I by cube" simulation is directly related to the shift control scheme used in the Staran.

In general, a cube interconnection cannot be simulated by a single PM2I connection (this follows from the networks' definitions). Thus, at least two transfers are required. To simulate the PE $p_{n-1}\ldots p_1 p_0$ to $p_{n-1}\ldots p_{i+1}\bar{p}_i p_{i-1}\ldots p_0$ cube connection in two steps, first have all PEs with a 0 in the ith bit position of their address use the $+2^i$ PM2I connection, and then have all the other PEs use the -2^i PM2I connection.

To simulate a PM2I connection by the cube network requires n transfers in the worst case. The proof that n transfers are needed involves the metric known as the Hamming distance. Let d be the Hamming distance, i.e., let $d(x,y)$ equal the number of bit positions in which x and y differ. The PM2I $+2^0$ interconnection connects PE $011\ldots 1$ to PE $100\ldots 0$. This means that it moves data a Hamming distance of n, i.e., $d(011\ldots 1,100\ldots 0) = n$. Each cube interconnection can move data a Hamming distance of only 1, i.e., from a PE to another PE which differs from it in only one bit position. Thus, to move data a Hamming distance of n, n transfers are needed.[42]

To perform any $+2^i$ PM2I interconnection with the cube network requires $n-i$ transfers. The algorithm is (1) move the data from PE $p_{n-1}\ldots p_1 p_0$ to $p_{n-1}\ldots p_{i+1}\bar{p}_i p_{i-1}\ldots p_0$ and (2) for $j=i+1$ until $n-1$, move data from PE $p_{n-1}\ldots p_1 p_0$ to PE $p_{n-1}\ldots p_{j+1}\bar{p}_j' p_{j-1}\ldots p_0$ if bits i to $j-1$ of $p_{n-1}\ldots p_1 p_0$ are all zeros.[43]

For example, for $N=8$ and $i=1$, the data from PE 011 goes to 001 and then goes to 101. The algorithm for -2^i is similar.

Table 1 shows the lower and upper bounds for all the simulations.[42,43] The methods for finding these bounds can also be used to study other single-stage network connections and to analyze network suitability for a particular implementation.

Table 1.
Entries in row i, column j are the lower and upper bounds on the number of transfers for network i to simulate network j, where $n = \log_2 N$.

		ILLIAC	PM2I	SHUFFLE-EXCHANGE	CUBE
ILLIAC	LOWER	—	$\sqrt{N}/2$	$1+\sqrt{N}/2$	$1+\sqrt{N}/2$
	UPPER	—	$\sqrt{N}/2$	$3\sqrt{N}-4$	$1+\sqrt{N}/2$
PM2I	LOWER	1	—	n	2
	UPPER	1	—	$2n-2$	2
SHUFFLE-EXCHANGE	LOWER	$2n-1$	$2n-1$	—	$n+1$
	UPPER	$2n$	$2n$	—	$n+1$
CUBE	LOWER	n	n	n	—
	UPPER	n	n	n	—

Conclusion

Although many SIMD interconnection networks have been proposed, there is little in the literature examining the relationships between different networks. The comparisons presented here should aid the system designer in choosing an appropriate network for a specific system. As for the future, more and more microprocessor or LSI-based SIMD machines are being proposed. The study, construction, and/or simulation of these different designs will bring new insights into the applications for SIMD machines and the interconnection network features needed to support them. ∎

Acknowledgments

The author thanks L. J. Siegel for her comments and suggestions. This work was supported by the Air Force Office of Scientific Research, Air Force Systems Command, USAF, under Grant No. AFOSR-78-3581. The United States Government is authorized to reproduce and distribute reprints for governmental purposes notwithstanding any copyright notation hereon.

References

1. M. C. Pease, "The Indirect Binary n-Cube Microprocessor Array," *IEEE Trans. Comput.*, Vol. C-26, No. 5, May 1977, pp. 458-473.

2. H. Sullivan, T. R. Bashkow, and K. Klappholz, "A Large Scale Homogeneous, Fully Distributed Parallel Machine," *4th Annual Symp. on Computer Architecture*, Mar. 1977, pp. 105-124.

3. H. S. Stone, "Parallel Computers," in *Introduction to Computer Architecture*, H. S. Stone, editor, Science Research Associates, Chicago, pp. 327-355.

4. A. J. Krygiel, "An Implementation of the Hadamard Transform on the STARAN Associative Array Processors," *1976 Int'l. Conf. on Parallel Processing*, Aug. 1976, p. 34.

5. D. Rohrbacker and J. L. Potter, "Image Processing with the Staran Parallel Computer," *Computer*, Vol. 10, No. 8, Aug. 1977, pp. 54-59.

6. W. J. Bouknight et al., "The Illiac IV System," *Proc. IEEE*, Vol. 60, Apr. 1972, pp. 369-388.

7. K. E. Batcher, "STARAN Parallel Processor System Hardware," *AFIPS Conf. Proc. 1974 NCC*, Vol. 43, May 1974, pp. 405-410.

8. P. M. Flanders et al., "Efficient High Speed Computing with the Distributed Array Processor," *Symp. on High Speed Computer and Algorithm Organization*, Apr. 1977, pp. 113-128.

9. L. Fung, "A Massively Parallel Processing Computer," *Symp. on High Speed Computer and Algorithm Organization*, Apr. 1977, pp. 203-204.

10. J. Keng and K. S. Fu, "A Special Computer Architecture for Image Processing," *1978 IEEE Comp. Soc. Conf. Pattern Recognition and Image Processing*, June 1978, pp. 287-290.

11. G. J. Lipovski, "On a Varistructured Array of Microprocessors," *IEEE Trans. Comp.*, Vol. C-26, No. 2, Feb. 1977, pp. 125-138.

12. G. J. Lipovski and A. Tripathi, "A Reconfigurable Varistructure Array Processor," *1977 Int'l. Conf. on Parallel Processing*, Aug. 1977, pp. 125-138.

13. G. J. Nutt, "Microprocessor Implementation of a Parallel Processor," *4th Annual Symp. on Computer Architecture*, Mar. 1977, pp. 147-152.

14. G. J. Nutt, "A Case Study of Simulation as a Computer System Design Tool," *Computer*, Vol. 11, No. 10, Oct. 1978, pp. 31-36.

15. H. J. Siegel, L. J. Siegel, R. J. McMillen, P. T. Mueller, Jr., and S. D. Smith, *An SIMD/MIMD Multimicroprocessor System for Image Processing and Pattern Recognition*, 1979 IEEE Comp. Soc. Conf. Pattern Recog. and Image Processing, Aug. 1979.

16. H. J. Siegel, P. T. Mueller, Jr., and H. E. Smalley, Jr., "Control of a Partitionable Multimicroprocessor System," *1978 Int'l. Conf. on Parallel Processing*, Aug. 1978, pp. 9-17.

17. G. M. Masson, G. C. Gingher, and S. Nakamura, "A Sampler of Circuit Switching Networks," *Computer*, Vol. 12, No. 6, June 1979, pp. 32-48.

18. H. J. Siegel, R. J. McMillen, and P. T. Mueller, Jr., "A Survey of Interconnection Methods for Reconfigurable Parallel Processing Systems," *AFIPS Conf. Proc. 1979 NCC*, Vol. 48, June 1979, pp. 387-400.

19. K. J. Thurber, "Circuit Switching Technology: A State-of-the-Art Survey," *Proc. COMPCON 78 Fall*, Sept. 1978, pp. 116-124.

20. K. J. Thurber, "Parallel Processor Architectures —Part 1: General Purpose Systems," *Computer Design*, Vol. 18, No. 1, Jan. 1979, pp. 89-97.

21. M. J. Flynn, "Very High-Speed Computing Systems," *Proc. IEEE*, Vol. 54, Dec. 1966, pp. 1901-1909.

22. D. J. Kuck, "A Survey of Parallel Machine Organization and Programming," *ACM Computing Surveys*, Vol. 9, Mar. 1977, pp. 29-59.

23. G. J. Lipovski and K. L. Doty, "Developments and Directions in Computer Architecture," *Computer*, Vol. 11, No. 8, Aug. 1978, pp. 54-67.

24. K. J. Thurber, *Large Scale Computer Architecture: Parallel and Associative Processors*, Hayden Book Company, Inc., Rochelle Park, N.J., 1976.

25. K. J. Thurber and L. D. Wald, "Associative and Parallel Processors," *ACM Computing Surveys*, Vol. 7, Dec. 1975, pp. 215-255.

26. D. Lawrie, "Access and Alignment of Data in an Array Processor," *IEEE Trans. Comput.*, Vol. C-24, No. 12, Dec. 1975, pp. 1145-1155.

27. K. E. Batcher, "The Flip Network in STARAN," *1976 Int'l. Conf. on Parallel Processing*, Aug. 1976, pp. 65-71.

28. H. J. Siegel, "Preliminary Design of a Versatile Parallel Image Processing System," *3rd Biennial Conf. on Computing in Indiana*, Apr. 1978, pp. 11-25.

29. H. J. Siegel and S. D. Smith, "Study of Multistage SIMD Interconnection Networks," *5th Annual Symp. on Computer Architecture*, Apr. 1978, pp. 223-229.

30. K. E. Batcher, "The Multidimensional Access Memory in STARAN," *IEEE Trans. Comput.*, Vol. C-26, No. 2, Feb. 1977, pp. 174-177.

31. L. H. Bauer, "Implementation of Data Manipulating Functions on the STARAN Associative Processor," *1974 Sagamore Computer Conf. on Parallel Processing*, Aug. 1974, pp 209-227.

32. S. W. Golomb, "Permutations by Cutting and Shuffling," *SIAM Review*, Vol. 3, Oct. 1961, pp. 293-297.

33. P. B. Johnson, "Congruences and Card Shuffling," *American Mathematical Monthly*, Vol. 63, Dec. 1956, pp 718-719.

34. H. S. Stone, "Parallel Processing with the Perfect Shuffle," *IEEE Trans. Comput.*, Vol. C-20, No. 2, Feb. 1971, pp. 153-161.

35. T. Lang and H. S. Stone, "A Shuffle-Exchange Network with Simplified Control," *IEEE Trans. Comput.*, Vol. C-25, No. 1, Jan. 1976, pp. 55-65.

36. T. Feng, "Data Manipulating Functions in Parallel Processors and Their Implementations," *IEEE Trans. Comput.*, Vol. C-23, No. 3, Mar. 1974, pp. 309-318.

37. S. D. Smith and H. J. Siegel, "Recirculating, Pipelined, and Multistage SIMD Interconnection Networks," *1978 Int'l. Conf. on Parallel Processing*, Aug. 1978, pp. 206-214.

38. G. R. Goke and G. J. Lipovski, "Banyon Networks for Partitioning Multiprocessor Systems," *1st Annual Symp. on Computer Architecture*, Dec. 1973, pp. 21-28.

39. S. D. Smith and H. J. Siegel, "An Emulator Network for SIMD Machine Interconnection Networks," *6th Annual Int'l. Symp. on Computer Architecture*, Apr. 1979, pp. 232-241.

40. C. Wu and T. Feng, "Routing Techniques for a Class of Multistage Interconnection Networks," *1978 Int'l. Conf. on Parallel Processing*, Aug. 1978, pp. 197-205.

41. S. E. Orcutt, "Implementation of Permutation Functions in Illiac IV-Type Computers," *IEEE Trans. Comput.*, Vol. C-25, No. 9, Sept. 1976, pp. 929-936.

42. H. J. Siegel, "Analysis Techniques for SIMD Machine Interconnection Networks and the Effects of Processor Address Masks," *IEEE Trans. Comput.*, Vol. C-26, No. 2, Feb. 1977, pp. 153-161.

43. H. J. Siegel, "Single Instruction Stream-Multiple Data Stream Machine Interconnection Network Design," *1976 Int'l. Conf. on Parallel Processing*, Aug. 1976, pp. 272-282.

44. H. J. Siegel, "Partitionable SIMD Computer System Interconnection Network Universality," *16th Annual Allerton Conf. on Communication, Control, and Computing*, Oct. 1978, pp. 586-595.

45. T. Lang, "Interconnections Between Processors and Memory Modules Using the Shuffle-Exchange Network," *IEEE Trans. Comput.*, Vol. C-26, No. 5, May 1976, pp. 496-503.

Howard Jay Siegel is an assistant professor in the School of Electrical Engineering at Purdue University and on the research staff of Purdue's Laboratory for Applications of Remote Sensing. His research interests include parallel processing, multimicroprocessor systems, speech processing, natural language processing, and image processing. His current activities include designing a partitionable SIMD/MIMD multimicroprocessor system for image processing.

Siegel received SB degrees in electrical engineering and in management in 1972 from MIT. He received the MA and MSE degrees in 1974, and the PhD degree in 1977, all from Princeton University. He is a member of ACM and IEEE, and chairman of the Central Indiana Chapter of the IEEE Computer Society. He is a member of Eta Kappa Nu and Sigma Xi honorary societies.

Reprinted from *Computer*, Volume 10, Number 8, August 1977, pages 54-59. Copyright © 1977 by The Institute of Electrical and Electronics Engineers, Inc.

Image Processing with the Staran Parallel Computer

Donald Rohrbacher and J.L. Potter
Goodyear Aerospace Corporation

Introduction

Although not designed with image processing specifically in mind, the Staran parallel processor has had a significant impact on that application area. The machine is fully programmable, yet when applied to image processing it has demonstrated speeds usually associated only with hardwired systems. The result is an ability to execute interactively (response time under 10 seconds) a number of sophisitcated image processing algorithms and provide a significant improvement in throughput for batch processing systems.

Here are a brief description of the Staran computer, a discussion of how it executes image processing functions, and a presentation of some of the results to date.

The Staran computer

The Staran computer, a "single-instruction-stream multiple-data-stream" processor, is in effect a large number of simple processors operating simultaneously under a single control. The basic architecture consists of a conventionally addressed control memory for program storage and data buffering, a control unit for sequencing and decoding instructions from control memory, and up to 32 array modules (see Figure 1). Figure 2 shows a simplified block diagram of an array module. Each array module consists of 256 simple processing elements. Each processing element is given enough logic and storage to perform bit-serial searches and arithmetic functions.

Multi-dimensional access memory. The multidimensional access memory contains 256 words, each 256 bits long. Under software control these words can be logically divided into fields of arbitrary length. Each memory access involves 256 bits. However, a wide variety of access modes are available (two access modes are illustrated in Figure 3). The bit slice access mode, which accesses one bit of all words in the memory, is necessary for many of the parallel operations (such as a field-to-field add). This operation results in all the processing elements (or a selected subset) simultaneously adding two numbers stored in different fields and storing the sum back into the memory. The

word slice access mode accesses all the bits of a single word and is particularly useful for I/O operations.

In addition to these two access modes, a wide variety of other access modes is possible. For example, 2 bits of every 2nd word, 4 bits of every 4th word, 8 bits of every 8th word, on up to 128 bits of every 128th word can be accessed.

With a memory read cycle time of better than 200 nanoseconds and a write cycle time of better than 400 nanoseconds, the bandwidth of one module is about 1.28 gigabits per second for reading and 0.64 gigabits per second for writing. A field-to-field add over all 256 words results in a raw processing rate of approximately 8 million 32-bit adds per second.

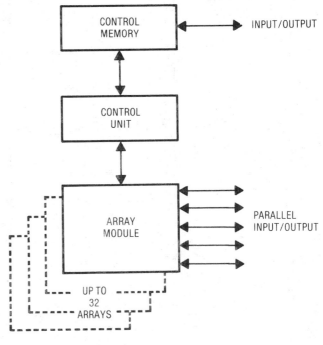

Figure 1. Staran modularity.

EHO182-6/81/0000/0119 © 1977 IEEE

Permutation network. Many applications require the processing elements to perform arithmetic operations with operand pairs that do not come from the same word. This means processing elements must be able to access more than one word in the memory. This is accomplished by passing the data through the permutation network. The network is capable of permuting the 256-bit vector read from the multidimensional access memory in a wide variety of ways. Figure 4 illustrates the case where each processing element is associated with a word of MDA memory shifted by two (note that it is an end-around

shift). Any shift of a power of two is possible with no loss in time. Shifts other than a power of two can be obtained by multiple passes through the permutation network.

In addition to shifting, the permutation network can also mirror the 256-bit vector. A mirror operation reverses the order of the bits and can be performed simultaneously with a shift. The mirroring capability can be used to provide a more efficient operation for some shifts. For example, a shift of 15 can be obtained in only two operations. The first is a combined mirror and shift of 1, and the second is a mirror and shift of 16.

The permutation network can also be used to perform shifts modulo any binary number with no time penalty. For example, Figure 5a illustrates a shift of 2 modulo 4 and Figure 5b a shift of 1 modulo 2.

One example of the use of the shifting network is in execution of the fast Fourier transform. The permutation network permits all the shifts, with no time penalty, found in the familiar butterfly diagram for the FFT. Therefore, the Staran is very efficient for frequency domain processing.

Image processing performance

Many image processing functions are well suited to the Staran architecture because they have an inherent parallelism. Since the computations associated with each pixel are the same for a given algorithm, they can be

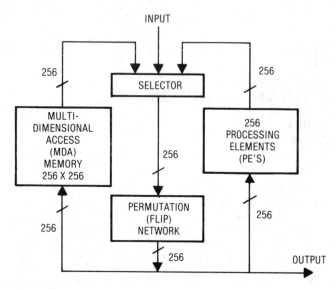

Figure 2. An array module.

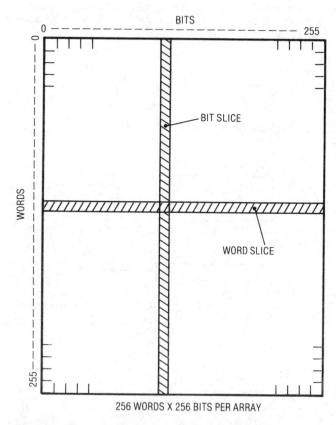

256 WORDS X 256 BITS PER ARRAY

Figure 3. Two access modes.

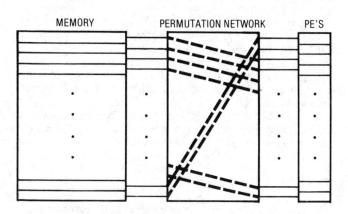

Figure 4. Staran communication.

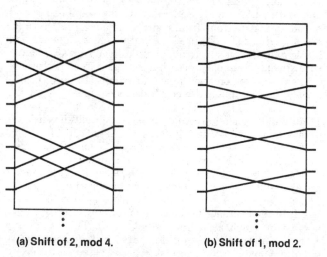

(a) Shift of 2, mod 4.　　(b) Shift of 1, mod 2.

Figure 5. Permutation network.

implemented in the single-instruction, multiple-data stream concept that is inherent in the Staran computer. This fact is evident in both a batch processing and interactive environment.

Batch processing. At the NASA Johnson Space Center, the Staran has been applied to a number of important image processing tasks in support of Lacie, or the Large Area Crop Inventory Experiment. The result has been a significant increase in throughput while reducing the burdens of IBM 360/75's in NASA's Mission Control Center. The Staran is connected to any one of the five 360/75's via a custom interface unit, and such key functions as iterative clustering and vector classification functions are off-loaded into the Staran.

Iterative clustering. The iterative clustering algorithm provides a means both for assigning measurement vectors to clusters and for evolving the statistical description of the reference clusters. The algorithm determines the "distance" of each measurement vector (of a set of such vectors) from the mean vector of each cluster and assigns each measurement vector to the "nearest" cluster. The statistics of all measurement vectors assigned to a particular class are determined and are used to modify the original clusters and cluster statistics. When the tasks described above are accomplished, the algorithm is considered to have undergone one "pass." Usually, several passes are executed before the iterative clustering process is terminated. Figure 6 shows typical Lacie results for 22,932 vectors under various channel (color bands) set sizes.

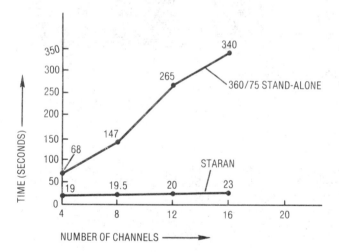

Figure 6. Iterative clustering timings.

Vector classification. The maximum likelihood classification algorithm involves essentially the calculation of the function representing the probability that a given vector belongs to a class and the determination of the most likely class among those defined for the vector.

The mixture density classification algorithm is similar to the maximum likelihood algorithm. The distinction is a derivative of the class statistics definition made in each case. The maximum likelihood classification algorithm utilizes a set of class statistics (mean and covariances) obtained for the population of the class as a whole; the mixture density function is formulated to treat a class as a union of independent subclasses, each of which is

described as a population having a complete set of (sub-) class statistics. Figure 7 shows mixture density timing results on LACIE images of 22,932 vectors under various channel set sizes and defined signatures. Maximum likelihood timing results are about 20% less for both computer systems.

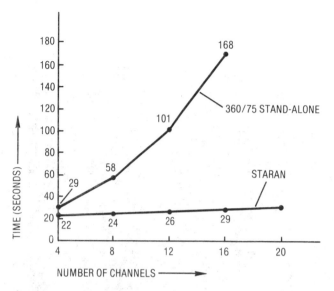

Figure 7. MIXDEN timings.

Interactive processing. Many image processing functions have been implemented on the STARAN at the Goodyear Aerospace Evaluation and Training Facility. Among these are some of the more frequently implemented point processing routines such as interactive grey-scale remapping, pseudocolor processing, and histogram computation and equalization. These functions are essentially serial in nature and can be performed in the Staran at about the same rate as in serial computers. In addition to the point processes, several area process functions have been implemented and still others have been analytically investigated to determine Staran performance. All of the functions studied and implemented can be executed in less than 10 seconds (including I/O), providing a truly comprehensive and interactive image processing capability.

Magnification. The magnification program implemented uses cubic convolution interpolation to calculate grey-scale values for points between those of the original image. The magnification program provides a complete interactive capability. The user positions the cursor over the center of the area to be magnified. He enters the magnification ratios (asymmetric magnification is possible by specifying different X and Y magnification ratios). The program determines from the magnification ratios and the center point if source data is needed from outside the image. If so, the center point is adjusted so that the input image data is available for a complete 512 by 512 output image. The entire magnification process takes less than 8 seconds at a 2.5 x 2.5 magnification.

The time required for the magnification routine alone is much less than 8 seconds. Actual timing measurements show that it takes only 588 milliseconds, which is estimated to be more than an order of magnitude faster than for a computer such as the CDC 6400. Figure 8 shows the original and a magnified image (2.5 x 2.5).

Figure 8a. Original image.

Figure 8b. Image magnified.

Convolution. Convolution is an image enhancement filtering technique which is performed in the space domain. Basically, convolution involves the modification of each image point as a function of the sum of the products of its near neighbors and an a priori weighting matrix.

The effect on one point of the image may be visualized by overlaying the original image, point-by-point, with the weighting matrix, where the central value of the weighting matrix is aligned with the image point of interest. Now each of the weights and its corresponding image point are multiplied. The sum of the resulting products then becomes the new value of the point of interest.

Figure 9 illustrates the effects of edge detection using a convolution matrix. Figure 9a is the original image and Figure 9b shows the results of edge detection. Figure 9c shows the result of superimposing 9a and 9b. This function takes about 700 milliseconds on the Staran. A comparable program on a serial computer such as the IBM 360/195 requires about 60 seconds.

Spatial warp. Spatial warp provides the capability of overlaying one image on another in exact pixel registration when the original images are misaligned. Common features in both images are identified and used to calculate, via a least-squares-fit, the coefficients required to map one grid onto the other. In the general case, the grid points of the warped image do not line up with the grid points of the other image. Consequently, an interpolation is required to determine the values of the points of the warped image at the grid points of the second image.

It takes an estimated* 2 milliseconds to calculate the warping function coefficients when 32 feature control points have been identified. The time required to identify the points was not included since this is normally done interactively where user time is much more significant than computer time. The coordinate transformations and pixel interpolation phase should take from 3.26 to 7.86 seconds depending on I/O configuration. Since the coefficient calculation time is small compared to the interpolation time, the total operation times approximates the interpolation times. It has been estimated to take from 1 to 3 minutes for a similar process on a CDC 6400.

Image filtering. In addition to the implemented space domain filtering (convolution) mentioned earlier, frequency domain and homomorphic filtering were also studied.

Due to the Staran's parallelism, one N-point fast Fourier transform can be performed in the Staran in $\log_2 N$ steps. Thus for $N = 512$, only nine steps are required. The time required to transform a 512 x 512 8-bit pixel image, filter it, and retransform it is estimated to take about 2.06 seconds for an 80 megabyte/second I/O and 9.48 seconds for a 0.6 megabyte/second I/O, compared to 1552 seconds for an HP 3000.

One form of homomorphic filtering consists of adding a step before and after a linear fast Fourier transform filter.

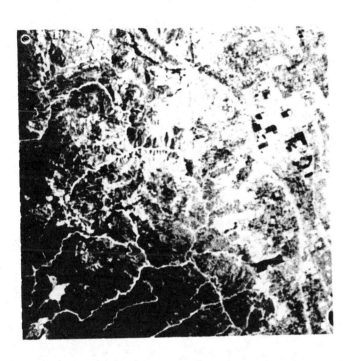

Figure 9. Convolution — (a) original image, (b) edge detection, and (c) views "a" and "b" superimposed.

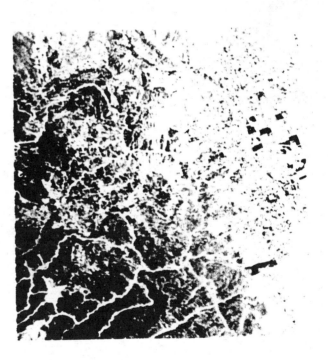

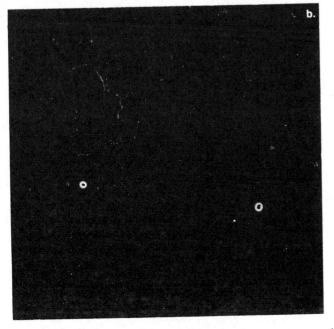

Prior to the FFT, the logarithm of the image data is taken, transforming the multiplicative signals into an additive space. After the data has been FFT filtered, it is transformed into the original multiplicative space by exponentation. Adding the two transforms to the FFT times results in times of about 3.5 seconds for an 80 megabyte/second channel and 14.4 seconds for a 0.6 megabyte/second I/O channel for the complete homomorphic filter operation.

*All times are based on 512 x 512 8-bit pixel images.

Summary

The Staran is a parallel processor whose computing power is located in the associated memory arrays. It is capable of performing traditional serial computations at contemporary rates while providing significant speed improvements in parallel applications.

The single most important aspect of image processing on the Staran is the fast execution time. This means that the user can try functions on an interactive basis. If, for example, an image is to be deblurred, study of the image will suggest a family of filters which may be helpful. In the normal situation, the long execution times make it impractical to try more than two or three filters. With the Staran it is possible to try many more functions in only a few minutes.

It should be emphasized that the functions described here are meant to represent a sample of the image processing functions which can be done by the Staran. Not only does the Staran perform well on image processing problems, but it can be used in many other applications (text searching, signal processing, and guidance and control, for example). ■

Bibliography

Batcher, K. E., "The Flip Network in STARAN," *Proc., 1976 International Conference on Parallel Processing*, pp. ___.

_____, "The Multi-Dimensional Access Memory in STARAN," *Proc., 1975 Sagamore Computer Conference on Parallel Processing*, pp. 167-xx.

Davis, E. W., "STARAN Parallel Processor System Software," *AFIPS Conf. Proc., 1974 NCC*, Vol. 43, pp. 17-22.

Faiss, R., J. Lyon, M. Quinn, and S. Ruben, "Application of a Parallel Processing Computer in LACIE," P. Enslow, Jr. (ed.), *Proc., 1976 International Conference on Parallel Processing*, pp. 24-32.

Morrill, C. D., "Parallel Processing Applied to Computer Image Generation," *First International Learning Technology Congress*, Washington, D. C., July 1976, pp. ___.

"Digital Image Processing and STARAN," GER-16336, Goodyear Aerospace Corp., Akron, Ohio, May 1976.

"Image Magnification," GER-16342, Goodyear Aerospace Corp., Akron, Ohio, August 1976.

Donald Rohrbacher is a section head in the Digital Technology Department at Goodyear Aerospace Corporation. He is responsible for systems development with an emphasis on the application of the Staran computer. His present responsibilities include the development of an interactive image processing system using the Staran computer. Rohrbacher received his BSEE from Ohio State University and his MSEE from the University of Syracuse.

J.L. Potter works on the development of image processing techniques and applications for the Staran computer at Goodyear Aerospace Corporation. Earlier he worked for Xerox and Bell Laboratories. Potter obtained his BA from the University of Iowa, his MA from Stevens Institute, and his PhD in computer science from the University of Wisconsin. He is a member of Phi Beta Kappa, Sigma Xi, and the ACM.

Reprinted from *Computer*, Volume 12, Number 3, March 1979, pages 53-61. Copyright © 1979 by The Institute of Electrical and Electronics Engineers, Inc.

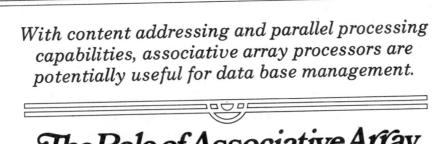

With content addressing and parallel processing capabilities, associative array processors are potentially useful for data base management.

The Role of Associative Array Processors in Data Base Machine Architecture

P. Bruce Berra
Ellen Oliver
Syracuse University

Associative memories and associative processors were extensively discussed in the literature of the late 1950's and early 1960's. Researchers then recognized the advantages of addressing data by content and parallel processing. More specifically, they recognized the potential advantages of these devices in information retrieval. However, since early devices required extensive hardware they were expensive, small, and difficult to work with. There was the added drawback of slow input and output. The time required for processing within the memory/array was negligible compared to load/unload time. Thus, this largely reduces the memory array speed advantage in comparison to more conventional devices.

Recent advances in LSI, VLSI, and memory technology have led to greatly reduced hardware costs with a concomitant reduction in size and increase in capability. These factors plus rising software and personnel costs have been instrumental in the renewed interest in associative memories and processors.

These devices are particularly important to data base management primarily because of two basic capabilities: content addressing and parallelism. That is, in searching for data these devices access by content rather than by hardware storage address, and do the searching in parallel. Because searching is a fundamental data base function, the renewed interest in utilization of associative memories and processors for data base management is understandable.

This article is concerned with the utilization of associative array processors of the STARAN[1] type in data base management. The basic organization consists of an associative array containing the data being processed, auxiliary/secondary memory for temporary or permanent data storage, and a wide bandwidth interface for use in rapidly staging data into the array.

Throughout this discussion we will assume that the relational data model[2,3] is utilized. We will view the data as two-dimensional arrays. The associative processor array is also two dimensional, thus yielding an efficient mapping between the structure of the data and the physical structure of the hardware.

Our discussion begins with a description of the architecture of associative devices, then reviews the literature in which bit/byte-slice associative array devices are utilized to search, retrieve, and update a data base. We give additional details on the searching of array-resident data and on a fast mass memory that keeps the array supplied with data. We conclude by discussing three general configurations in which associative array devices are utilized to search, retrieve and update a large data base ($> 10^9$ bits). In all cases data are staged into the associative array processor from auxiliary memory. We provide approximate timing data for each configuration.

The architecture of associative array processors

Yau and Fung[4] define an associative processor as a hardware device having an associative memory as one of its key components. When data are resident in the associative memory, the system can access the data by content and can perform search operations in parallel, such as exact match, greater than, less than, maximum, minimum, between limits, as well as Boolean operations. Yau and Fung have classified the architecture of associative processors into four categories according to the comparison process of

EHO182-6/81/0000/0125 © 1979 IEEE

their associative memories: (1) fully parallel, (2) bit-serial, (3) word-serial, and (4) block-oriented associative processors. We will be concerned only with *bit-serial* machines—also known as bit-serial, word-parallel associative processors since one bit column of all the words is operated on in parallel.* We will refer to them as *bit-slice* machines.

*Among associative processors of interest to data base management personnel are CASSM, DBC, RAP, and RARES. These block-oriented associative processors are discussed elsewhere in this issue.

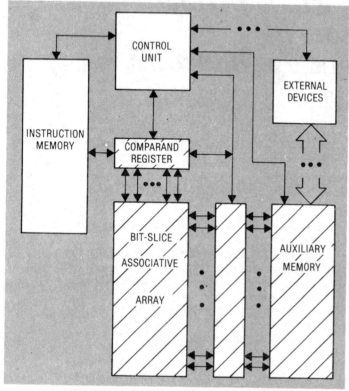

Figure 1. Block diagram of a STARAN-like bit-slice associative architecture. In this article we are concerned with the shaded areas—the comparand register, bit-slice associative array, and auxiliary memory.

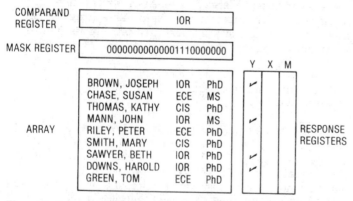

Figure 2. An associative memory. The array contains the data and the comparand register the argument. The mask register enables or inhibits bit slices of the array for an operation, and the response registers record search results, perform Boolean operations, and provide word selection capability.

One of the most notable bit-serial, word-parallel associative processors is the STARAN associative array processor built by the Goodyear Aerospace Corporation. Figure 1 is a general block diagram of a STARAN-like associative processor. Figure 2 shows the array, comparand register, mask register, and response registers. The array is the storage device containing the data, and the comparand register contains the argument. The mask register enables or inhibits bit slices of the array for a given operation, and the response registers record search results, perform Boolean operations, and provide word selection capability. Consider an example illustrating the functions of these units: The data, consisting of the name, department, and degree program for each student, are loaded in fixed-length predefined fields of the array. To find the names of all students enrolled in IOR, a query is executed by placing the argument IOR in the comparand, loading the mask register with ones in the bit positions to correspond to the department field and zeros elsewhere, and executing an exact match search. Those words matching the search criteria will set a response bit in the Y response register, and could subsequently be retrieved from the memory.

To illustrate the Boolean capabilities of such an arrangement, consider an addition to the above query: After finding all IOR students, the user decides to modify the query to retrieve each IOR student also enrolled in a PhD program. First, the responses to the previous search, which were recorded in the Y register, would be saved in the X register and the Y register would be cleared. The comparand argument would now become PhD, the mask would be altered to correspond to the degree field, an exact match search executed, and the result recorded in the Y register. The logical AND of the contents of the X register with the contents of the Y register would yield the desired response—in this case Brown, Sawyer, and Downs.

Early work with bit-slice associative memories/processors

In 1971, DeFiore et al[5] discussed the advantages of utilizing associative techniques for data base management. Fundamental to the discussion is the development of an algorithm to convert a hierarchical data model to a data structure called *associative normal form*, or ANF, which can be efficiently manipulated by an associative memory. Advantages of such an implementation include the elimination of an indexing scheme and the resultant decrease in storage, the capability of querying any field, and a greater flexibility to adapt to changing requirements.

Basically, the algorithm removes all non-simple domains. Consider the following occurrence of the non-simple domain Education History:

Personnel (name, position, title, education history)
Education History (degree, degree date)

The algorithm replaces Education History with μ to create the following ANF data structure:

Personnel (name, position, title, μ)
Education History (degree, degree data, μ)

where name, position, title, degree, degree date and μ are all simple domains.

DeFiore and Berra[6,7] describe a data base management system called Information System for Associative Memories, or IFAM. The system was implemented in 1970 at the Rome Air Development Center on an experimental associative memory developed by the Goodyear Aerospace Corporation. The memory operated in conjunction with a CDC 1604. The user interacted with the system via a Bunker Ramo BR-85 display console, a peripheral to the 1604.

The IFAM system, which utilized an ANF data structure, is compared with a sequential inverted list implementation of a personnel data file utilizing the criteria of retrieval, update, storage requirements, and flexibility. In both the sequential and associative implementations, the critical assumption is made that all data fit into main memory, thus limiting the generality of the results.

For retrieval and update, equations were developed to count the number of interrogations to main memory. Retrieval was evaluated for single and multi-criteria searches; updates were evaluated for single criteria. For single criteria searches, the ratio of the number of interrogations for the sequential system to the associative system was proportional to the logarithm of the length of the list being searched; for multi-criteria searches ratios of 50 to 1 were common. The ratio for updating as single item in a list of 16 was 30 to 1, but when all items on the list were updated the ratio dropped to 3 to 1. The equations developed to evaluate the storage requirements considered the number of bits used to store the data and any redundancies. Numerical results indicate that the sequential system requires 2 to 4.5 times as much storage. The associative system is the most flexible since all fields are potential indices.

Moulder[8] developed a research-oriented data base management system utilizing a STARAN associative array processor. The STARAN is connected to a Sigma 5 general-purpose computer via a custom input/output unit (CIOU) and a parallel head per track disk (PHTD) via a parallel input/output unit (PIOU). Also included in the system organization is an EAI analog computer and other peripheral devices. The PHTD is of particular interest in the configuration because it enables parallel data transfers to take place in the manner following. The surface of the disk is divided into 72 track sectors where 64 tracks are tied to STARAN; each sector has a capacity of 256 bits. To search the data base, one sector from each track is loaded into the STARAN in parallel and searched. For the PHTD used on this implementation, 100 μsecs were required to load a sector. In addition, STARAN can perform complex searches in 100 μsecs. Therefore, by loading and searching every

other sector, it is possible to search the entire data base in approximately two disk revolutions, assuming the entire data base is resident on one disk surface.

The data base utilized in this case was hierarchical in nature and reduced to a format similar to ANF. DBMS software was created to support the functions of data definition, file creation, interrogation and update. Preliminary results indicate that the STARAN can be effectively used to support the search operations of a DBMS and provide a flexible system requiring minimal software.

Linde, Gates, and Peng[9] describe a hypothetical byte-serial, word-parallel associative processor computer system, or APCS, designed to investigate real-time DBMS functions. The system architecture includes two associative processing units, a sequential processor, a parallel input/output channel, terminals and peripherals, and a large random access memory capable of transferring data to and from the associative memories at a rate of 1.6 billion bytes/sec.

The authors evaluated the APCS for search, retrieval, and update since they felt, after analyzing current operations, that these were the functions most able to utilize an associative processor. The analysis involved coding the search, retrieval, and update problems for both the APCS and an IBM 370/145, and then comparing program performance. After normalizing the APCS to the IBM 370/145, the authors found the APCS to be 32 to 110 times faster for search and retrieval and 15 to 210 times faster for update.

Advantages and limitations of bit-slice associative processors

Clearly, bit-slice associative processors have both advantages and disadvantages in the context of data base management.[10] Perhaps their greatest advantage is rapid search of array-resident data since the data can be searched by content and in parallel. And search is fundamental to such operations as retrieval of data, changing the value content of data already in the data base, sorting, and merging.

Another advantage is the mapping between the relational model and the physical structure of the associative memory since both can be viewed as two-dimensional arrays. This advantage also applies to the hierarchical and network structures albeit to a lesser extent. Another benefit is that any attribute can be viewed as an index since all bit positions in the array are treated equally.

In terms of updating, associative memories also have advantages. Consider a deletion. Once the record to be deleted has been located, the word-masking capability can be used to prevent that record from participating in further operations. Additions can be made to the bottom of any relation since order is not a prerequisite. Changes to a value are easily accomplished using the content addressability property to locate the value to be changed and then writing the new value in its place.

Finally, previous research indicates an advantage in terms of storage. Overhead in current systems, including pointers and lists utilized to improve retrieval and update performance, can be largely eliminated to conserve space.

Perhaps the most serious disadvantages in the utilization of bit-slice associative array processors in data base management are input/output speed and hardware cost. As previously noted, the data to be searched must be moved from secondary/auxiliary storage to the array. The time to load data into the array has been orders of magnitude greater than the time to search array-resident data, thus eliminating or at best greatly reducing the performance advantage of these devices. To correct this situation one must provide a high band-width interface linking the array with a fast, large memory holding all or part of the data base. Alternately, one could develop a staging scheme or bring data through a somewhat smaller fast buffer memory from more traditional secondary storage devices such as disk.

Providing additional interface hardware and a fast mass memory increases the cost of an already expensive piece of hardware. However, there are two mitigating factors. First, an additional functional capability is implemented in the hardware and removed from the software. With the current decreasing trend in hardware costs and increasing trend in software, we may well reach the crossover point before long. Second, current sequential systems cannot handle certain data base management applications. Some of these applications are so important that increased hardware costs are not a factor.

Array search and readout

In the following discussion on system configurations, the associative array unit is assumed to be a STARAN-like bit-slice word-parallel machine with four associative array modules, each 256 x 256 bits. We will also assume that this four-module array is large enough to hold eight pages of data, each page containing 128 x 256 bits. The page concept will be utilized throughout our analysis of subsequent configurations. Later we will convert the page measure to bytes and also show that eight pages is the same size as one track of a disk.

The array will be utilized to perform search operations. As mentioned previously, many kinds of searches can be performed in associative arrays. In terms of time required to search data, there are three general categories. The first category contains those searches utilizing the comparand to contain the argument to be processed against the data base; such searches are greater-than-or-equal-to-comparand, less-than-comparand, and equal-to-comparand. In general, using STARAN timing data, these searches require a time of approximately $(1 + 0.2n)$ μsecs, where n is the number of bits in the argument. If we use 256 as the maximum number of bits to be searched, we can perform this type of search in less than 53 μsecs.

The second category includes those occurring between fields of the associative array, such as equal-to-field, less-than-field, and greater-than-or-equal-to-field. Times for this type of search operation are on the order of $(3 + 0.5n)$ μsecs. In this case 128 is the maximum number of bits permitted in each of the fields of a word to be compared; therefore, this search will require a maximum of 67 μsecs.

The final category comprises those that will determine either the maximum or minimum value of a given field. Searches of this type can be performed in $(1.08 + 0.8n)$ μsecs. With 256 bits as the maximum field size, we find 205 μsecs a reasonable upper bound.

After a search has been performed, the result will be recorded in one of the response registers. As previously noted, the STARAN has three registers—X, Y, M—and search results are recorded in the Y register. Next, the Y register is used to locate those records that have responded to the query, and to read them from the array. In the STARAN, this requires less than 16 μsecs per 256-bit word. If we assume 10 responders per array load, a reasonable upper-bound estimate for readout time is 160 μsecs.

Our objective is to establish a reasonable upper-bound time for searching one array load (8 pages) of data, and for reading out the responding records, assuming 10 responses. Note that in the case of a maximum or minimum, we will have one response —the max or min. On the basis of the previous discussion, we conclude that most searches and readouts can be performed in less than 300 μsecs per array load.

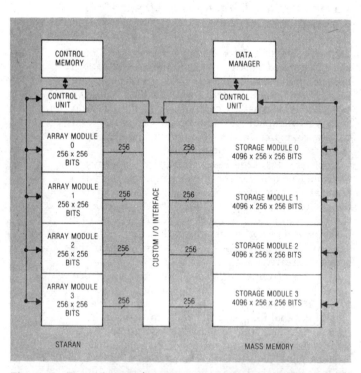

Figure 3. The STARAN/mass memory interface. Data transfers between the fast mass memory and the STARAN occur across an intelligent interface at a rate of about 3 x 10^9 bits per second.

128   COMPUTER

Fast mass memory

Farnsworth et al[11] report the results of a study to develop a giga-bit storage device compatible with the Rome Air Development Center's STARAN associative array processor. Although this design applies specifically to the STARAN, the concept is general enough to be applied to other associative processors. The results of this study are particularly important to the use of bit-slice associative array processors in data base management, since they indicate that technology has advanced to the point where I/O no longer has to be the bottleneck.

The organization of the mass memory closely mirrors the architecture of the STARAN. The STARAN at RADC contains four array modules, each 256 x 256 bits. Data transfers between the mass memory and the STARAN take place across an intelligent interface that can perform various data manipulation functions. There are 1024 parallel lines, with 256 bit-serial transfers required to fully load the array (Figure 3). Since transfer rates are 300 to 450 nsecs per bit slice, less than 115 μsecs are required to transfer 256 bit slices.

Data are stored within the mass memory in one of four non-volatile storage modules. Each storage module has the capacity to store up to 4096 randomly selectable blocks of 256 x 256 bits, enabling block transfers of up to 1024 bits at a time. Provision is made for transfers of fewer than 1024 parallel bits and 256 serial bits in any given block.

The block orientation for data storage enables pre-queueing of data. That is, once the starting address is located and the first bit slice moved via a shift register to the proper I/O port, the remaining bit slices in the block will be available for transfer without incurring the addressing and shifting overhead. The queue time is expected to be less than 50 μsecs. This implies that a maximum total time of 165 μsecs will be required to locate the data on the storage device and transfer it to the STARAN.

Three system configurations

Earlier, we reviewed associative processors, examined past work in utilization of bit-slice associative capabilities in data base management systems, discussed array search and readout, and finally described a fast mass memory to improve the performance of associative devices for DBMS applications. We can therefore conclude that associative technology is worth further investigation in the search for a solution to the very large data base problem. The question is how best to organize a system to take maximum advantage of these capabilities.

In this section we discuss three generalized system configurations utilizing currently available technology and offering a possible solution to the very large data base problem. All three systems are intended to be back-end data base computers which interface with a general-purpose host computer. In all cases we will assume the host can parse the query and utilize a dictionary or directory resident in the host so that the query is in an executable format when it reaches the back-end. Our primary concern, then, will be to demonstrate how these configurations can efficiently search, retrieve, and update large quantities of data. We will include a discussion of timing data for the configurations, based on published timing figures. Our reference for data relating to bit-slice associative memories/processors is the Goodyear STARAN associative array processor[1] in the RADC configuration—an associative memory with four modules, each 256 x 256 bits. Our reference for data relating to a mass storage device is the organization proposed by Farnesworth et al.[11] The data relating to disk is based on the standard IBM 3330.

Configuration 1. As shown in Figure 4, the first system we will examine has three major components: the associative array, an interface, and a fast mass memory. Data in the relational format are stored in the mass memory; when required for either a search, retrieval, or update, the data are moved to the associative array via the interface. Directory data could be utilized rather than data in the form of tuples. The following analysis would change slightly in that one would first search for a pointer to a tuple and then for the tuple itself. However, there is no loss of generality.

For this configuration we will assume that the array is similar to the STARAN array (1024 x 256 bits) and holds eight pages of data, each page 128 x 256 bits. The fast mass memory is as previously discussed and is divided into four modules as shown in Figure 3. That is, each module has a capacity of storing 8K pages of 128 x 256 bits (i.e., 32M bytes per module). Thus, there are 128M bytes which may be divided into 32K pages, each containing 128 x 256 bits (4K-bytes).

We are first interested in the amount of time required to locate a block of data to be transferred to the arrays. In this case we will assume that for any transfer we are locating a block consisting of eight

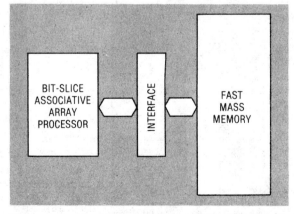

Figure 4. Configuration 1—data in relational format are stored in mass memory; when required for either a search, retrieval, or update, data are moved to the associative array via the interface.

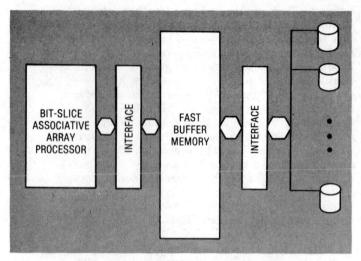

Figure 5. Configuration 2, a modification of Configuration 1, features a fast buffer memory interfaced to another level of storage.

contiguous pages (one array load). The study by Farnesworth et al indicates that a time of up to 50 μsecs may be required to locate the data and shift them to the I/O port.

After data are moved to the I/O port ready for transfer, they will go to the associative array via the interface. We assume that the interface has a 1024-bit bandwidth—i.e., there is one channel for each associative array word. Using the time obtained from Farnesworth et al, one bit slice can be transferred across the interface in a maximum of 450 nsecs. This means that 256 transfers of 1024 bits per transfer (one array load) can be accomplished in 115 μsecs—equivalent to a transfer rate of 280M bytes per second.

We are particularly interested in evaluating Configuration 1 for the data base operations of search, retrieval, and update. Recall that earlier we made the assumption that query parsing and data diction-

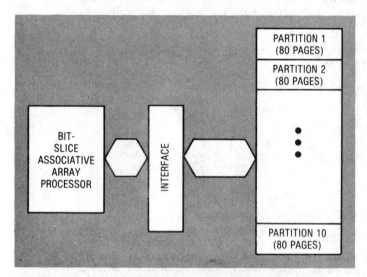

Figure 6. The array/fast buffer memory interface for Configuration 2. The fast buffer memory is partitioned and has dual ports.

ary/directory functions would be performed in the front-end host computer. We can also assume that any other desirable functions can be performed in the front-end. Therefore, we will consider the methodology and the amount of time required to perform searches, retrievals, and updates.

Consider the amount of time to perform any one of the search operations on an array load (eight pages) of data. The procedure is first to locate the data on the mass memory (50 μsecs); second to move the data across the interface (115 μsecs); and finally to search and retrieve up to 10 responders (300 μsecs). We can conclude that 500 μsecs, allowing for miscellaneous overhead, is a reasonable upper bound. The mass memory has a capacity to hold 32K pages. Therefore, the entire data base ($>10^9$) can be searched in

$$\frac{500\ \mu\text{secs}}{8\ \text{pages}} \times 32\text{K pages} = 2\ \text{seconds}$$

Three update operations are of interest to us—addition, deletion, and change. In each case, the data are read into the array, updated, and written into the mass memory. Records (tuples) can be added to the data base in at least two different ways. The first way is to look for the first page having an empty space and then to write into that space. The second way is to add the record to the last page. Deletions are accomplished by searching for the record to be deleted, marking it as deleted, and then using the word-masking capability to prevent the marked record from being read from the associative array back to the mass memory. Changes involve a search for the record to be changed, followed by an overwrite in the associative array, and finally a read back to the mass storage device.

Currently, a research effort is being conducted to model a system with Configuration 1.[12]

Configuration 2. As shown in Figure 5, Configuration 2 is a modification of Configuration 1. In addition to the array and the array-to-memory interface, there is a fast buffer memory interfaced to another level of storage. The data base is stored in the secondary moving head disk memory and staged through the smaller fast buffer memory to the associative array, where it is searched. From the associative array the data will either follow the reverse of the above path (i.e., update) or be returned to the user (retrieval).

The associative array of Configuration 2 and the interface to the fast buffer memory are assumed to be the same as found in Configuration 1. Therefore, the analysis of timing developed in the previous section will also be assumed here.

As shown in Figure 6, the fast buffer memory is smaller than the mass memory in Configuration 1, is partitioned, and has dual ports. Note that there are 10 partitions, each having a capacity of 80 pages. Recall the array can hold eight pages; therefore each partition will contain 10 array loads of data. The partitions are multiplexed so that the array will access data from one partition at a time and move it across the

130   COMPUTER

parallel interface. From the previous section, we know that 500 μsecs is a reasonable amount of time to allocate for the processing of eight pages (i.e., one array load). Therefore the search time for each partition is

$$\frac{500 \ \mu secs}{8 \ pages} \ x \ \frac{80 \ pages}{partition} = 5 \ msecs/partition$$

Since there are 10 partitions, a total of 50 msecs are required to process all of the data contained in the fast buffer memory. As stated above, the partitions are multiplexed, so that to avoid any bottleneck in the system we must be able to load any partition through the disk port in less than 45 msecs, since that is approximately the time when a partition is not being utilized by the array.

Consider the disk configuration and its interface to the fast buffer memory as shown in Figure 7. There are 100 disks divided into 10 banks, with each bank containing 10 disks. In other words, each fast buffer memory partition has a bank of 10 disks holding data for staging into that partition. The transfer will take place in parallel from all 10 disks across the interface until the partition is full.

Each disk is assumed to have 20 heads and 20 surfaces with 100 tracks per surface. Each track's capacity is equivalent to one array load of data (i.e., eight pages), or 32K bytes. We will assume a 20-msec revolution time and a maximum of 20 msecs for head positioning time. Allowing a maximum of one revolution to locate the data and a second revolution to read the data, one partition of the buffer memory can be filled in 40 msecs when the disk head is already in place.

As in the analysis of Configuration 1, the primary concern is how the configuration can perform the data base operations of search, retrieval, and update. Consider a search and retrieval. When a query is received, the first operation is to locate the data on the disk; in the worst case this will involve moving the heads (20 msecs) and rotating the disk almost a full revolution to the start of the block to be transferred (20 msecs)—a total of 40 msecs. The data will be read from all disks to all partitions in parallel; this operation will require 20 msecs. The array control will then access partition 1, load data into the array, search the array, and return the results, requiring 500 μsecs for the whole operation. Since each partition contains 10 array loads, a total of 5 msecs will be required to fully search a partition. After the first partition has been fully searched, the disk will begin to fill it with data. When partition 2 has been fully searched, it will be loaded from the disk while the array begins to access partition 3. The processing will continue in this fashion. At any point in time after the fast buffer memory has been initially loaded, one partition will be accessed by the array and all others will be in various stages of loading or waiting.

The buffer memory can be loaded 20 times before incurring a time penalty for disk arm movement. In terms of quantity of data, 20 tracks per disk x 100 disks x eight pages per track = 16,000 pages or

16,000 pages x 4K bytes per page = 64M bytes of data staged through the buffer without moving the disk arms. The time required to process these 64M bytes is 20 loads x 50 msecs per load = 1 second.

At this point in time, the heads will move to the next cylinder and the process will begin again. However, since the disk banks operate in parallel, the overhead for head movement will be incurred only once after each 20 loads. The process for search and retrieval of the entire data base will require that all 100 cylinders of the disk be searched. Since each cylinder requires 1 second, the search time for the entire data base will require 100 seconds plus overhead for disk head movement and initialization of the buffer. Therefore, we can conclude that the entire data base—

$$100 \ disks \ x \ \frac{20 \ surfaces}{disk} \ x \ \frac{100 \ tracks}{surface}$$

$$x \ \frac{8 \ pages}{track} \ x \ \frac{4K \ bytes}{page} = 6.4 \ x \ 10^9 \ bytes$$

—can be searched and up to four percent of the records retrieved in approximately 100 seconds.

Having discussed the procedure for search and retrieval, let us consider the process for updates. Again, we will consider additions, deletions, and changes. In general, the procedure will be to load the data into the array, perform the desired update opera-

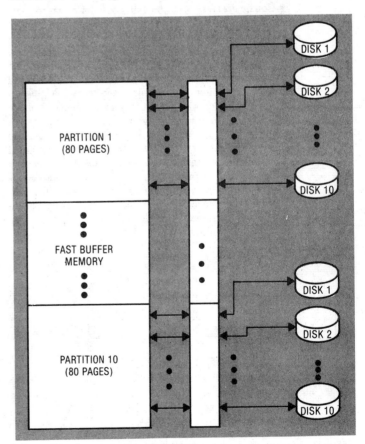

Figure 7. The fast buffer memory/disk interface for Configuration 2. Each partition has a bank of 10 disks.

tion, write the data from the array back into the partition they formerly occupied, and as a final step write the partition contents back to the disk before beginning another load operation. In the case of additions to the data base, there are two possibilities—single addition and multiple additions. For a single addition, an array load could be searched for an empty slot and the additional word written in. Multiple additions could be made at the end of the last page. Deletions would be handled by marking the tuple to be deleted and then using the word-masking capability to not write it from the array. Changes are handled by locating the tuple to be changed, overwriting the field(s) to be changed in the array, and then rewriting through the partition to the disk.

The time required for search and update will be longer than for search and retrieval, since the data must be read back to the disk via the partition. For any partition, the array processing time for search and update will require 5 msecs. Reading an array load to the partition from the array will require 300 nsecs. per bit slice x 256 bit slices = 76.8 μsecs, plus an overhead on the order of 25 μsecs. For each partition, this will be incurred 10 times; therefore a time on the order of 1 msec will be required for each partition. Overwriting the disk from the buffer will require a maximum of 40 msecs per partition. Thus the maximum total processing time per partition is 46 msecs.

Configuration 3. Figure 8 shows the third configuration we will consider, albeit somewhat briefly. The main difference between this configuration and Configuration 2 is the advanced secondary storage. As memory technologies develop we can expect faster and larger secondary memories with decreased costs. Examples of promising new technologies include charge-coupled devices and magnetic bubble memories. Concurrently, we can expect advances in disk technology which will provide for increased storage capability, faster access, and increased parallelism. In terms of Configuration 3 this will mean increased parallelism in the advanced secondary storage and a smaller fast buffer memory. There will also be a more even balance between the processing speed of the array and the ability to keep the array supplied with data.

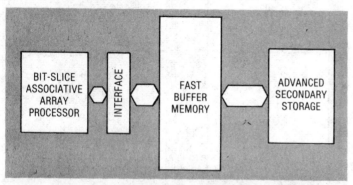

Figure 8. Configuration 3—this arrangement offers increased parallelism in the advanced secondary storage and a smaller fast buffer memory.

Associative array processors appear to be potentially useful in data base management environments. In particular, it is the content addressing and parallel processing capabilities which provide the advantage.

Early systems utilizing associative devices permitted data base operations of search, retrieval, and update to be effectively performed on an associative processor. The configurations discussed here have this same advantage. In Configuration 1, for example, one can search the entire data base of 128M bytes and retrieve up to four percent of the tuples in a time on the order of two seconds; in Configuration 2 one can search a data base of 6.4 x 10^9 bytes and retrieve up to four percent of the tuples in a time on the order of 100 seconds.

Historically, one of the primary disadvantages in utilizing associative array processors has been that the I/O time was orders of magnitude greater than the processing time. However, recent advances in memory technology make it possible to construct secondary storage/staging devices with speed/bandwidth requirements compatible with the associative array memory/processor. In particular, for the configurations used in these analyses, I/O times (including data location) are on the order of 200 μsecs and standard retrieval is on the order of 300 μsecs. This means that the I/O bottleneck of the early systems can be eliminated.

Another problem cited in the past was the small associative array size. However, RAM chips are currently available for associative memory construction in a 1024 x 256 bit configuration.[13] The STARAN-E uses 1K bipolar chips in conjunction with 8K MOS chips (i.e., two chips of 4K each) to create a module 9K x 256 bits. While the word length of 9K may not be desirable, the STARAN-E is indicative of the developments making a larger array a viable possibility.

One of our own current research efforts[14] combines an associative array with a word length on the order of 1K with a mass memory. Preliminary results indicate that the larger memory size can be effectively used to search, retrieve, and update a very large relational data base.

The other primary disadvantage in utilizing associative array processors has been cost. Obviously, the additional hardware which makes the associative array processor attractive and viable is expensive. However, as pointed out earlier, there are two mitigating factors. First, software and personnel costs are expected to continue upward while hardware costs decrease. Thus, a hardware solution may be more economical in the near future. Second, some important data base management applications cannot be undertaken using current sequential systems. In this case, cost is not a factor. ∎

References

1. Goodyear Aerospace Corporation, *STARAN Reference manual*, Revision 2, GER-15636B, Akron, Ohio, June 1975.

2. C. J. Date, *An Introduction to Database Systems*, Addison-Wesley, Reading, Mass., 1975.

3. D. C. P. Smith and J. M. Smith, "Relational Database Machines," in this issue.

4. S. S. Yau and H. S. Fung, "Associative Processor Architecture—A Survey," *Computing Surveys*, Vol. 9, No. 1, Mar. 1977, pp. 3-28.

5. C. DeFiore, N. Stillman, and P. B. Berra, "Associative Techniques in the Solution of Data Management Problems," *Proc. ACM National Conf.*, 1971, pp. 28-36.

6. C. DeFiore and P. B. Berra, "A Data Management System Utilizing an Associative Memory," *AFIPS Conf. Proc.*, Vol. 42, 1973 NCC, pp. 181-185.

7. C. DeFiore and P. B. Berra, "A Quantitative Analysis of the Utilization of Associative Memories in Data Base Management," *IEEE Trans. Computers*, Vol. C-23, No. 2, Feb. 1974, pp. 121-123.

8. R. Moulder, "An Implementation of a Data Management System on an Associative Processor," *AFIPS Conf. Proc.*, Vol. 42, 1973 NCC, pp. 171-176.

9. R. Linde, R. Gates, and T. Peng, "Associative Processor Applications to Real-Time Data Management," *AFIPS Conf. Proc.*, Vol. 42, 1973 NCC, pp. 187-195.

10. P. B. Berra, "Some Problems In Associative Processing Applications to Data Base Management," *AFIPS Conf. Proc.*, Vol. 43, 1974 NCC, pp. 1-5.

11. D. L. Farnesworth, C. P. Hoffman, and J. J. Shutt, *Mass Memory Organization Study*, Rome Air Development Center, TR-76-254, Sept. 1976.

12. S. Eilers, *Modeling a Relational Database for an Associative Processor*, PhD Research Proposal, Syracuse University, Sept. 1978.

13. K. E. Batcher, "STARAN Series E," *Proc. 1977 Int'l Conf. on Parallel Processing*, Aug. 1977, pp. 140-143.

14. E. Oliver, *RELACS, An Associative Computer Architecture to Support a Relational Data Model*, doctoral dissertation in preparation, Syracuse University.

P. Bruce Berra is professor and chairman of industrial engineering and operations research and a member of the faculty of computers and information science at Syracuse University. He has taught at the University of Michigan (Dearborn Campus), Boston University, and Purdue University. His industrial background includes service with IBM, Bendix, and Hughes.

He was general chairman of the 4th Workshop on Computer Architecture for Non-Numeric Processing, held in August 1978, and is area coordinator for data base management on the Technical Program Committee for the 1979 NCC. Currently chairman of the ACM Special Interest Group on Information Retrieval, he is a member of the Distinguished Visitor Program of the IEEE Computer Society. His research interests are in data base machines.

Berra received the BS and MS degrees from the University of Michigan and the PhD degree from Purdue University.

Ellen Oliver is a research assistant in the department of industrial engineering and operations research at Syracuse University, where she is a candidate for a PhD degree. Her current research interests include computer architecture for non-numeric processing and data base management.

Oliver received a BS from the University of Michigan and an MS from Syracuse University. She is a member of the IEEE and the ACM.

4. Multiprocessors

Multiprocessors are computer systems encompassing more than one general-purpose processor, each capable of executing a separate instruction stream, and all of them sharing a global memory. One of the most important components in a multiprocessor is the processor-memory interconnection network. The multiprocessors described in this chapter represent three of the many possible interconnection network alternatives.

The first multiprocessor is the S-1 described in the paper by Widdoes and Correll. The S-1, as many of the multiprocessors built in the past, consists of a few processors and a few memory modules interconnected through a crossbar switch. Other examples in this class include the Burroughs 5000 series, the Burroughs D825 command and control computer (Anderson et al., 1962), and Carnegie-Mellon's C.mmp (Wulf and Bell, 1972). A paper on the S-1 multiprocessor is included because it is the most recent of this group and because its design includes the interesting features of its predecessors as well as some new ones.

The second multiprocessor is Cm* from Carnegie-Mellon University. The interconnection used in Cm* consists of asynchronous busses; this allows the inclusion of processors and memory modules at a cost roughly linear in their number (crossbar switch cost grows as the product of the number of processors and memory modules). Thus, it is possible for Cm* to have a large number of processors (fifty are reported in the paper by Jones et al., (1979)). The major drawback of the interconnection network of Cm* is that it is slow.

The third multiprocessor is the Burroughs' FMP described in the paper by Lundstrom and Barnes. Even though it has not been built, a careful study of its feasibility and performance was done (Burroughs, 1979). The interconnection network chosen for this machine was the baseline network whose cost is proportional to N log N where N is the number of processors. This seems to be a good compromise between the costly crossbar switch and the slow asynchronous bus.

One of the problems affecting the performance of multiprocessors is memory interference. The paper by Chang, Kuck, and Lawrie surveys the studies made on this problem and presents some more optimistic results.

Independent processors provide the flexibility which makes multiprocessors ideal for the exploitation of parallelism in a range of applications where pipelined and array processors are not effective. An example in this range is presented in the paper by Fennell and Lesser.

The last paper in this chapter by Morenoff et al. describes how four processors, interconnected in a very simple way, were used to speed up the execution of a weather forecast program.

Two papers not included in this tutorial could be of interest to the reader. The first by Satyanarayanan (1980) describes several of the commercially available multiprocessors. The second, a survey paper (Jones and Schwarz, 1980) discusses many important issues like reliability, synchronization, and scheduling in multiprocessor systems; the discussion is based on the experience acquired at Carnegie-Mellon University with two experimental multiprocessors, C.mmp and Cm*.

EHO182-6/81/0000/0135 © 1981 IEEE

Reprinted with permission from *Energy and Technology Review*, September 1979. Copyright © 1979 by the Lawrence Livermore Laboratory Press.

THE S-1 PROJECT:
DEVELOPING HIGH-PERFORMANCE DIGITAL COMPUTERS*

L. Curtis Widdoes, Jr. and Steven Correll

University of California, Lawrence Livermore Laboratory, Livermore, CA 94550

Abstract

Under the auspices of the U.S. Navy, we are designing and implementing a multiprocessor (the S-1) with at least ten times the computational power of the Cray-1. Our first step is to develop a general-purpose uniprocessor with a performance level comparable to the Cray-1; the multiprocessor will then be made up of 16 of these uniprocessors, sharing a main memory. The uniprocessors can be used together for large problems or separately for several smaller problems. To reduce average memory-access time, each uniprocessor has a private cache memory. We have also developed a powerful design system (SCALD) that supports extremely efficient structured design of digital logic. Using advanced compiler and verification techniques, SCALD can complete the details of a computer design starting from a high-level specification.

Introduction

Our S-1 Project has as its general goal the development of advanced digital processing technology for potential application throughout the U.S. Navy. This work involves the design and implementation of extremely high-performance general-purpose computers.

The basic goals of the S-1 Project may be divided into development-oriented and research-oriented sets.

The primary development-oriented goal is to establish methods for faster design and implementation of advanced digital processors. Our approach to this goal includes the development of a design system that supports structured computer-aided logic design and the development of automated implementation and debugging techniques.

A second development-oriented goal is to provide prototype implementations of highly cost-effective digital processors against which the Navy may measure commercial offerings. We approach this goal in three ways: by developing a durable and extensible uniprocessor instruction-set architecture (the S-1 Native Mode) that will evolve in such a manner that the developing software base is unaffected by changes in the underlying hardware, by designing a common underlying hardware structure for a class of cost-effective, high-performance S-1 Uniprocessors, and by developing a multiprocessor architecture and implementation that allows the S-1 Uniprocessors to be used in a wide variety of applications, particularly those re-

quiring very large computing rates or high operational reliabilities.

Our primary research-oriented goal is to invent and evaluate in use the concepts and languages necessary to support practical, high-level, general-purpose digital logic design. A second goal is to provide a practical multiprocessor research environment, by implementing multiprocessor hardware with sufficient computing capability to solve real problems of interest to real users. At the same time, we intend to implement and evaluate a fundamental new multiprocessor architecture consisting of a fully-connected network of independent processors, each with a private, hardware-managed cache memory. Finally, we must invent and evaluate operating-system, language, and hardware constructs that will support the partitioning of single large problems across multiple independent processors.

The following sections divide discussion of the Project's work toward these basic goals into three categories: S-1 Multiprocessors, their constituent S-1 Uniprocessors, and the S-1 Design System that supports the design of these S-1 processors.

Multiprocessors

A multiprocessor is a network of computers that concurrently execute a number of independent instruction streams on separate data streams while closely sharing main memory. A multiprocessor design offers significant advantages over a uniprocessor design that provides an equivalent computation rate. The advantages result from the modularity inherent in a multiprocessor architecture and can be categorized as advantages of reliability, economy, and size.

The advantage of reliability has been validated by the very reliable commercial systems that handle, for example, banking transactions and computer network communications.[1] In a well-designed multiprocessor system, failure of a single module (for example, a component uniprocessor, a crossbar switch, or a memory bank) does not entail failure of the entire system. Indeed, the operating system for the S-1 Multiprocessor (called Amber) is intended to detect such module failures and automatically replace the function from the available complement of reserve modules.

Advantages of economy occur during both the design and the construction phases. The design cost per processing element is reduced asymptotically to zero as the processing element is replicated. The economy during construction is

---
*This work was performed under the auspices of the U.S. Department of Energy by Lawrence Livermore Laboratory under contract No. W-7405-ENG-48.

extremely important for semiconductors, since the unit replication cost of very large scale integrated-circuit chips varies nearly inversely with the replication factor, except for a small additive base cost.

Another economy is the potential reduction in the time between the design of the system and the delivery of the first operational unit. By replicating a relatively simple processing element many times and using a regular interconnection network, this time lag can be made very small; it is virtually independent of the processing power of the total system. As a result, the semiconductor technology used in a properly designed multiprocessor can be much more up to date than the technology used in a more complex processing structure. One additional economy results from the freedom of the multiprocessor designer to choose the most cost-effective uniprocessor element structure, regardless of the processing rate of the element.

Independent of these economic advantages is the advantage of size. Regardless of whether it is economical to build arbitrarily powerful uniprocessors, at some point it becomes physically impossible (with state-of-the-art technology). Multiprocessors, however, because of their modularity, can have larger processing rates. This advantage of multiprocessor structures is important because maximal computing rates will be necessary for certain applications (numerical weather prediction with its real-time constraints, for example) into the foreseeable future.

S-1 Multiprocessors

We are developing a multiprocessor that computes at an unprecedented aggregate rate on a wide variety of problems. Figure 1 is an artist's conception of the system. The S-1 Mark IIA Multiprocessor, to be implemented with second-generation S-1 Uniprocessors, each about as powerful as a Cray-1 computer, will have a computation rate

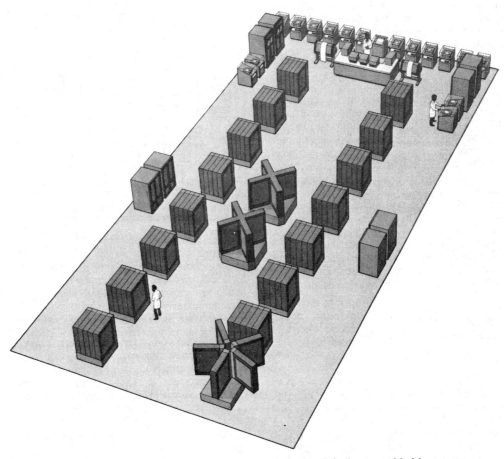

Fig. 1. The S-1 Mark IIA Multiprocessor system as it might be assembled in a computer center. The system includes 16 S-1 Mark IIA Uniprocessors (the beige and blue booklike devices arranged in two rows of 8 each along the sides of the room), 16 main memory banks (housed 4 each in the 2 blue cabinets on each side of the room near the middle of the rows of Uniprocessors), 2 Crossbar Switches (the X-shaped devices in the middle of the room) for transferring data between the Uniprocessors and the main memory, and peripheral equipment at the far end of the room, including disk drives, tape drives, printers, and a control console. The main memory shown consists of 128 million bytes but is expandable up to 16 billion bytes. The compact arrangement shown is not essential; the Uniprocessors and the memory banks may be hundreds of feet apart.

137

roughly ten times that of the Cray-1.* The Cray-1, in turn, has a performance two to four times greater than that of the CDC 7600 and outperforms all other existing computers in general numerical computation work.

Logical Structure

A typical S-1 Multiprocessor consists of 16 independent, identical S-1 Uniprocessors. Figure 2 shows the logical structure of the Mark IIA Multiprocessor. All 16 uniprocessors are connected to main memory through the S-1 Crossbar Switch. Each of the 16 memory banks can contain up to 1 billion bytes of semiconductor memory. Input and output are handled by peripheral processors (for example, LSI-11s); as many as eight can be attached to each S-1 Mark IIA Uniprocessor. The Synchronization Box is a shared bus connected to each member uniprocessor; one of its major functions is to transmit interrupts and small data packets from one uniprocessor to any subset of other uniprocessors in order to coordinate processing streams. Each module in an S-1 Multiprocessor is connected to a diagnostics-and-maintenance processor (an LSI-11) that allows convenient remote display-oriented maintenance and control of the multiprocessor.

All 16 S-1 Uniprocessors can execute independent instruction streams on independent data streams. Thus, all 16 uniprocessors can cooperate in the solution of a single large problem (for example, by means of a Monte Carlo-based algorithm, an increasingly popular and easily partitioned approach to physical simulation). The high-bandwidth, low-latency interprocessor communications provided by the Crossbar Switch facilitate the partitioning of physical simulation problems with little efficiency loss, but the 16 uniprocessors can also process completely independent tasks, so that each S-1 Uniprocessor might service a different set of users. Memory requests from the member uniprocessors are serviced by 16 memory banks with a aggregate maximum capacity of 16 billion nine-bit bytes. Any processor can uniformly access all of main memory through the S-1 Crossbar Switch. The programmer thus sees a huge, uniform address space, because each memory request from each uniprocessor is decoded by hardware in the Crossbar Switch and sent to the appropriate memory bank. The Crossbar Switch has a maximum peak bandwidth of more than 10 billion bits per second when all its 16 channels are transferring data simultaneously.

Cache Memory

The design of the S-1 Multiprocessor allows component uniprocessors and memory banks to be physically distributed over distances that are limited only by average bandwidth requirements (which degrade linearly with increasing cable length). To reduce the delays in accessing main memory that result from long cables, Crossbar-Switch transaction time, and relatively slow (but highly cost-effective) memory chips, each member uniprocessor contains private cache memories. These caches automatically

*Reference to a company or product name does not imply approval or recommendation of the product by the University of California or the U.S. Department of Energy to the exclusion of others that may be suitable.

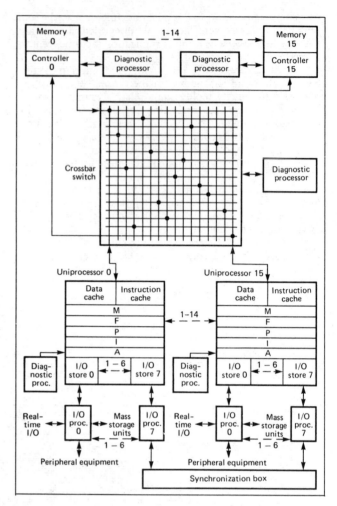

Fig. 2. The logical structure of the S-1 Mark IIA Multiprocessor, greatly simplified. Only the first and last of the 16 Uniprocessors, one of the two high-bandwidth Crossbar Switches, and the first and last of the 16 main memory banks are shown. As indicated, each of the Uniprocessors communicates with any part of the main memory through the Crossbar Switch. In the access pattern shown (dots at intersections of the Crossbar-Switch grid), each of the Uniprocessors is connected to a different memory bank. When two or more Uniprocessors request the same memory bank, the Crossbar Switch enforces queuing rules that guarantee each contender one turn in the contested memory bank before any other Uniprocessor has two. Private caches with very fast but expensive memory components within the member Uniprocessors effectively hide the combined latency of the switch and memory system.

(that is, without guidance from the programmer) retain recently referenced data and instructions in a relatively small amount of ultrahigh-performance memory, in the expectation that those data will be referenced again soon. Whenever a reference to such a retained datum or instruction is made, the information is immediately delivered directly from the cache, thus eliminating the need for a main-memory transaction. Although a similar efficiency can be realized if main memory contains a special high-speed area, such a design places on every programmer the burden of managing a variety of memory systems in order to maximize the efficiency of program execution.

The presence of caches in a multiprocessor necessarily introduces problems of cache coherence; that is, each uniprocessor must be able to read or write data in the other caches without any observable inconsistencies.[2] Without a guarantee of cache coherence, programming of certain problems in a cache-based multiprocessor would be inconceivably difficult.

The caches of the member uniprocessors of S-1 Multiprocessors are private in the sense that there are no special communication paths connecting the caches of one uniprocessor with the caches of any other uniprocessor; the cache coherence problem is therefore especially challenging. To solve it, the S-1 Multiprocessor includes a design closely related to one independently proposed in Ref. 2. A small tag is associated with each 16-word line in physical memory. This tag identifies the only member uniprocessor (if any) that has been granted permission to retain (that is, owns) the line with write access and all the processors that own the line with read access. The memory controller allows multiple processors to own a line with read access but responds with a special error flag when a request is received to grant read or write access for any line that is already owned with write access or to grant write access for any line that is already owned with read access. Any uniprocessor receiving such an access-denial response is responsible for requesting (through a simple interrupt mechanism) that other uniprocessors flush the contested line from their private caches. This procedure maintains cache coherence dynamically, and hence extremely efficiently, without requiring any effort by the programmer.

Error Detection and Correction

For reliability, all single-bit errors that occur in memory transactions are automatically corrected, and all double-bit errors are detected, regardless of whether the errors occur in the switch or in the memory system. For protection against single-point failures, the S-1 Multiprocessor allows permanent connection of multiple Crossbar Switches that can be selected electronically; the S-1 Multiprocessor can thus continue operating in the event of a single-switch failure. Furthermore, the Crossbar Switch can be configured electronically to keep a backup copy of every datum in memory, so that failure of any memory bank will not entail loss of crucial data. Each input–output peripheral processor may be connected to input–output ports on at least two uniprocessors, so failure of a single uniprocessor does not isolate any input–output device from the multiprocessor system. To make maintenance easier, each member uniprocessor, each crossbar switch, and each memory bank is connected to a diagnostic computer that can probe, report, and change the internal state of all modules that it monitors, with very high time and logic resolution.

S-1 Uniprocessors

We are developing a line of S-1 Uniprocessors to serve as the computational nodes in the S-1 Multiprocessor. The first-generation S-1 Uniprocessor (Mark I) has been implemented and evaluated in use,[3] the second-generation (Mark IIA) machine is under way, and future generations (Mark III, Mark IV, and Mark V) have been planned in varying amounts of detail. These generations of S-1 Uniprocessors vary greatly in performance because of generation-to-generation advances in microcode, hardware structure, and implementation technology. However, all of them can conform to an identical instruction-set architecture, thereby making software transportable from uniprocessors of any earlier generation to those of any later one.

Instruction-set Architecture

The instruction-set architecture of a computer consists of those principles of its operation that a programmer without a stopwatch is capable of observing; that is, it includes no timing information. The complete hardware and microcode structure that executes an instruction-set architecture is called the implementation. The implementation of the S-1 Mark IIA Uniprocessor has been designed to allow high-speed emulation of several existing instruction-set architectures, including the DEC-10 and Univac AN/UYK-7, in addition to the S-1 instruction-set architecture (S-1 Native Mode).

It was apparent early in the S-1 Multiprocessor design that no existing instruction-set architecture was suitable to serve as the S-1 Native Mode. Because then-existing instruction-set architectures had been designed under very different technology constraints than those expected to apply to S-1 systems, they variously suffered from address-space inadequacy, insufficient operations-code space, insufficient multiprocessing-oriented features, or adverse implications for high-performance implementations.

In response to this situation, we developed the S-1 Native Mode, which is probably the most widely reviewed high-performance computer architecture ever developed. Unlike the instruction-set architectures of previous high-performance computers (for example, the CDC STAR-100 or the Cray-1), which were developed by a few designers working behind corporate proprietary screens and were then frozen, the S-1 Native Mode has been analyzed, criticized, and revised by scores of computer scientists, engineers, and application specialists in industry, academia, and Government throughout the country. It has evolved over a period of three years, during design, implementation, and operational evaluation of the S-1 Mark I Uniprocessor prototype and during design of the S-1 Mark IIA Uniprocessor.

As a consequence of this unprecedentedly extensive peer review, the S-1 Native Mode is well developed—it contains a large, consistent set of features; it is highly extensible—it can easily include new features; it is general purpose—it contains features for compiler and operating system efficiency as well as for arithmetic-intensive and real-time applications; and it is carefully tuned—it facilitates high-performance implementations of S-1 Uniprocessors and S-1 Multiprocessors.

The S-1 Native Mode allows the programmer to address uniformly, without using base registers, 2 billion nine-bit bytes of main memory, 288 times more memory than the Cray-1 (although relatively low-performance machines with large address spaces have recently appeared on the market). Indeed, it was primarily to provide for adequate address space that a 36-bit word length was adopted for the S-1 Native Mode.

Huge memories are crucial for efficient solution of large problems, such as three-dimensional physical simulations and Monte Carlo-intensive studies, which are of great current interest in a wide variety of applications that range from imcompressible fluid flow studies to acoustic ray tracing in highly stratified media. The large memory addressability of the S-1 Native Mode essentially eliminates the programming costs associated with managing multiple types of computer system storage (for example, the SCM, LCM, drum, and disk memory hierarchy of the CDC 7600, to whose efficient management major portions of the careers of some programmers have been addressed). Memory technology has advanced so far since the development of small-address-space architectures such as the CDC 7600, the DEC PDP-10, and the IBM/360 that the current production cost to the S-1 Project of a 2-billion-byte main memory using 16K-bit memory chips is less than $10 million; its long-term rate of advance is so rapid that this cost can confidently be expected to decline by almost a factor of 2 each year for the next several years.

Most software produced for S-1 systems will be written in high-level compiled languages such as the developing DOD standard language, Ada. For ease of compiler writing and for rapid, efficient execution of the compiled code, these languages require certain features in the underlying instruction-set architecture. S-1 Native Mode is compiler-oriented: it is designed to support high-level languages in general, not one high-level language in particular, and it includes the full set of operators and addressing modes necessary for a simple compiler to produce efficient code. For example, S-1 Native Mode supports expression evaluation with a unique type of 2.5-operand instruction that allows the compilation of almost all forms of arithmetic expressions without using any move instructions (instructions which simply move data from one location to another without performing logical or arithmetic operations on them).

The extent of the compiler-orientation of an instruction-set architecture can be roughly measured by counting the number of instructions necessary to represent typical high-level language programs. We have observed that the CDC 7600 requires between two and three times as many instructions to represent FORTRAN programs as does the S-1 Native Mode; the bulk of additional CDC 7600 instructions are used in addressing computations. An experiment involving seven graduate-student programmers in the Computer Science Department at the University of California, Berkeley, showed that careful hand-coding of the PDP-11 requires an average of 1.5 times as many instructions to represent a variety of high-level language programs as does the S-1 Native Mode. These and related considerations lead us to assert that no high-performance machine available today has a more compiler-oriented instruction-set architecture than the S-1 Native Mode.

The S-1 Native Mode contains unprecedentedly comprehensive floating-point semantics. Floating-point numbers can be 18, 36, or 72 bits long, using 5, 9, and 15 bits, respectively, to represent the exponent of 2, and 13, 27, and 57 bits, respectively, to represent the signed fraction. The largest format is upwards compatible with the floating-point format of the Cray-1. The 36-bit format was designed to be the workhorse for virtually all numerical applications. The 18-bit floating-point format was specially designed to support real-time signal processing at many hundred

million floating-point operations per second, but it can be highly useful in any relatively low-precision application where processing speed is at a premium (as, for example, in Monte Carlo procedures).

Compared to conventional floating-point representations, S-1 floating-point formats offer one extra bit of precision because the high-order bit of the fraction is determined from the sign and is not explicitly represented. The S-1 Native Mode also allows floating-point operations to be correctly rounded in any of several different rounding modes. For example, stable rounding minimizes expected error, and diminished-magnitude, augmented-magnitude, floor, and ceiling roundings can be used to measure the actual error developed. The S-1 Native Mode includes special floating-point symbols (not-a-number, infinities, and epsilons) which allow programs to be created and exercised that will not malfunction because of transient generation of quantities so large or small that they cannot be represented as ordinary numbers in the computer. A computer arithmetic system containing such symbols is essential for efficient use of human resources in developing and using robust computer programs. [4]

Pipelining of Instructions

Pipelining is exemplified by an automobile production line, in which a number of automobiles are in production simultaneously, each in a different stage of completion; the time between completion of construction of one automobile and the next is roughly the delay of a stage in the assembly line, rather than the time required for a single car to pass through the entire line. A stream of instructions in a pipelined computer implementation is processed in a very similar fashion.

The S-1 Native Mode was designed especially to facilitate pipelined parallelism in the fetching and decoding of instructions, the associated fetching of instruction operands, and the eventual execution of instructions. Pipelined parallelism is a conceptually simple type of parallelism that can result in extremely high computer performance levels. In general, designers of advanced instruction-set architectures for commercial computers have given little consideration to the implications of extensive pipelining, because they have developed those architectures with medium- or low-performance implementations in mind. Furthermore, pipelining has thus far been used in modern computers primarily in the execution of instructions, where it appears in the streaming of vectors of operands through pipelined arithmetic or logical operation functional units.

S-1 Uniprocessors pipeline *the preparation* and execution of instructions that specify both scalar and vector operations. Every instruction proceeds through multiple pipeline stages, including instruction preparation, operand preparation, and execution. Some stages of the pipeline, particularly those dealing with operand address arithmetic and instruction execution, necessarily have a wide variety of functions, since the pipeline must process a wide range of instructions. This variability in operation is effected through the extensive use of microcode, an architecture-defining, very low-level program that precisely specifies the operation of every pipeline stage. The variability built into the microcode-controlled pipeline facilitates high-performance emulation of other computers (for example, the Navy's Univac AN/UYK-7). The S-1 Mark I and Mark IIA Uniprocessors are the first high-performance machines to incorporate instruction-preparation pipelines fully controlled by writable microcode.

Structure and Performance

Figure 3 shows the internal logical structure of the S-1 Mark IIA Uniprocessor. The machine consists of five microengines (extremely fast, relatively special-purpose programmable controllers) operating in parallel to provide high performance. Four of the microengines form the instruction pipeline, consisting of the instruction-fetch, instruction-decode, operand-preparation, and arithmetic segments. Some segments are internally pipelined (a level of detail not shown in Fig. 3). A single microengine handles memory traffic in parallel with the operation of the instruction pipeline. A one-processor system can be configured by connecting an S-1 Mark IIA Uniprocessor directly to a memory controller; this requires neither hardware nor microcode changes.

During the design of the S-1 Mark I and Mark IIA pipelines, we made significant advances in computer technology. The Mark I introduced a new, simple branch-prediction strategy to predict the outcome of each test-and-branch operation in an instruction stream before its execution, thereby allowing subsequent instructions to be prepared without disruption. The Mark I also refined the use of dual cache memories (one for instructions, one for data) to increase total cache bandwidth. The Mark IIA allows advance computation of simple operations in early pipeline stages; this technique minimizes idling of pipeline

stages because a computation (particularly, an operand-address computation) depends on some previous result. The Mark IIA includes refined control mechanisms to coordinate the operation of multiple pipeline stages controlled by the independent programmable microengines.

The S-1 Mark IIA also employs vector operations to achieve high performance. Vector operations use multiple functional units in the pipelined arithmetic module, to achieve a peak computation rate on the S-1 Mark IIA Uniprocessor of 400 million floating-point operations per second. Any fatal error encountered during a vector operation results in a precise interrupt, so the exact location of the error can be determined by the error-handling routine; this feature is regrettably rare on existing high-performance vector processors.

Status and Plans

The S-1 Mark I was developed to be a prototype for evaluating the S-1 Native Mode and its advanced hardware and to provide the necessary computational resources for the development of the S-1 Mark IIA hardware and software. Only one S-1 Mark I has been produced; it began operating late in 1977. Constituted of 5350 ECL-10K integrated circuits, it was designed to execute floating-point arithmetic only in microcode emulation and also contained a severely reduced instruction-preparation pipeline. On a small set of floating-point-intensive scientific benchmark codes written in Pascal, the S-1 Mark I has been observed to compute between 0.3 and 0.5 times as fast as the CDC 7600, although the judicious use of hand-coded routines in crucial

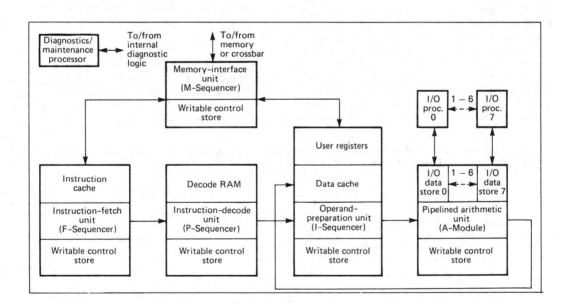

Fig. 3. The internal logical structure of the S-1 Mark IIA Uniprocessor. It consists of five distinct microengines that operate in parallel. Four of the microengines control the instruction pipeline, consisting of instruction-fetch, instruction-decode, operand-preparation, and arithmetic segments, each of which in turn is pipelined. One microengine controls memory transactions. All five microengines are controlled with writable microcode. The Uniprocessor also contains private cache memory.

inner loops on the CDC 7600 was found to increase that machine's overall performance relative to the Pascal-programmed Mark I to a speed advantage of fivefold, for our 16 000-line physical simulation code. Conversely, the maximum execution rate of the Mark I (10 million instructions per second), when combined with the powerful addressing modes and field-manipulating features of the S-1 Native Mode instruction-set architecture, permits it to execute a variety of non-floating-point-intensive codes significantly more rapidly than does the CDC 7600.

The second generation S-1 Uniprocessor, the Mark IIA, executes the same instruction set (the S-1 Native Mode) as the Mark I, but it has extensive hardware floating-point and vector operation capabilities. Its performance is expected to be comparable to that of the Cray-1 on scientific problems expressed in high-level languages such as Ada, Pascal, and FORTRAN, for just those applications in which the single-word floating-point format of the S-1 architecture is as useful as the substantially higher precision floating-point format of the Cray-1. The Cray-1 will assuredly retain primacy in high-precision, vector-intensive data processing relative to near-term S-1 Uniprocessors, since this type of computing capability cannot be justified for present or readily foreseen Navy applications, most of which stress relatively low precision, very high throughput data processing.

Table 1 shows the performance of the S-1 Mark IIA Uniprocessor compared to the CDC 7600 and the Cray-1 on several important DOE benchmark miniprograms. These miniprograms are representative of the full set used at LLL to compare the performance of advanced scientific computers; they accurately and concisely characterize the computation-intensive portions of extensive scientific code at LLL. The S-1 Mark IIA Uniprocessor computes these benchmarks at roughly the same speed as the Cray-1 and almost twice as fast as the CDC 7600. The CDC 7600 rate was measured using an optimizing compiler first available in 1974. The Cray-1 rates are based on actual performance measurements made in February, 1979, with a moderately mature optimizing and vectorizing compiler supplied by Cray Research, Inc. Although the Cray-1 executes more instructions per second than the Mark IIA, many Cray-1 instructions are expended in overhead computations. The S-1 results assume the use of 36-bit floating-point numbers, since high-precision arithmetic is often not necessary in LLL applications; however, neither the CDC 7600 nor the Cray-1 provides a low-precision floating-point format. For applications requiring high precision, the Mark IIA supports operations on the 72-bit floating-point format at roughly half the speed of operations on the 36-bit floating-point format. For low-precision applications, the Mark IIA supports operations on the 18-bit floating-point format at approximately twice the speed of operations on the 36-bit floating-point format.

The S-1 Mark IIA Uniprocessor is constituted of ECL-100K MSI circuits in performance-critical areas and ECL-10K circuits elsewhere. All Mark IIA circuits are standard, commercially available products. The transistor population of the Mark IIA's arithmetic unit alone is greater than that of the entire central processing unit of the Cray-1; gate circuit densities within this arithmetic unit are about 20 times greater than those in the Cray-1 central processing unit. The Mark IIA is in development at the present time; it is being packaged in the folded form shown in Fig. 4.

The S-1 Mark III is in an early design phase. Like the Mark I and Mark IIA Uniprocessors, the Mark III executes the S-1 Native Mode, but it is to be implemented completely in commercially available ECL-100K LSI circuits. While it will not achieve a large performance gain over the Mark IIA, it will be physically more compact because of its order-of-magnitude greater logic gate density.

We are moving as rapidly as possible toward using the technology of very large scale integrated circuits. The first generation presently planned to follow the Mark III will express the entire Mark III architecture on several VLSI chips, at a performance level at least as great as that of the Mark III.

S-1 Design System

The capabilities offered by semiconductor technology for the implementation of advanced computer designs are rapidly outpacing the capabilities developed for articulating the conception of those designs. To make best use of rapidly

Table 1. Comparison of the performances of the S-1 Mark IIA Uniprocessor, the Cray-1, and the CDC 7600. Data on Cray-1 and CDC 7600 taken from Ref. 5.

Mini-program	Miniprogram function	Computation rate, MFLOPS[a]				
		S-1 Mark IIA		Cray-1		
		Scalar[b]	Vector[c]	Scalar[d]	Vector[e]	CDC 7600
1	Hydro excerpt	9.1	59	9.3	71	5.3
2	Unrolled inner product	11	74	8.8	47	6.6
3	Inner product	8.0	65	4.4	62	4.6
5	Tridiagonal elimination	7.5	7.5	7.6	7.6	4.0
7	Equation-of-state excerpt	13	46	12.6	80	7.3

[a]MFLOPS stands for millions of floating-point operations per second.
[b]Assumes no use of vector capability.
[c]Assumes full vectorization.
[d]Obtained by turning off compiler vectorization.
[e]Obtained by turning on full compiler vectorization.

Fig. 4. The S-1 Mark IIA Uniprocessor. The package consists of identical pages. The pages unfold to expose all wire-wrap pins for maintenance. Ambient air blows up through the centers of the pages to cool the integrated circuits, which are mounted on the inside. Commercially available power supplies are mounted in the cabinet base.

improving semiconductor technology, we have developed the SCALD (Structural Computer-Aided Logic Design) System.[6]

SCALD is a graphics-based system for designing digital logic. It inputs a high-level description of a digital system and outputs magnetic tapes that are used by commercial automatic wire-wrap machines to build the hardware.

The main advantage of using SCALD is a drastic reduction in the amount of time required to design a large digital system. This reduction occurs because the designer can express his design in the same general level in which he thinks about it, freeing him from the task of actually drawing out all of the details of the logic and creating a wire list specifying its interconnection. Designs expressed in this high-level notation become much more comprehensible for all those who have to work with them—for computers, for computer designers, and for maintenance engineers. By reducing the amount of clerical work required of digital logic designers, SCALD reduces the number of designers required to execute a design project and the communication overhead per designer, thus increasing each designer's productivity and further reducing the total designer requirements of the project. Manpower savings well in excess of an order of magnitude may be realized; such savings have actually been demonstrated in practice during both the S-1 Mark I and Mark IIA design efforts.

SCALD allows designs to be recompiled rapidly when new integrated circuits become available; such circuits may simply take the place of low-level modules. Thus, a designer can quite effectively use a previous design to reduce his design time on a new project, thereby taking maximum advantage of the exponential rates of advance in component density and cost-effectiveness currently characterizing the semiconductor industry. In practice, considerable work may still be required to update a design to incorporate recent technology advances, but the required effort is likely to be much less than if the design were not expressed hierarchically.

SCALD also facilitates designing with very high accuracy, because SCALD performs design verification procedures that cannot be done by a human. Not only can SCALD verify syntactic details of the design (for example, that every gate input is connected to some output), but it can also verify that transmission lines are effectively free from signal reflections; it can certify that the logic networks defined by the designer do not contain timing errors, and it can demonstrate by simulation that the logical operation of the design is correct.

Historically, logic design has lagged far behind program design in terms of the ideals of structured design: that arbitrary modules be specified, each in terms of a few other modules, relatively independently, and that they communicate through well-defined interfaces. Logic is still typically hand-drawn by draftsmen; the specification language consists of drawings of the primitive logical elements available from integrated-circuit manufacturers and the physical connections between those logical elements. On the other hand, typical modern programming systems readily support the design of arbitrary modules (that is, routines), each in terms of a few other routines, and allow the specification of tightly structured interfaces between those routines. SCALD simply expresses these performance-proven software-engineering concepts in the world of hardware design.

SCALD consists of a set of computer programs. The Graphics Editor[7] enters drawings directly into a suitable computer, the Macro Expander compiles them, and the Router embeds them in a physical packaging system.

The Graphics Editor allows the designer to edit drawings at a graphics terminal and to print them out. The designer may create a library of shapes (macro bodies) that are generally abstractions of digital logic functions, though some may represent physical parts available from manufacturers. Each macro body is linked by name to a set of drawings, its macro definition. A macro is defined only once but may be used in the drawings any number of times. The designed system is then made up by connecting these macro bodies by lines indicating information flow. A single line in a drawing represents one or more signals (a signal vector) and may be named. Macro bodies have parameters, including parameter signal vectors. Names on signal vectors include a timing notation that allows SCALD to verify automatically (using real or estimated delays of wires and integrated circuits) that stated timing constraints will actually be satisfied by the digital logic when implemented in the specified physical package.

Figure 5 shows a sample midlevel drawing from the Mark IIA design; it represents several thousands of integrated circuits. The drawing shows the Mark IIA data cache and register file, operand queues, alignment network,

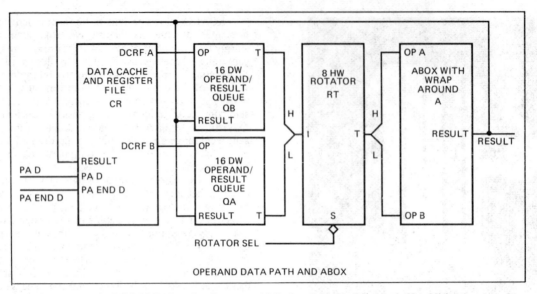

Fig. 5. A typical SCALD drawing from a middle level of the S-1 Mark IIA Uniprocessor design. This whole drawing defines a single block in a more general diagram at the next higher level. Each of the blocks in the drawing shown here is defined by a more detailed drawing at the next lower level. Thus a hierarchy is established that stretches from the most general abstraction down to the individual components of the computer. Many of these drawings can be used over and over again in the design; they are drawn once and then simply recalled by SCALD as needed. SCALD also generates a writing list, checks the design for mistakes and timing errors, and produces taped instructions for automatic wiring machines.

arithmetic module, and connections between those elements. This drawing represents the described portion of the machine accurately, in that hardware is automatically built using the drawings as a specification, but it is lacking in detail and requires definitions of its submodules for completeness.

The Macro Expander expands the design to individual integrated circuits by iteratively substituting the appropriate macro definition for each macro body in the drawings. The Macro Expander also verifies that designer-specified timing constraints are satisfied. The Macro Expander is largely technology-independent and is coded in transportable Pascal.

The Router reads an interconnection list produced by the Macro Expander and produces magnetic tapes that permit the design to be implemented by automatic and semiautomatic commercial machines. Extensive maintenance and debugging documentation is produced by the Router, which is also coded in transportable Pascal.

SCALD was used to design the S-1 Mark I and the S-1 Mark IIA. The Mark I design consisted of 211 high-level drawings (drawings used only once in the design) and 144 low-level drawings (drawings used several times). Low-level drawings form an investment in the particular technology chosen for implementation, since they have a high probability of being used again in subsequent designs. In contrast, high-level drawings represent an investment in the particular architecture being implemented and may be reused to recompile that architecture periodically into current, more cost-effective implementations. A total of two man-years was expended in the Mark I design work during an elapsed period of one calendar year.

Structured logic design consists of extending to logic design the essential power of the concepts and tools developed for simplifying the programming task; the savings in human labor expended in designing digital systems are potentially as great as those resulting from the use of compilers. Our experience has shown that SCALD has made the S-1 Mark I and Mark IIA designs more understandable, thus reducing the design efforts, enhancing design correctness, and facilitating generation of final documentation. The designs themselves serve as major portions of the final documentation because they are so readily understood; thus, the need for expensive and usually inaccurate post facto documentation has been greatly reduced. Furthermore, SCALD has increased the mutability of these designs; since macros are inherently isolated, changes in one macro definition usually require minimal changes in other parts of the design. Finally, the imposition of structure on the design and the use of computational resources in the verification task has resulted in designs of an unprecedented level of accuracy.

Summary

S-1 Project effort related to the development of high-performance computing machines is directed toward three major areas: the S-1 Multiprocessor, the S-1 Uniprocessor, and the S-1 Design System. S-1 Multiprocessors are rapidly extensible to very high powers and large memory capacities at uniprocessor cost-effectiveness levels and feature ultrareliable system performance. The S-1 Uniprocessors are general-purpose, emulation-oriented machines that are powerful and highly cost-effective and have advanced maintainability features. The S-1 Design System supports highly automated, general-purpose digital systems design and provides extensive construction and debug support of advanced computer systems.

Acknowledgments

This paper reports on work performed by the staff of the S-1 Project of the Lawrence Livermore Laboratory and the members of the software R&D teams of the Computer Science Department of Stanford University, which have operated under sub-contract to the Laboratory.

The S-1 Project has benefitted in fundamental fashions from the contributions of many people in academia, industry, and Government, and it is impossible to acknowledge our debt to even any significant fraction of them. However, it must be noted that the S-1 Multiprocessor concept is directly descended from the C.mmp Project of Carnegie-Mellon University's Computer Science Department, and we are indebted to Gordon Bell in this and many other respects. The hospitality and technical advice of Forest Baskett, Jerry Friedman, and John McCarthy of Stanford University during the Project's precarious early days was extremely valuable.

The U.S. Navy, the Project's sole sponsor, has provided enlightened and highly effective supervision in the persons of Norris Keeler, Tibor Horwath, and Joel Trimble. Edward Teller's research requirements midwifed modern scientific digital computing, and his continued keen interest in the application of computers to physical problems has profoundly impacted many related developments during the subsequent third of a century, at our Laboratory and elsewhere. His support and encouragement and that of his like-minded colleagues in our Laboratory, in the Department of Energy and Defense, and in the Congress have been crucial during the Project's inception and vital to its progress.

Notes and References

1. Such multiprocessors are described in "Tandem Non-Stop Systems," *Datapro Reports on Minicomputers*, Datapro Research Corporation, Delran, N.J. (1979), and in S. M. Ornstein *et al.*, "Pluribus—A Reliable Multiprocessor," *Proc. AFIPS 1975 Nat. Comp. Conf., Anaheim, 1975* (AFIPS Press, Montvale, N.J., 1975), vol. 44, p. 551.

2. L. M. Censier and P. A. Feautrier, "A New Solution to Coherence Problems in Multicache Systems," *IEEE Trans. Computers* C-27 (12), 1112 (1978).

3. S-1 Project Staff, *Advanced Digital Processor Technology Base Development for Navy Applications: The S-1 Project*, Lawrence Livermore Laboratory, Rept. UCID-18038 (1978).

4. J. T. Coonen, *Specifications for a Proposed Standard for Floating Point Arithmetic*, University of California, Berkeley, Electronics Research Laboratory Memorandum UCB/ERL M78/72 (1978).

5. F. McMahon, Lawrence Livermore Laboratory, private communication, October 1976.

6. SCALD is described in detail in "SCALD: Structured Computer-Aided Logic Design" and "The SCALD Physical Design Subsystem," written by T. M. McWilliams and L. C. Widdoes and published in *Proc. Ann. Design Automation Conf., 15th, Las Vegas, 1978* (IEEE, ACM, New York, 1978), p. 271.

7. D. Helliwell, *The Stanford University Drawing System*, Stanford Artificial Intelligence Laboratory, Palo Alto, California (1972).

Cm*—A modular, multi-microprocessor†

by R. J. SWAN, S. H. FULLER and D. P. SIEWIOREK

Carnegie-Mellon University
Pittsburgh, Pennsylvania

ABSTRACT

This paper describes the architecture of a new large multi-processor computer system being built at Carnegie-Mellon University. The system allows close cooperation between large numbers of inexpensive processors. All processors share access to a single virtual memory address space. There are no arbitrary limits on the number of processors, amount of memory or communication bandwidth in the system. Considerable support is provided for low level operating system primitives and inter-process communication.

INTRODUCTION

Cm* is an experimental computer system designed to investigate the problems and potentials of modular, multi-microprocessors. The initial impetus for the Cm* project was provided by the continuing advances in semiconductor technology as exemplified by processors-on-a-chip and large memory arrays. In the near future processors of moderate capability, such as a PDP-11, and several thousand words of memory will be placed on a single integrated circuit chip. If large computer systems are to be built from such chips, what should be the structure of such a "computer module?"

Initial versions of the Cm* architecture[1] grew in part as an extension to the modular design of systems from register transfer modules, or RTMs.[2] In addition there was substantial interest in the development of large multiprocessor systems such as Pluribus[3] and C.mmp.[4] Cm* is intended to be a testbed for exploring a number of research questions concerning multiprocessor systems, for example: potential for deadlocks, structure of inter-processor control mechanisms, modularity, reliability, and techniques for decomposing algorithms into parallel cooperating processes.

The structure of Cm* is very briefly described. There is a description of the address structure and discussion of the support given for the operating system. The use of the

addressing structure for inter-process communication and control operations is discussed. A companion paper[5] discusses the various mechanisms used to implement the complex address mapping and routing structure of Cm*. Some results from the performance modelling of Cm* are also presented. A second companion paper[6] describes the structure of the basic operating system and support software.

THE STRUCTURE OF Cm*

There is a surprising diversity of ways to approach the interconnection of processors into a computing system.[7] The processors could be interconnected with several serial I/O links to form a computer network; they could be interconnected in a tight synchronous fashion to build an array processor; or the processors could be organized to share primary memory. This last approach, a multiprocessor organization, was chosen for Cm* because it offers a closer degree of coupling, or communication, between the processors than would a multicomputer or network configuration. Multiprocessors also have a more general range of applicability than other multiple processor systems.

During the development of the Cm* structure a wide variety of multiprocessor switch structures were considered.[8] The basic structure selected is represented in Figure 1. The essential feature which distinguishes it from other multiprocessor structures is that shared memory is not separated from the processing elements, but rather a unit of memory and a processor are closely coupled in each module and a network of buses gives a processor access to nonlocal memory. This structure allows modular expansion of the number of processors and memory modules without a rapid increase in the interconnection costs. Memory can be shared even though there is no direct physical connection between the requesting processor and the required memory. For example, consider a request by processor, P1, to the memory, M4, in Figure 1. The address mapping element, K1, directs the reference from P1 onto the inter-module bus. The address is recognized by K2, which directs it onto a second inter-module bus. The reference is finally accepted by K4, which accesses the request memory location and passes back an acknowledgment or data to the requesting processor. The need for high inter-module

† This work was supported in part by the Advanced Research Projects Agency under contract F44620-73-C-0074, which is monitored by the Air Force Office of Scientific Research, and in part by the National Science Foundation Grant GJ 32758X. The LSI-11's and related equipment were supplied by Digital Equipment Corporation.

Reprinted with permission from the *Proceedings of the National Computer Conference*, Volume 46, 1977, pages 637-644. Copyright © 1977 by AFIPS Press.

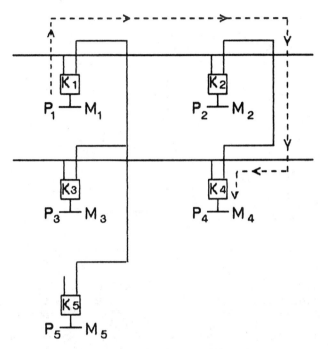

Figure 1—Canonical computer module structure

communication rates will be minimized if a large fraction of each processor's references to primary memory 'hit' the section of memory local to the processor. (Preliminary experiments in the fall of 1976 indicate that hit ratios of better than 90 percent can be expected provided that the code executed is normally held local to the processor.)

Deadlock with references to nonlocal memory

Almost all computer systems implement accesses from processor to primary memory with *Circuit Switching,* that is, a complete path is established from a processor to the memory being referenced. Circuit switching is not feasible for a structure like Cm* where local memory is also accessible as shared memory. Figure 1 shows the path used for P1 to access M4 via K2. Consider a concurrent attempt by P4 to access M1 via K2. With a circuit switch implementation, a situation could arise where P1 held its local memory bus and the bus connecting K2, while P4 also holds its own memory bus plus the bus connecting K4 to K2. Neither memory reference could complete without one processor first releasing the buses it holds. There are numerous situations where deadlock over bus allocation can occur. Resolving this deadlock requires, at the very least, a timeout and retry mechanism.

The alternative to circuit switching is *Packet Switching.* In a packet switched implementation, the address from the processor is latched at each level in the bus structure. Buses are not allocated for the full duration of a memory reference, but just for the time taken to pass a "packet," containing an address and/or data, from one node on the bus to another. Therefore packet switching allows signifi-

cantly better bus utilization and significantly reduced bus contention in Cm*-like structures. The use of packet switching eliminates the possibility of deadlock over bus allocation but introduces the possibility of deadlock over buffer allocation.[1,9] Buffers, or intermediate registers, are resources which can be provided very cheaply, relative to providing additional inter-Cm buses, with present technology.

*The actual structure of Cm**

Design studies indicated that very little performance loss would result from combining several individual Computer Modules into a cluster and providing a shared address mapping and routing processor, Kmap, which allowed communication with other clusters. Because the cost of the Kmap is distributed across many processors it can be endowed with considerable flexibility and power at relatively little incremental cost. Because of its commanding position in the cluster, the Kmap can ensure mutual exclusion on access to shared data structures with very little overhead.

The full structure of Cm* is shown in Figure 2. Individual Computer Modules, or Cm's, consist of a DEC LSI-11 processor, an Slocal and standard LSI-11 bus memory and devices. The processor is program compatible with PDP-11s; thus a large body of software is immediately available. The prime function of the Slocal, or local switch, is to direct references from the processor selectively either to local memory or to the Map Bus, and to accept references from the Map Bus to the local memory.

Up to 14 Computer Modules and one Kmap form a cluster. The Kmap, or mapping processor, consists of three major components. The Kbus arbitrates and controls the Map bus. The Pmap is a horizontally microcoded 150 ns cycle time processor. The basic configuration has 1 K × 80 bits of writable control store and 5K × 16 bits of bipolar RAM for holding mapping tables, etc. The third level of the Cm* structure is provided by the intercluster buses which allow communication between clusters. The Linc provides the interface to two intercluster buses.

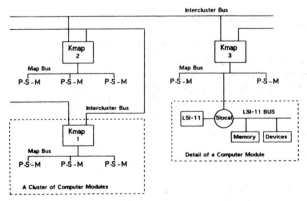

Figure 2—A simple 3 cluster Cm* system

There are no arbitrary limits to the size of a Cm* system. Memories, processors and Kmaps can be incrementally added to suit needs. Any processor can access any memory location in the system. The routing of a processor's reference to a target memory is transparent to the program, thus the system can be reconfigured dynamically in response to hardware failures.

ARCHITECTURE OF THE Cm* ADDRESS TRANSLATION MECHANISMS

Many of the more conventional aspects of the architecture of the Cm* system are consequences of using LSI-11's for the central processing elements. The organization and encoding of the instructions, interrupt and trap sequencing, and the 64K byte processor address space of a Cm* system are all a result of the PDP-11 architecture as implemented on the LSI-11. By selection of the LSI-11, however, we do not want to imply that the PDP-11 architecture is ideally suited to multiprocessor systems. The ideal solution would have been for us to have designed our own processors. However, practical considerations of time, money, and existing support software led us in early 1975 to recognize that by choosing the LSI-11 we could concentrate on those aspects of the Cm* architecture unique to multiprocessor systems. This section, and the following section on control structures, will discuss the Cm* architecture as we extended it beyond the standard PDP-11 architecture.

The addressing structure is one of the most important aspects of any computer architecture, it is even more significant when cooperation between multiple processors is to be achieved by sharing an address space. Denning[10] lists four objectives for a memory mapping scheme:

(a) Program modularity: the ability to independently change and recompile program modules.
(b) Variable size data structures.
(c) Protection
(d) Data and program sharing: allowing independent programs to access the same physical memory addresses with different program names.

For Cm*, where we are using processors with only a 64K byte address space, we must add the following requirement:

(e) Expansion of a processor's address space.

Cm* has a 2^{28} byte segmented virtual address space. Segments are of variable size up to a maximum of 4K bytes. There is a capability-based protection scheme enforced by the Kmap. The addressing structure provides considerable support for operating system primitives such as context switching and interprocess message transmission.

The path from processor to memory

The Slocal (see Figures 2 and 3) provides the first level of memory mapping. A reference to local memory is simply

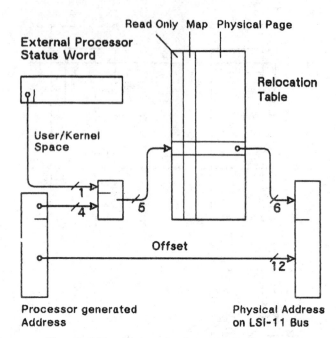

Figure 3—Addressing mechanism for local memory references

relocated, on 4K byte page boundaries, by the relocation table in the Slocal. As discussed above, it is assumed that most memory references will be made by processors to their local memory. Relocation of local memory references can be implemented with no performance overhead because the synchronous processor has sufficiently wide timing margins at the points where address relocation is performed. For segments which are not in a processor's local memory the relocation table has a status bit which causes the address to be latched, the processor forced off the LSI-11 bus, and a Service Request to be signalled to the Kmap. All transactions on the Map bus are controlled by the Map bus controller, or Kbus, which is a component of the Kmap. The address generated by the processor is transferred via the Map bus to the Pmap, the microprogrammed processor within the Kmap. If the reference is for memory within the cluster then the Pmap generates a physical address and sends it to the appropriate Slocal. If it is a write operation, data is passed directly from the source Slocal to the destination Slocal; the data does not have to be routed through the Kmap. The selected destination Slocal performs the requested memory reference and the processor in the destination Computer Module is not involved. When the reference is complete the Kbus transfers the data read from the destination Slocal directly back to the requesting processor via the Map bus and its Slocal.

If the processor references a segment in another cluster then the Pmap will transmit a request to the desired cluster via the Linc and the Intercluster buses. (See Figure 2.) If the destination cluster is not directly connected to the source cluster, that is, if it does not share a common intercluster bus, then the message will be automatically routed via intermediate clusters. When the message reaches the destination cluster, the memory reference is performed similar to a request from a processor within the cluster. An acknowledgment, or Return, message (containing data in the case of a read) is always sent back to the source cluster and subsequently to the requesting processor.

The addressing environment of a process

The virtual address space of Cm∗ is subdivided into up to 2^{16} *Segments*. Each segment is defined by a *Segment Descriptor*. The standard type of segment is similar to segments in other computer systems; it is simply a vector of memory locations. The segment descriptor specifies the physical base address of the segment and the length of the segment. Segments are variable in size from 2 bytes to 4 K bytes. However, other segment types may be more than simple linear vectors of memory; references to segments may invoke special operations. Segments may have the properties of stacks, queues or other data structures. Some segments may not have any memory associated with them, and a reference to the segment would invoke a control operation. For each segment type, up to eight distinct operations can be defined. For normal segments the operations are Read and Write. Conceptually, segments are never addressed directly; they are always referenced indirectly via a *Capability*. A capability is a two-word item containing the name of a segment and a *Rights* field. Each bit in the rights field indicates whether the corresponding operation is permitted on the segment.

To provide efficient support for context swapping, message-sending, etc., it is necessary for the Kmap microcode to understand some of the structure of an executable software module (variously called a process, activity, address space, etc.). Each executable software module is represented by an *Environment*, Figure 4. An environment is a three-level structure composed of segments. The first level in the structure is a *Primary Capability List*, CL[0]. The first entry in CL[0] is a Capability for a *State Vector*, which holds the process state while it is not executing on a processor. Entries CL[0](1) to CL[0](7) in the Primary Capability list may contain Capabilities for *Secondary Capability Lists* referred to as CL[1] through CL[7] respectively. The remaining entries in the Primary Capability List and all the entries in the Secondary Capability Lists contain Capabilities for segments which can be made directly addressable by the process when it executes. These may be code, data or any other type of segment. The provision of up to eight Capability Lists facilitates the sharing of segments and sets of segments by cooperating processes. A software module can only access those segments for which it has capabilities and perform only those operations permitted by the capabilities.

Virtual address generation

The processors in Cm∗, LSI-11s, can directly generate only a 16 bit address. This 64 K byte address space is

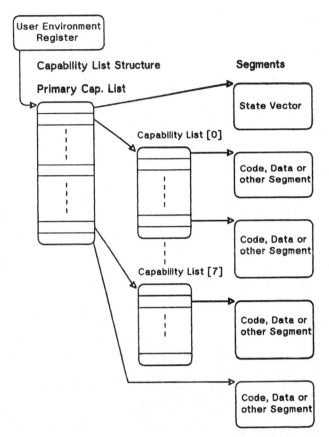

Figure 4—The environment of a user software module

divided into 16 pages of 4 K bytes each. Each page provides a window into the system-wide 2^{28} byte virtual address space, (see Figure 5) and can be independently bound to a different segment in the virtual address space. The top page in the processor's address space, page 15, is reserved for direct program interaction with the Kmap. This mechanism is analogous to the I/O page convention in standard PDP-11s. In page 15 there are 15 pseudo registers, called *Window Registers*. These define the binding between page frames in the processor's immediate address space and segments in the virtual address space. This binding is done indirectly via capabilities. Each window register holds an index for a capability in the currently executing software module's capability list structure. A Capability List index consists of a three bit field to select one of the up to eight Capability Lists, plus an offset within the C-List.

To overlay the processor's address space, i.e. to change the mapping from page frame to segment in the virtual address space, a program simply writes a new capability index into the appropriate window register. This overlay operation is completely protected; the program can only reference segments for which it has a Capability. The act of writing the Capability index into the window register activates the Kmap. The Kmap retrieves the selected Capability from main memory and places it in its "Capability cache." The Kmap adjusts its internal tables so that subse-

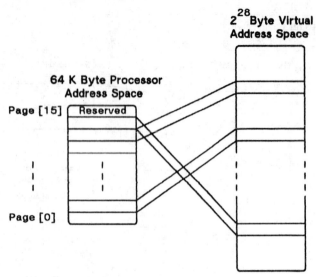

Figure 5—Windows from the processor's immediate address apce to the virtual address space

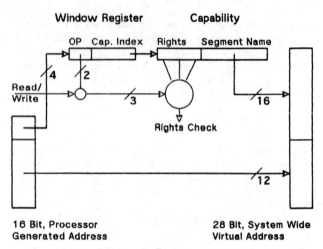

Figure 6—Conceptual virtual address generation and rights checking

quent references to the page frame will map to the segment specified by the Capability. If the segment is local to the processor then the Kmap may also change the relocation register in the Slocal so that references to the segment can be performed at full speed without the intervention of the Kmap. The Slocal, for cost and performance reasons, does not have the hardware necessary for bounds checking on variable sized segments. Thus only fixed size 4 K byte segments can be accessed without Kmap assistance.

The Cm∗ mechanism for address space overlaying should be contrasted with mechanisms in other computer systems. When executing a large program on a processor with a small immediate address space, the time taken to overlay the address space can have a crucial effect on performance. Measurements made of the execution of the operating system HYDRA on the C.mmp multiprocessor showed that relocation registers were being changed approximately every 12 instructions. (This does not, however, imply that user programs perform overlay operations this frequently.) Within the operating system this overlay operation is a single PDP-11 MOVE instruction because no protection is involved. However for user programs running under HYDRA, an overlay operation requires invocation of the operating system with several hundred instructions of software overhead. Subsequent optimization, and partial microcoding, have greatly reduced this overhead.

Figure 6 shows the conceptual translation from a 16 bit processor-generated address to a virtual address. The four high order address bits from the processor select one of 15 Window registers. The Window register holds an index for a Capability in the executing software modules Capability List structure. The 16 bit segment name from the selected Capability is concatenated with the 12 low order bits from the processor to form a 28 bit virtual address. Figure 6 also shows the read/write indicator from the processor being concatenated with two bits in the address expansion regis-

ters to form a three bit opcode. The correspondind bit in the Capability rights field is selected and tested. If the operation is not permitted then an error trap is forced.

Virtual to physical address mapping

The mapping from virtual to physical address depends on the location of the segment in the network and, of course, on the type of the segment. We begin with the case of a simple read/write segment residing within the same cluster as the processor referencing the segment. This mapping is shown in Figure 7. The segment name is used to access the corresponding segment descriptor. The descriptor provides

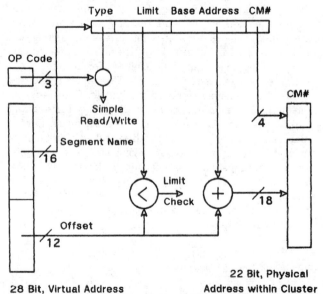

Figure 7—Virtual to physical address mapping for a variable sized segment

a limit value which is checked against the 12 bit offset in the virtual address. If the reference is out of the bounds of the segment then an error trap occurs. The offset is added to the physical base address from the descriptor. The resulting 18 bit value is a physical address within the 256 K byte address space of the computer module also specified in the descriptor.

If the virtual address references a segment outside the source cluster then the segment name is used to access an *Indirect Descriptor Reference* rather than the descriptor itself. The indirect reference simply indicates in which cluster the segment resides. The Kmap then passes the virtual address to that cluster via the inter-cluster buses. An alternative approach would be to have duplicate copies of the segment descriptors in every cluster. Thus the virtual-to-physical mapping could be done at the source cluster, with possibly some savings in overhead. However, any attempt to change the virtual-to-physical binding of a segment (e.g., moving it to a different memory module or onto backing store) would require an effectively simultaneous change to all copies of the segment descriptor. In a large network this operation would be slow and cumbersome, if not impossible. A further advantage to ensuring that only a single descriptor exists for each segment is that a *Lock Bit* can be provided in the descriptor. The lock bit can be used to ensure mutual exclusion for special segment operations.

The kernel address space

Each processor can execute in either of two address spaces. One is the *User Address Space* which was described above. The second is the *Kernel Address Space*, which is similar to a user address space with the addition of some mechanisms reserved for the operating system. The currently executing address space is selected by a bit in the Processor Status Word of the LSI-11. A *Kernel Environment* is similar to a User Environment; however segments at the third level of the Capability List structure (Figure 4) can be User Primary Capability Lists. That is, a Kernel Capability list structure can have user environments as substructures.

There are several additional pseudo registers provided in page 15 of the kernel address space. One of these, the *User Environment* register, holds an index for a Capability in the kernel environment which points to a user environment. This register specifies the current user environment for this processor. If the kernel writes a new index into the register the addressing state of the old user process is saved by the Kmap in the state vector part of the old user environment. The addressing state of the new user is then loaded from the specified new user environment. The addressing state is the value of the window and other system registers in page 15 of the executing program. Ideally, this operation, which performs a context swap by saving one addressing state and loading another, would also save the internal processor registers. Unfortunately there is no way for the Kmap to access the internal registers of an LSI-11. Thus internal registers must be saved and restored under program control.

THE USE OF THE ADDRESSING STRUCTURE FOR CONTROL OPERATIONS

The philosophy in Cm* is to implement all special control operations, such as interprocessor interrupts, by references to the physical address space. This not only avoids a proliferation of special control signals, but also allows the power of the system's address mapping and protection mechanisms to be applied to control operations.

The Slocal provides a three priority level interrupt scheme. An interrupt is invoked by writing into the appropriate physical address on the LSI-11 bus of the target processor. Thus an interrupt can be requested by a process anywhere in the network, provided the process has a Capability for a segment which maps to the correct physical address. Another example is the abort operation. If the appropriate bit is written, a NXM (Non Existent Memory) trap by the local processor is forced. This mechanism will be used when an error occurs during a remote reference by the processor.

The following examples show how references to special typed segments, or special operations on standard segments, are used to invoke microcoded operations in the Kmap.

Primitive lock operations

For processors in the PDP-11 family, most write operations are part of a read-modify-write sequence. In standard PDP-11s (including LSI-11's) this sequence is implemented as an indivisible, single bus operation. This improves performance by reducing bus overhead and allowing optimization of references to memory with destructive read operations (e.g., core and dynamic MOS memory). In C.mmp the indivisibility of these operations is maintained through the switch to shared memory. This allows the implementation of Locks and Semaphores because a memory location can be both tested and set without fear of an intervening access by some other processor. Indivisible read-modify-write operations to nonlocal memory will not be implemented in Cm* because of increased bus and memory contention and hardware complexity. We will provide an equivalent function by making use of the Kmap's ability to lock a segment descriptor while it makes a series of references to the segment. To implement a basic lock mechanism two special segment operations are defined:

Inspect the word addressed. If greater than zero, then decrement. Return the original value.

Increment the word addressed. Return the original value.

An inter-process message system

Message systems can provide particularly clean mechanisms for communication between processes.[11,12] In the past, a drawback to message systems has been the substantial operating system overhead in transferring a message from one process to another in a fully protected way. The architecture of Cm* provides an opportunity to build a fully protected message system which can be used with very low overhead.

A message port, or mail box, will be a special segment type. Messages will either be entire segments, passed by transferring capabilities, or will be single data words encoded as data capabilities. Two representative operations on Mailbox segments are:

Send(Message, ReplyMBox, MailBox)
  This transfers capabilities for a message and a reply mail box from the caller's Capability List to the Mailbox. If the Mailbox is full then the caller is suspended.
Receive(MailBox)
  If the mailbox contains a message then a Capability for the message and a Reply Mailbox will be transferred into the caller's Capability List. Otherwise the caller is suspended.

Provided that the above operations are successful, they are performed completely in Kmap microcode, and messages may be passed with probably less than 100 microseconds delay. If the operation cannot be completed because the Mailbox is full or empty, then the operating system is invoked to suspend the requesting process. The Kmap can also request the operating system to wake up a suspended process when the operation is complete.

DEVELOPMENT AIDS

The development of hardware and software for a new computer system is a major undertaking. We have attempted to ease this burden by using a variety of aids. All the major hardware components were drafted using an interactive drawing package (a version of the Standard Drawing Package). To facilitate the development of software, prior to the availability of hardware, a functional simulation of Cm* was programmed, which executes on C.mmp. Development of the Kmap hardware and microcode has been greatly benefited by the use of the "hooks" mechanism in the Kmap. This connection to the Kmap allows a program executing on an LSI-11 almost complete access to the internal state of the Kmap.

In order to expedite hardware debugging and software development, a host program development system was constructed. The host is connected to each Cm in the system by a Serial Line Unit (SLU) to allow down line memory loading and dumping from the associated Cm. In addition, the SLU makes console control functions for each LSI-11 available to the host computer.[16] The Host in turn is connected to a PDP-10 timesharing system.

CONCLUDING REMARKS AND PROJECT STATUS

Cm* is projected to be constructed in three stages. The first stage is a ten-processor, three Kmap system. The subse-

quent stages will include 30-processors and later 100-processors. Detailed hardware design began in late July, 1975. As of late summer, 1976, a three-processor, one-Kmap system was operational. It is expected that the first stage Cm* configuration will be operational in the second quarter of 1977. The initial operating system is described in Reference 6 and is being developed both on the Cm* simulator which runs on C.mmp and on the real hardware with the support of the Host Development system.

The essential features of the Cm* architecture have been presented. Both the coupling of a processor directly with each unit of shared memory and the three level bus structure which makes all memory accessible by every processor are primary features of the Cm* structure. Much of the sophistication in the architecture is associated with the address translation mechanisms. A description has been given of how the small processor address space of the PDP-11 is mapped into the larger global virtual address space of the Cm* system and how the global virtual address space is mapped onto the distributed physical address space of the Cm* system. A number of important aspects of the Cm* project are outside the scope of this paper and interested readers are referred to other papers for a more complete discussion.[5,6,8,9,13-15] Reliability and performance models have been developed concurrently with the hardware design of the system and have been used to guide several important decisions concerning the structure of the Cm* implementation.

ACKNOWLEDGMENTS

During the years its its initial development, many individuals have contributed to this project. Gordon Bell, Bob Chen, Doug Clark and Don Thomas contributed ideas to earlier versions of this architecture. Anita Jones and Victor Lessor have contributed to the present architecture. Miles Barel, Paulo Corrulupi, Levy Raskin and Paul Rubinfeld have all contributed to bringing the hardware to an early fruition. Kwok-Woon Lai and John Ousterhout are largely responsible for the successful development of the Kmap. Andy Bechtolsheim designed the Linc. Lloyd Dickman, Rich Olsen, Steve Teicher and Mike Titelbaum at Digital Equipment Corporation have provided information, ideas, and support critical to the success of the project.

REFERENCES

1. Fuller, S. H., D. P. Siewiorek, and R. J. Swan, "Computer Modules: An Architecture for Large Digital Modules," *Proceedings of the First Annual Symposium on Computer Architecture*, University of Florida, Gainesville. Also in ACM SIGARCH, *Computer Architecture News*, Vol. 2, No. 4, December 1973, pp. 231–236.
2. Bell, C. G., J. L. Eggert, J. Grason, and P. Williams, "The Description and the Use of Register Transfer Modules (RTMs)," *IEEE Transactions on Computers*, Vol. C-21, No. 5, May 1972, pp. 495–500.
3. Heart, F. E., S. M. Ornstein, W. R. Crowther, and W. B. Barker, "A New Minicomputer/Multiprocessor for the ARPA Network," *AFIPS Conference Proceedings*, Vol. 42, NCC 1973, pp. 529–537.

4. Wulf, W. A. and C. G. Bell, "C.mmp—A Multi-Mini-Processor," *AFIPS Conference Proceedings*, Vol. 41, part II, FJCC 1972, pp. 765–777.

5. Swan, R. J., A Bechtolsheim, K. Lai and J. Ousterhout, "The Implementation of the Cm* Multi-Microprocessor," *AFIPS Conference Proceedings*, Vol. 46, 1977 National Computer Conference.

6. Jones, A. K., R. J. Chansler, I. Durham, P. Feiler and K. Schwans, "Software Management of Cm*, a Distributed Multiprocessor," *AFIPS Conference Proceedings*, Vol. 46, 1977 National Computer Conference.

7. Anderson, G. A. and E. D. Jensen, "Computer Interconnection Structures: Taxonomy, Characteristics and Examples," *Computing Surveys*, 7, 4, December 1975, pp. 197–213.

8. Swan, R. J., S. H. Fuller and D. P. Siewiorek, "The Structure and Architecture of Cm*: A Modular, Multi-Microprocessor," *Computer Science Research Review* 1975-76, Carnegie-Mellon University, Department of Computer Science, Pittsburgh, Pa., December 1976, pp. 25-47.

9. Swan, R. J., L. Raskin, and A. Bechtolsheim, "Deadlock Issues in the Design of the Linc," Internal Memo, March 1976.

10. Denning, P. J., "Virtual Memory," *Computing Surveys*, Vol. 2, No. 3, September 1970, pp. 153-190.

11. Brinch-Hansen, *Per, Operating System Principles*, Chapter 8, "A Case Study: RC-4000," Prentice Hall, 1973.

12. Jefferson, David, "The Hydra Message System," to be published.

13. Ingle, Ashok and D. P. Siewiorek, "Reliability Modeling of Multiprocessor Structures," *Proceedings IEEE CompCon '76*, September 1976.

14. Ingle, Ashok and D. P. Siewiorek, "Reliability Models for Multiprocessor Systems with and without Periodic Maintenance," Computer Science Technical Report, Carnegie-Mellon University, September 1976.

15. Siewiorek, D. P., W. C. Brantley Jr., and G. W. Lieve, "Modeling Multiprocessor Implementations of Passive Sonar Signal Processing," Final Report, Carnegie-Mellon University. Pittsburgh, Pa. 15213, October 1975.

16. Van Zoren, H., "Cm* Host User's Manual," Department of Computer Science, Carnegie-Mellon University, December 1975.

17. Bell, C. G., R. C. Chen, S. H. Fuller, J. Grason, S. Rege, and D. P. Siewiorek, "The Architecture and Applications of Computer Modules: A Set of Components for Digital Design," *IEEE Computer Society International Conference*, CompCon 73, March pp. 177–180.

18. Bell, C. G. and A. Newell, *Computer Structures: Readings and Examples*, McGraw-Hill, New York, New York, 1971.

The implementation of the Cm∗ multi-microprocessor†

by RICHARD J. SWAN, ANDY BECHTOLSHEIM, KWOK-WOON LAI and JOHN K. OUSTERHOUT

Carnegie-Mellon University
Pittsburgh, Pennsylvania

Reprinted with permission from the *Proceedings of the National Computer Conference*, Volume 46, 1977, pages 645-655.
Copyright © 1977 by AFIPS Press.

ABSTRACT

The implementation of a hierarchical, packet switched multiprocessor is presented. The lowest level of the structure, a Computer Module, is a processor-memory pair. Computer Modules are grouped to form a cluster; communication within the cluster is via a parallel bus controlled by a centralized address mapping processor. Clusters communicate via intercluster busses. A memory reference by a program may be routed, transparently, to any memory in the system. This paper discusses the hardware used to implement the communication mechanism. The use of special diagnostic hardware and performance models is also discussed.

INTRODUCTION

The companion paper[1] has introduced Cm∗ as a large, extensible multiprocessor architecture. It has an unusually powerful and complex addressing structure which allows close, protected cooperation between large numbers of inexpensive processors. This paper describes the combination of hardware and firmware which implements the address space sharing and interprocessor communication mechanisms.

Cm∗ is a multiprocessor system as we define it (rather, than a network of independent computers) because the processors share a common address space. All processors have immediate access to all memory. The structure of Cm∗ is shown in Figure 1. The primary unit is the *Computer Module* or Cm. This consists of a processor, memory and peripherals interfaced to a local memory bus and a "local switch." The local switch, or *Slocal,‡* interconnects the processor, its local memory bus and the *Map Bus*. The Map Bus provides communication between up to fourteen Computer Modules within a *cluster,* and is centrally controlled by the *Kmap,* a high performance microprogrammed processor. Each Kmap interfaces to two *Intercluster busses,* by means of which it communicates with the other clusters in the system.

There is a system-wide 28 bit virtual address space. This address space is divided into *segments* with a maximum size of 4096 bytes. Programs refer to segments indirectly via *Capabilities,* which are two-word items containing the global name of a segment and specifying access rights to the segment. The processors have a 16 bit address space which is divided into 16 pages. A mechanism is provided which allows a program to associate any Capability it possesses (and hence any segment to which it is allowed access) with any page in its immediate address space. A full description of the address mapping scheme is given in Reference 1.

To demonstrate the viability of a structure it is necessary to build a pilot system with currently available components. To be a successful demonstration, the pilot system has to be a useful, economical computing resource in its own right. Therefore, in the Cm∗ network described here, many design tradeoffs were made on the basis of current technology and the resources available. The highly experimental nature of the project encouraged an emphasis on generality and ease of debugging in the hardware components, rather than just minimization of costs. There are many aspects of the detailed design which would have to be re-evaluated if the structure were to be implemented in a different technology or built as a commercial product. In particular the distribution of functions between the processors and the Kmap would be carefully reconsidered. The modular nature of Cm∗ makes it particularly suitable for implementation in LSI.

The second section of this paper illustrates the mechanism for memory references. The various hardware components of Cm∗ are described in the following six sections. The third section describes the processor-memory pairs and their interface to the Map Bus. In the fourth section opportunities for parallelism in the address mapping mechanism are considered. Three autonomous functional units of the Kmap are presented in later sections, and describes the

† This work was supported in part by the Advanced Research Projects Agency under contract number F44620-73-C-0074, which is monitored by the Air Force Office of Scientific Research, and in part by the National Science Foundation Grant GJ 32758X. The LSI-11's and related equipment were supplied by Digital Equipment Corporation.
‡ The names used for hardware components of Cm∗ are derived from PMS notation.[2] The leading, capitalized letter indicates the primary function of the unit, e.g., Computer, Processor, Kontroller, Link, Switch. The subsequent letters, optionally separated with a period, give some attribute of the unit. For example, Slocal is a local switch. Pmap is a mapping processor. The name Cm∗ derives from (Computer.modular)∗ where ∗ is the Kleene star.

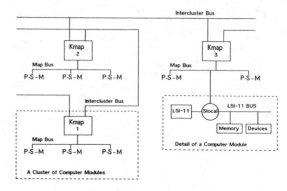

Figure 1—A simple 3 cluster Cm∗ SYSTEM

support given to hardware diagnosis and microcode development in the Kmap. For an effective implementation it was necessary to find a reasonable performance balance between system components. Some of the performance modelling which guided our judgment is presented in the last section.

THE MECHANISM FOR LOCAL AND NONLOCAL REFERENCES

Addresses generated by processors in a Cm* system may refer to memory anywhere within the system. Mapping of an address and routing to the appropriate memory are performed in a way that is totally transparent to the processor generating the address. If an address is to refer to the memory local to that processor, the memory reference is performed in a completely standard way except that the Slocal relocates the high-order four bits of the address. (See Figure 2.)

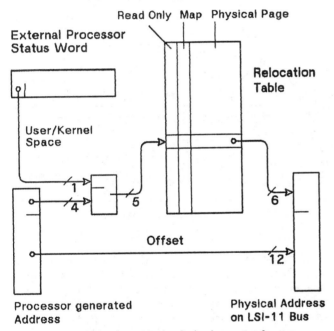

Figure 2—Addressing mechanism for local memory references

When the page being referenced is not local (i.e., the "Map" bit for the referenced page is set in the Slocal) a *service request* is made to the Kmap by the Slocal. Upon receiving the service request the Kmap executes a Map Bus cycle to read in the processor-generated address from the Slocal, as well as the number of the Cm making the request, and two status bits indicating which address space was executing on the processor and whether the reference was a read or a write (see Figure 3). If the segment being referenced is local to the cluster, the Kmap will use information cached in its high-speed buffers to bypass most of the processor-to-virtual-to-physical address mapping. Thus it can quickly translate from the page number referenced by the processor to a physical address consisting of the number of the Cm containing the physical location and an eighteen-bit local address. A second Map Bus transaction is executed to pass this address, and a bit indicating whether a read or a write is to be performed, to the destination Slocal. If the operation is a write, the data may be passed directly from the Cm making the reference to the Cm containing the word to be written. The destination

Slocal performs the read or write via a Direct Memory Access. When this is completed it issues a *return request* to the Kmap to acknowledge completion. A third Map Bus cycle is performed to transfer the data back to the processor that made the reference (in the case of a read) and to acknowledge completion of the reference so that the requesting processor may resume activity.

A second alternative when the Kmap receives an address to map is that the physical location being referenced is not local to the cluster. In this case the information cached in the Kmap for the page being referenced will not indicate a physical location directly; instead it will give a sixteen-bit segment name, the number of the cluster containing the physical memory allocated to the segment, and two bits used to extend the read/write bit to a three-bit *op code*.

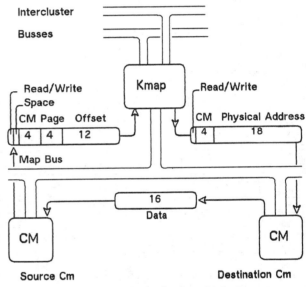

Figure 3—The mechanism for cluster-local references

This information is combined with the twelve low-order bits of the original processor address to form the full virtual address of the object being referenced. (See Figure 4.) The virtual address, along with the processor data (if a write is being performed) is sent via an Intercluster Bus to the Kmap of the cluster containing the segment (if there is no Intercluster Bus directly connecting the two Kmaps the message will be steered from Kmap to Kmap until it reaches the destination cluster). The destination Kmap will then map the virtual address to a physical one within its cluster. Map Bus transactions will be executed to pass the physical address (and data if needed) to an Slocal which in turn performs the operation and returns acknowledgment (and, perhaps, data) back to the destination Kmap. A return message is used to pass back acknowledgment and data to the Kmap of the originating cluster. Finally, this Kmap will relay the data and acknowledgment back to the initiating Cm to complete the reference.

Several points are worth noting with respect to the above schemes. Except at the local memory bus level, where conventional circuit switching is used, all communication is performed by *packet switching*. That is, buses are allocated only for the period required to transfer data. The data is latched at each interface, rather than establishing a continuous circuit from the source to the destination. This approach gives greater bus utilization and avoids deadlock over bus allocation. All transactions are completely interlocked with positive acknowledgment being required to signal completion of an operation (it is possible to allow a processor executing a nonlocal write to proceed as soon as the data for the write has been received by the Kmap or destination Slocal, without waiting for completion of the operation; however in this case the Kmap will expect to receive acknowledgment in place of the processor so that appropriate actions may be taken if none is received). The complete processor-to-virtual-to-physical address mapping is performed only in the case of intercluster references. As the locality of a reference increases the amount of this mapping that may be bypassed (and hence the speed of the reference) increases, with local caches of certain mapping information used to effect the bypass. An important charac-

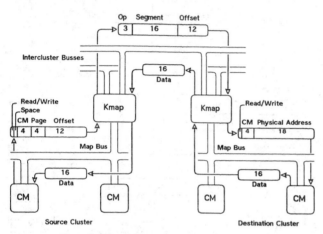

Figure 4—The mechanism for intercluster references

teristic of the addressing structure is that there is exactly one Kmap that may perform the virtual-to-physical mapping for a given segment. The requirement that all references to a segment occur with the cognizance of a single Kmap greatly simplifies the moving of segments and the implementation of operations requiring mutual exclusion.

THE COMPUTER MODULE

The first level of the Cm* network hierarchy is the *Computer Module*, or Cm. The Cm's provide both the memory and processing power for the multiprocessor system.

The decision to use a standard, commercially available processor (the DEC LSI-11) has had a considerable impact on the design. Use of a standard instruction set has made a large pool of software and software development aids directly available. The not inconsiderable effort to design and implement a new processor has been avoided.

At the software level, the prime disadvantage of the LSI-11 instruction set is that only 16 bit addresses can be directly manipulated. The companion architecture paper discusses in detail the mechanism used to expand a processor's address space from 16 bits to 28 bits.

The components of a computer module

A Computer Module, Figure 5, can act as a stand alone computer system. The standard commercially available components include the DEC LSI-11 processor and dynamic MOS memory. Any LSI-11 peripheral may be used on the bus, including serial and parallel interfaces, floppy and fixed head disks, etc. The standard 16 bit memory has been extended with byte parity. Memory refresh is normally performed by microcode in the LSI-11; however, the fact that a processor may be suspended indefinitely while awaiting the completion of a complex external reference has made it necessary to augment each Cm with a special bus device to perform refresh.

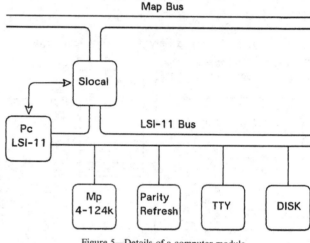

Figure 5—Details of a computer module

The most important component which has been added to each Cm is the Slocal. This provides the interface between the processor, the Map Bus and the LSI-11 Bus. The prime function of the Slocal is to selectively pass references from the processor to either the LSI-11 Bus or the Map Bus and to accept references from the Map Bus to the LSI-11 Bus. The Slocal also provides simple address relocation for references made by its processor to local memory. Figure 2 shows how this relocation is performed; the "Map Bit" in the local relocation table is set for pages which are not in the local memory of the processor.

In addition to the Local Relocation Table the Slocal provides a number of other control registers. All these registers are addressable as memory locations on the LSI-11 bus; however only the Kmap and highly privileged system code will have direct access to them. One of the key registers is the *eXternal Processor Status Word* (XPSW⟨15:8⟩). The LSI-11 implements only the low order byte of the standard PDP-11 *Processor Status Word* (PSW⟨7:0⟩). Logic in the Slocal (with assistance of standard signals from the LSI-11) allows the XPSW to be saved and restored during interrupt, trap and other operations in unison with the internal PSW. The XPSW allows selective enabling of various Slocal functions and controls a simple three level interrupt scheme. On power-up the XPSW is cleared, which disables all special operations by the Slocal including the relocation of local memory references. In this mode the processor acts as a bare, unmodified LSI-11. The Local Relocation Table can be initialized either by console operations, execution of local bootstrap code or remotely by any processor in the network. After initialization, enabling Reloc Mode (XPSW⟨11⟩) will allow local relocation and give access to the rest of the network.

Incorrect use of PDP-11 instructions such as HALT, RESET, Move-To-Processor-Status-word, Return from Interrupt, etc., can cause loss of a processor, garbling of an I/O operation or enable circumvention of the system's protection scheme. The Privileged Instruction Mode bit (XPSW⟨13⟩) enables logic in the Slocal which detects the fetching of any "dangerous" instruction. An immediate error trap is forced if an unprivileged program attempts to execute a privileged instruction.

Several registers in the Slocal are concerned with providing diagnosis and recovery information after a software or hardware error is detected. Almost all errors are reported to the processor by forcing a NXM (Non eXistent Memory) trap. This includes errors detected by the Kmap during remote references. The Kmap signals the error by writing to the "Force NXM" bit in an addressable register in the Slocal. The Local Error Register indicates the nature of the error and whether the erroneous reference was mapped. The "Last Fetch Address" register is updated to hold the address of the first word of an instruction every time the LSI-11 fetches a new instruction. If an error is detected, this register is frozen until the Local Error Register is explicitly cleared. Also frozen in the Local Error Register is a count of the number of memory references performed in the execution of the instruction. In conjunction, these two registers provide sufficient information to restore the state of the LSI-11 for retry of the instruction during which the error was detected.

The Slocal also provides two interrupt request registers. Interrupt enable bits in the external processor status word allow masking of the interrupt requests. Provided reference is permitted by the memory protection scheme, any processor in the network can interrupt any other processor simply by writing to the correct address.

Data paths for nonlocal references

An idealized form of the basic data paths and latches within a Cm* cluster is shown in Figure 6. Depending on the address generated, a reference from the processor is passed either to the local memory bus or to the Map Bus. A local memory reference is performed in a conventional way. For a nonlocal reference, the address (and possibly data) is latched and serviced request is issued to the Kmap. The broken line in Figure 6 shows the path of a read to the memory of another Cm in the cluster. The address from the source processor is read by the Kmap which translates it into a physical address within the memory of a Computer Module. This physical address is placed onto the Map Bus by the Kmap and latched at the target Cm. A conventional Direct Memory Access (DMA) cycle is performed by the destination Slocal, the data read is latched and the Kmap is again requested, this time with a return request. To complete the operation, the Kmap responds by transferring the

data over the Map Bus from the target Cm to the requesting Cm (this simply requires the latch at the target Cm to be enabled onto the Map Bus and the latch at the requesting Cm to be strobed). At this point the source processor, which was suspended, is given the data as if a normal memory reference had been performed.

This simplified description of a Computer Module has been presented to emphasize the simplicity of the basic mechanisms required for an intra-cluster reference in Cm*. In the actual implementation using the LSI-11 processor the data paths are rather different than the idealized structure shown in Figure 6. The differences are due primarily to the need to minimize the changes to the LSI-11. Although still simplified, Figure 7 is a more accurate representation of the

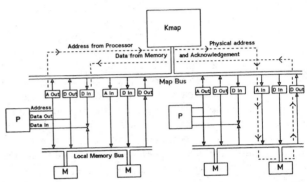

Figure 6—An idealized and simplified representation of the data paths in a cluster

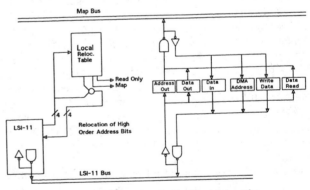

Figure 7—Simplified LSI-11—Slocal data paths

data paths and latches used to interface the LSI-11 and the LSI-11 bus to the Map Bus.

The processor board is modified so that the Local Relocation Table in the Slocal can be inserted in the data path of the four high order address bits. The timing margins in the processor's address path are wide enough to allow insertion of this delay without loss of performance. The LSI-11 Bus is the only data path from the processor for both local and nonlocal references. If the processor were permitted to hold the LSI-11 bus while waiting for completion of a nonlocal reference then references from other processors in the network to memory on the LSI-11 bus would be blocked. This could very easily lead to deadlock situations. To give greater concurrency and to eliminate the deadlock potential, the Slocal is able (using simple microcoded state sequence logic) to force the processor off the LSI-11 bus while it is waiting for completion of nonlocal references. While the processor is forced off the local bus the Slocal takes over DMA bus arbitration for the suspended processor.

CONCURRENCY WITHIN THE MAPPING MECHANISM

Early in the design of Cm∗ the speeds of the various components in the system began to appear as follows: the time for a "typical" Map Bus transaction was about 0.5 microseconds; the time required in the computational unit of the Kmap for an address mapping was 1-2 microseconds; the time to transfer a message on an Intercluster Bus was 2-4 microseconds; and the time for an Slocal to execute a read or write requested by the Kmap was 3-4 microseconds. In referring to the mechanisms for nonlocal mappings it can be seen that no single component is responsible for a very large fraction of the time required for a nonlocal reference. Thus if each cluster had a mapping concurrency of one (only one nonlocal reference could be processed at a time per cluster) both the utilization of the mapping components and the throughput of the mechanism would be low (the effect of concurrency on system performance is discussed quantitatively in a later section). In addition the possibility of deadlock in intercluster references is introduced.

The solution adopted for Cm∗ was to separate the four functions whose timings are given above and to allow a concurrency of eight in the mapping mechanism of each cluster. The packet-switched nature of Cm∗ yields cleanly to this approach, and requires only that queues be implemented to store messages at the interface between the components. Figure 8 depicts this structure, in which the Kmap has been logically sub-divided into three separate units: the *Kbus*, which is master of the Map Bus and controls all transactions on it; the *Pmap*, or mapping processor, which does all the address translation and maintains the cache used to speed up mapping; and the *Linc*, or intercluster link, which presides over the transmission of messages between clusters.

One other notion must be introduced before proceeding to a detailed discussion of the components of the Kmap, namely that of a *context*. Operations requiring mutual exclusion (for example, changing the virtual-to-physical mapping of the system) will be implemented in Cm∗ as memory references to "special" segments which will then cause the Kmap to perform the desired operations in a protected way. In general these operations will require several references by the Kmap to main memory. If the Pmap is to be used for other mappings while these main-memory references are being made by the Kbus and Slocals, there must be some means of saving and restoring its state so that processing can be resumed when the memory reference has been completed. The solution adopted is to provide registers in the Kmap to save and restore state for up to eight overlapping operations. A mapped operation in some stage of processing by the Kmap is referred to as a *context*. Each context has allocated to its exclusive use eight general-purpose registers and four sub-

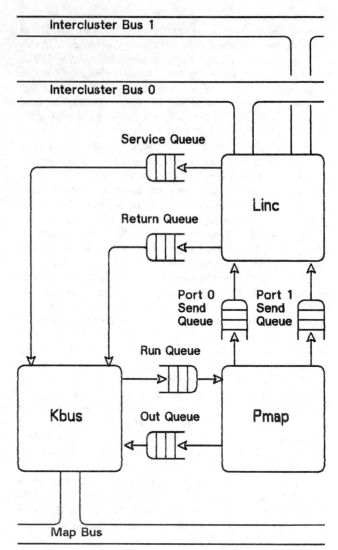

Figure 8—The components of the Kmap

routine linkage registers (one of which is used to save the microprogram address while awaiting the completion of Map Bus transactions).

The Kbus maintains the status of the eight Pmap contexts and allocates them to new service requests. The context number and other status are then placed in the *Run Queue* to signal the Pmap that the context is runnable. The mapping processor activates the context by removing its number from the Run Queue and starting execution of microcode at an address determined by the status bits. When the new context is activated the processor address is mapped, and a request for a main-memory reference is placed in the *Out Queue* (during this time the Kbus has been free to read in service requests or perform functions requested by the Pmap). A *context swap* is executed in the Pmap to deactivate the current context pending the completion of the memory reference and to activate the next one in the Run Queue. The Kbus transfers address and data to the destination Slocal, then processes other requests while the memory reference is being performed. When the memory reference is completed the Kbus either reads the acknowledgment and/or data back into the Kmap and places the context back in the Run Queue for reactivation, or it sends the acknowledgment back to the processor that originally made the service request (thereby completing the mapping operation) and marks the associated context as "free" for reallocation to a new service request. The fact that a context remains allocated to each nonlocal reference until that reference is completed (regardless of whether or not more Pmap processing is expected to be needed) means that if an error is detected the context can be reactivated and will have enough state information to handle the error in an intelligent fashion.

Communication between the Linc and Pmap is similar to that between the Kbus and Pmap; the Pmap queues a request for an intercluster message to be sent (separate queues are provided for each Intercluster Bus) and suspends the requesting context. When a return message is received for the context the Linc causes the Kbus to reactivate the context in the Run Queue. When an incoming intercluster message is received by one of the Linc's Intercluster Bus Ports, it is queued and a request is issued to the Kbus to allocate a free context to the request and activate it in the Run Queue.

THE KBUS AND THE MAP BUS

Because of the great variety of tasks it must perform and the necessity that it be able to respond to errors in an intelligent way, the Kbus was designed as a microprogrammed processor controlled by 256 40-bit words of read only memory. It has a microcycle time of 100 nanoseconds which is synchronized with the 150 nanosecond clock of the Pmap and Linc at 50 nanosecond intervals. Figure 9 shows the major elements of the bus controller.

The Map Bus contains 38 signals, of which 20 are bidirectional lines used to transmit addresses and data between the Slocals and Kbus of the cluster. The Kbus is master of all transactions on the bus; as such it specifies a source and destination for each cycle as well as status bits indicating the use of the data (address, data, etc.). The bus is synchronous, with the Kbus generating all of the strobes used to transmit data. Each Slocal is provided with private service and return request lines to the Kbus. The arbiter section of the Kbus scans these in a pseudo round robin priority scheme.

The Kbus maintains the queues and registers used for communication with the Pmap. The Run Queue contains eight eight-bit slots (and thus is guaranteed never to overflow), each containing a three-bit context name and five additional bits of activation status. The Out Queue contains four 39-bit entries. The Pmap loads this queue to request Kbus operations and must check its state before loading to insure that it never overflows. Each Out Queue slot contains an op code used to select one of thirty-two Kbus operations, and additional address, data, and context information relevant to the operation. Two registers are loaded by the Kbus on behalf of each Pmap context. They are readable only by the Pmap and writable only by the Kbus. The *Bus Data Register* contains the last data word read in from the Map Bus for the context and the *Bus Condition Register* gives control and status information for the transaction.

The Kbus is responsible for the allocation and deallocation of contexts, and maintains the status of each context

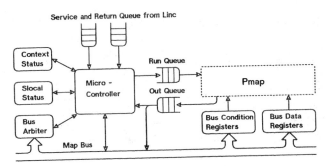

Figure 9—The components of the Kbus

for this purpose. It also keeps two additional bits of status for each context which are used to insure that, when a context suspends itself to await the execution of a main-memory reference or the sending of an intercluster message, an acknowledgment of the completion of the operation is received within a reasonable time (two milliseconds). If a suspended context times out it is forcibly reactivated with status bits indicating the error.

The Kbus also maintains nine bits of status for each Slocal in the cluster indicating whether the Slocal is busy with a Kmap-requested memory reference and, if so, what to do with the information returned at the end of the transaction. This status is set whenever a local memory reference is initiated and is used to insure that two contexts do not simultaneously try to request a memory access through the same Slocal.

THE PMAP, THE ADDRESS MAPPING PROCESSOR

The mapping processor of the Kmap, or Pmap, is a sixteen-bit horizontally microprogrammed processor. It occupies a central position within the Kmap, coordinating the activities of the other components. It is pipelined and has a cycle time of 150 nanoseconds. Microinstructions are 80 bits wide; a 1K*80 bipolar RAM is used as a writable microstore. The Pmap also uses a high-speed 5K*16 RAM to store the active Capabilities and segment descriptors. In addition to performing the basic address translation for the nonlocal references of a cluster, the Pmap must support certain operating system primitives, statistics gathering, and other experimental functions without excessive performance degradation.

Data paths

A register transfer level diagram of the Pmap is given in Figure 10. The main data paths consist of three internal high speed tri-state busses. Two of these, the *A* and *B busses*, take data from various sources and feed them to the inputs of the Arithmetic Logic Unit. The third bus, the *F Bus*, takes the ALU output and distributes it to various parts of the Kmap. The Kbus and Linc are also connected to these busses. Pipeline latches are used to overlap fetch of operands with current data operations.

The *Shift and Mask Unit* provides the ability to perform field-extraction on one of the ALU operands. This capability is important since the Pmap frequently deals with packed information in segment descriptors, intercluster messages, etc. The input to the Shift and Mask Unit is rotated by an arbitrary amount and then masked by one of 32 16-bit standard masks stored in a PROM.

For efficient address mapping, it is crucial that the Kmap have fast access to the information it needs to perform the virtual-to-physical address translation. This information consists largely of the active Capabilities and segment descriptors, of which up to 448 may exist in the cluster at a time (sixteen in each of two address spaces for each of

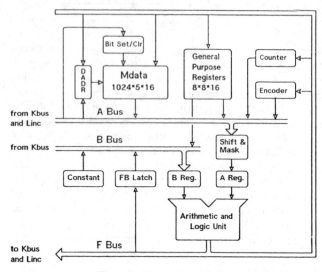

Figure 10—Data paths in the Pmap

fourteen processors). Although content addressable memory was not used because of the large capacity needed, the careful positioning of tables within the data memory, combined with a hash-coded list structure used for storing descriptors, has produced a cache-like structure.

The data memory, or Mdata, is divided into 1024 (expandable to 4096) *records,* each record containing five 16-bit words. The record organization was chosen because the segment descriptors, with cacheing information, fit comfortably within this 80-bit space. Each word has associated with it two parity bits, one for each byte. The memory is word addressable, with the record address coming from the *Data Address Register* (DADR) and three-bit word indices from fields in the current microinstruction. Thus once the record address of a descriptor or capability has been computed, the individual subwords may be accessed without expending further cycles to generate data memory addresses.

Data to be written in the Mdata may be taken either from the A Bus or F Bus. Because it is frequently necessary to set and clear status bits in segment descriptors (for example the "dirty" and "use" bits used for demand paging, and the lock bit used for mutual exclusion) bit set and clear logic is provided for data input from the A Bus. It provides for the setting or clearing of either or both of the two high-order bits of the input word. To further increase parallelism, it is possible to simultaneously read and write different words of the same record. It is therefore possible, say, to set the "use bit" in one word of a segment descriptor and at the same time extract the segment limit from another word of the same descriptor.

Microprogram sequencing logic

One characteristic of the Cm* address mapping algorithms is the large number of conditions to be tested. The service of a typical request will require testing of request status, operation type, and segment type and checking of the following conditions: protection violation, descriptor locked, segment localizable, etc. To perform address mapping within a reasonable number of cycles requires the Pmap to have a flexible multi-way branch capability.

A block diagram of the microprogram sequencing logic is given in Figure 11. A *Base Address* is selected from either the *Next Address* field in the current microinstruction or the output of the *Subroutine Linkage Registers.* Two bits in the microinstruction select the mode of branching (two-way, four-way, sixteen-way) and two three-bit fields control six 8-to-1 condition code multiplexers. Multi-way branching was implemented in the conventional way by OR'ing the selected condition codes with the Base Address. The address thus generated is stored in *MADR,* the *Microprogram Address Register,* to fetch the next microinstruction. There is a conditional override mechanism that can prohibit a potential 16-way branch. When the override condition is true, a branch is taken to a seventeenth location regardless of the value of the 16-way branch condition code.

Context considerations

There are a total of 64 general purpose and 32 subroutine linkage registers, allowing each context exclusive use of

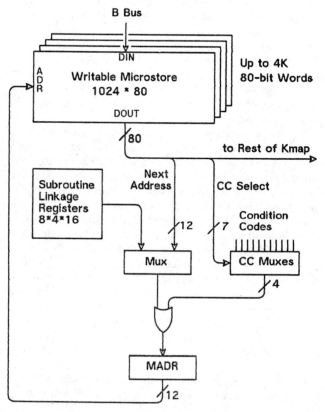

Figure 11—Microinstruction address generation logic

eight general purpose registers and four subroutine linkage registers. The *Current Context Number,* stored in the *Context Register,* selects the current register bank. Normally this register is loaded from the Run Queue when a context swap is executed. For diagnostic purposes the Pmap may directly load the Context Register, hence if required a microprogram may access the registers of any context. Each context may nest subroutine calls up to four levels deep. By convention, the zeroth linkage register is also used to store the reactivation address of a suspended context. The status bits in the Run Queue indicate whether a context is to be activated at its reactivation address (to continue an ongoing operation) or to be explicitly started at one of the first sixteen locations in the microstore (to begin a new operation, or handle certain error conditions).

THE LINC AND INTERCLUSTER BUS STRUCTURE

The Linc provides intercluster communication by connecting the Pmap to two *Intercluster busses.* Communication is in the form of short messages passed between Kmaps. Messages are stored in a *Message RAM* which is shared between the Pmap and the two Intercluster Bus *Ports.* Pointers to messages pass through an automatic system of queues. Messages are usually sent directly from source to destination cluster, but they can also be forwarded by intermediate clusters (thus allowing arbitrary network topologies to be constructed). Message routing is controlled by Pmap microcode. The goal in the Linc design was to provide fast, deadlock-free intercluster communication with a minimum of Pmap overhead.

Intercluster bus protocol

The Intercluster busses contain 26 lines: 16 data, 2 parity, and 8 control. They operate in an asynchronous, interlocked fashion at a transfer rate of 450 nanoseconds per word. Mastership is passed cyclically between requesting ports, effectively implementing a round robin priority scheme. The current bus master arbitrates future mastership in parallel with its current data transfers.

Intercluster messages consist of one to eight 16 bit words. The most common formats are shown in Figure 12. The header word contains a six bit identifier for source and destination cluster, the source context number and the complex bit. A return message has a unique source field of

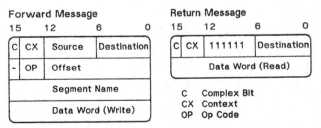

Figure 12—Standard message formats

all ones. The source context number is sent with the message to allow a direct reactivation of the suspended source context. The complex bit provides an escape mecha-

nism to other message formats, e.g., for error messages or block transfers.

Components of the linc (Figure 13)

Buffer space for messages is provided in the central 1K∗18 Message RAM, divided into 128 buffers of eight words each. This is sufficient to avoid any possibility of deadlock over buffer allocation except in very large systems.[3] The Pmap has priority for access to the Message RAM, although it is also directly accessible by the Ports. Several contexts may use the Linc in an overlapped fashion without interference since each context has private facilities for addressing message buffers. A context has two ways to address message buffers. It may use its context number to access a *reserved buffer* which is used for the creation of forward messages and to receive return messages. There is also a *Pmap Address Register* for each context to deal with incoming forward messages. Words within a buffer are selected by a Pmap microcode field. Each Port section has an address register and a word count register for accessing the Message RAM.

Five queues are maintained by the Linc. Two *Send Queues,* one for each Port, are used by the Pmap to request transmission of messages. To request that a message be sent on an Intercluster Bus, the Pmap places the address of the message buffer in the appropriate Send Queue. The *Free Queue* keeps the addresses of all the message buffers not currently in use. The *Service Queue* is used by the Linc to notify the Kbus and Linc of the addresses of incoming forward messages, and the *Return Queue* to request that the Kbus reactivate contexts when replies to their forward

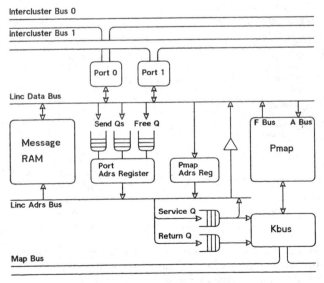

Figure 13—Components of the Linc

messages are received. All of the queues are implemented as partitions of a single 1K∗11 bipolar RAM.

The Linc uses the same 150 nanosecond clock as the Pmap. For diagnostic purposes the Pmap has access to almost all of the internal state of the Linc and may execute all the internal microcycles executable by the Ports.

An intercluster message transaction

A complete message transfer is shown in Figure 14. The Pmap at the source cluster creates the forward message in a reserved context buffer. Then its pointer is put into the appropriate Send Queue. The Linc pops the pointer off the Send Queue into the *Port Address Register,* acquires mastership of the corresponding bus and transfers the message, one word at a time, from its Message RAM onto the Intercluster Bus and into the Message RAM of the destination Linc.

At the destination side the receiving Port has already obtained a buffer from the Free Queue. If the message is received completely without error, then its pointer is placed into the Service Queue (if not, the message is ignored; a timeout will occur at the source). The Service Queue requests the Kbus to allocate a free Pmap context to service the message. It includes status bits to start up specific microcode. The context will transfer the pointer from the Service Queue into the Pmap Address Register and process the message, making appropriate main-memory references. It then creates a return message in the same buffer, setting the source field to ones to indicate this. On a Read, the data word will be appended. The buffer pointer of the completed return message is queued again in the Send Queue. When the message has been sent, the pointer is released into the Free Queue. At the original source the return message is placed in the reserved buffer for the requesting context. Its context number plus status is passed to the Return Queue and the context is reactivated to send data or an acknowledgment back to the requesting processor.

DEVELOPMENT AND DIAGNOSTIC AIDS

A common strategy used to aid in hardware and/or microcode development is to construct a software simulator

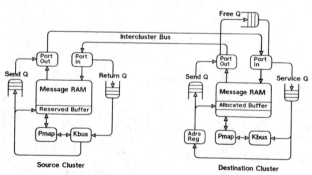

Figure 14—An intercluster message transaction

for the hardware. This allows initial debugging to be performed before the actual hardware is available and can provide a more comfortable environment in which to work. However, simulators are expensive both in terms of development effort and computer time; furthermore they cannot give an exact reflection of the hardware. Thus this approach leaves the final bugs to be found using the real hardware, and is of no aid in diagnosing component failures (rather than design errors). The alternative approach adopted for Cm* was to incorporate special hardware, called *Hooks*, directly into the Kmap for use in

hardware and microcode development. The interfacing of the Hooks to a standard LSI-11 allows extensive software support for hardware development and diagnostics while at the same time providing a convenient environment for the debugging of microcode on the real hardware.

The Hooks give to an LSI-11, referred to as the *Hooks Processor,* the ability to intimately examine and change the internal state of the Kmap. They provide the capability for the Hooks Processor to load microcode into the writable control store of the Pmap, read the values on the A and B busses of the Pmap, and to independently start, stop, and single-cycle the Pmap-Linc and Kbus clocks. An interrupt is generated for the Hooks Processor whenever the Pmap clock stops (either due to a microprogram-invoked halt or a memory parity error on the control or data stores). Furthermore, several of the internal registers of the Pmap have "twin registers" associated with them which may only be loaded by the Hooks Processor. These alternate registers may be enabled via the Hooks to override microprogram-controlled values. The presence of the Hooks added approximately ten percent to the cost of the Pmap while enormously reducing system development time.

PERFORMANCE: MEASUREMENTS AND PREDICTIONS

Before discussing the models used to estimate the performance of a Cm* cluster, several simple measurements (made on a cluster containing two processors) will be presented. The average time between memory references (including both code and data) made by a single LSI-11 executing entirely out of local memory varies between 2.5 and 4.0 microseconds, depending on the mix of instructions being executed. For a "typical" code sequence, based on measurements of compiled BLISS-11 programs, the inter-reference time was 3.0 microseconds. Measurements made on the same "typical" code sequence, except with all references mapped via the Kmap to the other processor in the cluster, yielded an average time between references of 7.7 microseconds. With the latter measurement there was no contention for use of the Map Bus, Kmap, or destination Slocal. Although no actual measurements were available at the time of this writing, it is expected that the time for intercluster references will be between 15 and 20 microseconds.

A simple queueing model was developed to estimate the performance of a cluster.[4] The model assumed an exponential distribution of nonlocal requests, exponential service time in the Pmap, and exponential distribution of the total non-Pmap overhead incurred during a nonlocal reference. It is assumed that the Pmap is the primary cause of contention hence the waiting time for other facilities is ignored. Figure 15 plots the results of this analysis. The relative rate of memory referencing in a cluster is plotted as a function of the number of active processors and their *hit ratio* to local memory.

Because of the inability of the queueing analysis to model contention for all cluster facilities it was feared that the results would prove to be an optimistic estimate of cluster performance. Therefore a series of simulations was performed in order to model more closely the true operation of a cluster.[5] The simulation and queueing results were in close agreement and so the simulation study will not be discussed further.

Figure 15 indicates that system performance is extremely dependent on the local hit ratio. It has been hypothesized that the local hit ratio would lie in the range between 85 and 95 percent, in which case the effect of the nonlocal references would be "reasonably" small. Unfortunately, this implies that code must be entirely local to the processor executing it. Two memory-intensive programs, a quicksort

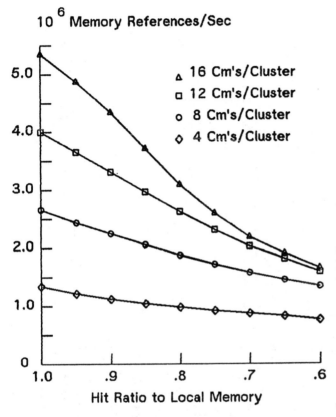

Local Reference Time = 3.0 uSec
External Service Time = 1.5 uSec
plus 6.5 uSec Constant Overhead

Figure 15—Absolute cluster performance

and a memory diagnostic, have been run on the initial Cm∗ system (one cluster, two modules). Measurements of the performance degradation when code and local variables are kept local but the area being sorted or diagnosed is moved to the other processor in the cluster indicate that local hit ratios of 90 percent or higher are being obtained in both cases. Expensive operating system functions such as block transfers are expected to lower this figure, but it is also expected that most user programs will make less intensive use of shared databases than the above examples.

The queueing model was used to predict the degradation of cluster performance if either the Pmap were made slower (and thus cheaper) or if the concurrency of the mapping mechanism were eliminated. The results for a cluster con-

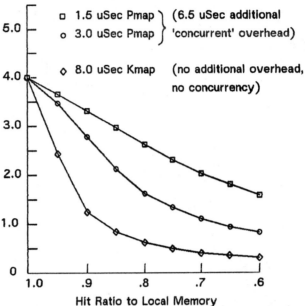

Figure 16—Cluster performance with slower Pmap or without concurrency between Pmap and Map Bus

taining twelve processors are shown in Figure 16. A slower Pmap was modelled by increasing its service time from 1.5 to 3.0 microseconds. The last model represents a cluster implementation where each external reference is carried to completion before servicing subsequent requests. This would be the situation if only one Pmap Context were provided, i.e., eliminating the concurrency between the Map Bus and the Pmap. Both the slow and non-concurrent clusters show enormous performance losses, especially at the low end of the 85 to 95 percent hit ratio range. The inability of slower or non-concurrent Kmaps to support large numbers of modules implies a need for more Kmaps per Cm∗ system. It also suggests that more intercluster communication will be required since each module will have fewer immediate neighbors.

CONCLUSION

Detailed hardware design of Cm∗ begain in late July, 1975. The initial goal of a 10 processor, three cluster system is expected to be realized in the first quarter of 1977. Considering the Kmap alone, the time from the beginning of design to a working prototype (excluding the Linc) was less than nine months. It is felt that this relatively short development time is due to extensive use of automated design aids, microprogramming at almost every level and the inclusion of additional hardware to aid in debugging. The Hooks facility in the Kmap has been particularly successful. However it will not be possible to declare the overall system a success until it is regularly and reliably supporting a community of satisfied users.

REFERENCES

1. Swan, R. J., S. H. Fuller, and D. P. Siewiorek, "Cm*: a Modular, Multi-Microprocessor", *AFIPS Conference Proceedings,* Vol. 46, 1977 National Computer Conference.
2. Bell, C. G. and A. Newell, *Computer Structures: Readings and Examples,* McGraw-Hill, New York, New York, 1971.
3. Swan, R. J., L. Raskin and A. Bechtolsheim, "Deadlock Issues in the Design of the Linc," Internal Memo, Computer Science Dept., Carnegie-Mellon University, March 1976.
4. Swan, R. J., S. H. Fuller, and D. P. Siewiorek, "The Structure and Architecture of Cm*: A Modular, Multi-Microprocessor," *The Computer Science Department Research Review 1975-1976,* Carnegie-Mellon University, December 1976.
5. Brown, K. Q., "Simulation of a Cm* Cluster," Internal Memo, Computer Science Dept., Carnegie-Mellon University, May 1976.

A CONTROLLABLE MIMD ARCHITECTURE[a]

by

Stephen F. Lundstrom
George H. Barnes
Burroughs Corporation
Paoli, PA 19301

Abstract -- A MIMD architecture targeted at 1000 Mflop/sec has been described to NASA. This system is targeted to be the Flow Model Processor (FMP) in the Numerical Aerodynamic Simulator. This paper describes the strategies adopted for making a many-processor multiprocessor controllable and efficient, primarily by decisions that are made at compile time. Hardware features include the division of memory into space private to each processor and space shared by all, and a hardware synchronization of all processors. The connection network, connecting 512 processors to 521 memory modules, is an essential element.

Two main constructs are needed in the language to control the architecture. First, an expression that a number of instances of a given section of code can be executed concurrently, and second, a determination as to whether variables are local to the instance or global to the entire program.

Performance validations used whole programs, not kernels. Simulation and analysis combine to demonstrate achievement of the goal of 1000 Mflop/sec on suitable programs and good performance on others.

Introduction

Present generation very-high-speed computers generally exploit vector algorithms for their highest performance. A study for NASA Ames Research Center was conducted to determine the feasibility of a "Flow Model Processor" (FMP) which could achieve a sustained computational rate of one billion floating point operations per second on complete aerodynamics flow programs [1]. It concluded that the dependence on vector operations for high throughput was no longer necessary.

Given that device technology has been fully utilized, parallelism can be used to achieve performance beyond that possible with a uniprocessor. Historically, two approaches have been used to achieve parallelism: a pipeline

where parallelism is achieved by each stage of the pipeline operating on a different step of successive operation, or an array of identical execution units each simultaneously evaluating the same instruction on different data. References [2,3,4, and 5] have recent examples of both. In either case the result is a vector machine where the data comes from orderly addresses in memory and the same instruction acts on each data element.

The Flow Model Processor makes use of the parallelism of a MIMD (multiple instruction stream, multiple data stream) architecture. The architecture includes specific features so that a single program can be issued to all the processors and result in cooperative execution on a single application for a single user.

This paper describes motivations behind the design and some of the strategies used to ensure controllability. The architecture described here avoids or sidesteps the limitation observed in some MIMD architectures which are unable to utilize more than a few processors effectively. The result is an architecture that is somewhat specialized to a class of applications (although much less specialized than a vector machine would be). This architecture exploits any concurrency inherent in the problem, whether or not that concurrency can be described as vector operations.

The problem was approached by first studying the aerodynamic applications [6]. These applications have a large numerical component, much inherent concurrency, and simple control structures. Due to the wide variation in the amount of computation that may concurrently proceed between times at which synchronization is required, efficient implementation of the synchronization function is required. Due to the many different natural modes of accessing data, a large memory equally accessible to all processors is required. Due to the practical limitation on the speed attainable in a large common memory, and due to the need for speed, an architecture is required which allows many memory accesses to be from memory local to each processor.

Software strategy is based on the premise that source text submitted to the compiler should

---

[a]This work was done for NASA under Contract NAS2-9897 and reported to them in [1].

Reprinted from *Proceedings of the 1980 International Conference on Parallel Processing*, 1980, pages 19-27. Copyright © 1980 by The Institute of Electrical and Electronics Engineers, Inc.

result in a single program being compiled for all processors in the array which will then execute it cooperatively. This premise is also advocated in [7]. From another point of view, the compiler emits a single program which is to be executed independently by each of the processors in the array. Included by this program are instructions which cause the processors to cooperate by sharing data and by synchronizing their actions appropriately when needed.

A second element of the strategy is to make certain decisions at compile time instead of run time. These decisions can then be supported by efficient hardware mechanisms, not by system software.

The functional constructs on which a language for this architecture is to be based can be compared to discussions previously found in the literature. A general discussion of parallel languages is found in [8]. Some proposed parallel languages are directed at the vector type of architecture, as in [9,10,11,12], others are not [13,14,15]. Some workers have proposed that the requisite parallelism can be found by starting from algorithms expressed in serial form [16,17] so that standard Fortran can be mapped onto various parallel architectures without language extensions. In the present case the architecture is such that the operations which can be done independently of each other and in parallel are whole sections of code, not restricted to single operations.

We believe that the architecture proposed here has several advantages over other parallel architectures previously proposed and that the simulations and performance validations reported below uphold this view. While no single feature of this architecture is by itself new, we believe the combination of features is. Some previously proposed architectures have all memory shared among all processors, [18, 19, 20, 21] but without processor private memory for data. In some cases, a central control processor is involved with the control of interconnections between processors, or from processors to memory [22]. N such centralized control is required here during execution of user programs. To our knowledge, fast hardware synchronization as seen here has not been proposed for MIMD architectures, although any SIMD machine, such as in [3], will be synchronized.

The development of the system concepts evolved from the applications to system architecture (involving both hardware and software) to a more detailed definition of both the hardware and software. In order to simplify the introduction of the software concepts, they will be preceded by a short summary of the hardware architecture. Following the software concept summary, a more detailed description of some parts of the hardware will be provided.

Hardware Overview

The block diagram of the proposed multiprocessor is shown in Figure 1. Salient features of this hardware are:

* A prime number of memory modules to reduce memory access conflicts.
* Separation of the memory space seen from each processor into a private part, and a section shared among all processors.
* A connection network whereby all processors can simultaneously request access to various memory modules.
* Hardware synhcronization, a P-way AND of the signal from each processor that marks its having gotten to a specific point in the program.

Each of the 512 processors has its own program counter, its own local memory for program and data, and its own connection to a shared memory. The shared memory is built of many (521) independently accessible modules. In order to provide connectivity between the processors and the memory modules, a connection network which has a complexity of $O(P \log(P))$, instead of the $O(P^2)$ complexity expected for a fully general cross-point network, was chosen. This choice satisfies both the economic requirements and the bandwidth requirements of the system. For discussion of the connection network, see [23].

Software

The expense involved in application software development and maintenance over the life of a system now often exceeds the total costs of operations support and acquisition/ amortization of the computational equipment especially in development environments. The development of any new capabilities for such environments must, therefore, carefully consider both efficient utilization of the computational facility and the efficiency with which application development can proceed. In the past, unfortunately, the emphasis has been almost entirely on efficient hardware utilization. The provision of capabilities to embed assembly or machine code within high-level languages such as FORTRAN are an example of this approach. One recently introduced extended FORTRAN supports both development, with application-oriented vector forms, and efficient hardware utilization [12].

The major concern during the study was the feasibility of a hardware system with the required sustained performance. Automatic conversion of standard FORTRAN was not required. Rather, the project emphasized the definition of FORTRAN extensions that provided efficient control of the hardware capabilities ease in application definition.

Language Overview

The basic language construct chosen for this

MIMD system was one of computational processes that proceed concurrently between appropriate synchronization points. This type of construct is clearly compatible with a MIMD system. Such a construct is also convenient for application descriptions in that it is more general than the vector forms currently in use. The concurrent processes may include boundary value computations and central value computations simultaneously. Thus, each program for the FMP has a structure of pieces of normal serial code, which describe the details of what must be done at a given time, or at a given element of some index set, embedded in a control structure that expresses the location of concurrency and where the synchronization must occur.

Three extensions to standard FORTRAN are proposed. The primary extension is the construct described above which allows the definition of the inherent concurrency in a process. This construct is called "DOALL". The second extension is a construct to allow the definition of index sets, called "DOMAIN"s. The third extension is a means for identifying the data or variable dependencies between the instances of various processes and for differentiating which variables or data are independent of the global process structure and are therefore local to a particular instance.

Domains

A means for describing index sets to the compiler is needed. In FMP FORTRAN such sets are called DOMAINs. A DOMAIN has an associated name and can be interpreted as a one or multi-dimensional index set. For example, the declaration
    DOMAIN/EYEJAY/: I=1, IMAX; J=1, JMAX
declares that there are IMAX*JMAX elements, each consisting of one pair of values of I and J, with values in the range shown. Standard set operators are allowed. For example, if one has also declared
        DOMAIN/KAY/: K=1,KMAX
then the cartesian product
        DOMAIN/IJK/: EYEJAY .X. KAY
defines a three-dimensional domain with extents in each dimension of IMAX, JMAX, and KMAX.

In the aero flow applications, only rectangular domains such as the example "IJK" were seen. Extensions to the domain concept will be needed for other applications. Simple modifications to domains can be implemented by conditional statements within the doall program segment.

In addition to their use in specifying the index sets for doalls as explained in the next section, domains can substitute for the iteration index sets in do loops, and for dimensionality in the declaration of arrays.

One convenient use of the DOMAIN construct is for the description of the geometry (or computational limits) of the problem. By naming the controlling index set, and referring to the index set by name throughout the rest of the program, changes relating to geometry need be made in only one place in the program.

DOALL Construct

The DOALL construct is the FMP FORTRAN extension for describing the inherent concurrency in a process. Figure 2 shows the conceptual flow of execution in this construct. Once the construct is entered, all individual parts may proceed simultaneously dependent on the availability of resources. Control is not allowed to pass beyond the construct until all individual parts (called instances) have completed whatever computation they are to do.

The doall construct consists of a "DOALL" header, followed by a doall program segment followed by a doall terminating delimiter. The header will contain a specification of a domain, perhaps by name. If the domain in the header is the domain "EYEJAY" as declared in the example of the previous section, and IMAX = 100 and JMAX = 50, then there are 5000 intances of the doall program segment to be executed. Each instance of the doall program segment can execute independently of, and without any interaction with, every other instance of the doall program segment. Within each instance, there may not be any references to computations within any other instance, but no restrictions on references to "old" values exist. The computation within each instance may be conditional on location in the model, on data, or on any other condition.

Hardware Support of the DOALL Construct

An issue is the mapping of the DOALL construct onto real processor resources. A DOALL construct execution begins when processors 0 through 511 pick up instance numbers 0 through 511. For a DOALL with I and J for instance variables as in the example above, each processor computes I and J values from the instance number by solving the equation
        instance number = $J*IMAX + I$
Specifically, I is instance number modulo IMAX and J is instance number DIV IMAX. When each processor has finished its instance of the DOALL program segments, it increments instance number by 512, computes new I and J values, and proceeds to iterate thus until the I and J values computed are outside the domain. Once the processor has completed all assigned instances, it drops down to a "WAIT" instruction. When all processors get to "WAIT", a 512-way AND of the WAITing state is used to create a "go" signal which causes all processors to step to the next construct or instruction. Thus, an essential feature to make the DOALL construct work is a fast hardware

synchronization operation. DOALL program segments can be as short as a single statement. A single-statement DOALL with regular subscripting on variables exactly corresponds to a vector operation in a vector machine and hence this MIMD architecture includes vector computations as a subset of its capabilities.

Waiting implies processor idle time. In the aerodynamic flow and weather codes which were analyzed during the study, the amount of processing per processor was nearly equal for all processors, and hence processor efficiency was high, the first processor to finish being only slightly ahead of the last.

Memory Allocation

System control is simplified by making decisions at compile time rather than having them made by system software art run time. The distinction between the various sorts of memory is made in the compiler with help from programmer declarations.

The potential four types of memory allocation are:

1. A variable or array element is visible to any part of the program, can be accessed from within any instance of a doall program segment, or from any serial section of code between doall program segments.

2. A variable is a temporary variable which need not remain defined after the end of the instance in which it is used.

3. A variable is so frequently accessed that each processor deserves to have its own local copy.

4. A one-to-one relationship between the elements of an array and the elements of a domain holds. Within the instances of a doall program segment over that domain, elements of that array are accessed in correspondence to the relationship.

The exact form of the declarations for helping the compiler make appropriate assignments of different data to different types of space is still under discussion. It is clear that some analysis on the compiler's part is possible; an array which is subscripted with the instance variables inside a doall must be either type 1 or type 4, for example. If the language is to be an extended Fortran, each common area must contain variables of only one category.

The sets of memory declarations suggested to date contain some common features. First, there is a declaration to the effect that a variable is shared (type 1). Second, there is a declaration (or default) that a variable is temporary to the instance (type 2). Third, there is a means for

declaring that a set of variables is of type 4. This last is the "INALL" declaration. The INALL declaration couples a variable or array with the dimensionality and index set of a domain. For example, the declaration

INALL/EYEJAY/ C1, C2, A(5)

declares that there is an element of C1, an element of C2 and five elements of A associated with each element of the domain "EYEJAY". When there is a doall construct over the domain "EYEJAY (I,J)" then these variables can be used with the doall program segment and each instance will have its own copy. Referring to a variable such as C2 either without subscripts, or with "centered subscripts" i.e., "C2(I,J)", is permissible and functionally identical. Outside of doalls over "EYEJAY", these three identifiers will identify arrays which have dimensionality C1(IMAX,JMAX), C2(IMAX,JMAX), and A(IMAX, JMAX,5) respectively.

Given that there are two kinds of memory space, memory private to each processor and memory shared by all processors, variables of type 2 and type 3 will be found in processor private memory, and type 1 would be in shared memory. If a variable of type 4 is only accessed within doalls over the appropriate domain, and always on centered subscripts, it can be held in the private memories of the processor that will compute the instances that are in one-to-one correspondence with the appropriate array elements.

Parallel Functions

Some common parallel operations and first-order linear recurrences would be supported by new intrinsics.

Parallel sum. Consider a variable defined within each instance at the end of a doall. The parallel sum of all those variables is created, which will then be accessible after the end of the doall. 512 such variables can be summed in 9 steps using interprocessor communication. Similar parallel functions are parallel AND, parallel OR, and MAXIMUM across all instances.

First-order linear recurrence. Given quantities B(I) and C(I) in each instance of a doall whose index set is I=1, IMAX, form the sequence A(I) = A(I-1)*B(I) + C(I). A(0) is given as an initial value. As with the parallel sum, this function can be implemented in N steps when IMAX = 2^N. [24]

Other Software Issues

Although the mechanisms shown demonstrate that one can design a langauge to enhance control of the MIMD machine by imposing structure and regularity on the MIMD interprocessor interactions at compile time, there are certain issues which have to be resolved before fixing on a final design for the language.

One issue is a trade between making memory allocation decisions based on programmer declarations and making allocation decisions by compiler analysis. Many users of high-throughput machines insist on being able to control every detail of machine action, out of fear that the vendor's compiler will be inefficient if left to its own devices.

Using Fortran as a starting point raises an issue that might not arise with some other starting point because of the requirement in Fortran for separate compilation. At compile time the compiler must distinguish between a subroutine called within a doall program segment where each instace of the doall calls its own copy, and a subroutine called outside the doall which runs on the array as a whole. The simplest solution would be to distinguish between the two kinds of subroutine by a difference in the SUBROUTINE statements.

"Every instance of the doall program segment must be independent of and free from any side effects that would interfere with any other instance of the same doall program segment". This over-simplified statement is true at the first level of understanding of the working of the machine. However, steps taken to enforce this rule are subject to a trade between authoritarian and libertarian schools of programming. There is no hardware limitation on the processors fetching or storing any variable in shared memory at any point in the program. Since the relative timing between actions that occur in different instances of the doall is not controlled, this allows for data accesses and definitions to occur in an uncontrolled order. Hence there is a question about the enforcement of data precedence. Absolute enforcement by the compiler, so that code which is emitted is guaranteed to be free of data precedence violations, may be undesirable. First, such a compiler will be unable to detect all cases in which the instances are independent of each other and as a result will forbid certain useful functions. Second, for some applications [25] a change in the sequence of performing the computations will change the result to another, different, but still acceptable result. One does not wish to forbid such programs. However, if the compiler made no check, gave the user no help, unnecessary errors might be committed. The following rule is observed to cover all cases that arise in the aero flow and weather codes, and appears simple to implement. "If an array element in shared memory is used on the right side of an assignment statement within a doall program segment then any assignment to that array in the same doall program segment must be on centered subscripts and will be held in a "new" copy of the array. The "new" copy will replace the old copy of the array at the time of synchronization at the end of the doall."

Hardware Details

Instead of implementation details, discussion below will concentrate on how hardware features support the langauge extensions.

Processor

Analysis of the aerodynamic flow and global weather model programs (provided by NASA Ames during the NASF Feasibility Study as samples of typical application programs) showed that up to several thousand processors could efficiently work in parallel. In these cases, the actual number of processors supplied is irrelevant over a large range; only total throughput matters. The design intent was to supply a processor that had maximum throughput at minimum cost. The trade-off evaluation was based on assumptions of the technology suitable for 1983 delivery and on the desire to limit complexity to control project risk. The result was 512 processors, each having capability of about 3Mflop/sec.

Each processor has independent integer and floating-point execution units with limited instruction look-ahead. To hide access time of the shared memory, each processor has a one-slot queue, called the "CN Buffer", which manages accesses to the shared memory while other processor operations go on concurrently. A processor-local memory of about 32K words is appropriate to the applications studied.

Shared Memory

In reference (1), the shared memory is called "Extended Memory" (EM). It consists of a prime number of memory modules (521) in order to reduce conflicts for the case that the pattern of accesses from the processors forms a regular pattern [26,27].

All processors independently compute accesses in shared memory, and independently access memory. Given that processor no. i is to access shared memory address A(i) the processor will compute address-within-module given by

$$L(i) = A(i) \text{ DIV } 512$$

and module number

$$M(i) = A(i) \text{ modulo } 521$$

When the addresses being accessed by the processors form a vector with constant stride the formula for the A(i) is

$$A(i)=A(0)+p*i$$

Here the M(i) fall into 512 different memory modules because p and the number of memory modules are relatively prime. This is the basis for claiming that a prime number of memory modules makes certain kinds of accessing "conflict-free".

Features for Fault Tolerance

Because of the flexibility of the connection network, a simple method of providing spare processors and memory modules is planned. Each

CN buffer contains a "replacement unit directory" to redirect connections around spare units. Single error correction, double error detection (SECDED) code covers all memory and transfers through the connection network. The connection network, being duplexed, has a simplex mode of operation as backup.

Staging Memory

Staging memory is called "Data Base Memory" in (1) where a size of 128 Mwd is assumed. Later discussions have centered on a size of 256 Mwd. Transfer rates must be on the order of 50 Mwd per second to and from shared memory. Access time requirements make disk undesirable. If staging memory were to be built of semiconductor components, then 256k-bit chips would be desirable.

The design and control of the staging memory has no surprises. The structure is one of a dual port memory. One port responds to requests from the coordinator for high-speed transfers between staging memory and Extended Memory. The other port is externally controlled and provides the high-speed data path to the rest of the system.

Connection Network

The connection network is used like a dial-up network, with any processor requesting connection to any memory module at any time, with the concommittant "message" being an address plus one word of data either stored to or fetched from the memory module involved. All processors could request simultaneously. Blockage must be low enough that the average added delay due to blockage is small compared to the time due to cable delays, access time of the memory module and memory conflicts. In addition processors must be treated "fairly". In the intended applications all processors have an equal amount of work to do. If any processor had a low probability of making its connections through the connection network, then that slower processor would tend to be the last processor arriving at the synchronization points, thereby slowing up the whole system.

The chosen configuration (Figure 3) is called the "baseline" network by Wu and Feng 28]. We first derived it as an isomorphism to the Omega network of Lawrie [29]. A parallel paper [22] discusses the design and validation of the connection network showing that it indeed performs as desired.

The time it takes to make a connection from any one of the 512 processors to any one of the 521 memory modules is estimated at 120 ns., barring conflicts or blockage. The throughput analysis of the FMP assumed a path width of 11 bits. During throughput analysis of the FMP, a particular distribution of shared memory conflicts and of blockage in the connection network was assumed. After the simulations to evaluate performance were nearly finished, simulation of the connection network [23] showed that the assumed delays were in fact correct.

Synchronization

Synchronization is mechanized by the WAIT instruction. A processor continues to execute WAIT until a "go" signal is received. The "go" signal is the 512-way AND of a signal emitted by each waiting processor. Synchronization ensures that no processor tries to fetch new data until that data has in fact been produced, perhaps by the slowest processor, in the preceding DOALL construct.

Figure 4 shows a mechanism whereby the 512-input AND gate is implemented as a tree-form cascade of 8-input AND gates (Figure 4 is actually drawn for a 27-input AND gate implemented as a cascade of 3-input AND gates; the number of levels in the tree comes out the same in either case). The root node of the tree reflects the "GO" signal back to all processors when the "AND" output is true at the root node. Note that the spare processors must always appear to be waiting even when being serviced or checked off-line from the primary problem.

The total delay from the last processor accessing a WAIT instruction until the "go" signal reaches all processors has been estimated at 160 ns.

Performance Validation

NASA had supplied two complete three-dimensional aerodynamic flow codes, solutions of the time-averaged Navier Stokes equations, and some weather codes. Three of these programs were completely analyzed. The method of analysis was to determine the calling sequence, the path of execution through the entire program, with notations as to how often each section of the code was called. Appropriate DO loops were converted into concurrent "DOALL" constructs in which DO iterations are converted into DOALL instances. Representative sections of the programs were exercised in simulation to determine running time. Other sections had their running estimated based on how their parameters were related to the parameters of the simulated sections. The most significant parameter was the number of floating point operations per reference to the shared memory. The running time and number of floating point operations in each section are each summed to give the running time for the whole program and the number of floating point operations for the whole program. The quotient of these two totals is then the throughput for the entire program in terms of floating point operations per second. Details are in [1] in Appendix A.

The results of this analysis are summarized in Table I. In brief, performance met the target of 1.0 Gflop/sec for favorable aerodynamic applications, and varied from 0.5 Gflop/sec on up for other suitable applications. The chemistry and radiation portions of the global circulation model were not vectorized, but consisted of a doall with one instance at each point on the globe; the doall program segment having much data dependent branching within it.

Conclusion

A generalization of vector architectures for high-throughput numerical computing has been presented. The lack of any need to vectorize the application should make it more widely applicable than are the current generation of vector machines. Validation using actual application programs supports the expectation of high throughput.

The three programming constructs are the parallel execution of many instances of the same code, the use of named index sets, and the concept of two types of memory, one private to a single instance, the other shared across the entire program.

Acknowledgements

In any project of this size, many people contribute. The authors have singled out, for special acknowledgement of their contributions, Howard Pearlmutter and Philip E. Shafer.

References

[1] Final Report, Numerical Aerodynamic Simulation Facility Feasibility Study, Contract No. NAS2-9897 Burroughs Corporation, Paoli, PA, for NASA Ames, March 1979.

[2] R. M. Russell, "The Cray-1 Computer System", Communications of the ACM, Volume 21, No. 1 January 1978, pp. 63-72.

[3] P. M. Flanders, D. J. Hunt, S. F. Reddaway, D. Parkinson, "Efficient High Speed Computing with the Distributed Array Processor", in High Speed Computer and Algorithm Organization, ed. D. J. Kuck, et al, Academic Press, 1977, pp. 85-89 (SIMD).

[4] R. A. Stokes, "Burroughs Scientific Processor", in High Speed Computer and Algorithm Organization, ed., D. J. Kuck et al, Academic Press, 1977 pp. 85-89.

[5] L. Fung, "A Massively Parallel Processing Computer", in High Speed Computer and Algorithm Organization, ed., D. J. Kuck et al, Academic Press 1977, pp. 203-204 (MPP).

[6] D. R. Chapman, "Computational Aerodynamics Development and Outlook", Dryden Lectureship in Research, 17th Aerospace Sciences Meeting 1979 NASA Technical Report 79-0129.

[7] T. Christopher, O. El-Dessouki, M. Evens, P. Greene, A. Hazra, W. Huen, A. Rastogi, R. Robinson, and W. Wojciechowski, "Uniprogramming a Network Computer", 1978 International Conference on Parallel Processing IEEE, Computer Society, Long Beach CA, 1978, pp. 312-138.

[8] D. J. Kuck, "A Survey of Parallel Machine Organization and Programming", Computing Survey, Volume 9, No. 1 (March 1977), pp. 29-60.

[9] D. H. Lawrie, T. Layman, D. Baer, J. M. Randal, "Glypnir - A Programming Language for Illiac IV", Communications of the ACM, Volume 18, No. 3, March 1975, pp. 157-164.

[10] E. W. Davis "STARAN Parallel Processor System Software", AFIPS National Computer Conference, 1974, pp. 17-22.

[11] J. R. Dingledine, H. G. Martin, and W. M. Patterson, "Operating System and Support Software for PEPE", Sagamore Conference on Parallel Processing, Proceedings, 1973 IEEE, pg. 170-178 (claims to describe PFOR).

[12] Burroughs Corporation, Burroughs Scientific Processor (BSP) Fortran Reference Manual, Ref. No. 1118338, February 1980, Paoli, PA.

[13] J. B. Dennis, D. P. Misunas, and C. K. Leung, "A Highly Parallel Processor Using a Data Flow Machine Language", Computation Structures Group Memo. 134, MIT, January 1977.

[14] P. Brinch-Hansen, "The Programming Language Concurrent Pascal", IEEE Transactions on Software Engineering, June, 1975, pp. 199-207.

[15] J. P. Anderson, "Program Structure for Parallel Processing", Communications of the ACM, Volume 8, No. 13 (December 1965), pp. 431-155. (Very early discussion of "conventional" multiprocessors).

[16] D. J. Kuck, P. P. Budnick, S. C. Chen, E. W. Davis, Jr., J. C. Han, P. W. Kraska, D. H. Lawrie, Y. Muraoka, R. E. Strebendt, and R. A. Towle, "Measurements of Parallelism in Ordinary Fortran Programs", IEEE Computer, Vol. 7, No. 1, pp. 37-46, Jan, 1974.

[17] Leslie Lamport, "Parallel Execution of DO Loops", Communications of the ACM, Volume 17, No. 2, February 1974, pp. 83-93.

[18] R. J. Swan, S. H. Fuller, D. P. Siewiorek, "Cm*, a Modular, Multiprocessor", in "Collection

of Papers on Cm*", Technical Report, Computer Science Dept., Carnegie-Mellon University, February, 1977.

[19] W. A. Wulf, C. G. Bell, "C.mmp - A Multi-mini-processor", AFIPS Conference Proceedings Vol. 14, Part II, FJCC 1972, pp. 765-777.

[20] H. J. Siegel, P. T. Mueller, Jr., and H. E. Smalley, Jr., "Control of a Partitionable Multi-microprocessor System", Proceedings of the 1978 International Conference on Parallel Processing, IEEE Computer Society, 1978.

[21] Burton J. Smith, "A Pipelined, Shared Resource MIND Computer", Proceedings of the 1978 International Conference on Parallel Processing, IEEE Computer Society, 1978.

[22] R. Kober, C. H. Kunzia, "SMS - A Multi-processor Architecture for High Speed Numerical Calculations", Proceedings of the 1978 Inter-atnional Conference on Parallel Processing, IEEE Computer Society, 19781.

[23] G. H. Barnes, "Design and Validation of a Connection Network for Many-processor Multi-processor Systems", this conference.

[24] S. C. Chen, D. J. Kuck, "Time and Parallel Processor Bounds for Linear Recurrence System", IEEE Transactions on Computers, Volume C-24, No. 7, July 1975, pp. 701-717.

[25] Gerald M. Baudet "Asynchronous Iterative Methods for Multiprocessors", Journal of the ACM, Volume 25, No. 2, April 1978, pp. 226-244.

[26] P. Budnick and D. J. Kuck, "The Organization and Use of Parallel Memories", IEEE Transactions on Computers, December 1971.

[27] Roger C. Swanson, "Interconnection for Parallel Memories to Unscramble p-ordered Vectors, IEEE Transactions on Computers, November 1974.

[28] C. Wu and T. Feng, "Routing Techniques for a Class of Multistage Interconnection Networks", Proceedings of the 1978 International Conference on Parallel Processing, IEEE Computer Society, 1978.

[29] D. H. Lawrie, "Access and Alignment of Data in an Array Processor", IEEE Transactions on Computers, C-24 (1975), pp. 1145-1155.

Table I

Performance Summary

Case	Grid Size	No. Time Step	Thru put, Gf/s	Run Time min.
Implicit	100x 50x200	100	1.01	6
Explicit	100x100x100	100	0.89	9
Weather	89x144x 9	1008	0.53	4.5
FFT	512 to 4096	-	0.45-0.7	-

Implicit = Implicit Aero Flow Code
Explicit = Mixed Explicit/Implicit Aero Flow Code
Weather = Global Circulation Model
FFT   = Fast Fourier Transform

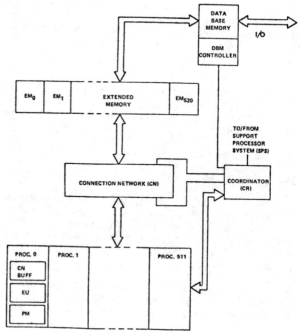

Fig. 1. Block Diagram

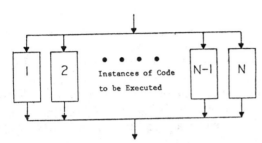

Fig. 2. Flowchart, Concurrent Construct

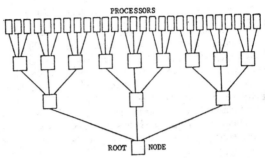

Fig. 4. Tree Form of AND Implementation

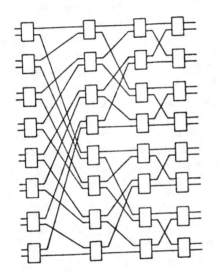

Fig. 3. Form of Connection Network

173

On the Effective Bandwidth of Parallel Memories

DONALD Y. CHANG, STUDENT MEMBER, IEEE, DAVID J. KUCK, MEMBER, IEEE, AND DUNCAN H. LAWRIE, MEMBER, IEEE

Reprinted from *IEEE Transactions on Computers*, Volume C-26, Number 5, May 1977, pages 480-489. Copyright © 1977 by The Institute of Electrical and Electronics Engineers, Inc.

Abstract—The object of this paper is to bring together several models of interleaved or parallel memory systems and to expose some of the underlying assumptions about the address streams in each model. We derive the performance for each model, either analytically or by simulation, and discuss why it yields better or worse performance than other models (e.g., because of dependencies in the address stream or hardware queues, etc.). We also show that the performance of a properly designed system can be a linear rather than a square root function of the number of memories and processors.

Index Terms—Array memory system, parallel memory bandwidth, parallel memory performance, memory interference, multiprocessor performance.

I. INTRODUCTION

ONE of the great advantages of multiprocessor organizations is that the relatively expensive primary and secondary memory can be shared by several relatively inexpensive processors. A primary weakness in such systems is that as the number of processors and resulting address streams grows, the effective system bandwidth drops off due to memory conflicts. If the number of parallel memory units is increased in an effort to enhance memory and system bandwidth, the effective rate of growth of these bandwidths is an important question. In commercially available systems, 4 processors and perhaps 8 to 16 memories have been limiting numbers, in contrast to much higher numbers of memories in array machines.

In parallel or pipeline machines, 64 or more memories are used in parallel to deliver a sufficiently high bandwidth. These machines are often accessing arrays of data for which special storage schemes can be used to provide conflict-free access [2], [11]. However, on some occasions they must perform random accesses; for example, whenever they access an array with subscripted subscripts.

In the past ten years, a variety of analytical results have been obtained concerning interleaved or parallel memories. Most of the results have been presented in a rather abstract way, without any clearly stated machine interpretations. We will interpret these results below and also provide some new results.

There are two key questions on which the validity and usefulness of these models turn. They are:

1) What kind of dependence is assumed in the memory access sequence?

2) What kind of queueing mechanism is assumed for retaining unserviced accesses?

There are several other questions which relate to the usefulness of the model but are of less importance in determining the general form of the results. These include how control dependence is handled and whether we study the steady-state or transient memory bandwidth. These are interrelated questions, and control dependence is also related to data dependence.

In these terms, we briefly summarize some of the results. Hellerman's model [9] can most reasonably be interpreted to assume no data dependence between successive memory accesses and to have no provision to queue conflicting addresses. It is also a steady-state model. Thus, it scans an infinite string of addresses, blocking when it finds the first duplicate memory unit access request.

In various models, Coffman and his co-workers [3]–[5], [7] extended the above to include a type of queueing and to separate data accesses from instruction accesses. These papers further introduced address sequences which were not necessarily uniformly distributed. These models also assumed that no dependencies existed in the address sequence.

Ravi [12] introduced a model which was more realistic for multiprocessor machines. He allows each processor to generate an address and compute the number of addresses which can be accessed without conflict, in a steady-state sense. He effectively assumes a sequential data dependence in the addresses generated by each processor. A similar model has been introduced by Bhandarkar [1].

In this paper the above results are extended in several ways. First, it is shown analytically that Ravi's model yields an effective memory bandwidth which is linear in the number of memory units. Several models are given with queues in the processors and in the memories to show the differing effects on bandwidth of such queues and methods used for managing the queues. Several types of dependencies are assumed to exist, some as in the Ravi model and others which include dependencies between the processors. In all of these models, we show that the effective bandwidth of m memories can be made to be $0(m)$. The models are useful for either multiprocessor or array machines.

In the models which follow we assume a parallel memory system, i.e., we assume that at a given instant of time some number of memory access requests are issued by the processors, conflicts are detected and resolved, and all m memory modules are then cycled together. However, our results should also indicate the performance of other types of interleaved memory systems, e.g., where processors and

Manuscript received September 22, 1975; revised February 17, 1976 and June 23, 1976. This work was supported in part by the National Science Foundation under Grant NSF DCR73-07980 A02.

The authors are with the Department of Computer Science, University of Illinois, Urbana, IL 61801.

EHO182-6/81/0000/0174 © 1977 IEEE

174

memories are operating asynchronously or where access requests arrive at random times. For the remainder of this paper we will use the words interleaved and parallel interchangeably, even though we are referring specifically to a parallel memory system.

Thus, we conclude that for array or multiprocessor machines, the proper use of m parallel memories can lead to effective bandwidths which are $0(m)$. This is much more encouraging than the $0(m^{1/2})$ which was derived from earlier, simpler models.

II. DEPENDENCY

In order to clarify some of the differences between the following models it is necessary to discuss some of the attributes of the address stream. We assume a stream of addresses which represent requests for memory accesses generated by a program or programs, and these addresses can be instruction addresses, data addresses, or both. Between any two such addresses there may be what we call a *dependency*. We define a dependency as a logical relationship between two addresses such that the second address cannot be accessed (written or read) until after the first has been accessed. We further define four classes of dependency as illustrated in Fig. 1, where each node represents a memory address (request for access) and each link a dependency.

Clearly, the class of dependency has a bearing on the performance of an interleaved memory system. For example, if we assume Class A, then we cannot access one address until its predecessor has been accessed and we can get no speedup from interleaving—our bandwidth will be 1. On the other hand, if we could assume Class D, then with sufficient hardware we could get the maximum possible effectiveness from interleaved memories.

Each dependency class can be thought of as a minimal assumption about the actual dependencies which must be accounted for in a real instruction stream. For example, given an address stream with dependencies as shown in Fig. 2, we could say these dependencies are "covered" by Class A or Class B dependencies but not by Class C or D.

Thus, any of the following models which assume Class A or Class B dependencies will correctly or conservatively predict the preformance, given the address stream of Fig. 2. Models assuming Class C or D would yield overly optimistic results. It is easy to see that the four classes of dependency are ordered, e.g., any dependencies covered by Class B must also be covered by Class A, etc.

Note, however, that we are only concerned with these dependencies as they are seen by a memory service unit. Thus, while the original address stream may have dependencies which can only be covered by Class A, sufficient lookahead and queueing hardware (cf., Tomasulo [16]) might allow the memory service unit to effectively ignore dependencies, and service addresses in any order at least over large portions of the address stream. Sophisticated compiler techniques might also be used to rearrange

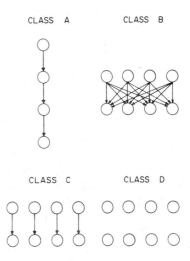

Fig. 1. Dependency classes.

dependencies to allow assumption of a less restrictive class of dependencies.

We might associate each dependency class with some computer architecture. For example, Class A corresponds to a uniprocessor, monoprogrammed machine which has no capability for detecting or bypassing dependencies. For such a machine we would have to assume Class A since the addresses would have to be serviced in strict order. Similarly, Class B might correspond to a multifunction machine (e.g., GDC 6600) or array machine (e.g., TI ASC or Illiac IV), Class C to a multiprocessor machine (e.g., B6700 or Univac 1110), and Class D to a machine capable of instruction level multiprogramming (from a large number of jobs), or a machine with sufficient lookahead and queueing hardware to allow dependencies to be bypassed (e.g., IBM 360/91).

It is also possible to associate each dependency class with certain classes of program segments. For example, the data dependencies corresponding to each program segment below can be minimally covered by Class B, C, and D dependencies, respectively.

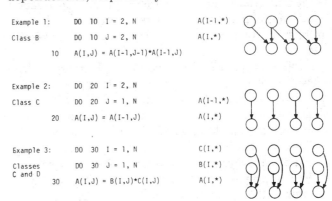

Notice the program segment in Example 3 is really Class C. However, we can consider the fetch requests for the arrays *B* and *C* to belong to Class D, so that we can use models of Class D dependencies at least in a piecewise fashion. The extent to which we could exploit the independence of these fetches would, of course, depend on the

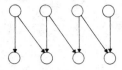

Fig. 2. Dependency covered by class B.

presence of data queues and instruction lookahead hardware in a particular machine.

Clearly, neither an architecture nor program alone determines a dependency class. This must be done by considering both. In the following we associate each class with one of the following models of interleaved memory performance. We leave it to the reader to decide which dependency class he can assume, given a specific architecture and program, and thus which performance model to use.

III. INTERLEAVED MEMORY MODELS

In this section we will discuss the models by Hellerman [9], Snowdon, Burnett, and Coffman [7], and Ravi [12], and we will also present three new models. In each case our measure of performance will be the effective bandwidth of the memory system which is usually defined to be the average number of memory accesses per memory cycle. We make the usual distinction between steady-state bandwidth and average bandwidth (which includes the effects of initial and/or final transients), and present one or both of these measures for each model. Some of our results are analytic, others have been obtained by simulation. Details of the analyses and simulation are deferred to the Appendices. We now present these models in an order corresponding to the ordering of the dependence class to which they are applicable.

Models for Class B Dependencies

Our first model, which we designate model I, works on an address stream with dependencies covered by Class B (see Fig. 1). Thus, we assume we have our addresses arranged in groups such that there are no dependencies within a group but there may be dependencies between groups. We further assume each group contains exactly p addresses.

By an address we mean an ordinary memory address. However, we are only concerned with that part of the address which designates the memory number. Hence, we shall assume that an address is any integer between 0 and $m - 1$ where m is the total number of memories.

An example of a machine which might work like this would be an array processor with p processors which must satisfy all p memory requests for one vector before proceeding to the next p requests.

As each group of addresses is issued, each memory module receives zero, one, or more access requests. In those memories where more than one request is received, one request is satisfied and the remaining requests must wait for subsequent memory cycles. This process can be seen graphically in Fig. 3.

Obviously, the bandwidth of this model depends on the maximum height of the distribution in Fig. 3. In the above case, the maximum height is 3 so we access 10 words in 3 memory cycles. We can define the bandwidth of this case to be 10/3 (words/cycle). Thus, the steady-state bandwidth of the model can be found by computing the expected value of the maximum height H_{av} of the request distribution where H_{av} can be shown to be (see Appendix A)

$$H_{av} = \sum_{h=1}^{p} h g(h)$$

$$= \sum_{h=1}^{p} h$$

$$\times \frac{\sum_{j=1}^{\lfloor p/h \rfloor} \left(\prod_{k=0}^{j-1} \binom{p-k \cdot h}{h} \right) \binom{m}{j} f_{p-j \cdot h}(m-j, h-1)}{m^p}$$

where the function $g(h)$ is the probability that the maximum height of the distribution is h.

Given H_{av}, we can compute the steady-state bandwidth $B_{ss} = p/H_{av}$. In Fig. 4 we plot B_{ss} as a function of p for fixed ratios $r = p/m$. One of the important things to notice in Fig. 4 is that the bandwidth appears to be linear in p for a fixed ratio of p/m.

Models for Class C Dependencies

Ravi [12] presented a model which, while not explicitly stated as such, is based on Class C dependencies. During each cycle, p access requests are generated. Ravi gives a formula for computing the average number of *distinct* integers in a group of p integers chosen uniformly from the integers 0 to $m - 1$. He takes this value to be the steady-state bandwidth. This is a well-known combinatorial problem and the solution is

$$B_{ss} = \sum_{k=1}^{t} k \frac{k! S(p,k) \binom{m}{k}}{m^p} \tag{3.1}$$

where $t = \min(m,p)$, $S(p,k)$ is the Stirling number of the second kind, and $k! S(p,k)$ is the number of ways to put p distinct requests into k distinct memory modules with each module holding at least one request.

Actually, (3.1) can be reduced to a very simple closed form, that is

$$B_{ss} = m \left[1 - \left(1 - \frac{1}{m} \right)^p \right].$$

We show this derivation in Appendix B.[1] If we plot this result against p for fixed ratios $r = p/m$, we get a family of curves which are asymptotically linear as shown in Fig. 5. This is not surprising since the above result can be further reduced to an asymptotic form by using the fact that

---

[1] As this paper was going to press, we learned of the earlier work of Strecker [15] in which this same result was derived by a different argument. Several interesting variations were also considered there.

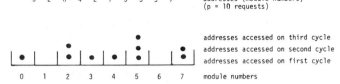

Fig. 3. Address accessing by model I.

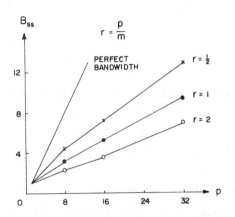

Fig. 4. Steady-state bandwidth for model I as a function of p for fixed $r = p/m$.

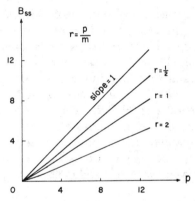

Fig. 5. Bandwidth of Ravi's model.

$$\lim_{p \to \infty} \left(1 - \frac{1}{m}\right)^p = \frac{1}{e^r}$$

Substituting this into the above equation, we get

$$\lim_{p \to \infty} B_{ss} = m \left[1 - \frac{1}{e^r}\right] = m\,\gamma(r),$$

$$\text{where } \gamma(r) = 1 - \frac{1}{e^r}$$

or

$$\lim_{p \to \infty} B_{ss} = \frac{p}{r}\left[1 - \frac{1}{e^r}\right] = p\,\xi(r),$$

$$\text{where } \xi(r) = \left(1 - \frac{1}{e^r}\right)\Big/ r$$

which is a linear function of either m or p, given a constant p/m ratio r. This linearity is important, and we will refer to it again in a later section.

Ravi essentially considered an abstract combinatorial

problem. We now ask if this model corresponds to any real machine. (In all fairness, we must point out that Ravi never claimed to satisfy Class C dependencies. In fact, he did not discuss dependencies at all.) First, we consider a multiprocessor system. Assume that each processor generates addresses as shown below for $p = 4$, $m = 5$.

processor

$$
\begin{array}{cccc}
0 & 1 & 2 & 3 \\
\hline
3 & 2 & 2 & 2 \\
4 & 3 & 0 & 1 \\
1 & 0 & 3 & 4
\end{array}
\Biggr\} \text{ addresses (module numbers)}
$$

Ravi would count the bandwidths as 2, 4, and 4, respectively (from the top), and would compute an average bandwidth for these three samples as $(2 + 4 + 4)/3 = 10/3$. He simply dropped unserviced requests between cycles—an unreasonable assumption in practice. But if we assume that no processor can issue a new request until its previous request is satisfied (Class C dependency), then the requests in the above example would be serviced as follows, where an x represents a request which cannot be satisfied due to a memory conflict.

Cycle 1:	3	2	x	x
Cycle 2:	4	3	2	x
Cycle 3:	1	0	x	2
Cycle 4:	—	—	0	1
Cycle 5:	—	—	3	4.

We would measure the bandwidth during the first three cycles as 2, 3, and 3, respectively, which differs from Ravi's result. The point is that in a sample with multiple conflicts (>2), Ravi only counts the sample once, but in fact the extra conflicts can go on to degrade later memory cycles. Thus, we would expect that Ravi's result would be somewhat optimistic.

In order to determine how optimistic Ravi's result might be, we define model II which works essentially like the above multiprocessor example. We assume p independent address streams, each uniformly distributed. We further assume that in any given stream, no address can be accessed until its predecessor has been accessed. Thus, at the beginning of a cycle, each processor attempts to get its next address accessed. Since there may be conflicts, some control function will decide which processor in each conflict group will be serviced. Those processors not being serviced will reissue their addresses during the next cycle.

Bhandarkar [1] uses a Markov chain method to solve this model. He presents a rather nice algorithm to evaluate the transition matrix of this Markov chain. However, his algorithm is very time-consuming. For example, with $p = 16$ and $m = 16$ it takes one hour of computation time on a DEC-10 system. Since analysis of this model is so time-consuming, we have used simulation techniques to determine the steady-state bandwidth of this model. Our results are shown in Fig. 6 along with Ravi's result.

Notice that in fact the results for model II are linear in p but are slightly worse than Ravi's result. The difference

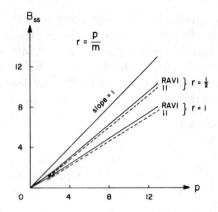

Fig. 6. Results for model II and for Ravi's model.

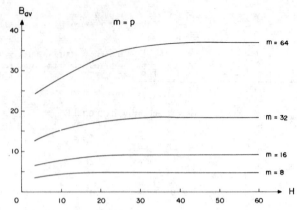

Fig. 7. Average bandwidth of model II as a function of the length H of each address stream using LEFT algorithm.

is no doubt due to a combination of the point discussed above and statistical error in the simulation. In fact, our results are very close to Bhandarkar's results [1], which are 6 to 8 percent lower than Ravi's results. In any event, the difference is barely significant at least for the values of p and r shown in Fig. 6.

Another interesting question about Class C models is the average versus the steady-state bandwidth. That is, let us assume that each independent address stream is finite with length H, so that the total number of addresses is $p \cdot H$. We can simulate this and determine the number of cycles, T, needed to access all $p \cdot H$ requests. We then define the average bandwidth to be $B_{av} = p \cdot H/T$. Results for these simulations are shown in Fig. 7 for various values of H and m, given $m = p$. (In fact, the steady-state bandwidths given previously were determined from the asymptotic value of curves like those shown in Fig. 7.)

Before proceeding any further, we need to discuss in more detail the conflict resolution process. As mentioned earlier, whenever a group of processors issues a set of addresses which are in conflict, a control function decides which processor in each conflict group will be serviced. When determining the steady-state bandwidth, the details of this process are unimportant. However, for the average bandwidth, we must consider them. Suppose this function always chooses to service the leftmost (LEFT) (lowest numbered) processor in each conflict group. Then, the leftmost processors will, on the average, get more requests serviced than those on the right, and will finish H requests sooner. The rightmost processors will then have to continue longer, thus increasing T and decreasing B_{av}. We define two other functions which should improve B_{av}: random selection (RAND), and least-used first (LUF). Under RAND, a processor is selected for service randomly in each conflict group. Under LUF, the processor in each conflict group which has had the least addresses accessed is selected.

We define the instantaneous bandwidth $B(t)$ to be the number of addresses accessed in cycle t. In Fig. 8, we plot $B(t)$ versus t for the three conflict resolution schemes. As we might have expected, using the LEFT algorithm, $B(t)$ begins to taper off much sooner and thus T_{LEFT} occurs much later (since the integral under each curve must equal

$p \cdot H$). RAND is the next best algorithm and of course LUF is best.

Models for Class D Dependencies

The addresses under Class D have no dependencies, and models which ignore dependencies, legitimately or otherwise, correspond to this class.

The first such model was presented by Hellerman [9]. Hellerman assumes a single stream of addresses. Addresses are examined in order until the first duplicate memory number is found. These first k distinct addresses are then accessed in parallel. Since these addresses are accessed in parallel, and since the first duplicate can occur anywhere, we must assume all the addresses are independent and have no dependencies. Hellerman apparently stops access of the first duplicate not because of data dependencies (although dependencies are not completely uncorrelated with duplicate memory numbers), but because it is assumed there is no hardware to allow us to look past the first duplicate.

The steady-state bandwidth for Hellerman's model can be taken to be the average length of an initial string of duplicate-free integers, i.e., the distance to the first duplicate. By a simple argument [8], the probability that k is the length of a string of distinct integers can be shown to be

$$P(k) = \frac{k(m-1)!}{m^k(m-k)!}.$$

Then the average length (and hence the steady-state bandwidth) will be

$$B_{ss} = \sum_{k=1}^{m} k\, P(k) \qquad (3.2)$$

$$= \sum_{k=1}^{m} \frac{k^2(m-1)!}{m^k(m-k)!}. \qquad (3.3)$$

When $1 \le m \le 45$, Hellerman found a good numerical approximation of the above equation to be $m^{0.56}$, or approximately $\sqrt{m}$. The error is no more than 4.3 percent.

Recently, Knuth and Rao [10] have shown a closed form for Hellerman's bandwidth:

$$B_{ss} = \sqrt{\frac{\pi m}{2}} - \frac{1}{3} + \frac{1}{12}\sqrt{\frac{\pi}{2m}} + 0(m^{-1}). \quad (3.4)$$

This confirms the fact that Hellerman's bandwidth is indeed aymptotic to $\sqrt{m}$.

Hellerman's model is the source of the frequently cited result that the effectiveness of an interleaved memory system is approximately equal to the *square root* of the number of memories. Notice, however, that this result applies to addresses in Class D, while for even more restrictive dependency classes we find that the effectiveness of interleaved memories is *linear* in m. This square root result is thus not inherent in interleaved memory systems nor is it due to dependencies, but is due simply to the assumption that we must stop examining addresses at the first duplicate.

Burnett and Coffman [4] introduced another generalization of the Hellerman model. They assumed that the addresses are *not* uniformly distributed but are determined by two parameters α and β. They assumed that the probability of a request addressing the next module in sequence (modulo m) will be α and the probability of addressing any other module out of sequence will be β, where $\beta = (1 - \alpha)/(m - 1)$. Or formally, let $y_1, y_2, \cdots, y_i, y_{i+1}, \cdots$ denote the input request stream, then

$$P(y_1 = j) = 1/m, j \in \{0, 1, \cdots, m-1\}$$
$$P(y_{i+1} = (y_i + 1) \bmod m) = \alpha, \quad i = 1, 2, \cdots$$
$$P(y_{i+1} = l) = \beta, \qquad l \neq (y_i + 1) \bmod m, i = 1, 2, \cdots.$$

For example, when $m = 8$ the eight-length sequence 06723145 would have probability $1/8\, \alpha^3\beta^4$. For this model it can be shown (see Appendix C) that

$$B_{ss} = \sum_{k=1}^{m} \sum_{j=0}^{k-1} \alpha^j \beta^{k-1-j} \sum_{h=1}^{k-1-j} (-1)^n$$
$$\cdot \binom{j+n}{n}\binom{k-1}{j+h}(m-j-n-1)_{k-j-n-1}.$$

The interesting result is that as α increases, the bandwidth increases exponentially. In any real program we would expect a nontrivial α because of the serial nature of instruction addresses and vector addresses. Thus, the result of Hellerman's model is conservative for this reason as well. (In fact, all the results in this paper will tend to be conservative since we usually assume a uniform address distribution.)

Coffman, Burnett, and Snowdon [7] later introduce a queue into their model which allows us to look beyond the first duplicate. Thus, we examine the address stream and each time we find a duplicate it is placed in a queue of size L. Without this queue, the address stream is blocked whenever an attempt is made to access a busy memory. With this queue, the address stream is not blocked unless a busy memory access is attempted and the queue is full. Their result shows the use of a queue can greatly improve the bandwidth. For example, if $\alpha = 0.25$ and $m = 16$, the bandwidth is about 4.5 when no queue is used but jumps

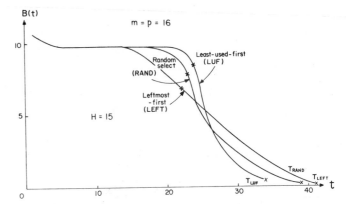

Fig. 8. Addresses accessed in cycle t for three conflict resolution functions.

to 9.5 if a queue of length 4 is used. Clearly, as $L \to \infty$ the bandwidth approaches m.

We now introduce our model III which includes a request queue of size Q in each memory module. We again assume p processors (or request generators) and m memory modules. At the beginning of every memory cycle, each processor issues a request to access a memory module. A memory module may receive zero, one, or more than one such request. Each memory selects for access a request from its queue of previous requests or, if the queue is empty it accepts one of the current requests. It then attempts to queue the remaining requests according to some algorithm (e.g., LUF, LEFT, or RAND). If a memory receives more requests than it can queue, then the processors which submitted the unqueueable requests are blocked and will resubmit their request during the next memory cycle. (Further details of this model can be found in [6].) Notice that if $Q = 0$, this model is equivalent to our model II. If $Q \geq 1$, then we have effectively increased the number of outstanding requests which the memories can try to access and thus the effective bandwidth should be improved. We shall show that this is indeed the case.

Notice, however, that with $Q \geq 1$ it is possible for a processor to have more than one request satisfied in one memory cycle (e.g., its current request in one memory plus some previously queued requests in other memories). Thus, the processors must be capable of accepting during one memory cycle the result of several memory requests. This can mean additional hardware in the form of extra data paths and/or queues.

Since this model is difficult to analyze, we again use simulation to get our results. We define Q to be the size of each memory queue and H to be the total number of requests generated by a processor. Fig. 9 shows the average bandwidth B_{av} as a function of H for various values of m (assuming $m = p$ and using the LEFT algorithm).

As we can see, adding queues to the memories does improve the bandwidth of the system (see also Fig. 10). The average bandwidth can again be improved by using a better conflict resolution algorithm (which only needs to be applied when a queue is full). By using LUF we get a 27 percent improvement over LEFT.

Fig. 10 shows the B_{ss} curves as a function of p, where

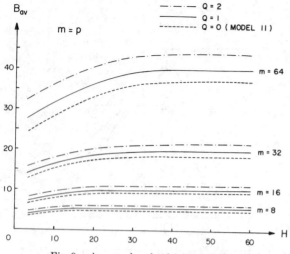

Fig. 9. Average bandwidth of model III.

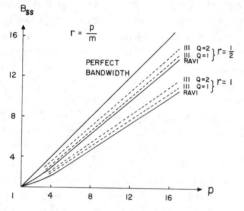

Fig. 10. Steady-state bandwidths.

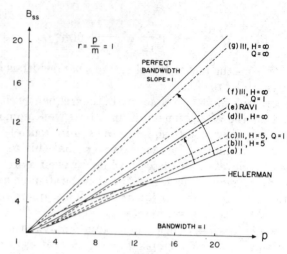

Fig. 11. Comparison of the bandwidths of various models.

again we define $B_{ss} = \lim_{H \to \infty} B_{av}$. Apparently, if we build a queue in each memory module, the resulting bandwidth will be larger than what Ravi or our model II would predict. The reason is simple. No matter what the new requests are, the requests left in queues can only enhance the bandwidth.

Fig. 10 shows that when $r = 1$, we get an approximate 5 percent improvement over Ravi's model if we use memory queues of length 1, and an approximate 10 percent improvement over Ravi's model if we use a queue of length 2. Clearly, this model displays the best performance among all the models. However, this model can only be used for Class D dependency since it does not preserve the order of the requests. It also requires significantly more hardware for queues, queue management, data transmission, etc.

IV. CONCLUSION

Comparison of Performances

In order to compare the performances of these models, we summarize their bandwidth curves in one graph. Fig. 11 shows the bandwidth versus p curves when $m = p$. Of course, perfect bandwidth (slope = 1 line) is the best we can ever achieve, so that no model will surpass it. Also none

will fall below the $B_{av} = 1$ line, which is the worst case and corresponds to type A problems. All the performances lie between these two lines.

Line a is the analytical result of model I when $m = p$. All analytical results can be viewed as the steady-state bandwidth. This line is the lower bound of both model II and model III, since it corresponds to the special case of $H = 1$. Line e is the Ravi result when $r = 1$ ($B_{ss} = p(1 - 1/e)$), which is the upper bound for model II. So the performance of model II swings from line a to line e. When we increase H, the bandwidth curve will move from a to b, which corresponds to $H = 5$, then to d when H gets very large.

Line f is the steady-state bandwidth of model III with queue length 1; it is above Ravi's line. When we increase the queue length, the bandwidth curve keeps going up until reaching line g, which corresponds to infinite queue length. So the bandwidth of model III has an even wider range, which goes from line a to line g.

From this diagram, one can get a rough idea of how good these models can be and how they change with respect to the parameters. For other ratios of m and p, the relative positions of these curves remain the same. When r gets smaller (more memory modules than processors) all the curves move upward, and when r gets larger they move downward.

The most important thing about this diagram is that all the bandwidth curves, both steady state and transient, are linear when we fix the ratio r. This linearity has important implications for the design of multiprocessor machines. In Fig. 11 we also indicate Hellerman's curve, which is proportional to the square root of p, rather than linear.

Comparison of Costs

Another important thing we should consider is the cost to implement the models (see also Chang [6]). Models I and II have very similar structure and control. The cost depends on the complexity of the conflict resolution box and the switching network. A simple design might be very cheap. As mentioned before, model I needs only the sim-

TABLE I

Model	Dependency Type	Performance	Usefulness
I	B	worst linear	Vector, SIMD machines.
Ravi	C	good	MIMD machines, standard multiprocessor machine executing independent tasks.
II	C	good	
Hellerman	D	square root	Tomasulo type machines, or SIMD, MIMD machines executing programs or parts of programs with no dependencies
Coffman, Burnett and Snowdon	D	good	
III	D	best	

plest circuit, so the cost of building it would not be high. For model II, however, a very good conflict resolution scheme such as LUF would increase the cost.

Hellerman's model needs only a very simple control unit, so the cost will be low. Coffman, Burnett, and Snowdon's model [7] needs only an extra queue and a relatively simple control unit, so its cost will also be rather low.

From a bandwidth point of view, model III is the best one. However, as we discussed in the last section, this model needs a more complicated conflict resolution circuit and switching network. Besides, it is very expensive to build queues into the memory. Overall then, the cost of this scheme is highest of all the models.

An additional cost which we have not discussed is that associated with special control unit functions (e.g., Tomasulo algorithm [16]) or sophisticated compiler techniques which allow us to take advantage of the least possibly restrictive dependency class or to alter the request stream so that the memories see a less restrictive class. This cost is dependent on the total system design. For example, it is easy to assume Class C dependencies in a multiprocessor, multiprogrammed machine (p independent request streams from p programs in p processors). On the other hand, the amount of hardware/software we would need to produce Class D requests in a monoprogrammed, monoprocessor would be very high. A detailed discussion of these costs is beyond the scope of this paper.

Summary

Table I summarizes the performances and usefulness of all the models discussed in this paper. Together with that information is the dependency class for each model. This table shows the overall result, which can be used as a guide for memory design.

In this paper we have attempted to provide further in-

sight into the nature of the bandwidth of interleaved memory systems by bringing together several different models and exposing some of the underlying assumptions about the request streams. Clearly, the bandwidth for a given number of processors and memories is determined by several factors. First, the degree of dependence between addresses can be seen to affect bandwidth by observing the curves for models I, II, and III in Fig. 11. Thus, if we can reduce dependencies by program transformations at compile time and/or by special hardware (e.g., Tomasulo [16]) at run time, or if we take advantage of existing dependence patterns as in Classes B, C or D, at least over portions of a program, then we can improve bandwidth.

Second, as dependence decreases, bandwidth can be further improved by using some form of queueing hardware. This effect can be seen by observing the difference in Fig. 11 between Hellerman's model (no queueing), Coffman, Burnett, and Snowdon's model [7] (some queueing), and our model III (more queueing).

Finally, we have tried to dispel the popularly held notion that interleaved memory performance is necessarily a function of the square root of the size of the system. Models I, II, and III, and Ravi's model all display a linear improvement with increasing p for a fixed p/m ratio.

APPENDIX A

Derivation of H_{av} for Model I

The expression in the numerator of $g(h)$ is the total number of sequences such that at least one module number occurs exactly h times and other module numbers occur no more than h times. The denominator m^p is the number of all possible sequences with repetitions. The ratio thus gives the probability function.

Notice that there might be more than one number that

occurs h times. The maximum number of such numbers (each occurs exactly h times) is $\lfloor p/h \rfloor$ which serves as the upper limit of the summation.

The product of the binomial coefficients is the total number of ways to choose $j*h$ positions out of p positions so as to distribute those j numbers with each occurring exactly h times. $\binom{m}{j}$ chooses j numbers from m possible module numbers.

$f_{p-j*h}(m-j, h-1)$ takes care of the rest of the positions. The function $f_n(m,s)$ is the number of ways to distribute n distinct objects into m distinct boxes such that each box contains at most s objects. This is the coefficient of the $t^n/n!$ term of the following generating function:

$$(1 + t + t^2/2! + \cdots + t^s/s!)^m = \Sigma f_n(m,s) t^n/n!$$

The solution will be the following recurrence:

$$f_n(m,s) = m f_{n-1}(m,s) - m \binom{n-1}{s} f_{n-1-a}(m-1,s).$$

The boundary conditions are

$$f_n(m,s) = m^n \qquad if\ n \leq s$$
$$f_{s+1}(m,s) = m^{s+1} - m$$
$$f_{s+2}(m,s) = m^{s+2} - m - (m)_2(s+2)$$
$$f_{s+3}(m,s) = m^{s+3} - m - (m)_2 \binom{s+4}{2}$$
$$- (m)_3 \binom{s+3}{2}.$$

This can be found in [13, ch. 5].

APPENDIX B

Simplification of Ravi's Bandwidth Equation

Ravi's bandwidth equation (3.1) is repeated here:

$$B_{ss} = \sum_{k=1}^{t} k \frac{k! \, S(p,k) \binom{m}{k}}{m^p}, \qquad \text{where } t = \min(m,p).$$

$$\text{(B1)}$$

This equation can be simplified to a simple closed form of m and p only. Since the upper limit t has two different possible values, we will split the derivation into two different cases: one for $t = m$ and one for $t = p$, but the results of the two cases will be the same.

First, let $t = p$, i.e., $p \leq m$. Equation (B1) becomes

$$B_{ss} = \sum_{k=1}^{p} \frac{k \, k! \, S(p,k) \binom{m}{k}}{m^p}.$$

Let us take a look at the numerator. Since

$$k k! \binom{m}{k} = m (m-1)(m-2) \cdots (m-k+1) k$$

$$= m (m-1)(m-2) \cdots (m-k+1)(m-(m-k))$$
$$= m^2(m-1) \cdots (m-k+1)$$
$$- m (m-1) \cdots (m-k)$$

$$= m k! \binom{m}{k} - m k! \binom{m-1}{k},$$

the numerator becomes

$$m \sum_{k=1}^{p} \left(k! \binom{m}{k} - k! \binom{m-1}{k} \right) S(p,k)$$

$$= m \sum_{k=1}^{p} k! \binom{m}{k} S(p,k) - m \sum_{k=1}^{p} k! \binom{m-1}{k} S(p,k).$$

By the definition of Stirling numbers of the second kind:

$$m^p = \sum_{k=1}^{p} k! \binom{m}{k} S(p,k).$$

Thus, the above expression becomes

$$m^{p+1} - m(m-1)^p.$$

Hence, when $p \leq m$, (B1) can be simplified to be

$$B_{ss} = \frac{m^{p+1} - m(m-1)^p}{m^p} = m[1 - (1 - 1/m)^p].$$

Now let $t = m$, i.e., $p > m$. We cannot use the same trick again since the upper limit is not p any more. Instead we substitute $\Sigma_{i=1}^{k} (-1)^i \binom{k}{i}(k-i)^p$ for $k! S(p,k)$ and we get

$$B_{ss} = \sum_{k=1}^{m} \frac{k \left(\sum_{i=0}^{k} (-1)^i \binom{k}{i} (k-i)^p \right) \binom{m}{k}}{m^p}.$$

The upper limit of the summation in the numerator can be changed to $k - 1$, since when $i = k$, $(k-i)^p$ becomes 0.

Now, we just expand these two summations and place the $m(1 + m)/2$ terms in an upper triangle (for $k = 1$, we get one term; for $k = 2$, we get two terms; etc.), then all terms on a diagonal have the same factor and the coefficients change regularly. We start from the upper right corner and sum the terms diagonally, and we get expression (B2) for the numerator.

$$m^{p+1} - m(m-1)^p + \sum_{i=2}^{m-1} a_i (m-i)^p \qquad \text{(B.2)}$$

where

$$a_i = \sum_{j=0}^{i} (-1)^j (m-i+j) \binom{m}{m-i+j} \binom{m-i+j}{j}.$$

It is easy to prove that a_i is equal to 0 for all i:

$$\sum_{j=0}^{i} (-1)^j (m - i + j) \binom{m}{i} \binom{i}{j}$$

$$= \sum_{j=0}^{i} (-1)^j (m - i + j) \binom{m}{i} \binom{i}{j}$$

$$= \binom{m}{i} m \sum_{j=0}^{i} (-1)^j \binom{i}{j} - i \sum_{j=0}^{i} (-1)^j \binom{i}{j}$$

$$+ \sum_{j=0}^{i} (-1)^j j \binom{i}{j}$$

$$= 0$$

since

$$\sum_{j=0}^{i} (-1)^j \binom{i}{j} = 0 \text{ and } \sum_{j=0}^{i} (-1)^j j \binom{i}{j} = 0.$$

So only the first two terms in expression (B2) survive and the others become 0. Thus, for $p > m$, B_{ss} is the same as that for $p \leq m$, or .

$$B_{ss} = m[1 - (1 - \frac{1}{m})^p].$$

APPENDIX C

Derivation of B_{ss} for Burnett and Coffman's Model

According to Burnett and Coffman [4], the bandwidth of their generalized Hellerman model is

$$B_{ss} = \sum_{k=1}^{m} \sum_{j=0}^{k-1} \alpha^j \beta^{k-1-j} C_m(j,k)$$

where $C_m(j,k)$ is the total number of k-length sequences with j α-transitions (addressing the next module in sequence) and $k - 1 - j$ β-transitions (addressing any other module out of sequence) and the first request is 0. In their paper they give a complicated recursive solution. Later in [14], Stone shows an improvement to their solution. Here we are going to show a direct solution by using a combinatorial argument.

A well-known inclusion-exclusion theorem says

$$e_j = s_j - \binom{j + 1}{1} S_{j+1} + \binom{j+2}{2} S_{j+2} - \cdots$$

$$+ (-1)^{k-1-j} \binom{k - 1}{k - 1 - j} S_{k-1}$$

$$= \sum_{n=0}^{k-1-j} (-1)^n \binom{j + n}{n} S_{j+n}$$

where e_j is the number of objects that have exactly j properties and S_j is the number of objects that have at least j properties. If we define a property to be that an α-transition must occur at a certain position in a k-length sequence, then $e_j = C_m(j,k)$.

It can be shown [6] that

$$S_j = \binom{k - 1}{j} (m - j - 1)_{k-j-1}$$

so

$$C_m(j,k) = e_j = \sum_{n=1}^{k-1-j} (-1)^n \binom{j + n}{n}$$

$$\cdot \binom{k - 1}{j + n} (m - j - n - 1)_{k-j-n-1}.$$

Substituting this back into the bandwidth equation, we have

$$B_{ss} = \sum_{k=1}^{m} \sum_{j=0}^{k-1} \alpha^j \beta^{k-1-j} \sum_{n=1}^{k-1-j} (-1)^n \binom{j + n}{n}$$

$$\cdot \binom{k - 1}{j + n} (m - j - n - 1)_{k-j-n-1}.$$

REFERENCES

[1] D. P. Bhandarkar, "Analysis of memory interference in multiprocessors," *IEEE Trans. Comput.*, vol. C-24, pp. 897–908, Sept. 1975.
[2] P. Budnik and D. J. Kuck, "The organization and use of parallel memories," *IEEE Trans. Comput.*, vol. C-20, pp. 1566–1569, Dec. 1971.
[3] G. J. Burnett and E. G. Coffman, Jr., "A study of interleaved memory systems," in *1970 Spring Joint Computer Conf., AFIPS Conf. Proc.*, vol. 36, pp. 467–474.
[4] ——, "A combinatorial problem related to interleaved memory systems," *J. Ass. Comput. Mach.*, vol. 20, pp. 39–45, Jan. 1973.
[5] ——, "Analysis of interleaved memory systems using blockage buffers," *Commun. Ass. Comput. Mach.*, vol. 18, pp. 91–95, Feb. 1975.
[6] D. Y. Chang, "Analysis and design of interleaved memory systems," M.S. thesis, Univ. Illinois, Urbana-Champaign, Dep. Computer Sci. Rep. 75-747, Aug. 1975.
[7] E. G. Coffman, Jr., G. J. Burnett, and R. A. Snowdon, "On the performance of interleaved memories with multiple-word bandwidth," *IEEE Trans. Comput.*, vol. C-20, pp. 1570–1573, Dec. 1971.
[8] H. Hellerman, *Digital Computer System Principles.* New York: McGraw-Hill, 1967, pp. 228–229.
[9] ——, "On the average speed of a multiple-module storage system," *IEEE Trans. Comput.*, vol. C-15, p. 670, Aug. 1966.
[10] D. E. Knuth and G. S. Rao, "Activity in an interleaved memory," *IEEE Trans. Comput.*, vol. C-24, pp. 943–944, Sept. 1975.
[11] D. Lawrie, "Access and alignment of data in an array processor," *IEEE Trans. Comput.*, vol. C-24, pp. 1145–1155, Dec. 1975.
[12] C. V. Ravi, "On the bandwidth and interference in interleaved memory systems," *IEEE Trans. Comput.*, vol. C-21, pp. 899–901, Aug. 1972.
[13] J. Riordan, *An Introduction to Combinatorial Analysis.* New York: Wiley, 1958.
[14] H. S. Stone, "A note on a combinatorial problem of Burnett and Coffman," *Commun. Ass. Comput. Mach.*, vol. 17, pp. 165–166, Mar. 1974.
[15] W. D. Strecker, "An analysis of the instruction execution rate in certain computer structures," Ph.D. dissertation, Carnegie-Mellon Univ., June 1970.
[16] R. M. Tomasulo, "An efficient algorithm for exploiting multiple arithmetic units," *IBM J. Res. Develop.*, vol. 11, pp. 25–33, Jan. 1967.

Donald Y. Chang (S'74) was born in Fukien, China, on April 5, 1949. He received the B.S. degree in electrical engineering from the National Taiwan University, Taipei, China, and the M.S. degree in computer science from the University of Illinois, Urbana-Champaign, in 1971 and 1975, respectively.

In 1973 he attended the University of California, Berkeley. Since January 1974, he has been a Research Assistant with the Department of Computer Science, University of Illinois, where he is currently working toward his Ph.D. degree in computer science. His current research interests include computer organization and architecture, memory organizations, and computer system performance evaluation.

David J. Kuck (S'59–M'69), for a photograph and biography, see p. 153 of the February 1977 issue of this TRANSACTIONS.

Duncan H. Lawrie (S'66–M'73) received the B.A. degree from DePauw University, Greencastle, IN, the B.S.E.E. degree from Purdue University, Lafayette, IN, and the M.S. and Ph.D. degrees in computer science from the University of Illinois, Urbana-Champaign.

He is currently an Assistant Professor of Computer Science, University of Illinois. Prior to joining the faculty, he held the position of Senior Research Programmer with the Illiac IV project at the University of Illinois, where he was in charge of language development and served as manager of the computer center. His current areas of research include the design of hardware and software for high-speed computer systems, specialized architectures for information retrieval systems, and network theory.

Dr. Lawrie serves as a referee for the IEEE TRANSACTIONS ON COMPUTERS as well as several national conferences, and as a reviewer for *Computer Reviews*. He also serves as a consultant to industry and government. He is a member of the Association for Computing Machinery, the American Association for University Professors, and several honorary services.

Parallelism in Artificial Intelligence Problem Solving:

A Case Study of Hearsay II

RICHARD D. FENNELL AND VICTOR R. LESSER

Abstract—The Hearsay II speech-understanding system (HSII) (Lesser *et al.* [11], Fennell [9], and Erman and Lesser [6]) is an implementation of a knowledge-based multiprocessing artificial intelligence (AI) problem-solving organization. HSII is intended to represent a problem-solving organization which is applicable for implementation in a parallel hardware environment such as C.mmp (Bell *et al.* [2]). The primary characteristics of this organization include: 1) multiple, diverse, independent and asynchronously executing knowledge sources (KS's), 2) cooperating (in terms of control) via a generalized form of the hypothesize-and-test paradigm involving the data-directed invocation of KS processes, and 3) communicating (in terms of data) via a shared blackboard-like data base in which the current data state is held in a homogeneous, multidimensional, directed-graph structure. The object of this paper is to explore several of the ramifications of such a problem-solving organization by examining the mechanisms and policies

underlying HSII which are necessary for supporting its organization as a multiprocessing system. In addition, a multiprocessor simulation study is presented which details the effects of actually implementing such a parallel organization for use in a particular application area, that of speech understanding.

Index Terms—Artificial intelligence (AI) problem solving, data-directed control, multiprocessors, parallelism, speech understanding, synchronization, system organization.

INTRODUCTION

MANY artificial intelligence (AI) problem-solving tasks require large amounts of processing power because of the size of the search space that needs to be examined during the course of problem solution. This is especially true for tasks that involve the interpretation of real-world perceptual data which is generally very noisy (e.g., speech and image understanding systems). For example, a speech-understanding system capable of reliably understanding connected speech involving a large vocabulary is likely to require from 10 to 100 million instructions

Manuscript received September 5, 1975; revised August 27, 1976. This research was supported by the Defense Advanced Research Projects Agency under Contract F44620-73-C-0074 and monitored by the Air Force Office of Scientific Research.

R. D. Fennell was with the Department of Computer Science, Carnegie-Mellon University, Pittsburgh, PA 15213. He is now with the Federal Judicial Center, Washington, DC 20005.

V. R. Lesser is with the Department of Computer Science, Carnegie-Mellon University, Pittsburgh, PA 15213.

Reprinted from *IEEE Transactions on Computers*, Volume C-26, Number 2, February 1977, pages 98-111. Copyright © 1977 by The Institute of Electrical and Electronics Engineers, Inc.

per second (mips) of computing power, if the recognition is to be performed in real time.[1] Recent trends in technology suggest that this computing power can be economically obtained through a closely coupled network of asynchronous "simple" processors (involving perhaps 10 to 100 of these processors), (Bell *et al.* [3], and Heart *et al.* [10]). The major problem (from the problem-solving point of view) with this network multiprocessor approach for generating computing power is in specifying the various problem-solving algorithms in such a way as to exhibit a structure appropriate for exploiting the parallelism available in the multiprocessor network.

The Hearsay II speech-understanding system (HSII) (Lesser *et al.* [11], Fennell [9], and Erman and Lesser [6]) currently under development at Carnegie-Mellon University represents a problem-solving organization that can effectively exploit a multiprocessor system. HSII has been designed as an AI system organization suitable for expressing knowledge-based problem-solving strategies in which appropriately organized subject-matter knowledge may be represented as knowledge sources capable of contributing their knowledge in a parallel data-directed fashion. A *knowledge source* (KS) may be described as an agent that embodies the knowledge of a particular aspect of a problem domain and is useful in solving a problem from that domain by performing actions based upon its knowledge so as to further the progress of the overall solution. The HSII system organization allows these various independent and diverse sources of knowledge to be specified and their interactions coordinated so they might cooperate with one another (perhaps asynchronously and in parallel) to effect a problem solution. As an example of the decomposition of a task domain into KS's, in the speech task domain there might be distinct KS's to deal with acoustic, phonetic, lexical, syntactic, and semantic information. While the speech task is the first test of the multiprocessing problem-solving organization of HSII, it is believed that the system organization provided by HSII is capable of supporting other knowledge-based AI problem-solving strategies (Erman and Lesser [6]), as might be found in vision, robotics, chess, natural language understanding, and protocol analysis. In fact, work is under way which further tests the applicability of the HSII organization for the analysis of natural scenes (Ohlander [13]) and as a model for human reading (Rumelhart [17]).

The rest of this paper will explore several of the ramifications of such an organization by examining the mechanisms and policies underlying HSII which are necessary for supporting its organization as a multiprocessing problem-solving system. First, an abstract description of a class of problem-solving systems is given using the production system model of Newell [12]. Then, the HSII organization is described in terms of this model. The various decisions made during the course of design necessitated the introduction of various multiprocessing mechanisms (e.g., mechanisms for maintaining data localization and data integrity), and these mechanisms are discussed. Finally, a simulation study is presented which details the effects of actually implementing such a problem-solving organization in a multiprocessor environment.

THE MODEL

An Abstract Model for Problem Solving

In the abstract, the problem-solving organization underlying HSII may be modeled in terms of a "production system," (Newell [12]). A *production system* is a scheme for specifying an information processing system in which the control structure of the system is defined by operations on a set of *productions* of the form $P \rightarrow A$, which operate from and on a collection of data structures. P represents a logical antecedent, called a *precondition,* which may or may not be satisfied by the information encoded within the dynamically current set of data structures. If P is found to be satisfied by some data structure, then the associated *action A* is executed, which presumably will have some altering effect upon the data base such that some other (or the same) precondition becomes satisfied. This paradigm for sequencing of the actions can be thought of as a data-directed control structure, since the satisfaction of the precondition is dependent upon the dynamic state of the data structure. Productions are executed as long as their antecedent preconditions are satisfied, and the process halts either when no precondition is found to be satisfied or when an action executes a stop operation (thereby signalling problem solution or failure, in the case of problem-solving systems).

The HSII Organization: A Production System Approach

The HSII system organization, which can be characterized as a "parallel" production system, has a centralized data base which represents the dynamic problem solution state. This data base, which is called the *blackboard,* is a multidimensional data structure, the fundamental data element of which is called a *node.* For example, the dimensions of the HSII speech-understanding system data base are informational level (e.g., phonetic, surface-phonemic, syllabic, lexical, and phrasal levels), utterance time (speech time measured from the beginning of the input utterance), and data alternatives (where multiple nodes are permitted to exist simultaneously at the same level and utterance time). The blackboard is readable and writable by any precondition or KS process (where a KS process is the embodiment of a production action, to use the terminology of production systems). Preconditions are procedurally oriented and may specify arbitrarily complex tests to be performed on the data structure in order to decide precondition satisfaction. In order to avoid executing these precondition tests unnecessarily often, they

---

[1] The Hearsay I (Reddy *et al.* [14]–[16] and Erman [5]) and Dragon (Baker [1]) speech-understanding systems require approximately 10 to 20 mips of computing power for real-time recognition when handling small vocabularies.

in turn have *pre-preconditions* which are essentially monitors on relevant primitive data base events (e.g., monitoring for a change to a given field of a given node in the data base, or a given field of any node in the data base). Whenever any of these primitive events occurs, those preconditions monitoring such events become schedulable and, when executed, test for full precondition satisfaction. Testing for precondition satisfaction is not presumed to be an instantaneous or even an indivisible operation, and several such precondition tests may proceed concurrently.

The KS processes representing the production actions are also procedurally oriented and may specify arbitrarily complex sequences of operations to be performed upon the data structure. The overall effect of any given KS process is usually either to hypothesize new data which are to be added to the data base or to verify (and perhaps modify) data previously placed in the data base. This follows the general *hypothesize-and-test* problem-solving paradigm wherein hypotheses representing partial problem solutions are generated and then tested for validity; this cycle continues until the verification phase certifies the completion of processing (and either the problem is solved or failure is indicated). The execution of a KS process is usually temporally disjoint from the satisfaction of its precondition; the execution of any given KS process is not presumed to be indivisible; and the concurrent execution of multiple KS processes is permitted. In addition, a precondition process may invoke multiple instantiations of a KS to work on the different parts of the blackboard which independently satisfy the precondition's pattern. Thus, the independent data-directed nature of precondition evaluation and KS execution can potentially generate a significant amount of parallel activity throught the concurrent execution of different preconditions, different KS's, and multiple instantiations of a single KS.

The basic structure and components of the HSII organization may be depicted as shown in the message transaction diagram of Fig. 1. The diagram indicates the paths of active information flow between the various components of the problem-solving system as solid arrows; paths indicating control activity are shown as broken arrows. The major components of the diagram include a passive global data structure (the *blackboard*) which contains the current state of the problem solution. Access to the blackboard is conceptually centralized in the *blackboard handler* module,[2] whose primary function is to accept and honor requests from the active processing elements to read and write parts of the blackboard. The active processing elements which generate these data access requests consist of *KS processes* and their associated *preconditions*. Preconditions are activated by a *blackboard monitoring mechanism* which monitors the various write-actions of

[2] The blackboard handler module could be implemented either as a procedure which is called as a subroutine (with appropriate protected critical sections) from precondition and KS processes, or as a process which contains a queue of requests for blackboard operations sent by precondition and KS processes. In the implementation discussed in this paper, the former method is used.

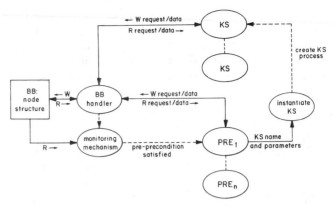

Fig. 1. Simplified HSII system organization.

the blackboard handler; whenever an event occurs which is of interest to a particular precondition process, that precondition becomes schedulable.[3] If, upon further examination of the blackboard, the precondition finds itself "satisfied," the precondition may request a process instantiation of its associated KS to be established, passing the details of how the precondition was satisfied as parameters to this instantiation of the KS. Once instantiated, the KS process can respond to the blackboard data condition which was detected by its precondition, possibly requesting further modifications be made to the blackboard, perhaps thereby triggering further preconditions to respond to the latest modifications. This particular characterization of the HSII organization, while overly simplified, shows the data-driven nature of the KS activations and interactions. A more complete message transaction diagram for HSII will be presented in a subsequent section.

HEARSAY II MULTIPROCESSING MECHANISMS

In order to adapt the HSII organization to a multiprocessing environment, mechanisms must be provided to support the individual localized executions of the various active and ready processes and to keep the processes from interfering with one another, either directly or indirectly. On the other hand, mechanisms must also be provided so that the various active processes may communicate with one another so as to achieve the desired process cooperation. Since the constituent KS's are assumed to be independently developed and are not to presume the explicit existence of other KS's, communication among these KS's must necessarily be indirect. The desire for a modular KS structure arises from the fact that usually many different people are involved in the implementation of the set of KS's, and, for purposes of experimentation and KS performance analysis, the system should be able to be reconfigured easily using alternative subsets of KS's. Communication among KS's takes two primary forms: data base monitoring for collecting pertinent data event information for future use (*local contexts* and precondition activation),

[3] During the period between when the precondition process is first scheduled and the time it is executed, the monitoring for relevant data base events continues. Thus, a precondition process, when finally executed, may check more than one part of the data base for satisfaction.

and data base monitoring for detecting the occurrence of data events which violate prior data assumptions (*tags* and *messages*). The following paragraphs discuss these forms of data-base monitoring and their relationship to the data-access synchronization mechanisms required in a multiprocess system organization.

Local Contexts

Interprocess communication (and interference) among KS's and their associated preconditions occurs mainly via the global data base, as a result of the design decisions involved in trying to maintain process independence. It is therefore not surprising that the mechanisms necessary to bring about the desired process cooperation and independence are based on global data-base considerations. The global data base (the *blackboard*) is intended to contain only dynamically current information. Since preconditions (being data-directed) are to be tested for satisfaction upon the occurrence of relevant data-base changes (which are historical *data events*), and since neither precondition testing nor action execution (nor the sequential combination of the two) is assumed to be an indivisible operation, localized data bases must be provided for each process unit (precondition or action) that needs to remember relevant historical data events. These localized data bases, called *local contexts* in HSII, which record the changes to the blackboard since the precondition process was last executed or since the KS process was created, provide personalized operating environments for the various precondition and KS processes. A local context preserves only those data events[4] and state changes relevant to its owner. The creation time of the local context (i.e., the time from which it begins collecting data events) is also dependent upon the context owner. Any given local context is built up incrementally: when a modification occurs to the global data base, the resulting data event is distributed to the various local contexts interested in such events. Thus, the various local contexts retain a history of relevant data events, while the global data base contains only the most current information.

Data Integrity

Since precondition and KS processes are not guaranteed to be executed uninterruptedly, these processes often need to assure the integrity of various assumptions they are making about the contents of the data base;[5] should these assumptions become violated due to the actions of an in-

tervening process, the further computation of the assuming process may have to be altered (or terminated). One way to approach the problem of data integrity is to guarantee the validity of data assumptions by disallowing intervening processes the ability to modify (or perhaps even to examine) critical data. The HSII system provides two forms of locking primitives, *node-* and *region-locking,* which can be used to guarantee exclusive access to the desired data. Node-locking guarantees exclusive access to an explicitly specified node in the blackboard, whereas region-locking guarantees exclusive access to a collection of nodes that are specified implicitly based on a set of node characteristics. In the current implementation of HSII, the region characteristics are specified by a particular information level and time period of a node. If the blackboard is considered as a two-dimensional structure with coordinates of information level and time, then region-locking permits the locking of an arbitrary rectangular area in the blackboard. Region-locking has the additional property of preventing the creation of any new node that would be placed in the blackboard area specified by the region by other than the process which had requested the region-lock. Additional locking flexibility is introduced by allowing processes to request read-only access to nodes or regions (called *node-* or *region-examining*); this reduces possible contention by permitting multiple readers of a given node to coexist, while excluding any writers of that node until all readers are finished. The system also provides a "super lock," which allows an arbitrary group of nodes and regions to be locked at the same time. A predefined linear ordering strategy for nonpreemptive data-access allocation (Coffman *et al.* [4]) is applied by the "super lock" primitive to the desired node- and region-locks so as to avoid the possibility of data-base deadlock.

The technique of guaranteeing data integrity through exclusive access is applicable only if all the nodes and regions to be accessed and modified are known ahead of time and thus are able to be locked simultaneously. The sequential acquisition of exclusive access to nodes and region, without intervening unlocks, can result in the possibility of deadlock. In the HSII blackboard, nodes are interconnected to form a directed graph structure; because it is possible to establish an arbitrarily complex interconnection structure, it is often very difficult for a KS process to anticipate the sequence of nodes it will desire to access or modify. Thus, the mechanisms of exclusive access cannot always be used to guarantee data integrity in a system with a complex data structure and a set of unknown processes. Furthermore, even if the KS can anticipate the area in the blackboard within which it will work and thereby request exclusive access to this area, the area may be very large, leading to a significant decrease in potential parallel activity by other processes waiting for this locked area to become available.

An alternative approach to guaranteeing data integrity is to provide a means by which a process (precondition or KS) may place data assumptions about the particular state of a node or group of nodes in the data base (the action of

---

[4] The information which defines a data event consists of the locus of the event (i.e., a data node name and a field name within that node) and the old value of the field (the new value being stored in the global data base).

[5] There are two different forms of data integrity that need to be differentiated: syntactic (system) and semantic (user). For example, a syntactic consistency requirement associated with a list structure is that each element of the list contains a pointer to another valid list element; whereas, a semantic consistency requirement, which relates to how the list structure is interpreted by a KS, could be that the values associated with adjacent list elements are always less than 100 apart. Both types of data integrity are dealt with in this paper, but the main focus of the discussion in this section is on semantic consistency.

putting these assumptions in the blackboards is called *tagging*). If these assumptions are invalidated by a subsequent blackboard modification operation of another process, then a *message* indicating this violation is sent to the process making the assumption. In the meantime, the assuming process can proceed without obstructing other processes, until such time as it intends to modify the data base (since data-base modification is the only way one process can affect the execution of another). The process must then acquire exclusive access to the parts of the data base involved in its prior assumptions (which parts will have been previously *tagged* in the data base, thereby defining a *critical data set*) and check to see whether the assumptions have been violated (in which case, messages indicating those violations would have been sent to the process). If a violation has occurred, the assuming process may wish to take alternative action; otherwise, the intended data base modifications may be made as if the process had had exclusive access throughout its computation. This tagging mechanism can also be used to signal the KS process that the initial conditions in the blackboard (i.e., the precondition pattern) that caused the precondition to invoke it have been modified; this is accomplished by having the precondition tag these initial conditions on behalf of the KS process prior to the instantiation of the KS.

Thus, the HSII organization provides mechanisms to accomplish two forms of data integrity assurance: the various data-base locking mechanisms described previously provide several ways to acquire exclusive or read-only data access; and the data-tagging facility allows data assumptions to be placed in the data base without interfering with any process' ability to access or modify that area of the data base (with data invalidation warning messages being sent by data-base monitors whenever the assumptions are violated).

To provide a basis for the discussion in the subsequent sections of this paper, Fig. 2, depicting the various components of the HSII organizational structure, is offered. The diagram is a more detailed version of the message transaction model presented previously. The new components of this diagram are primarily a result of addressing multiprocessing considerations. As in the earlier, more simplified organizational diagram, the dynamically current state of the problem solution is contained in the *blackboard*. The blackboard not only contains data *nodes,* but also records data-monitoring information (*tags*) and data-access synchronization information (*locks*). Access to the blackboard is conceptually centralized in three modules. As before, the *blackboard handler* module accepts read and write data-access requests from the active processing elements (the *KS processes* and their *precondition processes*). A *lock handler* coordinates node- and region-lock requests from the KS processes and preconditions, with the ability to block the progress of the requesting process until the synchronization request may be satisfied. A *monitoring mechanism* is responsible for accepting *data-tagging* requests from the KS process and

preconditions, and for sending *messages* to the tagging processes whenever a tagged data field is modified. It is also the responsibility of the monitoring mechanism to distribute *data events* to the various *local contexts* of the KS processes and preconditions, as well as to activate precondition processes whenever sufficient data events of interest to those preconditions have occurred in the blackboard.

Associated with each active processing element is a local data structure, the *local context,* which records data events that have occurred in the blackboard and are of interest to that particular process. The local contexts may be read by their associated processes in order to find out which data nodes have been modified recently and what the previous values of particular data fields were. The local contexts are automatically maintained by the blackboard monitoring mechanism.

Upon being activated and satisfied, precondition processes may instantiate a KS (thereby creating a *KS process*), passing along the reasons for this instantiation as parameters to the new KS process and at the same time establishing the appropriate data-monitoring connections necessary for the new process. The *scheduler* retains the actual control over allocating hardware processing capability to those KS processes and precondition processes which can best serve to promote the progress of the problem solution.[6]

EXPERIMENTS WITH AN IMPLEMENTATION

The preceding sections of this paper have presented the mechanisms necessary for implementing a knowledge-based problem-solving system such as HSII in a multiprocessing environment. The present sections will discuss the various experiments that have been performed in an attempt to characterize the multiprocessing performance of the HSII organization in the speech-understanding task.

HSII Multiprocess Performance Analysis through Simulation

In order to gain insight into the various efficiency issues involving multiprocess problem-solving organizations, a simulation model was incorporated within the uniprocessor version of the HSII speech-understanding system.[7]

---

[6] One way a scheduler might help in reducing (or eliminating) global data-base access interference is to schedule to run concurrently only processes whose global data demands are disjoint. Such a scheduling policy could even be used to supplant an explicit locking scheme, since the global data-base locking would be effectively handled by the scheduler (albeit probably on a fairly gross level). Of course, other factors may rule out such an approach to data-access synchronization, such as an inability to make maximal use of the available processing resources if only data-disjoint processes are permitted to run concurrently, or the inability to know in advance the precise blackboard demands of each KS instantiation. Nonetheless, the information relating to the locality of KS data references is useful in scheduling processes so as to avoid excessive data-access interference (thereby improving the effective parallelism of the system).

[7] This system was programmed on the DECsystem-10 computer in an Algol-like language, SAIL (Swinehart and Sproull [18]), using SAIL's multiprocessing facilities (Feldman *et al.* [8]).

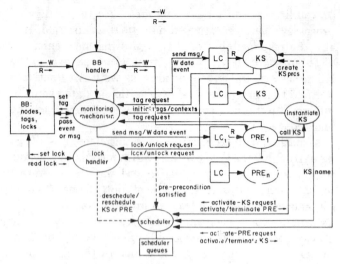

Fig. 2.   HSII system organization.

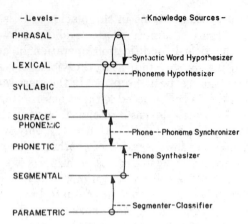

Fig. 3.   Simplified HSII, KS, and information level configuration.

The HSII problem-solving organization was not itself modeled and simulated, but rather the actual HSII implementation (which is a multiprocessing organization even when executing on a uniprocessor) was modified to permit the simulation of a closely coupled multiprocessor hardware environment.

There were four primary objectives of the simulation experiments: 1) to measure the software overheads involved in the design and execution of a complicated, data-directed multiprocess(or) control structure, 2) to determine whether there really exists a significant amount of parallel activity in the speech-understanding task, 3) to understand how the various forms of interprocess communication and interference, especially that from data-access synchronization in the blackboard, affect the amount of effective parallelism realized, and 4) to gain insight into the design of an appropriate scheduling algorithm for a multiprocess problem-solving structure. Certainly, any results presented will reflect the detailed efficiencies and inefficiencies of the particular system implementation being measured, but hopefully the organization of HSII is sufficiently general that the various statements will have a wider quantitative applicability for those considering similar multiprocess control structures.

The HSII Speech Understanding System: The Simulation Configuration

The configuration of the HSII speech-understanding system, upon which the following simulation results were based, consists of eight generic KS's that operate on a blackboard containing six information levels. The KS's used in the simulation were as follows: the *segment classifier*, the *phone synthesizer* (consisting of two KS's), the *phoneme hypothesizer*, the *phone-phoneme synchronizer* (consisting of three KS's), and the *rating policy module* (see Fig. 3). These KS's are activated by half a dozen permanently instantiated precondition processes which are continuously monitoring the blackboard data base for

events and data patterns relevant to their associated KS's. Due to the excessive cost of the simulation effort (and due to the limited stages of development of some available KS's), this configuration represents only a subset of a more complete system which currently contains approximately 15 KS's. Lesser *et al.* [11] contains a more detailed description of the blackboard and the various KS's for the more complete HSII speech-understanding system.

Simulation Mechanisms and Simulation Experiments

The various multiprocessor simulation results were obtained by modifying the flow of control through the usual HSII multiprocessing organization to allow simulation scheduling points every time a running process could interact in any way with some other concurrently executing process. Such points include blackboard data base accesses and data-base access synchronization points (including attempts to acquire data-base resources, both at the system and user levels, and any resulting points of process suspension due to the unavailability of the requested resource, as well as the subsequent points of process wake-up for retrying the access request). Simulation scheduling points were also inserted whenever a data modification warning message (triggered by modifying a tagged data field) was to be sent, as well as whenever a process attempted to receive such a message. The scheduling mechanism itself was also modified to allow for the simulated scheduling of multiple processing units, while maintaining the state information associated with each processor being simulated (such as the processor clock time of that simulated processor and the state of the particular process being run on that processor). The simulation runs were performed so as to keep the processor clock-time of each processor being simulated in step with one another (the simulation being *event-driven*, rather than *sampled*), thereby allowing for the accurate measurement and comparison of concurrent events across processors. Most of the results presented here were achieved by using a single set of KS's (as described above), with a single speech-data input utterance, keeping the data-base locking structure and scheduling algorithms essentially fixed, while varying the number of simulated (identical) processors. Several runs were also performed to test the effects of altering the KS set, altering the locking structure, and altering the mode of data input (the normal input mode being a utterance-time-ordered introduction of input data which simulates real-time speech input).

Measures of Multiprocessing Overhead: Primitive Operation Timings

Time measurements of various primitive operations were made using a 10-μs hardware interval timer. Some of the timed primitive operations (such as those involving simple data-base access and modification) were not especially reliant upon the fact that the problem-solving organization involved multiple parallel processes, whereas others (such as those involving process instantiation and process synchronization) were directly related to the multiprocess aspects of the organization (and might even be taken in part as overhead when compared to alternative single-process system organizations). The times for the various system operations, as shown in Table I, should be read as relative values, comparing the multiprocess-oriented operations with the data-accessing operations to get a relative feel for the overheads involved in supporting and maintaining the multiprocess organization of HSII. Keep in mind that such time measurements are highly dependent on the particular implementation and can change fairly radically when implemented differently.

Table I gives timing statistics relating to the costs involved in maintaining the shared blackboard data base. Two sets of statistics are given, one set showing the operation times without the influence of data-access synchronization (blackboard locking) and one set with the locking structures in effect. These two sets of times give a quantitative feeling for the cost of data-access synchronization mechanisms in this particular implementation of HSII. The figures given include the average runtime cost per operation, the number of calls (in this particular timing run) to each operation (thereby showing the relative frequencies of operation usage), and the percentage of the overall run time consumed by each operation. With respect to the individual entries, *create.node* is a composite operation (involving many field-writes and various local context updates) for creating blackboard nodes. The *read.node.field* and *write.node.field* operations are used in accessing the individual fields of a node. Note that included in any given field-read or field-write operation is the cost of perhaps tagging (or untagging) that particular field (or its node). The various functions of the blackboard monitoring mechanism are contained within the field-write operations. Thus, also included in the field-write operation is the cost of distributing the data event resulting from the write operation to all relevant precondition and KS process local contexts, as well as the cost of sending tag messages to all processes which may have tagged the field being modified; these additional costs are also accounted for independently in the *send.msgs.and.events* and *notify.sset* table entries. Field-write operations are also responsible for evaluating

TABLE I
Primitive Operation Times

	% total runtime		mean time (ms)		number of calls	
	w/o lock	w/ lock	w/o lock	w/ lock	w/o lock	w/ lock
Blackboard Accessing:						
create.node	6.96	4.15	35.81	50.77	287	287
read.node.field	5.06	15.68	0.31	2.03	23577	25279
write.node.field	14.13	7.75	13.96	18.44	1493	1476
Process Handling:						
invoke.ks	5.29	2.30	22.64	23.64	345	342
create.ks.prcs	0.75	0.31	3.21	3.22	345	342
ks.cleanup	8.20	5.24	35.06	53.94	345	342
invoke.pre	0.10	1.04	10.44	10.59	14	14
create.pre.prcs	0.42	0.40	8.53	19.57	72	72
Local Context Maintenance:						
transfer.tags	7.12	2.99	9.12	9.17	1152	1149
delete.all.tags	0.52	0.22	2.01	2.03	383	380
notify.sset	6.52	3.01	2.63	2.92	3665	3626
send.msgs.and.events	4.04	2.12	3.68	4.68	1021	1594
receive.msg	0.36	0.15	1.00	1.01	531	530
read.cset.or.sset	0.11	0.05	0.84	0.84	192	192
Data Access Synchronization:						
lock! (overhead)	---	7.78	---	57.47	---	476
unlock! (overhead)	---	3.22	---	23.78	---	476
lock.node	---	2.32	---	2.94	---	2770
exam.node	---	9.34	---	2.40	---	13675
lock.rgn	---	0.11	---	1.77	---	227
write.access.chk	---	0.41	---	0.98	---	1470
read.access.chk	---	14.45	---	1.60	---	31761

any pre-preconditions associated with the field being modified and activating any precondition whose pre-precondition is satisfied. Included in the cost of reading a data field (e.g., *read.node.field*) is the cost of verifying the access right of the calling process to the node being read (which could involve a temporary-locking operation[8] the cost of which is also given independently in the *lock.node* table entry); this access-right checking cost is also separately accounted for by the *read.access.chk* operation. It should be noted that because most of the mechanisms required to implement a data-directed control structure are embedded in the blackboard write operations, the time to execute a write operation is significantly more expensive than a read operation. However, the actual cost in terms of total runtime of implementing a data-directed control structure is comparatively small in the HSII speech-understanding system, because the frequency of read operations is much higher than that of write operations. If this relative frequency for read and write operations holds for other task domains (e.g., vision, robotics), then a data-directed control structure (which is a very general and modular type of sequencing paradigm) seems to be a very reasonable framework within which to implement such tasks.

Table I also relates the costs of process handling within HSII. Process invocation and process creation are separated (the former being a request from a precondition or KS process to the scheduler to perform the latter), and the costs are accounted separately, as in *invoke.ks* and *crea-*

[8] If a process has not previously locked the node to which it desires access and the process does not have any other node locked, then the system will temporarily lock the node for the duration of the single read or write operation, without the process having explicitly to request access to the node. This locking operation is required in order to guarantee the internal consistency of the list data structure of a node.

te.ks.prcs. Ks.cleanup is the cost of terminating a KS process; preconditions never get terminated. The cost of initializing and terminating a KS process (i.e., *invoke.ks* and *ks.cleanup*) is due to the overheads involved in maintaining local contexts, locking structures, and database monitoring (tagging), all of which are necessitated by the multiprocess nature of the HSII organization. However, in a relative sense, this is not expensive, since the total overhead associated with process-handling amounts to only about 9 percent of the overall execution time.

Additionally, local context maintenance costs are given in Table I, since they are also a cost of having asynchronous parallel processes. While individual tag creation and deletion is handled by the primitive field-read and field-write operations, tags may be transferred from a precondition to the KS it has invoked via *transfer.tags* and destroyed at termination of a process via *delete.all.tags*. As noted above, *send.msg.and.events* and *notify.sset* are suboperations of the field-write operations and represent the cost of distributing data-event notifications to all relevant local contexts. *Receive.msg* is the operation used by precondition or KS processes to receive a tagging message (or perhaps wait for one, if one does not yet exist); and *read.-cset.or.sset* is the operation for retrieving the information from a local context.

Finally, Table I gives the costs associated with the data-access synchronization mechanism. *Lock!* and *unlock!* represent the overhead costs of locking and unlocking a group of nodes specified by the process requesting access rights. These two operations are among the most complex routines in the HSII operating system, the complexity arising from having to coordinate the allocation of database resources by two independent access allocation schemes (node-locking and region-locking). This coordination is necessary in order to avoid any possibility of data base deadlock by maintaining a homogeneous linear ordering among all data resources (nodes and regions). The costs of *lock!* and *unlock!* do not include the time spent in performing the actual primitive locking operations. The primitive lock costs are given by *lock.node* (lock a node for exclusive access), *exam.node* (lock a node for read-only access), and *lock.rgn* (lock a region for exclusive access). The access-checking operations (*write.access.chk* and *read.access.chk*) are used by the blackboard accessing routines discussed above.

These timing statistics can be used to determine the amount of system overhead incurred in running precondition and KS processes under the HSII operating system. The following summary statistics are offered, given as percentages of the total execution time, the percentages being calculated so as to avoid overlapping between categories (e.g., blackboard access synchronization costs are factored out of blackboard reading costs):

Blackboard reading	16 percent
Blackboard writing	4 percent
Internal computations of processes	34 percent
Local context maintenance	10 percent
Blackboard access synchronization	27 percent
Process handling	9 percent

Another way of viewing these figures is that approximately half of the execution time involves multiprocessor overheads (i.e., local context maintenance, blackboard access synchronization, and process handling). Based on the assumption that this multiprocess overhead is independent of the parallelism factor achieved,[9] then a parallelism factor of 2 or greater is required in order to recover the multiprocess overhead.

Effective Parallelism and Processor Utilization

Several experiments were run to measure the parallelism achieved using varying numbers of identical processors. Each of these experiments was run with the KS set described previously, using the same input data (introduced into the data base in such a manner as to simulate real-time speech input), the same blackboard locking structure, and the same scheduling algorithm, while varying the number of (identical) processors. An example of the output by the simulation, for the case of eight processors, is displayed in Fig. 4. To comment on these activity plots, the " # runnable processes" plot gives the number of processes either running or ready to run at each simulation scheduling point; the " # running processes" plot gives the number of actively executing processes at each scheduling point; the " # ready processes" plot shows the number of processes awaiting assignment to a processor at each scheduling point; and the " # suspended processes" plot gives the number of processes blocked from executing because of data-access interference or because they are waiting on the receipt of a tagging message.

Referring to Fig. 4(c), notice the spiked nature of the ready-processes plot. This is a result of delaying the execution of a precondition (due to the limited processing power available) beyond the point in time at which its pre-precondition is first satisfied: the longer a precondition is delayed, the more data events it is likely to accumulate in the meantime, and the more KS processes it is likely to instantiate once it does get executed; hence the spiked nature of the resultant ready-processes plots for configurations of few processors. As parallel processing power increases, preconditions can more often be run as soon as their pre-preconditions are intitially satisfied, and the spiking phenomenon subsides.

As an example of how these activity plots have been used in upgrading the performance of the implementation, compare Fig. 5 to Fig. 4(c). Fig. 5 depicts the process activity under the control of an earlier scheduler which did not attempt to perform load balancing with respect to ready preconditions; and as a result of not increasing the

---

[9] This assumption, based on timing statistics from a series of runs with different numbers of processors, seems valid except for the cost of context swapping and process suspension, which depends upon the amount of data-base interference and the number of processors.

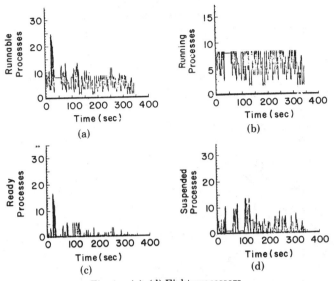

Fig. 4. (a)–(d) Eight processors.

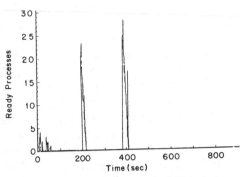

Fig. 5. Eight processors: Old scheduling strategy.

relative scheduling priority of preconditions as they received more and more data events, the activity spike phenomenon referred to above became predominant, to the extent of reducing process activity to a synchronous system while the long-time waiting precondition instantiates a great many KS processes all at once. Fig. 4(c) shows the activity on the same number of processors, but using a somewhat more intelligent scheduling algorithm, with a resulting reduction in the observed spiking phenomena. This improved scheduling strategy is the one used for all plots presented herein.

In addition to the plots described above, various other measures were made to allow an explicit determination of processor utilization and effective parallelism for varying numbers of processors. Referring to Table II, one can get a feeling for the activity generated by employing increasing numbers of processors. All simulations represented in Table II were run for equivalent amounts of processing effort with respect to the results created in the blackboard by the KS activity. The final clock time of the multiprocessor configuration being simulated is given in simulated real-time seconds, and the accumulated processor idle and lost times are also given. *Idle time* is attributed to a processor when it has no process assigned to it and there are no ready processes to be run; *lost time* is attributed when the process on a processor is suspended for any reason and there are no ready processes which could be swapped in to replace the suspended process. Processor utilization (calculated using the final clock time and processor idle and lost times) is given in Table II; Fig. 6 shows the corresponding effective parallelism (speed-up), based on the processor utilization factors of Table II.

The speed-up for this particular selection of KS's is appreciable up to four processors, but drops off substantially as one approaches sixteen processors. In fact, a rather distressing feature of this effective parallelism plot is that the speed-up actually decreases slightly in going from eight processors to a sixteen-processor configuration (from a

TABLE II
Processor Utilization

number of prcrs (all times in secs)	1	2	4	8	16	32 (special*)
KS instantiations	355	401	423	421	415	434
PRE activations	82	126	173	213	200	229
multiprcr clock time	1076	634	389	350	351	43
total idle time	9	15	37	380	2608	867
total lost time	0	5	34	900	1546	0
avg cxt swaps	0	309	942	368	9	0
avg prcr utilization	99%	98%	95%	54%	26%	37%
effective # prcrs	0.99	1.96	3.80	4.32	4.16	11.84
utilization speed-up	1.00	1.98	3.84	4.36	4.20	11.96

* The 32-processor column represents an experiment which was run under special conditions, to be explained below, and should not be compared directly to the other columns of the table.

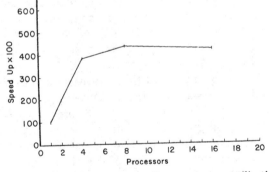

Fig. 6. Effective parallelism according to processor utilization.

speed-up of 4.36 over the uniprocessor case, down to 4.20). This may be explained by noting that both the eight- and sixteen-processor runs had approximately equal final clock times; but in the sixteen-processor case, the number of runnable processes never exceeded sixteen processes, so any ready process could always be accommodated immediately. As a result, the number of KS instantiations and precondition activations fell off a bit from the eight-processor case, because the preconditions were more likely to be fully satisfied the first time they were activated (since all ready-processes, KS processes in particular, could be executed immediately and complete their intended actions sooner, so that when a precondition came to be activated, it would more likely find its full data pattern to be satisfied); thus, preconditions would not often be aborted, having to be retested upon receiving a subsequent data event. However, running fewer preconditions resulted in much more idle time for the sixteen-processor configuration (the increase in lost time indicated in Table II is an artifact of having too many processors available, since suspended processes would tend to remain on otherwise idle processors rather than being swapped off the processor—note the rather dramatic decrease in context swaps indicated by Table II for the sixteen-processor case). The result is a lower proportionate utilization of the processor configuration, and hence a decrease in the effective parallelism from the eight-processor configuration to the sixteen-processor configuration.

Due to the limited state of development of the total set of KS's, the set of KS's used in the simulation was necessarily restricted;[10] so the fact that these plots indicate that not more than about four to eight processors are being effectively utilized is not to say that the full HSII speech-understanding system needs only eight processors. One might ask that if only 4.16 processors of the sixteen-processor configuration are being totally utilized (see Table II), what is the maximum potential effective parallelism, given this set of KS's? To answer this question, an experiment was performed in which effectively infinite processing power was provided to this KS set and all data-access interference was eliminated (by removing the locking structure overheads and blocking actions); the scheduling algorithm was kept unchanged, as was the input data, although the input data stream was entered so as to be instantaneously available in its entirety (rather than being introduced in a simulated real-time, "left-to-right" manner). The results of this experiment are summarized by the 32-processor column of Table II (32 processors was an effective infinite computing resource in this case, since eight of the processors were never used during the simulation). Notice that no lost time was attributed to the run, due to the absence of locking interference; and the resultant processor utilization was 37% of 32 processors, or 11.84 totally utilized processors. Thus, data-base interference caused by particular data-base accessing patterns and associated locking structures of the KS set used in the experiment significantly affected processor utilization; if the use of the locking structures could be accomplished in a more noninterfering manner, the speed-up indicated by the eight- or sixteen-processor configurations could be increased substantially. The next section will analyze in detail the exact causes for this data base interference, and propose changes to the KS locking structure so as to reduce potential interference.

Table III presents some other system configurations to show effective processor utilizations under varying con-

TABLE III
System Configuration Variations

experiment description	multiprcr clock	total idle	total lost	% util	effective # prcrs
8 KS's, 6 PRE's 16 prcrs, w/ lock l-to-r input	351	2608	1546	26%	4.16
8 KS's, 6PRE's 32 prcrs, w/o lock instantaneous input	43	867	0	37%	11.84
9 KS's, 7 FRE's 16 prcrs, w/ lock l-to-r input	148	854	726	33%	5.28
9 KS's, 7 PRE's 16 prcrs, w/ lock instantaneous input	155	839	784	35%	5.60
9 KS's, 7 PRE's 32 prcrs, w/o lock instantaneous input	13	226	0	46%	14.72

ditions. The first row repeats the statistics of the sixteen-processor case of Table 2; the second row is a summary of the 32-processor case of Table II, as described above. Three further data points are offered to indicate the effects of increasing the size of the KS set. The last three rows of Table III involve experiments using an expanded KS set consisting of the KS's of all the previous runs plus the *Syntactic Word Hypothesizer* and its precondition. Simulations were performed to evaluate the effects of this expanded KS set on a sixteen-processor configuration with the locking structure in effect, presenting the input data in the usual "left-to-right" manner, as well as in the instantaneous manner used in the infinite-processor test. Comparing the results (in Table III) to the original sixteen-processor run, the "left-to-right" input scheme achieved a processor utilization of 33 percent, up 7 percent from the smaller KS set case; and by presenting all input data simultaneously, the utilization rose to 35 percent. The fifth row of Table III represents the results of providing effectively infinite computing power (only 25 processors were ever used during the run) to the expanded KS set and eliminating all data access interference, in the same manner as for the experiment of the second row. In this "optimal" situation for the expanded KS set, processor utilization was measured at 46%, or 14.72 totally utilized processors. Again, it may be noted that a more effective (less interfering) use of the locking structures can result in substantial increases in processor utilization and effective parallelism.

The addition of the syntactic word hypothesizer was able to achieve the increases in utilization noted in Table III because it operates on information levels that are used by only one other KS (the phoneme hypothesizer) in the basic KS set; hence, the process interference introduced by adding this KS was minimal. Unfortunately, the development of KS's at an information levels which more directly conflict with those of existing KS's has been limited, so direct experimentation on the interfering effects of such KS's could not be performed; but based on the observations comparing the 32-processor without-lock experi-

[10] The particular set of KS's chosen for use in the simulation experiments happened to be an effectively bottom-up speech recognition system. It is expected that as top-down KS's are added, the system will work in a more combined top-down and bottom-up fashion thereby increasing the potential parallelism (since the top-down KS's will presumably not interfere with the execution of the bottom-up KS's as much as additional competing bottom-up KS's would).

ments to the original sixteen-processor with-lock runs, substantial interference due to ineffective use of the locking structure would be expected in such cases of adding "competing" KS's. One mitigating circumstance which could alleviate such interference was noted in the "instantaneous" input case of the expanded KS set case, as compared to the "left-to-right" input case: if process activity can be spread across the utterance-time dimension of the blackboard, process interference would decrease—but interference due to data-access synchronization interference can easily overwhelm this improvement.

Execution Interference Analysis

As previously described, there are two methods in the HSII system for preserving data integrity: 1) guaranteeing exclusive access through the use of node- and region-locking primitives, and 2) placing data assumptions in the blackboard, through tagging primitives, which when violated cause a signal to be sent to the process making the assumption. There is an interesting balance in terms of execution overhead and execution interference between these two techniques. The region-locking technique is least costly in terms of execution overhead and is the easiest to embed in a program but causes the most execution interference. This is in contrast to the use of tagging which is the most costly in terms of execution overhead and is the most difficult to embed in a program but causes the least execution interference.[11] Both these methods were used for guaranteeing data integrity in the precondition and KS set that was used in the simulation experiments.

In structuring each KS so as to preserve its data integrity, no *a priori* assumptions were made about the non-modifiability of any blackboard data that KS used in its processing (i.e., it was assumed that any blackboard information that the KS read could perhaps be modified by some other concurrent KS). This self-contained approach to the design of a KS's locking and tagging structure is required if the modularity of the system, with respect to deletion or addition of KS's, is to be preserved.

The KS's that were used in the simulation experiments were not originally designed so that they could be interrupted at arbitrary points in their processing, and consequently they lacked the appropriate locking and tagging structure to guarantee data integrity in a multiprocess(or) environment. The addition, as an afterthought, of the appropriate locking and tagging structure to these KS's was sometimes quite difficult. This was an especially serious problem when an attempt was made to put tagging

primitives into KS's which had internal backtracking control structures for searching the node graph structure in the blackboard. This difficulty arises because previously made data assumptions (tags in the blackboard) associated with a partial path (sequence of nodes in the blackboard) must be removed upon discovering that the path cannot be successfully completed. Thus, most of the KS's in the experiment did not use tagging as a method of guaranteeing integrity, but rather used a combination of node- and region-locking. However, preconditions, which have a much simpler structure and generally do not write in the blackboard, were modified to use the tagging mechanism. In addition, to further simplify KS locking structures, region-locking was used wherever possible. This excessive use of region-locking was mainly responsible for the significant amount of interference among processes which caused the effective processor utilization to go from an optimal 12 to a realized 4 (see Table II).

Table IV contains the simulation results relating to the data-access interference experienced by precondition and KS processes, for varying numbers of processors. This table is an extension of Table II, which was discussed in the previous section (i.e., the underlying simulation runs were the same for both tables). Execution interference was measured by recording the amount of process suspension (also called *descheduling*), which results from processes being temporarily blocked in their attempts to gain access to some part of the blackboard data base.[12] As might be expected, as process activity increases with increasing numbers of processors, the possibility of execution interference increases (see table entries on "deschedules/ primitive lock"). This phenomenon stops at eight processors because in these simulation experiments there were rarely more than eight processes executing at any given moment. At the same time, with more and more processing power available, the likelihood of suspended processes being unblocked and becoming available for further processing increases as the number of processors increases (see table entries on "deschedule duration"). This phenomenon is also indicated by the significant decrease in processor context swaps per deschedule (i.e., with more processors, it becomes less likely that when a process is suspended there will be another process ready to execute).

The major conclusion that can be drawn from this table is that the decrease in processor utilization caused by the locking structure is not due to the high rate of data-access interference (i.e., at most only 6 percent of the primitive

---

[11] An alternative approach to these two methods for maintaining data integrity which was not explored in the simulations is the following paradigm: 1) accumulate the critical data set without the use of tagging or locking; 2) lock the critical data set, perhaps by using a single region-lock which encloses the entire critical data set; and 3) always reverify that the critical data set meets the necessary assumptions before performing the desired modifications. This alternative approach can potentially lead to less interference and lower system overhead for maintaining data integrity than the other two approaches if the following conditions are met: 1) the KS examines a large number of nodes before finally determining the small number of them that meet the desired criteria (i.e., the critical data set); and 2) the cost of reverifying this small critical set is much less costly than the initial search to construct it.

[12] The number of deschedules attributed to a process is also related to the granularity of the process-blocking mechanism. For example, processes could be blocked upon trying to gain access to a region and then relegated to waiting in a set of processes which are waiting on *any* region at that information level in the blackboard; or the wait set could be divided according to the individual regions being waited upon. While it is more expensive in the former strategy to determine whether, upon receiving an unlock wake-up signal for the wait set, which particular members of the wait set are really reschedulable, this strategy does have the advantage of causing fewer context swaps. Both strategies were tried and it was found that the more complex strategy led to higher throughput. The simpler strategy resulted in a significant number of unnecessary context swaps because the average number of suspended processes waiting at the same level was quite large.

TABLE IV
Data-Access Characteristics

number of prcrs (all times in secs)	1	2	4	8	16
avg BB accesses/KS	54.4	52.8	54.5	53.9	56.4
avg BB accesses/PRE	96.7	68.7	55.7	48.2	51.1
avg prim locks/KS	27.9	27.4	28.0	25.7	26.9
avg prim locks/PRE	96.7	68.7	55.7	48.2	51.1
avg dsched/prim lock(KS)	0	0.020	0.060	0.055	0.053
avg dsched/prim lock(PRE)	0	0.009	0.026	0.045	0.040
avg dsched duration/KS	0	5.08	5.69	1.75	1.90
avg dsched duration/PRE	0	3.95	1.91	1.35	1.86
avg cxt swaps	0	309	942	368	9
avg cxt swaps/dsched	0	1.03	0.97	0.75	0.01

locks result in deschedules) but rather from the long duration over which descheduled processes are blocked. This deschedule duration, in the optimal case of 16 processors, where processes do not have to wait for an available processor, is approximately 2 s, which is very close to the average run time of a KS. This long duration occurs because the KS locking structures typically involve executing region-locks at the beginning of the KS execution. The region-locks define the entire blackboard area (and perhaps even more) that the KS will either examine or modify during its entire execution. The locks are then released only at the termination of the KS execution. Thus, if data-access interference (i.e., a primitive lock deschedule) occurred because of a previously executed region-lock, the suspended process would very likely not be unblocked until the KS executing the region-lock had completed its processing.

Another important point that can be drawn from these simulation studies is that the self-contained approach used to develop KS locking structures, which makes no assumptions about the nature of processing of other KS's in the system, may lead to a significant amount of unnecessary interference. This unnecessary interference occurs because of the way in which KS processes actually cooperate indirectly through the blackboard. The majority of modifications that KS's make to the blackboard occur through the addition of new independent nodes rather than by modifying or deleting existing structures. Thus, most KS changes to the blackboard do not directly interfere with the concurrent processing of other KS's. In addition, due to the data-directed, incremental and error-correcting nature of KS processing, these new additions to the blackboard are eventually processed and the appropriate blackboard structure generated based on this new information. The data from the simulations run without locking confirm these observations since approximately the same results were produced as the system with locking. Thus, it seems that making some assumptions about the basic nature of KS processing can significantly reduce process interference and the overhead required to maintain data integrity. It should be pointed out that it is not being claimed that all explicit synchronization code embedded in a KS for guaranteeing data integrity can

be removed; but there is the feeling the self-correcting nature of information flow in the system will make the majority of this code unnecessary. Besides, there is still a need for temporary locks on nodes when reading and writing in order to guarantee the internal consistency of the node data structure, as well as a need for region-locking so as to avoid the creation of duplicate copies of the same node.

Finally, it is once again stated that the results presented here are derived from a rather limited selection of KS processes. However, it is hoped that the system organization (including the data-base design) is of sufficiently general character that these particular results at least give a feeling for the results that might be expected using a different set of KS processes to solve the same or different problems.

SUMMARY AND CONCLUSIONS

This paper has presented an organization for a knowledge-based AI problem-solving system which is designed to take maximum advantage of any separability of the processing or data components available within that organization. KS's are intended to be largely independent and capable of asynchronous execution in the form of KS processes. Overall system control is distributed and primarily data-directed, being based on events occurring in a globally shared blackboard data base. The intercommunication (and interdependence) of the various KS processes is minimized by making the blackboard data base the primary means of communication, thereby exhibiting an indirection with respect to communication similar to the indirect data-directed form of process control. Such a problem-solving organization is believed to be particularly amenable to implementation in the hardware environment of a network of closely coupled asynchronous processors which share a common memory. The HSII, which has been developed using the techniques for system organization described here, has provided a context for evaluating the multiprocessing aspects of this system architecture.

In specifying the blackboard as the primary means of interprocess communication, particular attention was paid to resolving the data-access synchronization problems and data-integrity issues arising from the asynchronous data-access patterns possible from the various independently executing parallel KS processes. A nonpreemptive data-access allocation scheme was devised in which the units of allocation could be linearly ordered and hence allocated according to that ordering so as to avoid data deadlocks. The particular units of data allocation (locking) were chosen as being either blackboard nodes (node-locking) or abstract regions in the blackboard (region-locking). The region-locking mechanism views the potential blackboard as an abstract data space in which access rights to abstract regions could be granted without regard to the actual data content of these regions.

Another area of concern relating to the use of a shared blackboard-like data facility has to do with the assumptions made by the various executing KS's concerning issues of data integrity and localized data contexts. Since the blackboard is intended to represent only the most current global status of the problem solution state, mechanisms were introduced to allow individual KS's to retain recent histories (in the form of local contexts) of modifications made to the dynamic blackboard structure. Local contexts provide KS's with the ability to create a local data state which reflects the net effects of data events which have occurred in the data base since the time of the KS's activation. Combined with the blackboard data-tagging capabilities, local contexts also provide a means by which KS's can execute quite independently of any other concurrently executing KS's (and without interfering with the execution progress of any of these processes).

In an attempt to improve the problem-solving efficiency of a multiprocessor implementation of the system by increasing the amount of potential parallelism from KS activity, the logical functions of precondition evaluation and KS execution were split into separate processing entities. A precondition process is responsible for monitoring and accumulating blackboard data events which might be of interest to the KS associated with the precondition; and when the appropriate data conditions for the activation of the KS exist in the blackboard, the precondition instantiates a KS process, giving to the new process the data context in which the precondition was satisfied. The activation of the precondition itself is also data-directed, being based on monitoring for primitive blackboard modifications.

In order to indicate the nature of the performance of the HSII organization when run in a closely coupled multiprocessor environment, a simulation system was embedded into the multiprocess implementation of HSII on the DEC system-10. Given the knowledge-based decomposition of a problem-solving organization as prescribed by the HSII structure, effective parallelism factors of four to six were realized even with a relatively small set of precondition and KS processes, with indications that up to fourteen processors could be totally utilized, given appropriate usage (or structuring) of the data-access synchronization

mechanisms. Experiments thus far have indicated that careful use of the locking structure is required in order to approach the optimal utilization of any given processor configuration. An extended use of noninterfering tagging seems to be indicated, along with a reduction in the use of region-locking (perhaps substituting region-examining or node-locking wherever possible). In addition, it is felt that the basic self-correcting nature of information flow in the HSII system, may obviate the need for most uses of explicit synchronization techniques to maintain data integrity. Studies are under way to determine whether other types of symbol manipulation problems can be structured for a multiprocessor without a major use of explicit synchronization techniques by employing such a self-correcting information flow paradigm as is used in HSII. Measurements were also made of various system level primitive operations which indicate that overhead to support the multiprocessing aspects is approximately 100 percent; thus, with a parallelism factor of 2 or greater the multiprocess overheads can be recovered. While all these results are based on a small set of KS's in the particular task domain of speech understanding, they seem to indicate that the HSII organization is indeed applicable for efficient use in a closely coupled multiprocessor environment.

ACKNOWLEDGMENT

We wish to acknowledge the contributions of the following people: L. Erman for his major role in the design and development of HSII, R. Reddy for many of the basic ideas which have led to the uniprocessor version of the problem-solving organization described here, and G. Gill for his untiring efforts in systems implementation.

REFERENCES

[1] J. K. Baker, "The DRAGON system—An overview," in *Proc. IEEE Symp. Speech Recognition*, Carnegie-Mellon Univ., Pittsburgh, PA, Apr. 1974, pp. 22–26; also in *IEEE Trans. Acoustics, Speech, and Signal Processing*, vol. ASSP-23, pp. 24–29, Feb. 1975.
[2] C. G. Bell *et al.*, "C.mmp: The CMU multi-mini-processor computer," Comp. Sci. Dep., Carnegie-Mellon Univ., Pittsburgh, PA, Tech. Rep., 1971.
[3] C. G. Bell, R. C. Chen, S. H. Fuller, J. Grason, S. Rege, and D. P. Siewiorek, "The architecture and application of computer modules: A set of components for digital systems design," presented at the *COMPCON 73*, San Francisco, CA, 1973.
[4] E. G. Coffman, M. J. Elphick, and A. Shoshani, "System deadlocks," *Comput. Surv.*, vol. 3, pp. 67–78, 1971.
[5] L. D. Erman, "An environment and system for machine understanding of connected speech," Ph.D. dissertation, Comp. Sci. Dep., Stanford Univ., Stanford, CA; also, Comp. Sci. Dep., Carnegie-Mellon Univ., Pittsburgh, PA, Tech. Rep., 1974.
[6] L. D. Erman, and V. R. Lesser, "A multi-level organization for problem solving using many, diverse, cooperating sources of knowledge," in *Proc. 4th Int. Joint Conf. on Artificial Intelligence*, Tiblesi, Georgia, USSR, pp. 483–490, 1975.
[7] L. D. Erman, R. D. Fennell, V. R. Lesser, and D. R. Reddy, "System organizations for speech understanding: Implications of network and multiprocessor computer architectures for AI," *IEEE Trans. Comput.*, vol. C-25, pp. 414–421, Apr. 1976.
[8] J. A. Feldman *et al.*, "Recent developments in sail—An Algol-based language for artificial intelligence," *Proc. FJCC*, 1972.

[9] R. D. Fennell, "Multiprocess software architecture for AI problem solving," Ph.D. dissertation, Comp. Sci. Dep., Carnegie-Mellon Univ., Pittsburgh, PA, Tech. Rep., 1975.

[10] F. E. Heart, S. M. Ornstein, W. R. Crowler, and W. B. Barker. "A new minicomputer/multiprocessor for the ARPA network," in *Proc. AFIPS*, NDD42, pp. 529–537, 1973.

[11] V. R. Lesser, R. D. Fennell, L. D. Erman, and D. R. Reddy, "Organization of the Hearsay II speech understanding system," in *Proc. IEEE Symp. Speech Recognition*, Carnegie-Mellon Univ., Pittsburgh, PA, Apr. 1974; also in *IEEE Trans. Acoustics, Speech, and Signal Processing*, vol. ASSP-23, pp. 11–23, Feb. 1975.

[12] A. Newell, "Production systems: Models of control structures," in *Visual Information Processing*, W. C. Chase, Ed. New York: Academic Press, 1973, pp. 463–526.

[13] R. B. Ohlander, "Analysis of natural scenes," Ph.D. dissertation, Comp. Sci. Dep., Carnegie-Mellon Univ., Pittsburgh, PA, Tech. Rep., 1975.

[14] D. R. Reddy, "Eyes and ears for computers," Comp. Sci. Dep., Carnegie-Mellon Univ., Pittsburgh, PA, Tech. Rep., Keynote Speech presented at Conf. on Cognitive Processes and Artificial Intelligence, Hamburg, Apr. 1973.

[15] D. R. Reddy, L. D. Erman, and R. B. Neely, "A model and a system for machine recognition of speech," *IEEE Trans. Audio and Electroacoust.*, vol. AU-21, pp. 229–238, June 1973.

[16] D. R. Reddy, L. D. Erman, R. D. Fennell, and R. B. Neely, "The HEARSAY speech understanding system: An example of the recognition process," in *Proc. 3rd Int. Joint Conf. on Artificial Intelligence*, Stanford, CA, pp. 185–193; also in *IEEE Trans. Comput.*, vol. C-25, pp. 422–431, Apr. 1976.

[17] D. E. Rumelhart, "Towards an interactive model of reading," Center for Human Information Processing, Univ. of California at San Diego, La Jolla, CA, Tech. Rep. 56, Mar. 1976.

[18] D. Swinehart and R. Sproull, "SAIL," Stanford AI Proj. Operating Note 57.2, Comp. Sci. Dep., Stanford Univ., Stanford, CA, 1971.

Richard D. Fennell was born in Pittsburgh, PA, on June 1, 1947. He received the B.S. degree in physics from Rensselaer Polytechnic Institute, Troy, NY, in 1969, and the Ph.D. degree in computer science from Carnegie-Mellon University, Pittsburgh, PA, in 1975.

He is currently with the Federal Judicial Center, Washington, DC, serving as Chief of Software Systems Research and Development. He is also a Consulting Research Computer Scientist at Carnegie-Mellon University. Dr. Fennell was the President of APL Software Systems, Inc., and a software consultant for Digital Equipment Corporation, Maynard, MA. He is a member of Sigma Pi Sigma.

Victor R. Lesser was born in New York, NY, on November 21, 1944. He received the A.B. degree in mathematics from Cornell University, Ithaca, NY, in 1966, and the M.S. and Ph.D. degrees from Stanford University, Stanford, CA, in 1969 and 1972, respectively.

He was a Research Associate in the Computer Science Department at Carnegie-Mellon University, Pittsburgh, PA, from 1972 to 1974. He currently holds the position of Research Computer Scientist there. In addition to work on system organizations for speech understanding, his research interests include computer architecture, particularly multiprocessor systems and microprogramming.

Reprinted with permission from *Spring Joint Computer Conference*, Volume 38, 1971, pages 39-48. Copyright © 1971 by AFIPS Press.

4-way parallel processor partition of an atmospheric primitive-equation prediction model

by E. MORENOFF

Ocean Data Systems, Inc.
Rockville, Maryland

and

W. BECKETT, P. G. KESEL, F. J. WINNINGHOFF and P. M. WOLFF

Fleet Numerical Weather Central
Monterey, California

INTRODUCTION

A principal mission of the Fleet Numerical Weather Central is to provide, on an operational basis, numerical meteorological and oceanographic products peculiar to the needs of the Navy. Toward this end the FNWC is also charged with the development and test of numerical techniques applicable to Navy environmental forecasting problems. A recent achievement of this development program has been the design, development, and beginning in September 1970, operational use of the FNWC five-layer, baroclinic, atmospheric prediction model, based on the so-called "primitive-equations," and herein defined as the Primitive Equation Model (PEM).

The PEM was initially written as a single-processor version to be executed in one of the two FNWC computer systems. In this form the PEM was exercised as a research and development tool subject to improvement and revision to enhance the meteorological forecasts being generated.

The development reached a point in early 1970 where the PEM was skillfully simulating the essential three-dimensional, hemispheric distribution of the atmospheric-state parameters (winds, pressure, temperature, moisture, and precipitation). Its ability to predict the generation of new storms, moreover, was particularly encouraging. The FORTRAN coded program, however, required just over three hours to compute a set of 36 hour predictions. To be of operational utility, it was clear that several types of speed-ups were in order.

The principal effort in the development of the operational version of the PEM was directed at partitioning the model to take advantage of all possible computational parallelism to exploit the four powerful central processing units available in the FNWC computer installation. Additional speed-ups involved machine language coding for routines in which the physics were considered firm, and the substitution of table look-up operations for manufacturer supplied algorithms. The resultant four-processor version of the PEM was considered ready for final testing in August 1970, four months after work was initiated.

The one-processor version of the PEM required 184 minutes of elapsed time for the generation of 36-hour prognoses. The four-processor version, on the other hand, requires only one hour of elapsed time to produce the same results.

This paper summarizes the principal factors involved in the successful operation of the 4-processor version of the PEM. Operating System modifications needed to establish 4-way inter-processor communications through Extended Core Storage (ECS) are described in the second section. The PEM structure is described in the third section. The partitions into which the PEM is divided are examined in the fourth section. The fifth section is devoted to the methods employed for synchronizing the execution of the partitions in each of the multiple processors and the model's mode of operation. The results of the PEM development and reduction to operational use are summarized in the last section.

FNWC COMPUTER SYSTEMS COMMUNICATIONS

The Fleet Numerical Weather Central operates two large-scale and two medium-scale computer systems as

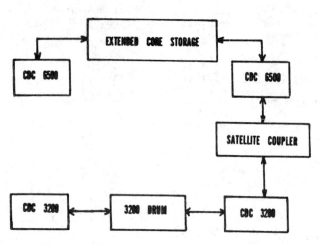

Figure 1—FNWC computer system configuration

shown in Figure 1. The two CDC 2200 computer systems communicate with each other through a random access drum. One of the CDC 3200 computers is linked to one of the CDC 6500 computers by a manufacturer-supplied satellite coupler. The two dual-processor CDC 6500 computer systems are linked with each other through the one million words of Extended Core Storage (ECS).

Normally, the ECS is operated in such a manner that 500,000 words are assigned to each of the two CDC 6500 computer systems with no inter-communication permitted. A mechanism was developed by the FNWC technical staff allowing authorized programs in each of the four central processors of the two CDC computer systems to communicate with each other and, at the same time, be provided with software protection from interference by non-authorized programs.

There are three classifications of ECS access, normal, master and slave, designated for each job in the system by an appropriate ECS access code and a pass key. For normal ECS access these fields are zero. If the ECS access code field designates a job as a master, then the associated pass key will be interpreted as the name of ECS block storage assigned to that job. A slave has no ECS assigned to it but is able to refer the ECS block named by its pass key.

A master job in one of the CDC 6500's may have slave jobs in the other CDC 6500. A communication mechanism called 1SI was established between the operating systems by FNWC technical staff to facilitate implementation of the master-slave ECS access classification. 1SI is a pair of bounce PP routines (one in each machine) which provide a software, full duplex block multi-plexing channel between the machines via ECS. Messages and/or blocks of data may be sent over

this channel so that 1SI may be used to call PP programs in the other machine or to pass data such as tables or files between the machines.

Obtaining a master/slave ECS access code is accomplished by two PP programs: ECS and 1EC. A job wishing to establish itself as a master first requests a block of ECS storage in the same manner of a normal access job. Once obtained, the labeling of this block of ECS storage is requested by calling the PP program ECS with the argument specifying the desired pass key and the access code for a master. The program ECS searches the resident control point exchange areas (CPEA) for a master with the same pass key. If one is found the requesting job is aborted even if the program ECS used 1SI to call 1EC in the other machine. 1EC will perform a similar search of the CPEA in its own machine and return its findings to the program ECS via 1SI. If the other machine is down, or if no matching key can be found, the label is established, otherwise the requesting job is aborted. Before returning control to the requesting job, the program ECS increments the ECS parity error flag and monitors via a special monitor function developed at FNWC. A non-zero value of this flag has the effect of preventing ECS storage moves in the half of ECS assigned to the particular machine.

Similarly, a job wishing to establish itself as a slave calls the PP program ECS with the appropriate pass key and access code. ECS searches its own machine's CPEA for a master with a matching key. If none is found, 1EC is called on the other machine via 1SI and the search is repeated in the other CPEA. If still none is found, this fact is indicated to the requesting job. If a match should exist in either machine, the original ECS will have the address (ECRA) and field links (ECFL) of the requesting job saved in its CPEA and will be given the ECRA and ECFL of the matching master.

Modifications made to the ECS storage move program allow ECS storage moves in a machine with no master present. Modifications to the end of job processor reset the ECRA and ECFL of slaves to their values and decrement the ECS parity error flag in the monitor when a master terminates.

ATMOSPHERIC PREDICTION MODEL STRUCTURE

Several developmental variations of a five-layer baroclinic atmospheric prediction model, based on integrations of the so-called primitive equations, were designed and developed by Kesel and Winninghoff[1] in the 1969-1970 period at FNWC Monterey.

The governing equations are written in flux form in a

manner similar to Smagorinsky et al.,[2] and Arakawa.[3] The corresponding difference equations are based on the Arakawa technique. This type of scheme precludes nonlinear computational instability by requiring that the flux terms conserve the square of an advected parameter, assuming continuous time derivatives. Total energy is conserved because of requirements placed upon the vertical differencing; specifically, the special form of the hydrostatic equation. Total mass is conserved, when integrated over the entire domain. Linear instability is avoided by meeting the Courant-Fried-richs-Lewy criterion.

The Phillips[4] sigma coordinate system is employed in which pressure, P, is normalized with the underlying terrain pressure, π. At levels where sigma equals 0.9, 0.7, 0.5, 0.3, and 0.1, the horizontal wind components, u and v, the temperature, T, and the height, Z, are carried. The moisture variable, q, is carried at the lowest three of these levels. Vertical velocity, $w \equiv -\dot{\sigma}$, is carried at the layer interfaces, and calculated diagnostically from the continuity equation. See Figure 2.

The Clarke-Berkovsky mountains are used in conjunction with a Kurihara[5] form of the pressure-force terms in the momentum equations to reduce stationary "noise" patterns over high, irregular terrain.

The Richtmyer centered time-differencing method is used with a ten-minute time step, but integrations are recycled every six hours with a Matsuno (Euler backward) step to greatly reduce solution separation. The mesh length of the grid is 381 kilometers at 60 North. The earth is mapped onto a polar stereographic projection for the Northern Hemisphere. In the calculation of map factor and the Coriolis parameter, the sine of the latitude is not permitted to take on values less than that value corresponding to 23 degrees North.

Lateral diffusion is applied at all levels (sparingly) in order to redistribute high frequency components in the mass and motion fields. Surface stress is computed at the lowest layer only.

A considerable part of the heating "package" is fashioned after Mintz and Arakawa,[6] as described by Langlois and Kwok.[7] The albedo is determined as a function of the mean monthly temperature at the earth's surface. A Smagorinsky parameterization of cloudiness is used at one layer (sigma equals 0.7), but based on the relative humidity for the layer between 0.7 and 0.4. Dry convective adjustment precludes hydrostatic instability. Moisture and heat are redistributed in the lowest three layers by use of an Arakawa-Mintz small-scale convection parameterization technique. Small-scale convective precipitation occurs in two of the three types of convection so simulated. Evaporation and large-scale condensation are the main source-sink terms in the moisture conservation equa-

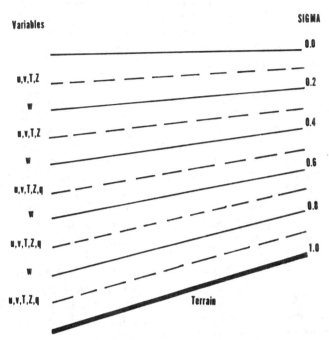

Figure 2—Diagram of levels and variables

tion. Evaporation over land is based on a Bowen ratio, using data from Budyko.

In the computation of sensible heat flux over water, the FNWC-produced sea surface temperature distribution is held constant in time. Over land, the required surface temperature is obtained from a heat balance equation. Both long- and short-wave radiative fluxes are computed for two gross layers (sigma = 1.0 to 0.6 and from 0.6 to 0.2). The rates for the upper gross layer are assigned to the upper three computational levels. Those rates for the lower gross layer are assigned to the lower two computational levels.

The type of lateral boundary conditions which led to the over-all best results is a constant-flux *restoration technique* devised by Kesel and Winninghoff, and implemented in January 1970,

The technique was designed to accomplish the following objectives:

a. To eliminate the necessity of altering the initial mass structure of the tropical-subtropical atmosphere as is the case when cyclic continuity is used.

b. To eliminate the problems associated with the imposition of rigid, slippery, insulated-wall boundary conditions; particularly those concerning the false reflection of the computational mode at outflow boundaries.

c. To preserve the perturbation component in the

aforementioned areas in the prognostic period (although no dynamic prediction is attempted south of 4 North the output is much more meteorological than fields which have been fattened as required by cyclic continuity).

The procedure is as follows: All of the distributions of temperature, moisture, wind, and terrain pressure are preserved at initial time. A field of restoration coefficients which vary continuously from unity at and south of 4 North to zero at and north of 17 North is computed. At the end of each ten minute integration step the new values of the state variables are restored back toward their initial values (in the area south of 17 North) according to the amount specified by the field of restoration coefficients. The net effect of this procedure is to produce a fully dynamic forecast north of 17 North, a persistence forecast south of 4 North, and a blend in between. The mathematical-physical effect is that the region acts as an energy sponge for externally (outwardly) propagating inertio-gravity oscillations.

The basic inputs associated with the initialization procedure are the virtual temperature analyses for the Northern Hemisphere at 12 constant pressure levels distributed from 1000 MBS to 50 MBS, height analyses at seven of these pressure levels, moisture analyses at four levels from the surface up to 500 MBS. In addition, the terrain height, sea level pressure and sea surface temperature analyses are used.

Several types of wind initialization have been tried: geostrophic winds (using constant Coriolis parameter); linear balance winds; full balance winds; winds obtained by use of an iterative technique. Aside from geostrophic winds the quickest to compute is the set of non-divergent winds derived from solution of the so called linear balance equation. These are entirely satisfactory for short-range forecasts (up to three days).

The degree of prediction skill currently being observed from the tests is very gratifying. It is clear that little or nothing is known about the initial specification of these parameters over large areas of the Northern Hemisphere, particularly over oceans and at high altitudes.

As noted at the start of the section, the equations are written in flux form and an Arakawa-type conservative differencing scheme is employed. No attempt will be made to exhibit herein a complete set of the corresponding difference equations, since it is well beyond the scope of this paper to do so. Rather, it will suffice to show the main continuous equation forms (using only symbols such as H, Q, and F, to denote all of the diabatic heating effects, moisture source and sink terms, and surface stress, respectively).

There are five prognostic equations, one of which must be integrated prior to parallel integration of the remaining four. These are the continuity equation, the east-west momentum equation, the thermodynamic energy equation, and the moisture conservation equation. Heights (geopotentials) are computed diagnostically from the hydrostatic equation (the scaled vertical equation of motion). Vertical velocities are calculated from a form of the continuity equation. The pressure-force terms are shown in their original forms. [The pressure surfaces are actually synthesized "locally" about each point, by means of the hypsometric conversion of pressure changes to geopotential changes; and geopotential differences are computed on these pressure surfaces.] This Kurihara-type modification tends to reduce inconsistent truncation error when differencing the terrain pressure (which remains fixed in any column) and geopotentials of sigma surfaces (the "smoothness" of which varies with height).

A. East-West Momentum Equation

$$\frac{\partial \pi u}{\partial t} = -m^2\left\{\frac{\partial}{\partial x}\left(\frac{uu\pi}{m}\right)+\frac{\partial}{\partial y}\left(\frac{uv\pi}{m}\right)\right\}+\pi\frac{\partial(wu)}{\partial \sigma}$$

$$+\pi vf-m\left\{\frac{\partial \phi}{\partial x}+RT\frac{\partial \pi}{\partial x}\right\}+K\nabla^2 u\pi+F_x$$

B. North-South Momentum Equation

$$\frac{\partial \pi v}{\partial t} = -m^2\left\{\frac{\partial}{\partial x}\left(\frac{uv\pi}{m}\right)+\frac{\partial}{\partial y}\left(\frac{vv\pi}{m}\right)\right\}+\pi\frac{\partial wv}{\partial \sigma}$$

$$-\pi uf-m\left\{\pi\frac{\partial \phi}{\partial y}+RT\frac{\partial \pi}{\partial y}\right\}+K\nabla^2 v\pi+F_y$$

C. Thermodynamic Energy Equation

$$\frac{\partial \pi T}{\partial t} = -m^2\left\{\frac{\partial}{\partial x}\left(\frac{\pi uT}{m}\right)+\frac{\partial}{\partial y}\left(\frac{\pi vT}{m}\right)\right\}$$

$$+\pi\frac{\partial(wT)}{\partial \sigma}+H\pi+K\nabla^2\pi T$$

$$+\frac{RT}{c_p\sigma}\left\{-w\pi+\sigma\left[\frac{\partial \pi}{\partial t}+m\left(u\frac{\partial \pi}{\partial x}+v\frac{\partial \pi}{\partial y}\right)\right]\right\}$$

D. Moisture Conservation Equation

$$\frac{\partial e\pi}{\partial t} = -m^2\left\{\frac{\partial}{\partial x}\left(\frac{\pi ue}{m}\right)+\frac{\partial}{\partial y}\left(\frac{\pi ve}{m}\right)\right\}+\pi\frac{\partial(we)}{\partial \sigma}+Q\pi$$

where Q = moisture source/sink term

E. Continuity Equation

$$\frac{\partial \pi}{\partial t} = -m^2 \left\{ \frac{\partial}{\partial x}\left(\frac{u\pi}{m}\right) + \frac{\partial}{\partial y}\left(\frac{v\pi}{m}\right) \right\} + \pi \frac{\partial w}{\partial \sigma}$$

F. Hydrostatic Equation

$$\frac{\partial \phi}{\partial \sigma} = -\frac{RT}{\sigma}$$

PARTITIONING THE MODEL

The PEM may be considered in three distinct sections: the data input and initialization section; the integration section repeated in each forecast time step; and the output section. Each sixth time step, the basic integration section is modified to take into consideration the effects of diabatic heating. This includes incoming solar radiation, outgoing terrestrial radiation, sensible heat exchange at the air-earth interface, and evaporation, Condensation processes, in contrast, are considered every time-step. Each thirty-sixth time step, the results of the preceding forecast hours are output and the integrations reiterated.

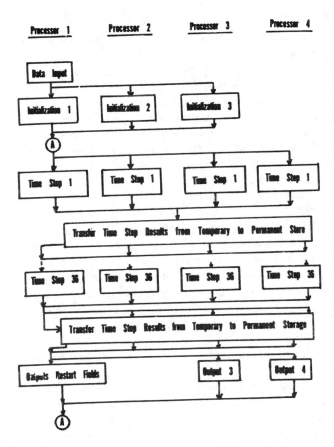

Figure 3—Overall model partition structure

The basic structure of the PEM, as represented by the governing set of difference equations and the method of their solution, is naturally suited for partitioning for parallel operation and concurrent execution in multiple processors. The particular partitioning implemented was selected in order to insure approximately equal elapsed time for the execution of concurrently operating partitions. Four-way partitions were principally employed, although both three-way and two-way partitions were introduced where appropriate.

The basic partition of the model was based on the observation that during each time step in the forecast process the momentum equations in the east-west and north-south directions, the thermodynamic energy equation, and the moisture equation could each be executed concurrently in each of four different processors. By virtue of the centered time-differencing method, the forcing functions to be evaluated in the solution of each of these equations require data generated during the preceding time step and accessed on a read only basis during the current time step. Hence parallel processing could be achieved by providing separate temporary locations for storage of intermediate results during execution of a time step by each processor *and* by providing a mechanism to insure that each processor is at the same time step in the solution of its assigned equation and, where required, at the same level within that time step.

With this four-way partitioning within the basic time step as a starting point, additional possibilities for simultaneity in the model's operation were observed and further partitions developed. For example, prior to the execution of the four-way partitioning within each time step a three-way partition was implemented which allowed the continuity equation to be solved for the interface vertical velocities and the local change of lower boundary pressure at the same time that geopotential-field correction terms are generated. The model's initialization section was similarly partitioned three ways and the output section two ways. Finally, the heating effects computations were implemented as a three-way partition.

The four-way, three-way and two-way partitions were packaged and compiled as four separate programs, one for each of the four FNWC processors. The overall structure of the partitioned model is illustrated in Figure 3. Following completion of the output section at time step (36), the integration sequence is recycled from time step (1) as shown.

Processor 1 is designated as the "master" processor and Processors 2, 3, and 4 as the "slave" processors, both in the sense described in the inter-computer communications section and in the sense that each time step is initiated by command from Processor 1 and termi-

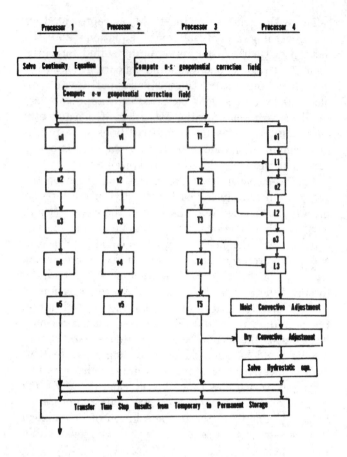

Figure 4—Typical time step partition structure

through integration of the east-west and north-south oriented momentum equations, the thermodynamic energy equation and the moisture conservation equation, respectively. The variable L represents the computation of the effects of the large scale condensation process.

Once the computations of the u_i, v_i and T_i ($i=1, 2, 3, 4, 5$) are initiated in Processors 1, 2, and 3, respectively, they proceed independently of one another to the end of the time step. Each "i" value represents another layer in the five-layer atmospheric model.

An added consideration is introduced into the computations of Processor 4, however. Before the effects of the large scale condensation process can be computed for a layer, both the Thermodynamic Energy equation and the Moisture Conservation equation must be solved at that layer. Hence, a level of control is required to synchronize the execution of Processor 4 with Processor 3 within the individual time step computations. Further, the Dry Convective Adjustment computation in Processor 4 requires the completion of all five layers of the Thermodynamic Energy equation before it can be initiated so that a second level of intra-step control is required. At the conclusion of the Dry Convective Adjustment computation, the Hydrostatic equation is integrated in Processor 4 to obtain the new geopotential fields. The time step is concluded with the transfer of intermediate time step results from temporary to permanent storage.

The basic time-step partition structure is modified each sixth time step to include the effects of a diabatic heating. The heating section was implemented as a three-way partition illustrated in Figure 5. Additional intra-step level control is required to synchronize the execution of each of the partitions as shown in the figure. Note that the heating partition in Processor 3 is itself divided to allow as great a degree of simultaneity as possible with the execution of partitions in Processors 1 and 2.

The output section, executed each thirty-sixth time step (at the completion of six forecast hours), is partitioned as shown in Figure 6. The output section partitions were placed in Processors 3 and 4 principally for central memory space considerations, more central memory being available in these processors than in Processors 1 and 2. The basic function of each output partition is co-ordinate transformation of the forecast variables and conversion to forms suitable for the user community.

Each output partition is initiated by command from Processor 1. Processor 4 may immediately begin processing of the east-west and north-south momentum equation variables but must wait on the transformation of the Phi fields until Processor 3 has completed the

nated by Processor 1 acknowledgment of a "complete" signal emanating from each of Processors 2, 3, and 4. At the completion of each step, results from the computations of that time step are transferred from temporary to permanent locations in storage and the next time step initiated. Once again, the transfer is initiated by command from Processor 1 and terminated by Processor 1 acknowledgment of a transfer complete signal received from Processors 2, 3, and 4.

The structure of a typical time step partition is illustrated in Figure 4. At the start of the time step a three-way split is initiated by Processor 1 during which time Processor 1 integrates the continuity equation to obtain vertical velocities and Processors 2 and 3 compute the ten pressure-force-term geopotential correction fields in the east-west and north-south directions, respectively. At this time Processor 4 is not executing a portion of the model and may either be idling or operating on an independent program in a multi-programmed mode. The completion of the assigned tasks by Processors 2 and 3 are signaled to Processor 1 which then initiates the basic four-way split. The variables u, v, T and e represent the new values of the variables obtained

Preprocessor program. A three-way partition was not implemented since the Preprocessor must be completed prior to the transformation of the Thermodynamic energy equation and moisture conservation equation variables.

To increase total system reliability a checkpoint restart procedure was designed and coded. At each output step (6, 12, 18, ..., 72 hours) all of those data fields required to restart the PEM are duplicated from their permanent ECS locations onto a magnetic tape by Processor 1, at the same time that Processors 3 and 4 are processing the output forecast fields. The essential difference between these two data sets is that the restart fields contain the variables on sigma surfaces as opposed to the pressure surface distributions required by the consumers.

The "restart" procedure itself requires less than a minute. If the prediction model run is terminated for any type of failure (hardware, software, electric power, bad input data, etc.), the restart capability ensures that the real time loss will be less than ten minutes.

In addition to the four processor version of the Atmospheric Prediction Model a two-processor version was also implemented. The primary motivation for the second implementation was to provide a back-up capability with graceful degradation which could be operated in the event one or two of the central processing units were down for extended periods. The two-pro-

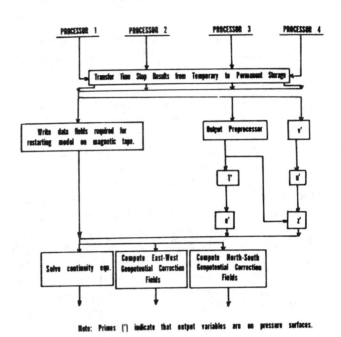

Note: Primes (') indicate that output variables are on pressure surfaces.

Figure 6—Output partition structure

cessor version will also be used as the vehicle for further research and development efforts to improve the meteorological and numerical aspects of the model, and the quality (skill) of the resultant forecasts.

PARTITION SYNCHRONIZATION AND EXECUTION

The parallel execution of the multiple partitions is realizable because it is possible to postulate a mechanism by which the operation of each partition in each of the multiple processors can be exactly synchronized. This mechanism is an adaptation to the requirements of the PEM and the characteristics of the FNWC computer installation of a general program linkage mechanism known as the Buffer File Mode of Operation.[8,9,10]

Implicit in the Buffer File Mode of Operation is the concentration of all inter-program communications through Buffer Files. A Buffer File is a set of fixed length blocks organized in a ring structure and placed in each data path from one program to another. The program generating the data to be passed places the data into the Buffer File once its operations on that data have been completed. The program to receive the data finds the data to be operated on in the Buffer File.

The flow of data through the Buffer File is unidirectional; that is, one program may only write data to the Buffer File and the other may only read data from the

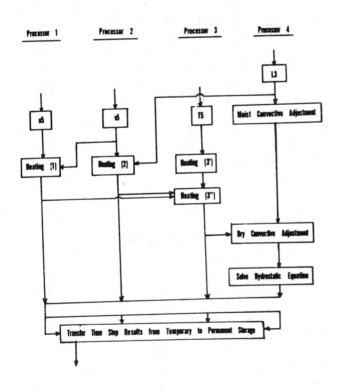

Figure 5—Influence of heating on time step computation

Buffer File. Pointers are maintained which indicate which blocks in the Buffer File have last been written into and read from by the two programs involved in the data transfer. The Buffer File Mode of Operation can be used to synchronize the operation of otherwise asynchronously operating programs in the same or different processors by either of two methods.

In the first instance, program synchronization is effected by regulating the streaming of data through the Buffer File from one program to another. The program writing data to a Buffer File cannot proceed beyond the point in its execution when it is necessary to place data into the Buffer File and there is no room for additional data in the Buffer File. Similarly, a program reading data from the Buffer File cannot proceed beyond the point in its execution when it requires data from the Buffer File and there is no additional data in the Buffer File. The execution of a program, either waiting for additional data in its input Buffer File or for additional space in its output Buffer File, is temporarily delayed, and thereby brought into synchronization with the execution of the other program.

In the second instance, program synchronization is effected by conveying "change of state" or "condition" information from one program to the other. The Buffer File block size is chosen on the basis of the quantity of information to be passed between programs. The internal state change of a program is noted as a block of data in that program's output Buffer File. The fact that there has been a change in state of the program can readily be sensed by the other program which then can read the block of data from the Buffer File. The second program can determine the nature of the change in state of the first program by examination of the data in the block it has read from the Buffer File.

The bi-directional transfer of the program state information is realized by the introduction of Buffer File pairs. The first Buffer File can only be read from by the first program and written to by the second program, while the second can only be read from by the second program and written to by the first program. This method of exchanging state information between programs not only provides a mechanism for synchronizing the execution of two otherwise asynchronously executed programs, but also eliminates the internal program housekeeping which would normally be needed to coordinate the accesses and the sequences of such accesses of the programs to the program state information.

The PEM synchronization mechanism, referred to herein as the Partition Synchronization Mechanism (PSM), is based on the latter alternative. The application of the PSM to the multi-processor FNWC com-

puter environment requires the Buffer Files to reside in some random access storage device jointly accessible by each of the processors. The device which satisfies this requirement is the ECS, operated in the manner previously described.

A pair of Buffer Files is assigned between each two partitions for which bi-directional transfer of state information is required. Hence in the typical time step partition structure illustrated in Figure 4 and amplified in Figure 5, Buffer File pairs are assigned between partitions resident in Processors 1 and 2, 1 and 3, 1 and 4, 2 and 4, and 3 and 4.

The nature of the change of state information to be passed between any pair of partitions in the PEM is whether or not one partition has reached a point in its execution where sufficient data has been developed to allow the other partition to initiate or continue its own execution. This can be represented as a single "GO-NO GO" flag to be sensed by the second partition. Hence, in the PEM the Buffer File recirculating ring structure reduced to a simple single one word block maintained in ECS.

Referring to Figure 3, it can be seen that the issuance of a "GO-NO GO" signal by a partition is equivalent to either a command to "split" the straight line execution of the model into multiple partitions or to "join" the execution of the multiple partitions into a lesser number of partitions. A five character Buffer File naming convention was established to facilitate identification of which process was involved.

The first two characters of the name serve to identify whether the Buffer File is associated with an inter-step or inter-level signal; the former is designated by the characters "IS" and the latter by the characters "IL". The third character specifies whether a split ("S") or a join ("J") is being signaled. The fourth and fifth characters specify the Processors in which the partitions writing and reading the Buffer File are located respectively. Hence Buffer File ISS12 is used by the partition resident to Processor 1 to split its operation by initiating execution in Processor 2 in going from one time step to another.

When the PEM is to be executed the four programs of which it is comprised are loaded, one into each of the four Processors. The programs in Processors 2, 3 and 4 are immediately halted upon initiation and manually delayed until the program in Processor 1, the master Processor, has been assigned the necessary ECS for the model's execution and has initialized all Buffer Files to reflect a NO GO condition. Processors 2, 3 and 4 are then permitted to enter a programmed loop in which each periodically tests a Buffer File to determine when it may initiate processing of its first partition.

While in this programmed loop the slave Processors may either be engaged in the execution of unrelated programs or simply remain in a local counting loop.

Upon completion of the data input phase of its operation, Processor 1 removes the hold on the execution of Processors 2 and 3 which then proceed with the initialization phase while Processor 4 remains at the hold condition. At the completion of its portion of the initialization phase, Processor 1 holds until receipt of a GO signal from Processors 2 and 3, signifying the completion of their assigned partitions. Processors 2 and 3 again enter a hold status after providing the GO signal to Processor 1. Finally, Processor 1 initiates the iterative integration section by signaling the GO condition for Processors 2, 3 and 4. At the completion of the execution of the partitions in Processors 2, 3 and 4 the master Processor is notified via the appropriate Buffer Files and each once more enters the hold condition and remains there until Processor 1, having verified that each partition has been completed, signals the transfer of the time step results from temporary to permanent storage. This process then continues to repeat itself, modified as previously described in each sixth and thirty-sixth time step.

Inter-level holds and go's are generally implemented in the same manner as the inter-step holds and go's described in the preceding paragraph. There is one exception, however. In the partition executed in Processor 4 in the iterative integration section, a separate Buffer File is provided to control the initiation of the execution of the large scale condensation effects computation at each of levels 1, 2 and 3. The separate Buffer file at each level is predicated on the need to allow the partition in Processor 3 to proceed on with its execution after signaling the start of execution of Processor 4 at each level *without* waiting for an acknowledgment of completion of that level by Processor 4.

This emphasizes a particularly important aspect of the operation of the PEM. The execution of the partitions in the different processors cannot get out of synchronization with one another. Each is always working on the same time step at the same time. If the partition in one of the Processors is delayed, for example, while that Processor solves a higher priority problem, then all the Processors at the completion of the processing of their partitions will hold until the delayed Processor "catches-up." The execution of the partitions will not fall out of synchronization.

CONCLUSIONS

The Atmospheric Prediction Model developed at FNWC was partitioned to be operated in a 4-Processor

and a 2-Processor configuration, in addition to the 1-Processor configuration for which it was initially designed. The 4-Processor version is currently in operational use at FNWC while the 2-Processor version provides a back-up capability in the event of equipment malfunction and a new research and development tool.

A Partition Synchronization Mechanism was developed for purposes of synchronizing the execution of the partitions being executed in each of the multiple processors. The nature of PSM is such as to insure that each partition is always operating on data in the same time step. The ability to guarantee this synchronization implies it is possible to allow other independent jobs to co-exist and share what computer resources are available with the Partitioned Atmospheric Prediction Model.

The PSM fully utilizes modifications to the operating systems of each of the two CDC 6500 dual processor computers to allow programs in each of the four processors to communicate with each other using ECS. In addition to the intercomputer communications the FNWC operating system modifications insure software protection from interference by non-authorized programs.

As a consequence of employing the 4-Processor version of the Atmospheric Prediction Model, the same meteorological products were generated in 60 minutes rather than the 184 minutes required of the 1-Processor version. This reduction in time allowed the incorporation of a new and more powerful output section and the extension of the basic forecast period from 36 hours to 72 hours. The 72 hour forecast is produced in an elapsed time of 2 hours.

The next step in the evolution of the FNWC PEM involves expanding grid size from 63×63 points to 89×89 points. To accommodate the additional central memory and processing requirements required of such a shift in grid size, partitioning of the horizontal domain rather than the computational burden is under consideration. It is estimated that partitioning the horizontal domain will reduce overall central memory requirements by one-half and allow the 72 hour forecast on the expanded grid to be performed in only four hours as opposed to the five and one-third hours required by the current partitioning method. The results of these new efforts will be reported on in a later paper.

REFERENCES

1 P G KESEL F J WINNINGHOFF
*Development of a multi-processor primitive equation
atmospheric prediction model*

207

Fleet Numerical Weather Central Monterey California
Unpublished manuscript 1970

2 J SMAGORINSKY S MANAGE
L L HOLLOWAY JR
Numerical results from a 9-level general circulation model of the atmosphere
Monthly Weather Review Vol 93 No 12 pp 727-768 1965

3 A ARAKAWA
Computational design for long term numerical integration of the equations of fluid motion: Two dimensional incompressible flow
Journal of Computer Physics Vol 1 pp 119-143 1966

4 N A PHILLIPS
A coordinate system having some special advantages for numerical forecasting
Journal of Meteorology Vol 14 1957

5 Y KURIHARA
Note on finite difference expression for the hydrostatic relation and pressure gradient force
Monthly Weather Review Vol 96 No 9 1968

6 A ARAKAWA A KATAYAMA Y MINTZ
Numerical simulation of the general circulation of the atmosphere
Proceedings of WMO/IUGG Symposium of NWP Tokyo 1968

7 W E LANGLOIS H C W KWOK
Description of the Mintz-Arakawa numerical general circulation model
UCLA Dept of Meteorology Technical Report No 3 1969

8 E MORENOFF J B McLEAN
Job linkages and program strings
Rome Air Development Center Technical Report TR-66-71 1966

9 E MORENOFF J B McLEAN
Inter-program communications, program string structures and buffer files
Proceedings of the AFIPS Spring Joint Computer Conference Thompson Books pp 175-183 1967

10 E MORENOFF
The table driven augmented programming environment: A general purpose user-oriented program for extending the capabilities of operating systems
Rome Air Development Center Technical Report TR-69-108 1969

5. Dataflow Processors

Dataflow processors are based on the idea that data availability should control the execution of a program, much as tokens control the firing of nodes in Petri nets (Peterson, 1977). By their nature, dataflow machines do not require the explicit inclusion of synchronization instructions when they are programmed; synchronization is embedded in the semantics of their machine languages.

The idea of a dataflow processor is not new; it appears as early as 1963 in a paper by Seeber and Lindquist (1963) and multifunction processors like the CDC 6600 (Thornton, 1970) and the IBM 360/91 (Tomasulo, 1967) are examples of dataflow processors.

In these machines, instructions will automatically wait for the availability of their operands before being executed.

Dennis's paper presented in Section 5.1 presents a good summary of many of the recently proposed dataflow processors. Smith's paper describes Denelcor's HEP computer. Even though this computer is not a dataflow computer as described by Dennis, it is related to dataflow machines because of its synchronization mechanism.

In section 5.2, we present a paper by Dennis and Weng on the use of dataflow computers for weather prediction as one example of an application of these computers.

209

EHO182-6/81/0000/0209 © 1981 IEEE

Reprinted from *Proceedings of the First International Conference on Distributed Computing Systems*, October 1979, pages 430–439. Copyright © 1979 by The Institute of Electrical and Electronics Engineers, Inc.

THE VARIETIES OF DATA FLOW COMPUTERS[1]

Jack B. Dennis
Laboratory for Computer Science
Massachusetts Institute of Technology
Cambridge, Massachusetts 02139

Abstract -- Architectures of computer systems based on data flow concepts are attracting increasing attention as an alternative to conventional sequential processors. This paper discusses and contrasts several approaches to data flow computation representative of current work on experimental prototype machines.

Introduction

The architects of future computer systems face three challenges -- an architectural concept that successfully addresses these challenges will prove a major breakthrough toward computer systems that have high performance and contribute to easing the software problem.

1. Achieve high performance at minimal hardware cost.

This has always been an objective of computer architecture. Of course, the nature of the architecture required changes as one traverses the range of scale from microprocessing to super-computer, and as applications and technology evolve.

2. Utilize effectively the capabiliities of LSI technology.

Using · LSI devices effectively in medium to large scale computers is a generally recognized problem without generally accepted solutions. Architectures are needed which use large numbers each of a few part types which have a high logic-to-pin ratio. The most popular suggestion having these characteristics is a large number of interconnected microcomputers; however sufficiently good schemes for interconnecting and programming them have not been forthcoming.

3. Programmability

Any radical departure from conventional architectures based on sequential program execution must address the problem that the existing body of software methodology and

tools may not be applicable. The architects of supercomputers and multiprocessor systems have not addressed this challenge, trusting that the "software problem" can be successfully attacked by the "software people." This is fallacious.

A good way to ensure that a radical architecture is programmable is to make the computer system a *language-based* design. This means the system is designed as a hardware interpreter for a specific *base language* in terms of which programs to be run on the system must be expressed [10]. However, much of the work on language-based architecture has not been fruitful because the languages chosen (Fortran and Algol, for example) embody some of the principal limitations of conventional machines (global memory), and lack generality (no provision for expressing concurrency).

Computer designs based on principles of data flow are attracting increasing interest as an alternative to architectures derived from conventional notions of sequential program execution. These new designs offer a possible solution to the problem of efficiently exploiting concurrency of computation on a large scale, and they are compatible with modern concepts of program structure and therefore should not suffer so much from the difficulties of programming that plague other approaches to highly parallel computation: array and vector processors, and shared-memory multprocessor systems.

Fundamentally, the data flow concept is a different way of looking at instruction execution in machine level programs -- an alternative to the Von Neuman idea of sequential instruction execution. In a data flow computer, an instruction is ready for execution when its operands have arrived -- there is no concept of "control flow," and data flow computers do not have program location counters. A consequence of data-activated instruction execution is that many innstructions of a data flow program may be available for execution at once. Thus highly concurrent computation is a natural accompaniment of the data flow idea.

The idea of data driven computation is old [21, 22], but it is only in recent years that architectural schemes have been developed that can support an interestingly general level of user language, and are attractive in terms of anticipated performance and practicality of construction. Work on data

1. This research was supported by the Lawrence Livermore Laboratory of the University of California under contract 8545403.

driven concepts of program structure and on the design of practical data driven computers is now in progress in at least a dozen laboratories in the United States and Europe. Several processors using data-driven instruction execution have been built, and more hardware projects are being planned.

Most of this work on architectural concepts for data flow computation is based on a program representation known as *data flow program graphs* (Dennis [11]), which evolved from work of Rodriguez [19], Adams [3] and Karp and Miller [16]. In fact, data flow computers are a form of language-based architecture in which program graphs are the base language. As shown in Fig. 1, data flow program graphs serve as a formally specified interface between system architecture on one hand and user programming language on the other. The architect's task is to define and realize a computer system that faithfully implements the formal behavior of program graphs, while the language implementer's task is to translate source language programs into their equivalent as program graphs.

The techniques used to translate source language programs into data flow graphs [7] are similar to the methods used in conventional optimizing compilers to analyze the paths of data dependency in source programs. High level programming languages for data flow computation should be designed so it is easy for the translator to identify data dependence and generate program graphs that expose parallelism. The primary sources of difficulty are unrestricted transfer of control, and the "side effects" resulting from assignment to a global variable or to input arguments of a procedure. Removal of these sources of difficulty not only makes concurrency easy to identify, but programs have better structure -- they are more modular, and are easier to understand and verify.

These implications of data flow for language designers are discussed by Ackerman [1]. Moreover, new programming languages have been designed specifically for data flow computations: ID developed at Irvine [4] and VAL designed at MIT [2, 18].

This paper presents a sample from the variety of architectural schemes devised to support computations expressed as data flow program graphs. We explain data flow graphs by means of examples, and show how they are represented as collections of *activity templates*. Then we describe the basic instruction handling mechanism using activity templates that is characteristic of most current projects to build prototype data flow systems. We discuss the reasons for the different hardware organizations used by various projects, in particular, the different approaches to communicating information between parts of a data flow computer.

Data Flow Programs

A data flow program graph is made up of actors connected by arcs. One kind of actor is the operator shown in Fig. 2

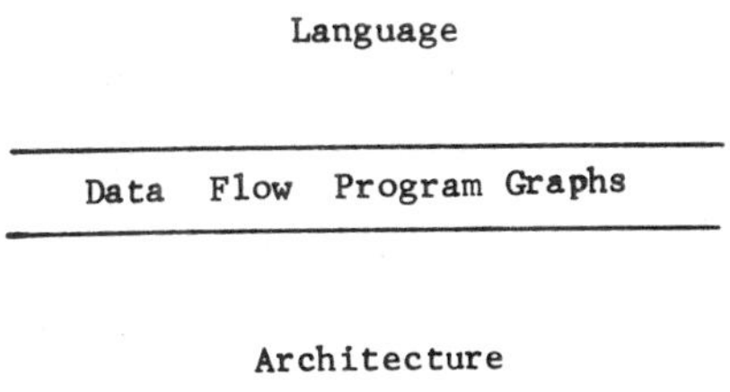

Language

Data Flow Program Graphs

Architecture

Fig. 1. Program graphs as a base language.

which is drawn as a circle with a function symbol written inside -- in this case + -- indicating addition. An operator also has input arcs and output arcs which carry *tokens* bearing values. The arcs define paths over which values from one actor are conveyed by tokens to other actors.

Tokens are placed on and removed from the arcs of a program graph according to *firing rules*, which are illustrated for an operator in Fig. 3. To be *enabled*, tokens must be present on each input arc, and there must be no token on any output arc of the actor. Any enabled actor may be *fired*; in the case of an operator, this means removing one token from each input arc, applying the specified function to the values associated with those tokens, and placing tokens labelled with the result value on the output arcs.

Operators may be connected as shown in Fig. 4 to form program graphs. Here, presenting tokens bearing values for x and y at the two inputs will enable computation of the value

$$z = (x + y) * (x - y)$$

by the program graph, placing a token carrying the result value on output arc z.

To understand the working of data flow computers, it is useful to introduce another representation for data flow

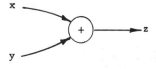

Fig. 2. Data flow actor.

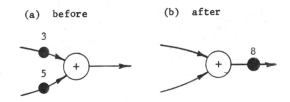

(a) before   (b) after

Fig. 3. Firing rule.

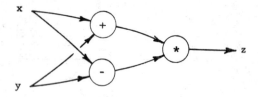

Fig. 4.   Interconnection of operators.

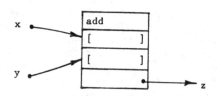

Fig. 5.   An activity template.

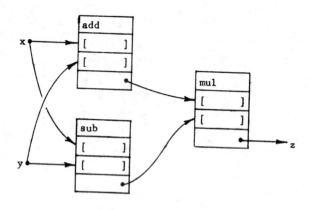

Fig. 6.   Configuration of activity templates
for the program graph of Fig. 4.

programs -- one that is much closer to the machine language used in prototype data flow computers. In this scheme, a data flow program is a collection of *activity templates*, each corresponding to one or more actors of a data flow program graph.   An activity template corresponding to the plus operator (Fig. 2) is shown in Fig. 5. There are four fields for (1) an operation code specifying the operations to be performed; (2) two *receivers*, which are places waiting to be filled in with operand values; and (3) destination fields (in this case one), which specify what is to be done with the result of performing the operation on the operands.

An *instruction* of a data flow program is the fixed portion of an activity template and consists of the operation code and the destinations.

instruction:
    <opcode, destinations>

Fig. 6 shows how activity templates are joined to represent a program graph, specifically the composition of operators in Fig. 4. Each destination field specifies a target receiver by giving the *address* of some activity template and an *input* integer specifying which receiver of the template is the target.

destination:
    <address, input>

Program structures for conditionals and iteration are illustrated in Fig. 7 and Fig. 8. These make use of two new data flow actors, *switch* and *merge*, which control the routing of data values. The switch actor sends a data input to its T or F output according as a boolean control input is **true** or **false**. The merge actor forwards a data value from its T or F input according to its boolean input value.

The conditional program graph and implementation in Fig. 7 represent computation of

y := (if x > 3 then x + 2 else x - 1) * 4

and the program graph and implementation in Fig. 8 represent the iterative computation

while x > 0 do x := x - 3

Execution of a machine program consisting of activity templates is viewed as follows: When a template is activated by the presence of an operand value in each receiver, the contents of the template from an *operation packet* of the form

operation packet:
    <opcode, operands, destinations>

Such a packet specifies one *result packet* having the form

result packet:
    <value, destination>

for each destination field of the template. Generation of a

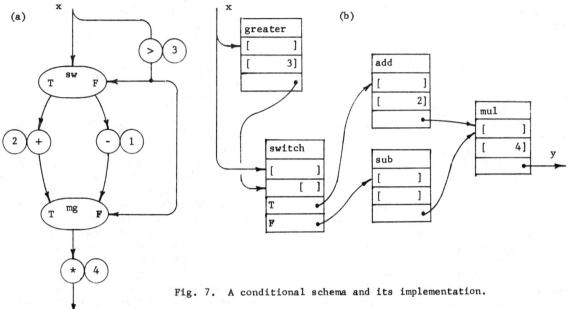

Fig. 7. A conditional schema and its implementation.

result packet, in turn, causes the value to be placed in the receiver designated by its destination field.

Note that this view of data flow computation does not explicitly honor the rule of program graphs that tokens must be absent from the output arcs of an actor for it to fire. Yet there are situations where it is attractive to use a program graph in pipelined fashion, as illustrated in Fig. 9a. To faithfully represent this computation the *add* instruction must not be reactivated until its previous result has been used by the *multiply* instruction. This constraint is enforced through use of *acknowledge signals* which are generated by specially marked destinations (*) in an activity template, and in general are sent to the templates that supply operand values to the activity template in question (Fig. 9b). The enabling rule now

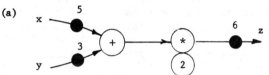

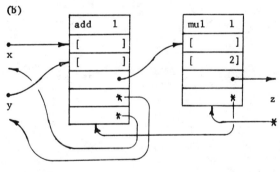

Fig. 9. Pipelining in data flow programs.

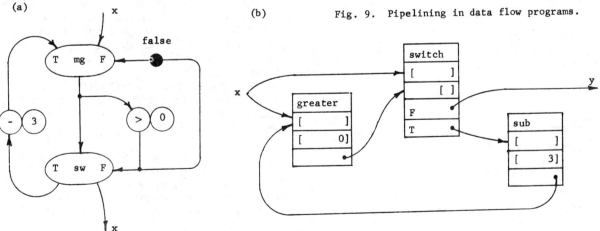

Fig. 8. An iterative schema and its implementation.

213

requires that all receivers contain values, and the required number of acknowledge signals have been received. This number (if nonzero) is written adjacent to the opcode of an activity template.

The Basic Mechanism

The basic instruction execution mechanism used in a number of current data flow projects is illustrated in Fig. 10. The data flow program describing the computation to be performed is held as a collection of activity templates in the *Activity Store*. Each activity template has a unique address which is entered in the *Instruction Queue* unit (A FIFO buffer store) when the instruction is ready for execution.

The *Fetch* unit takes an instruction address from the Instruction Queue and reads the activity template from the activity store, forms it into an operation packet, and passes it on to the *Operation Unit*. The Operation Unit performs the operation specified by the operation code on the operand values, generating one result packet for each destination field of the operation packet. The *Update* unit receives result packets and enters the values they carry into operand fields of activity templates as specified by their destination fields. The Update unit also tests whether all operand and acknowledge packets required to activate the destination instruction have been received, and, if so, enters the instruction address in the Instruction Queue.

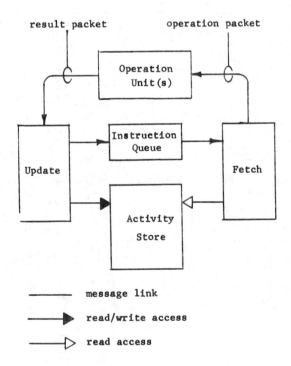

Fig. 10. Basic instruction execution mechanism.

During program execution, the number of entries in the Instruction Queue measures the degree of concurrency present in the program. The basic mechanism of Figure 10 can exploit this potential to a limited but significant degree: once the Fetch unit has sent an operation packet off to the Operation Unit, it may immediately read another entry from the Instruction Queue without waiting for the instruction previously fetched to be completely processed. Thus a continuous stream of operation packets may flow from the Fetch Unit to the Operation Unit so long as the Instruction Queue is not empty.

This mechanism is aptly called a "circular pipeline" -- activity controlled by the flow of information packets traverses the ring of units leftwise. A number of packets may be flowing simultaneously in different parts of the ring on behalf of different instructions in concurrent execution. Thus the ring operates as a "pipeline" system with all of its units actively processing packets at once. The degree of concurrency possible is limited by the nummber of units on the ring and the degree of pipelining within each unit. Additional concurrency may be exploited by splitting any unit in the ring into several units which can be allocated to concurrent activities. Ultimately, the level of concurrency is limited by the capacity of the data paths connecting the units of the ring.

This basic mechanism is essentially that implemented in a prototype data flow processing element built by a group at the Texas Instruments Company [8]. The same mechanism, elaborated to handle data flow procedures, was described earlier by Rumbaugh [20], and a new project at Manchester University (see below) uses a different variation of the same scheme.

Data Flow Multiprocessor

The level of concurrency exploited may be increased enormously by connecting together many processing elements of the form we have described to form a *data flow multiprocessor* system. Figure 11a shows many processing elements connected through a communication system, and Fig. 11b shows how each processing element relates to the communication system. The data flow program is divided into parts which are distributed over the processing elements. The activity stores of the processing elements collectively realize a single large address space, so the address field of a destination may select uniquely any activity template in the system. Each processing element sends a result packet through the communication network if its destination address specifies a nonlocal activity template, and to its own Update unit otherwise.

The communication network is responsible for delivering each result packet received to the processing element that holds the target activity template. Such a network, in which each packet arriving at an input port is transmitted to the output specified by information contained in the packet, is called a *routing network*.

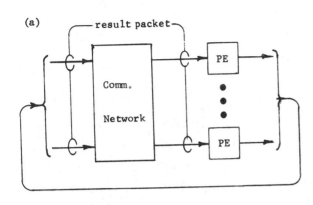

(a)

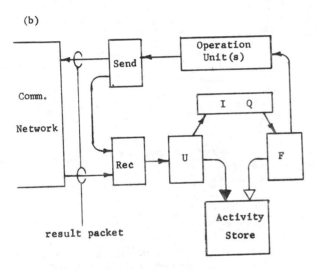

(b)

Fig. 11. Data flow multiprocessor.

The characteristics required of a routing network for a data flow multiprocessor differ in two important ways from the properties demanded of a processor/memory switch for a conventional multiprocessor system. First, information flow in a routing network is in one direction -- an immediate reply from the target unit to the originating unit is not required. Second, since each processing element holds many enabled instructions ready for processing, some delay can be tolerated in transmission of result packets without slowing down the overall rate of computation.

The "cross bar switch" used in conventional multiprocessor systems meets requirements for immediate respoonse and small delay by providing for signal paths from any input to any output that are established on request and maintained until a reply completes a processor/memory transaction. This arrangement is needlessly expensive for a data flow multiprocessor and a number of alternative network structures

have been proposed. The ring form of communication network has been used in many computer networks and has been used by Texas Instruments to couple four processing elements in their prototype data flow computer. The ring has the drawback that delay grows linearly with size, and there is a fixed bound on capacity.

Several groups have proposed tree-structured networks for communicating among processing elements [9, 15, 17]. Here, the drawback is that the traffic density at the root node may be unsatisfactorily high. Advantages of the tree are that the worst case distince between leaves grows only as $\log_2 N$ (for a binary tree), and that many pairs of nodes are connected by short paths.

The packet routing network shown in Fig. 12 is a structure currently attracting much attention. A routing network with N input and N output ports may be assembled from $(N/2) \log(N)$ units each of which is a 2 x 2 router. A 2 x 2 router receives packets at two input ports and transmits each received packet at one of its output ports according to an address bit contained in the packet. Packets are handled first come, first served, and both output ports may be active concurrently. Delay through an N x N network increases as $\log_2 N$ and capacity rises nearly linearly with N. This form of routing network is described in [23], and several related structures have been analyzed for capacity and delay [6].

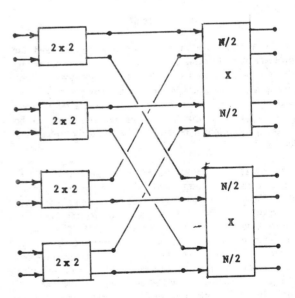

Fig. 12. Routing network structure.

Token Labelling

An experimental data flow computer being constructed at Manchester University, England [24], uses an elaboration of the basic mechanism designed so more than one instance of an instruction may be active at a time. This feature provides for overlapped execution of successive cycles of an iteration, and makes possible a natural machine level implementation of procedure application.

The Manchester processing element design is sketched in Fig. 13. In place of the Activity Store there is an *Instruction Store* and a *Matching Store*. Since more than one instance of execution of an instruction is allowed, the result packet format is extended to include a *label* field used to distinguish instances of the target instruction. No longer can arrived operand values be held in a single activity template for an instruction. Rather, instructions are divided into just two classics -- those that require only one operand, and those that require two operands -- and result packets include an indicator *count* of how many operands the target instruction requires. For single operand instructions, the one result packet is sent directly to the Instruction Store, where the instruction is fetched and an operation packet constructed. For two-operand instructions, the first result packet to arrive at the Matching Store is held until the second result packet arrives. Then information from the two result packets is combined and sent on to the Instruction Store where an operation packet is constructed. The matching store is an associative memory that uses the address and label fields of a result packet as its search key.

The MIT Architecture

In a data flow multiprocessor (Fig. 11) we noted the problem of partitioning the instructions of a program among the processing elements so as to concentrate communication among instructions held in the same processing element. This is advantageous because the time to transport a result packet to a nonlocal processor through the routing network will be longer (perhaps much longer) than the time to forward a result locally.

At MIT, an architecture has been proposed [12, 13] in response to an opposing view: Each instruction is equally accessible to result packets generated by any other instruction, independent of where they reside in the machine. The structure of this machine is shown in Fig. 14. The heart of this architecture is a large set of Instruction Cells, each of which holds one activity template of a data flow program. Result packets arrive at Instruction Cells from the Distribution Network. Each Instruction Cell sends an operation packet to the Arbitration Network when all operands and signals have been received. The function of the Operation Section is to execute instructions and to forward result packets to target instructions by way of the Distribution Network.

As drawn in Fig. 14, this design is impractical if the Instruction Cells are fabricated as individual physical units since the number of devices and interconnections would be

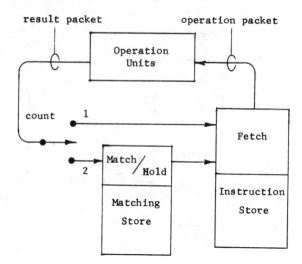

operation packet:

   <opcode, operands, destination>

result packet:

   <value, label, destination>

destination:

   <address, input, count>

Fig. 13. Data flow processor with labels.

enormous. A more attractive structure is obtained if the Instruction Cells are grouped into blocks and each block realized as a single device. Such an Instruction Cell Block has a single input port for result packets, and a single output port for operation packets. Thus one Cell Block unit replaces many Instruction Cells together with the associated portion of the Distribution Network.

Moreover, to further reduce the number of interconnections between Cell Blocks and other units, a byte-serial format for result and operation packets is chosen.

The resulting structure is shown in Fig. 15. Here, several Cell Blocks are served by a shared group of functional units $P_i, ..., P_k$. The Arbitration Network in each section of the machine passes each operation packet to the appropriate functional unit according to its opcode.

The number of functional unit types in such a machine is likely to be small (four, for example), or just one universal functional unit type might be provided in which case the arbitration network becomes trivial.

The relationship between the MIT architecture and the basic mechanism described earlier becomes clear when one

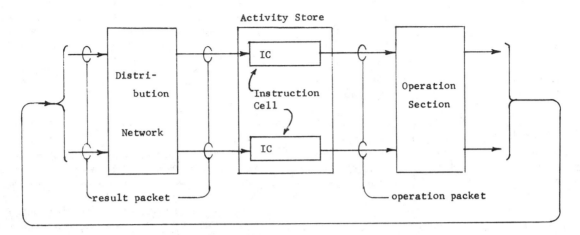

Fig. 14. MIT data flow processor.

considers how a Cell Block unit would be constructed. As shown in Fig. 16 a Cell Block would include storage for activity templates, a buffer store for addresses of enabled instructions and control units to receive result packets and transmit operation packets that are functionally equivalent to the Fetch and Update units of the basic mechanism. The Cell Block differs from the basic data flow processing element in that the Cell Block contains no functional units, and there is no shortcut for result packets destined for successor instructions held in the same Cell Block.

Discussion

In the Cell Block machine, communication of a result packet from one instruction to its successor is equally easy (or equally difficult depending on your point of view) regardless of how the two instructions are placed within the entire activity store of the machine. Thus the programmer need not be concerned that his program might run slowly due to an unfortunate distribution of instructions in the activity store address space. In fact, a random allocation of instructions may prove to be adequate.

In the data flow multiprocessor, communication between two instructions is much quicker if these instructions are allocated to the same processing element. Thus a program may run much faster if its instructions are clustered so as to minimize communication traffic between clusters, and each cluster is allocated to one processing element. Since it may be handling significantly less packet traffic, the communication network of the data flow multiprocessor will be simpler and

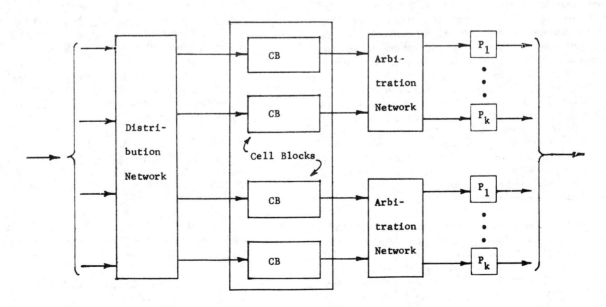

Fig. 15. Practical form of the MIT architecture.

217

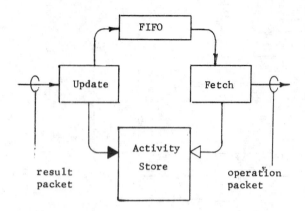

Fig. 16. Cell Block implementation.

less expensive than the Distribution Network of the MIT machine. Whether the cost reduction justifies the additional programming effort is a matter of debate, and depends on the area of application, the technology of fabrication and the time frame under consideration.

Although the routing networks in the two forms of data flow processor have a much more favorable growth of logic complexity (N log N) with increasing size than the switching networks of conventional multiprocessor systems, their growth is still more than linear. Moreover, closer examination reveals that in all suggested physical structures for N x N routing networks, the complexity as measured by total *wire length* grows as $O(N^2)$. This fact shows that interconnection complexity still places limits on the size of practical multi-unit systems which support universal intercommunication. If we need yet larger systems, it appears we must settle for arrangements of units that only support immediate communication with neighbors. It is not at all clear how such a system could support a general approach to program construction. A variety of views are currently held as to the circumstances which would favor construction of machines having only local interconnections. A view implicit in most proposals for distributed computing systems is that the programmer (or, alternatively, a *very* smart compiler) will plan how the computation should be distributed so as to optimize resource utilization. A corollary of this view is that programming such systems will be at least as difficult as programming a conventional single processor system; that is, this form of distributed architecture makes no contribution to ameliorating the software problem.

Another view is that the system itself should dynamically allocate its resources among portions of the computation to be performed so that in each interval of computation, only local interactions are required. This view is consistent with current advanced thinking about programming languages and methodology. For this to be possible, very flexible mechanisms must be built into the hardware to support dynamic reallocation of processing and memory resources without

imposition on the programmer. Systems proposed from this viewpoint include the Irvine data flow architeture [5], the Utah project toward a demand driven implementation of applicative Lisp [17], and an operational concept of data flow program execution developed by Weng [14, 25]. Whether these proposals can be developed into practical computer systems is an open question.

Extensions

The forms of data flow architecture discussed in this paper are limited in several significant ways. There is no specific mechanism in these systems to provide efficient support for data structures, and only the Manchester University machine incorporates even rudimentary support for multiple instances of instruction execution such as required for implementing concurrent or recursive procedure activations. Moreover, in each of these systems, all instructions are held in the same level of storage and there is no provision for "caching" instructions, so programs beyond some limiting size become impractical due to their need to occupy relatively fast storage.

A variety of proposals have been made of approaches to overcome these limitations of current prototype construction projects, but none have yet reached the stage that even experimental construction of a machine is warranted. It will be fascinating to see how these concepts evolve over the coming decade.

References

[1] W. B. Ackerman, "Data Flow Languages," Proc. of the ACM 1979 National Computer Conference (June 1979), pp. 1087-1095.

[2] W. B. Ackerman and J. B. Dennis, VAL -- A Value Oriented Algorithmic Language, Preliminary Reference Manual, Laboratory for Computer Science, M.I.T., Technical Report TR-218 (June 1979), 80 pp.

[3] D. A. Adams, A Computation Model With Data Flow Sequencing, Computer Science Dept., School of Humanities and Sciences, Stanford University, Technical Report CS 117 (December 1968).

[4] Arvind, K. P. Gostelow, and W. Plouffe, An Asynchronous Programming Language and Computing Machine, Dept. of Information and Computer Science, University of California, Irvine, Technical Report 114a (December 1978), 97 pp.

[5] Arvind, and K. P. Gostelow, "A Computer Capable of Exchanging Processors for Time," Information Processing 77, North Holland (1977), pp. 849-854.

[6] G. A. Boughton, Routing Networks in Packet Communication Architectures, Dept. of Electrical Engineering and Computer Science, M.I.T., S.M. Thesis (June 1978).

[7] J. D. Brock and L. B. Montz, "Translation and Optimization of Data Flow Programs," Proceedings of the 1979 International Conference on Parallel Processing (August 1979).

[8] M. Cornish, Private communication, Texas Instruments Corp., Austin, Texas.

[9] A. Davis, "A Data Flow Evaluation System Based on the Concept of Recursive Locality," Proc. of the ACM 1979 National Computer Conference (June 1979), pp. 1079-1086.

[10] J. B. Dennis, "On the Design and Specification of a Common Base Language," Proc. of Symposium on Computers and Automata, Polytechnic Press, Polytechnic Institute of Brooklyn (1971).

[11] J. B. Dennis, "First Version of a Data Flow Procedure Language," Lecture Notes in Computer Science, 19, Springer-Verlag (1974), pp. 362-376.

[12] J. B. Dennis, and D. P. Misunas, A Preliminary Architecture for a Basic Data-Flow Processor, Laboratory for Computer Science, M.I.T., CSG Memo 102 (August 1974), 27 pp.

[13] J. B. Dennis, C. K. C. Leung, and D. P. Misunas, A Highly Parallel Processor Using a Data Flow Machine Language, Laboratory for Computer Science, M.I.T., CSG Memo 134-1 (June 1979), 33 pp.

[14] J. B. Dennis, and K. Weng, "An Abstract Implementation for Concurrent Computation With Streams," Proceedings of the 1979 International Conference on Parallel Processing (August 1979).

[15] A. Despain and D. Patterson, "X-Tree: A Tree Structured Multi-Processor Computer Architecture," Proceedings of the 5th Annual Symposium on Computer Architecture (April 1978), pp 144-150.

[16] R. M. Karp, and R. E. Miller, "Properties of a Model for Parallel Computations: Determinacy, Termination, Queueing," SIAM J. of Applied Mathematics (November 1966), pp. 1390-1411.

[17] R. M. Keller, G. Lindstrom, and S. S. Patil, "A Loosely-Coupled Applicative Multi-processing System," Proc. of the ACM 1979 National Computer Conference (June 1979), pp. 613-622.

[18] J. R. McGraw, "VAL -- A Data Flow Language," these proceedings.

[19] J. E. Rodriguez, A Graph Model for Parallel Computation, Laboratory for Computer Science, M.I.T., Technical Report TR-64 (September 1969).

[20] J. E. Rumbaugh, "A Data Flow Multiprocessor," IEEE Trans. on Computers (February 1977), pp. 138-146.

[21] R. R. Seeber and A. B. Lindquist, "Associative Logic for Highly Parallel Systems," Proc. of the AFIPS Conference (1963), pp. 489-493.

[22] R. M. Shapiro, H. Saint and D. L. Presberg, Representation of Algorithms as Cyclic Partial Orderings, Applied Data Research, Wakefield, Mass., Report CA-7112-2711 (December 1971).

[23] A. R. Tripathi and G. J. Lipovski, "Packet Switching in Banyan Networks," Proceedings of the 6th Annual Symposium on Computer Architecture (April 1979), pp. 160-167.

[24] I. Watson and J. Gurd, "A Prototype Data Flow Computer With Token Labelling," Proc. of the ACM 1979 National Computer Conference (June 1979), pp. 623-628.

[25] K. Weng, An Abstract Implementation for a Generalized Data Flow Language, Laboratory for Computer Science, M.I.T., Technical Report, forthcoming.

A PIPELINED, SHARED RESOUCE MIMD COMPUTER

Burton J. Smith
Denelcor, Inc.
Denver, Colorado 80205

Abstract -- The HEP computer system currently
being implemented by Denelcor, Inc., under contract to the U.S. Army Ballistics Research Laboratory is an MIMD machine of the shared resource
type as defined by Flynn. In this type of organization, skeleton processors compete for
execution resources in either space or time.
In the HEP processor, spatial switching occurs
between two queues of processes; one of these
controls program memory, register memory, and
the functional units while the other controls
data memory. Multiple processors and data
memories may be interconnected via a pipelined
switch, and any register memory or data memory
location may be used to synchronize two processes on a producer-consumer basis.

Overview

The HEP computer system currently being implemented by Denelcor, Inc., under contract to
the U.S. Army Ballistics Research Laboratory is
an MIMD machine of the shared resource type as
defined by Flynn [1]. In this type of organization, skeleton processors compete for execution
resources in either space or time. For example,
the set of peripheral processors of the CDC 6600
[5] may be viewed as an MIMD machine implemented
via the time-multiplexing of ten process states
to one functional unit.

In a HEP processor, two queues are used to
time-multiplex the process states. One of these
provides input to a pipeline which fetches a three
address instruction, decodes it, obtains the two
operands, and sends the information to one of
several pipelined function units where the operation is completed. In case the operation is a
data memory access, the process state enters a
second queue. This queue provides input to a
pipelined switch which interconnects several data
memory modules with several processors. When the
memory access is complete, the process state is
returned to the first queue. The processor organization is shown in Figure 1, and the over-all
system layout appears in Figure 2.

Each processor of HEP can support up to 128
processes, and nominally begins execution of a
new instruction (on behalf of some process) every
100 nanoseconds. The time required to completely
execute an instruction is 800 ns, so that if at
least eight totally independent processes, i.e.
processes that do not share data, are executing
in one processor the instruction execution rate
is 10^7 instructions per second per processor. The
first HEP system will have four processors and
128K words of data memory.

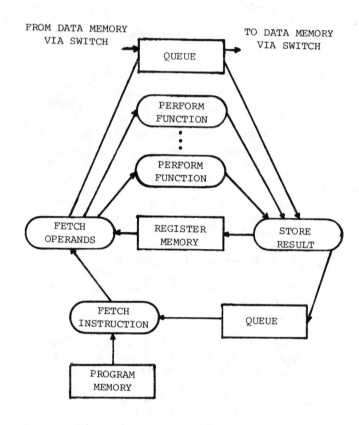

Figure 1. Processor Organization

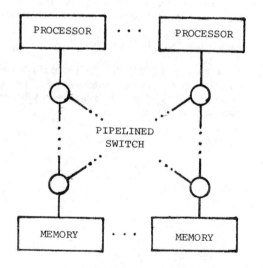

Figure 2. Overall System Layout

Reprinted from *Proceedings of the 1978 International Conference on Parallel Processing*, 1978, pages 6-8. Copyright
© 1978 by The Institute of Electrical and Electronics Engineers, Inc.

EHO182-6/81/0000/0220 © 1978 IEEE

HEP instructions and data words are 64 bits wide. The floating point format is sign magnitude with a hexadecimal, seven-bit, excess-64 exponent. All functional units can support one instruction execution every 100 nanoseconds except the divider, which can support this rate momentarily but is slower on the average.

Tasks

Since HEP attains maximum speed when all of its processes are independent, a simple set of protection mechanisms is incorporated to allow potentially hostile users to execute simultaneously. A domain of protection in HEP is called a task, and consists of a set of processes with the same task identifier (TID) in their process state. The TID specifies a task status word which contains base and limit addresses defining the regions within the various memories accessible by the processes in that task. In this way, processes within a task may cooperate but are prevented from communicating with those in other tasks. Processes in different tasks or processors may communicate via data memory if they have an overlapping allocation there.

Processes are a scarce resource in HEP; in addition, the synchronization primitives used in HEP make processes difficult to virtualize. As a result, the maximum number of processes a task will use must be specified to the system when the task is loaded. It is the job of the operating system to insure that its total allocation of processes to tasks does not exceed the number available, so that a create fault (too many processes) can only occur when one or more tasks have created more processes than they were allocated. In this event, the offending task or tasks (not necessarily the task that actually caused the create fault) are removed from the processor.

Protection violations, create faults, and other error conditions arising within a process cause traps. A trap is the creation of a process executing in a supervisor task. There are a total of sixteen tasks available in each processor; eight of these are user tasks and the other eight are corresponding supervisor tasks. When any process in it, and a process is created in the corresponding supervisor task to handle the condition. This scheme is not used for create fault, however; a create fault suspends execution of all processes (regardless of task) except those actually handling the fault.

Create fault occurs before all processes have been used to allow any create instructions in progress within the pipeline to complete normally and to allow for the creation of the create fault handler process. All other traps in HEP are precise in the sense that no subsequent instructions will be executed from the offending task, a useful feature when one is trying to debug a concurrent algorithm.

Synchronization

The synchronization of processes in HEP is made simple by virtue of the fact that any register or data memory location can be used to synchronize two processes in a producer-consumer fashion. This requires three states in general: a reserved state to provide for mutual exclusion, a full state, and an empty state. The execution of an instruction tests the states of locations and modifies them in an indivisible manner; typically, an instruction tests its sources full and its destination empty. If any of these tests fails, the instruction is reattempted by the process on its next turn for servicing. If all tests succeed, the instruction is executed; the process sets both sources empty and the destination reserved. The operands from the sources are sent to the function unit, and the program counter in the process state is incremented. When the function unit eventually writes a result in the destination location that was specified in the instruction it sets the destination full. Provisions are made to test a destination full rather than empty, to preserve the state of a source, or to totally override the state of a source or destination with the proviso that a reserved state may not be overridden except by certain privileged instructions. Input-output synchronization is handled naturally by mapping I/O device registers into the data memory address space; an interrupt handler is just a process that is attempting to read an input location or write an output location. I/O device addresses are not relocated by the data memory base address and all I/O-addressed operations are privileged.

Switch

The switch that interconnects processors and data memories to allow memory sharing consists of a number of nodes connected via ports. Each node has three ports, and can simultaneously send and receive a message on each port. The messages contain the address of the recipient, the address of the originator, the operation to be performed by the recipient, and a priority. Each switch node receives a message on each of its three ports every 100 nanoseconds and attempts to retransmit each message on a port that will reduce the distance of that message from its recipient; a table mapping the recipient address into the number of a port that reduces distance is stored in each node for this purpose. If conflict for a port occurs, the node routes one of the contending messages correctly and the rest incorrectly. To help insure fairness, an incorrectly routed message has its priority incremented as it passes through the node, and preference is given in conflict situations to the message(s) with the highest priority.

The time required to complete a memory operation via the switch includes two message transmission times, one in each direction, since the success or failure of the operation (based on the state of the memory location, i.e. full or empty) must be reported back to the processor so that it can decide whether to reattempt the operation or not. The propagation delay through a node and its associated wiring is 50 nanoseconds. Since a message is distributed among two (or three) nodes at any instant, the switch must be two-colorable to avoid conflicts between the beginning of some message and the middle part of another. When the switch fills up due to a high conflict rate, misrouted massages begin to "leak" from the switch. Every originator is obliged to reinsert a leaking message into the switch in preference to inserting a new message. Special measures are taken when the priority value reaches its maximum in any message to avoid indefinite delays for such messages; a preferable scheme would have been to let priority be established by time of message creation except for the large number of bits required to specify it.

FORTRAN Extensions

Two extensions have been made to FORTRAN to allow the programmer to incorporate parallelism into his programs. First, subroutines whose names begin with "$" may execute in parallel with their callers, either by being CREATEd instead of CALLed or by executing a RESUME prior to a RETURN. Second, variables and arrays whose names begin with "$" may be used to transmit data between two processes via the full-empty discipline. A simple program to add the elements of an array $A is shown in Figure 3. The subroutines $INPUT and $OUTPUT perform obvious functions, and the subroutine $ADD does the work of adding up the elements. There are a total of 14 processes executing as a result of running the program.

```
C       ADD UP THE ELEMENTS OF
C       THE ARRAY $A
        REAL $A(1000),$S(10),$SUM
        INTEGER I
        CREATE $INPUT($A,1000)
        DO 10 I=1,10
        CREATE $ADD($A(100*I-99),$S(I),100)
  10    CONTINUE
        CREATE $ADD($S,$SUM,10)
        CREATE $OUTPUT($SUM,1)
        END

C       NOELTS ELEMENTS OF $V
C       ARE ADDED AND PLACED IN $ANS
        SUBROUTINE $ADD($V,$ANS,NOELTS)
        REAL $V(1),$ANS,TEMP
        INTEGER J, NOELTS
        TEMP=0.0
        DO 20 J=1,NOELTS
        TEMP=TEMP+$V(J)
  20    CONTINUE
        $ANS=TEMP
        RETURN
        END
```

Figure 3. HEP FORTRAN Example

Applications

As a parallel computer, HEP has an advantage over SIMD machines and more loosely coupled MIMD machines in two application areas. The first of these involves the solution of large systems of ordinary differential equations in simulating continuous systems. In this application, vector operations are difficult to apply because of the precedence constraints in the equations, and loosely coupled MIMD organizations are hard to use because a good partition of the problem to share workload and minimize communication is hard to find. Scheduling becomes relatively easier as the number of processes increases [3], and is quite simple when one has one process per instruction as in a data flow architecture [4].

A second type of application for which HEP seems to be well suited is the solution of partial differential equations for which the adjacencies of the discrete objects in the model change rapidly. Free surface and particle electrodynamics problems have this characteristic. The difficulty here is one of constantly having to rearrange the model within the computer to suit the connectivity implied by the architecture. Tightly coupled MIMD architectures have little implied connectivity. Associative SIMD architectures of the right kind may perform well on these problems, however.

Conclusion

The HEP system described above represents a compromise between the very tightly coupled data flow architectures and more loosely coupled multicomputer systems [2]. As a result, it has some of the advantages of each approach: It is relatively easy to implement parallel algorithms because any memory location can be used to synchronize two processes, and yet it is relatively inexpensive to implement large quantities of memory. In addition, the protection facilities make it possible to utilize the machine either as a multiprogrammed computer or as an MIMD computer.

References

[1] Flynn,M.J. "Some Computer Organizations and Their Effectiveness", IEEE-C21 (Sept. 1972).

[2] Jordan,H.F. "A Special Purpose Architecture for Finite Element Analysis", International Conference on Parallel Processing (1978).

[3] Lord,R.E. "Scheduling Recurrence Equations for Parallel Computation", Ph.D. Thesis, Dept. of Computer Science, Wash. State Univ. (1976).

[4] Rumbaugh,J. "A Data Flow Multiprocessor", IEEE-C26, p. 138 (Feb. 1977).

[5] Thornton,J.E. "Parallel Operation in the Control Data 6600", Proc. FJCC vol 26, part 2, p. 33 (1964).

Reprinted with permission from *High Speed Computer and Algorithm Organization*, 1977, pages 143-157. Copyright © 1977 by Academic Press.

APPLICATION OF DATA FLOW COMPUTATION TO THE WEATHER PROBLEM[1]

Jack B. Dennis
Ken K.-S. Weng
MIT Laboratory for Computer Science

ABSTRACT

Computer processors and memory systems organized to execute programs in data flow form show promise of overcoming the barrier to highly parallel computation without concomitant loss of programmability. The principles and advantages of data flow programming and computer architecture are illustrated in this paper by their application to a general atmosphere circulation model for numerical weather forecasting. The paper develops the structure of a data flow program for a basic global circulation model and discusses the performance achievable for this computation by a data flow computer.

I. INTRODUCTION

The past decade has witnessed the evolution of data flow languages from primitive concepts of data driven instruction execution [1, 2, 3] to fully developed schemes for representing algorithms in a form that exposes the natural concurrency of their parts [4, 5, 6, 7]. Recently, several interesting proposals have been advanced for organizing computer hardware to interpret data flow programs in a data driven mode [8, 9, 10, 11]. Although each of these authors makes a good case that his proposed system implements a well defined level of data flow language, their effectiveness as instruments for performing practical computations has not been demonstrated.

The aim of the present paper is to help fill the gap by studying the performance potential of a data flow computer. In an earlier study [12] submitted for publication, we evaluated the performance of a limited data flow machine for the fast Fourier transform computation. Here we use a more general data flow language that includes data structure operations on arrays, and we describe the structure of a corresponding extended data flow computer. Since data flow computers differ radically in structure from conventional machines, meaningful comparisons are only possible through the study of specific applications. For the present study, we have chosen a global general circulation model (GCM) for numerical weather forecasting.

[1]This research was supported in part by the National Science Foundation under grant DCR75-04060, and in part by the Advanced Research Projects Agency of the Department of Defense under contract N00014-75-C-0661.

223

In Section II of the paper we describe the general circulation model; the structure of a corresponding data flow program is developed in Section III. Section IV presents the overall structure of a data flow computer appropriate for the language used to express the GCM computation. In Section V the manner in which array operations are handled by the machine is studied in detail because efficient processing of arrays is crucial to realizing high performance in the GCM computation. Our performance study is presented in Section VI; this analysis shows how a one hundred-fold improvement in computation rate for the GCM computation may be achieved by a data flow computer.

II. THE GENERAL CIRCULATION MODEL

The General Circulation Model used in this study is the GISS fourth order model developed by Kalnay-Rivas, Bayliss and Storch [13] in which the atmospheric state is represented by the surface pressure, the wind field, temperature, and the water vapor mixing ratio. These state variables are governed by a set of partial differential equations in the spherical coordinate system formed by latitude (ϕ), longitude (λ) and normalized atmospheric pressure (σ). In this fourth order model, the computation is carried out on a three-dimensional grid that partitions the atmosphere vertically into K levels and horizontally into M intervals of longitude and N intervals of latitude of size $\Delta\lambda$ and $\Delta\phi$, respectively.

We denote a value of a state variable (the temperature for example) by T(i, j, k) where i, j and k index over the ϕ, λ and σ coordinates, respectively. The model computes each state variable for the next time instant using "leap frog" integration: Thus the temperature T^N(i, j, k) for the next time instant is computed from the temperature T^P(i, j, k) for the preceding time instant and the time derivative $\partial/\partial t \, T^C$(i, j, k) evaluated for the current time instant

$$T^N(i, j, k) = T^P(i, j, k) + 2\Delta t \frac{\partial}{\partial t} T^C(i, j, k)$$

The main computation is the evaluation of the time derivatives of the state variables from the current atmospheric state using the physical laws that govern the atmosphere.

In addition to the main computation, three additional computations must be performed to make the scheme workable: (1) Polar computation -- computation of state variables at the poles is treated as a special case; (2) Filtering -- to ensure stability in spite of the convergence of longitude lines toward the poles, spatial filtering is used to suppress high frequency waves at high latitudes; (3) Sum-of-Neighbors -- since the leap frog integration rule is inherently unstable, an averaging computation is performed once every so many time steps.

The GISS model has been implemented in Fortran and runs on an IBM 360/95 machine equipped with 4 megabytes of addressable core memory. Using a grid having nine vertical levels, 72 intervals of longitude, 45 intervals of latitude, and a time step of five minutes, this implementation can simulate one day of atmospheric activity in about one hour of computer time. Reliable long-range forecasts require that the simulation be carried out on a finer grid for more time steps, and thus demand a much faster processing rate.

III. THE DATA FLOW PROGRAM

To present the structure of the data flow program for the General Circulation Model, we shall use the language of data flow schemas [5] in terms of which the concurrency of execution of the computation on a data flow processor can be easily seen. In practice we envision that programs prepared for execution on a data flow computer will be written in a high-level textual language. The design of a high level language that permits straightforward translation into data flow schemas has been studied by Weng [14].

To construct a data flow program for the GCM computation, we represent the atmospheric state by a nested array data structure; for example, the temperature component T of the state is of type Al where

$$\text{type } Al = \underline{\text{array}} \ 0..M+3 \ \underline{\text{of}} \ A2$$

$$\text{type } A2 = \underline{\text{array}} \ 0..N+3 \ \underline{\text{of}} \ A3$$

$$\text{type } A3 = \underline{\text{array}} \ 0..K+1 \ \underline{\text{of}} \ \underline{\text{real}}$$

The South and North poles correspond to latitude indices $i = 1$ and $i = M+2$, and the values for longitude indices $j \in [N-1..N+3]$ are copies of the values for $j \in [0..4]$.

The new values of each state variable are computed for $i \in [2..M+1]$, $j \in [2..N+1]$, and $k \in [1..K]$; the remaining components of the data structure provide neighboring values for the fourth order spacial difference formulas along the boundaries of the horizontal grid.

The overall structure of the GCM computation, represented as a data flow schema, is shown in Fig. 1. In this figure, the notation $T(i, j, *)$ denotes the K+2-element array containing the temperature values for horizontal grid point (i, j); $T(i, *, *)$ is the array containing all temperature values on the ith line of latitude; and $T(*, *, *)$ is the complete data structure of temperature values. The figure shows the blocks making up the data flow computation of the next temperature state $T^N(*, *, *)$ from the preceding state $T^P(*, *, *)$ and current values of all state variables including $T^C(*, *, *)$. The next state data structure and the current state data structure become the current state and preceding state for the next cycle of computation (the data paths and control for this are omitted in Fig. 1 for simplicity).

The data flow schema in Fig. 1 is organized so the parallelism of the GCM computation is exposed in two major ways: First, in the main computation, evaluation of the time derivative is carried out concurrently for all K atmospheric levels. This is accomplished by using K copies of the data flow program appropriate for a single grid point. Second, the main computation program block is coded so sets of data values for successive cells of the horizontal grid are processed concurrently by the several stages of the program block. Thus the streams of K+2-element arrays entering the main computation block are processed in pipeline fashion.

The function of each <u>get</u> operator (defined in Fig. 2a) is to convert each array arriving at its a-input into a stream of component values selected from the array by successive elements of the sequence of integers presented at the s-input. Each <u>get</u> operator in the first rank of Fig. 1 converts the temperature data structure $T(*, *, *)$ into a stream of M arrays where each

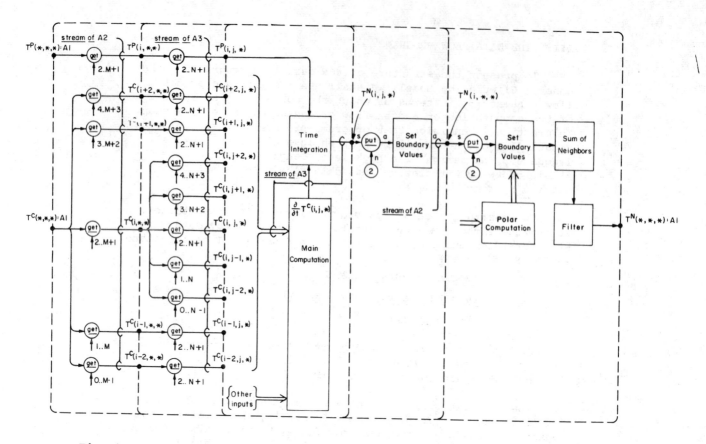

Fig. 1. Structure of a data flow program for the General Circulation Model.

array holds the temperature values for one latitude line. The second rank of <u>get</u> operators further converts the state data structure so each element of the resulting streams is a K+2-element array of values for all grid points having the same horizontal coordinates.

The output of the main computation and time integration is M streams of N arrays apiece, each containing the K+2 temperature values $T^N(i, j, *)$ for one horizontal grid point. The <u>put</u> operator converts each stream into an array of type <u>array</u> 2..N+1 <u>of</u> A3 with components representing $T^N(i, j, *)$, for $j \in [2..N+1]$, the set of new temperature values for the ith latitude line. The block labelled Set Boundary Values adds to the resulting array the temperature values for the boundary indices $j \in [0, 1, N+1, N+3]$, yielding an array of type A2 representing $T^N(i, *, *)$. A final <u>put</u> operator generates the array containing as components the temperature values $T^N(i, *, *)$ for $i \in [2, .., M+1]$. The full array of temperature values $T^N(*, *, *)$ is obtained by adding boundary values for $i \in [0, 1, M+2, M+3]$ using the results of the polar computation. This array is further averaged and filtered to ensure computational stability before becoming the next value of the current atmospheric state.

Data flow schemas for the <u>get</u> and <u>put</u> operators are shown in Fig. 2. These schemas are composed of data flow *actors* [5] interconnected by links that convey data and truth values from one actor to another. In addition to the basic actor types introduced in [5], these schemas use some special actors to implement operations on streams of values [14]: A stream is represented in a data flow schema by a sequence of value-bearing tokens followed by a special token called an *end-of-stream token.* The actor est generates an end-of-stream token; the predicate eos yields true if an end-of-stream token is received and false otherwise.

IV.   THE DATA FLOW COMPUTER

Now we are ready to explain how our data flow program for the GCM computation will run on a data flow computer. The organization of a computer that implements the appropriate level of data flow language is shown in Fig. 3. This machine is similar in structure to the data flow processor described in [12], but the machine provides, in addition to the basic scalar operations and control mechanisms, support for data structure operations in its Structure Processor.

Before discussing operation of the Structure Processor, let us review the basic scheme of operation of the data flow

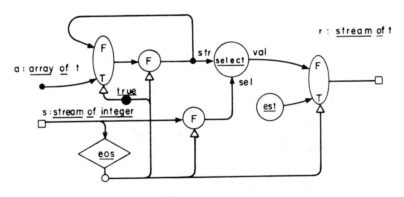

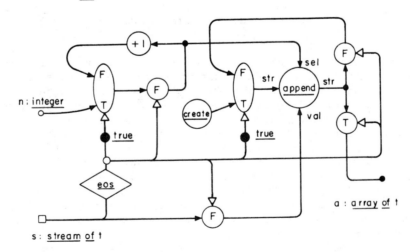

Fig. 2.   *The get and put operators as data flow schemas.*

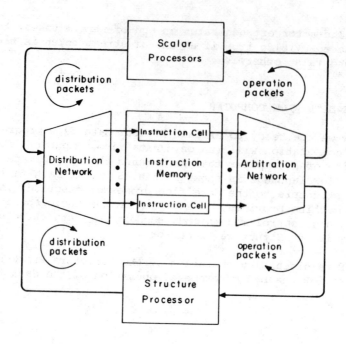

Fig. 3. Structure of the data flow computer.

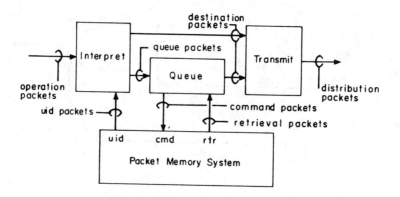

Fig. 4. The Structure Processor.

machine. Each Instruction Cell in the Instruction Memory holds
one instruction which corresponds to an actor of a data flow
program. Once an Instruction Cell has received (via the Distribution Network) all required operand values and the necessary
number of acknowledge signals, the Cell is *enabled* and delivers
its contents to the Arbitration Network for transmission to the
appropriate Processor. The result value produced by the Processor is transmitted through the Distribution Network to the
Instruction Cells which require it as an operand, and *acknowledge* signals are sent to control the enabling of Cells. Even
though roughly 20 microseconds may be required for an instruction to be enabled, sent to the Processing Section, executed, and
the results transmitted back to other Instruction Cells, the computer is capable of high performance because a large number of
instructions may be in various stages of execution simultaneously.

In this form of data flow processor, congestion of the Distribution Network is possible if Instruction Cells are reenabled

228

repeatedly without waiting for previously generated results to be consumed by other Instruction Cells; this congestion can even lead to deadlock -- the complete cessation of computation (see [12]). We avoid these problems of congestion and deadlock by requiring that an Instruction Cell not be reenabled until the data and control packets generated by the previous execution of the instruction have been absorbed by their destination cells. Machine language programs which satisfy this condition are said to be *safe*. Safety is achieved through the use of acknowledge signals generated by an instruction to control the enabling of instructions that produce the data required by the instruction.

V. THE STRUCTURE PROCESSOR

The Structure Processor receives operation packets calling for the data structure operations create, select and append. Earlier concepts for the design of structure processors have been given by Rumbaugh [10] and by Misunas [15]. As shown in Fig. 4, the Structure Processor consists of a Packet Memory System [16] and three units -- the Interpret, Queue and Transmit units -- which make up the Structure Controller.

The Packet Memory: The function of the Packet Memory System is to hold representations of data structures and to provide the means for storing and accessing their components. Each data structure value held in the Packet Memory has a *unique identifier* which serves to represent the structure value in all units outside the Structure Processor. Within the Packet Memory, a data structure value (we consider here only arrays) is represented by an *item* of the form

$$(i, (c_m, \ldots, c_n), r)$$

in which

i	is the unique identifier of the data structure value.
$c_m, \ldots, c_n$	are either all real number representations, or all unique identifiers of component structure values. Some components may be undefined, and c_k is then nil.
r	is a reference count used to detect when all references to the item have disappeared indicating that the item may be deleted from the Packet Memory.

The state of the Packet Memory is fixed by giving the collection of items held and the set of unique identifiers available for creation of new items. The behavior of the Packet Memory is conveniently specified by giving the state changes for each of the five basic transactions:

Store Transaction: In response to a *store* command packet ⟨STO, i, k, c⟩ at port cmd the item having unique identifier i is modified to have a component $c_k = c$ (the previous value of c_k is lost). If no item exists with unique identifier i, then a new item is created having $c_k = c$ as its sole component, and with its reference count set to one.

Retrieval Transaction: If a *retrieval* command packet
⟨RTR, i, k⟩ arrives at port cmd and an item
(i, (c_m, ..., c_n), r) exists where m ≤ k ≤ n, then
a retrieval packet ⟨i, k, c_k⟩ is sent at port rtr.

Up and Down Transactions: The command ⟨UP, i⟩ adds one to
the reference count of item i; the command ⟨DWN, i⟩
decrements its reference count by one. If the reference count is reduced to zero by a down command,
the item is deleted from the collection of items
held by PM and its unique identifier i is added to
the set of available unique identifiers, and the
reference count for each data structure component is
decremented.

Unique Identifier Generation: A unique identifier packet ⟨i⟩
is sent at port uid, and the unique identifier i is
removed from the set of available unique identifiers.

In [16] we have shown how the Packet Memory can be structured to handle many transactions concurrently at a high
throughput rate.

The Structure Controller: The function of the Structure
Controller is to implement the data structure operations create,
append and select in terms of the memory transactions supported
by the Packet Memory System. In the GCM data flow program these
data structure operations occur only in the blocks labelled Set
Boundary Values and the get and put routines which transform arrays into streams and vice versa; these routines have been specified as data flow schemas in Fig. 2.

To achieve the desired level of performance, it is important to exploit the capability of the Packet Memory to handle
many transactions concurrently, while permitting the memory system to be slow in responding to individual retrieval requests.
Thus the get routine as written in Fig. 2a is unsatisfactory because the select actor is not reenabled until after the result
of its previous execution has been sent. Consequently, repeated
execution of the select actor can occur only at a rate determined by the retrieval delay of the Packet Memory, and no overlap of retrieval requests is realized.

The desired overlapped execution of select operations can
be achieved through the choice of an appropriate machine level
instruction set and careful design of the Structure Controller.
The Interpret unit of the Structure Controller interprets the
data structure operations producing sequences of commands that
it sends to the Packet Memory System. The Transmit unit generates result and acknowledge packets for distribution to Instruction Cells as called for by the instructions in operation
packets. The Queue unit is the heart of the Structure Controller; it holds an entry for each select operation that has
been initiated but not completed. Each entry includes the
unique identifier and selector that specify the value to be obtained, and the destinations to which copies of the result are
to be sent. Operation of the Structure Processor must be such
that the results of selection are sent to the destination cell
exactly in the order of select actor initiation even though
variations in retrieval delay cause retrieval packets to be returned out of sequence from the Packet Memory. Otherwise, the
components of the arrays constructed by the put operators of
the GCM program would be incorrectly indexed. The function
of the Queue module is to ensure that results of select operations are sent by the Structure Controller in the same order
as the corresponding operation packets are received. When a

retrieval packet is received from the Packet Memory, a matching
entry in the Queue is found and the retrieval value appended
to the entry. Result packets are generated from entries containing retrieved values as they reach the end of the queue.

Correct pipelined operation of select actors in the data
flow program requires that after a result packet is sent to
an Instruction Cell by the Structure Processor, no further result packet is sent until an acknowledge signal has been received indicating that the Instruction Cell is ready to receive it. This provision requires a machine level get routine
that is more elaborate than a direct encoding of the scheme in
Fig. 2a, but the details will not be covered here. Further
discussion of the machine encoding of safe data flow programs
may be found in [12].

The put routine in Fig. 2b generates an array by appending
successive elements to the empty data structure. If each result of an append operation is viewed as a distinct value, as
in the usual data flow semantics, a new copy of the partial array must be created in the Packet Memory each time an append
operation is executed. In most cases, as in the put routine,
each new partial array value is used only as input to the next
instance of append, and it is unnecessary to retain the input
array after execution of append. Therefore the append operation is implemented by the Structure Controller by adding a
component to an existing item in the Packet Memory System. It
is the responsibility of the programming system to ensure that
no attempt is made to reference the old data structure value
once the append operation is initiated.

VI. PERFORMANCE

We now turn to the analysis of the processing capacity of
the data flow processor necessary to achieve the desired one
hundred-fold performance over IBM 360/95 on which the GISS model
is implemented. The 360 implementation simulates one day of atmospheric activity in about one hour using a 9 $\times$ 45 $\times$ 72 grid and
a five-minute time step. To increase this performance by two
orders of magnitude implies that our data flow computer must be
able to complete all operations for computing new values of the
state variables for one group of K grid points at the same latitude and longitude each 40 microseconds.

For the data flow computer shown in Fig. 3, the computation
rate will be determined by which part of the machine is the bottleneck for the flow of operation and result packets. We proceed by determining the throughput required of each part of the
machine if the desired performance level is to be achieved.

Analysis of the complete data flow program partially
sketched in Fig. 1 reveals that the machine level program will
occupy about 13,000 Instruction Cells and that computation of
the new state for all grid points with the same horizontal coordinates requires processing approximately 7000 operation packets,
of which 2700 are multiplications or divisions, 2700 are additions or subtractions, 900 are data structure operations, and
700 are other miscellaneous operations. If the data flow computer is to complete this processing in 40 microseconds, the
Scalar Processors must be able to handle operation packets at
150 MHz and the Structure Processor must be capable of handling
data structure operations at 25 MHz. The routing networks must
be able to perform packet switching at 175 MHz. These rates
may be achieved by using many processors and structuring the

Arbitration and Distribution Networks for concurrent transmission of many packets.

In addition to these throughput requirements, we must ensure that the instruction processing time (the time interval from the instant an Instruction Cell becomes enabled to the instant all result and acknowledge packets have been received by other Instruction Cells) is small enough that instructions are enabled at the necessary rate. If a block of a data flow program is constructed to make the most effective use of the pipeline capability of the data flow computer, the period of repeated use of any actor is twice the instruction execution delay. This is because one execution cycle is needed to compute a result value and forward it to the next actor, and a second cycle is needed to return an acknowledge signal. We conclude that the two routing networks (the Arbitration and Distribution Networks) must be constructed so the instruction execution delay is no more than 20 microseconds.

Finally, the memory access time for retrieval requests handled by the Packet Memory must not be so large that values of the new atmospheric state are not available when they are needed. Since a time step is completed only once every 125 milliseconds, this requirement is easily met. However, the Queue unit of the Structure Controller must be large enough to hold all retrieval requests which have not been completed by the Packet Memory. For the arrival rate of 25 MHz even a one millisecond retrieval delay would require a capacity of 25,000 entries in the Queue, thus the Packet Memory should be implemented with storage devices having an access time well under a millisecond.

VII. CONCLUSION

Our study of the General Circulation Model as a data flow computation shows that a very high computation rate can be realized if the units of our proposed data flow computer operate at the assumed rates. This level of performance results from exposing and exploiting the inherent concurrency of the computation on a global basis. In contrast, the "lookahead" machines such as the IBM 360/195 attempt to discover parallelism through execution-time analysis of data dependencies in a small fragment of a sequential program. The vector and array machines can effectively use their highly parallel operation only to the extent that the programmer (or the compiler) can invent ways of encoding problem data into vectors or arrays that take advantage of the machine's power. Since the high performance of a data flow computer results from exposing large numbers of operations for concurrent execution, the speed with which each operation is executed is not crucial; thus a very powerful machine could be built using a large number of relatively slow logic devices. Since our data flow machines are composed of many units of similar type, these machines are ideal for effective application of LSI technology.

The open questions concerning the feasibility of practical data flow computers are: What physical structure should the Structure Controller and the Packet Memory System have? Can these units, which make up the Structure Processor, achieve the throughput assumed in our analysis? How difficult will it be to construct and debug such a large asynchronous system? How much will it cost to build data flow computers? The last question can be answered only by developing complete logic designs for the critical components of the machine. Each of these questions is under study in the Data Flow Project at the MIT Laboratory for Computer Science.

REFERENCES

1. Seeber, R. R., and Lindquist, A. B., "Associative Logic for Highly Parallel Systems," Proc. of the AFIPS Conference 24, 489-493 (1963).

2. Shapiro, R. M., Saint, H., and Presberg, D. L., "Representation of Algorithms as Cyclic Partial Orderings," Report CA-7112-2711, Applied Data Research, Wakefield, Mass., 1971.

3. Miller, R. E., and Cocke, J., "Configurable Computers: A New Class of General Purpose Machines," Report RC 3897, IBM Research Center, Yorktown Heights, N. Y., June 1972.

4. Rodriguez, J. E., "A Graph Model for Parallel Computation," Technical Report MAC TR-64, Laboratory for Computer Science, Mass. Inst. of Technology, Cambridge, Mass., 1969.

5. Dennis, J. B., "First Version of a Data Flow Procedure Language," Lecture Notes in Computer Science 19, 362-376, Springer-Verlag, New York, 1974.

6. Kosinski, P. R., "A Data Flow Language for Operating Systems Programming," SIGPLAN Notices 8, 89-94 (1973).

7. Bahrs, A., "Operation Patterns," Lecture Notes in Computer Science 5, 217-246, Springer-Verlag, New York, 1974.

8. Dennis, J. B., and Misunas, D. P., "A Computer Architecture for Highly Parallel Signal Processing," Proc. of the ACM 1974 National Conference, 402-409 (1974).

9. Dennis, J. B., and Misunas, D. P., "A Preliminary Architecture for a Basic Data-Flow Processor," Proc. of the Second Annual Symposium on Computer Architecture, IEEE, 126-132 (1975).

10. Rumbaugh, J. E., "A Data Flow Multiprocessor," IEEE Trans. on Computers C-26, 138-146 (February 1977).

11. Arvind, and Gostelow, K., "A New Interpreter for Data Flow Schemas and Its Implications for Computer Architecture," Technical Report 72, Department of Information and Computer Science, University of California, Irvine, 1975.

12. Dennis, J. B., Misunas D. P., and Leung, C. K., "A Highly Parallel Processor Using a Data Flow Machine Language," submitted for publication.

13. Kalnay-Rivas, E., Bayliss, A., and Storch, J., "Experiments with the 4th Order GISS Model of the Global Atmosphere," Proc. of the Conference on Simulation of Large-Scale Atmospheric Processes, Hamburg, Germany (1976), to be published.

14. Weng, K.-S., "Stream-Oriented Computation in Recursive Data Flow Schemas," Technical Memo 68, Laboratory for Computer Science, Mass. Inst. of Technology, Cambridge, Mass., 1975.

15. Misunas, D. P., "Structure Processing in a Data-Flow Computer," Proc. of the 1975 Sagamore Computer Conference on Parallel Computation, IEEE, 230-234 (August 1975).

16. Dennis, J. B., "Packet Communication Architecture," Proc. of the 1975 Sagamore Computer Conference on Parallel Processing, IEEE, 224-229 (August 1975).

6. Special-Purpose Parallel Architectures

As the design costs for digital processors have decreased, special-purpose processors have become increasingly viable. However, it should be pointed out at the onset that the term "special-purpose processor" is hard to define precisely. Although it can be argued that no one makes general-purpose processors any more and that every processor is special-purpose today, we follow the general consensus and adopt a more narrow definition. By the term "special-purpose processor" we mean a processor designed to satisfy one application. That many special-purpose processors have a high degree of parallelism should not be surprising. Often, designers take advantage of the inherent parallelism in the application without having to face the overhead needed to support general-purpose parallelism.

Papers in this chapter do not cover all the applications for which special-purpose parallel processors have been proposed or built. Since a description of all applications would be an impossible task, we have selected surveys of the special-purpose processors that have been designed for three applications. These coincide with the applications cited in Chapters 2 through 5, so that the reader may have some means of ascertaining whether or not the claims of special-purpose processor advocates are justified. The first two papers describe partial-differential equation applications. The paper about the SMS 201 describes a multi-microprocessor machine designed for weather prediction. The paper by Jordan *et al.* discusses how to tune an architecture to a specific application, in this case, solving finite element problems. Several designs are evaluated and the one which best solves the problem is implemented. Compare these two papers with the papers in Section 2.2. The next paper in this section, by Preston *et al.*, surveys special-purpose processors used for image processing. The application is for medical image processing, by no means the only medical application of parallel processing. Computer-assisted tomography (CAT) is another example (Gilbert and Harris, 1980). Compare the paper by Preston *et al.* to the paper by Rohrbacker and Potter in Section 3.2. The last paper in this chapter, by Smith and Smith, is a survey of special-purpose processors for database applications. Compare these special-purpose processors to the application of an array processor to database processing found in the paper by Berra and Oliver in Section 3.2

Special-purpose parallel processors have been proposed for many other applications, for example, to solve signal processing problems (e.g., FFT machines and digital filters), and to solve military problems (such as Ballistic Missile Defense). Several of these architectures have been reported in the *Proceedings of the International Conference on Parallel Processing* and the *Proceedings of the International Symposium on Computer Architecture*.

SMS - A MULTIPROCESSOR ARCHITECTURE FOR HIGH SPEED NUMERICAL CALCULATIONS

R. Kober, Ch. Kuznia
Research Laboratories
Siemens AG
Otto-Hahn-Ring 6, D-8000 Munich 83, West Germany

Reprinted from *Proceedings of the 1978 International Conference on Parallel Processing*, 1978, pages 18-23. Copyright © 1978 by The Institute of Electrical and Electronics Engineers, Inc.

Abstract -- The architecture, organization and application of the SMS multiprocessor system, a MIMD-structure for high speed numerical computations, are outlined.
The now operational SMS 201 with 128 combined microprocessors is capable of executing 30 000 floating point operations per second (FLOPS); by using high speed LSI circuits the newly designed SMS 3 will have a speed of 18 Million FLOPS.
The SMS-System features central coordination of the processor modules, private program and data memory for each module, a data exchange method via decentraliced communication memories and a self-synchronized computing scheme. The implementation of a global weather model shows a typical application: program structure and computation times for this example are discussed. With the introduction of the SMS 3, which yields an improvement factor of 300 over the SMS 201, the performance of todays large mainframes will be surpassed.

Introduction

Many motivations lead to investigations of multiprocessor systems, for instance: to build a cheap computer system, to increase reliability or to achieve high processing power /1-9/. The Structured Multiprocessor System (SMS) is a parallel architecture, which (besides beeing useful for nonnumerical applications) mainly pursues the high speed computer idea for the solution of large numerical problems /10-13/. Typical appications are picture processing, solving of partial differential equations for weather prediction or aerodynamic problems etc, circuit simulation, and control or supervision of complex processes /5, 14-18/.

Architecture and Organization of the SMS

The SMS concept combines the advantages of array processors of the ILLIAC IV-type /2/ on one side and of "decentralized" multiprocessor systems like the C.mmp or he Cm* /7, 8/ on the other side. It features a central control of the processor modules as known from the array processors. It allows a clear organization of software. But the level of parallelism is high, namely at the program level, as used in decentralized multiprocessor systems. This fact has two important advantages: Firstly it is possible, to translate a real problem, consisting of a number of coupled subproblems, in a natural way into subprograms for the processor modules. (In section 4 we describe the task allocation scheme for the example of the global weather forecast). Secondly the amount of data exchanges between the modules, representing the real interactions between the subproblems, is small compared to the amount of calculation done by each module task.

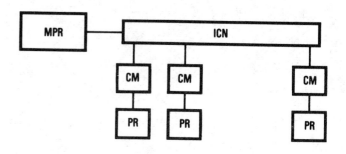

Figure 1: SMS-Architecture

Figure 1 shows the architecture of the SMS. A number of identical modules, each consisting of a processor PR with program and data memory, and of a communication memory CM, are connected via an interconnection network ICN to a main processor MPR.

The communication memories are one main characteristic of the SMS concept. They accomplish a soft coupling of the modules: Each module has only access to its own CM. All communications between the modules, and between modules and main processor are controlled and carried out by the main processor via these CMs.

The second main characteristic is a self synchronized computing scheme in a repetetive sequence of three phases:

- The control phase, in which the main processor selects and starts the module programs,
- The computation phase, in which the modules carry out their tasks, and - after all modules have completed their tasks -
- The communication phase, in which the results of each module are broadcast to the other modules.

This clear and straightforward organization avoids problems like access conflicts, synchronization problems and deadlocks /7, 10/. Nevertheless a high computing power can be achieved. For homogeneous problems, that is for equal module tasks, (in content and execution time) the computing power can be characterized by

- The instruction stream of all module processors (MIPS, MFLOPS)[a]
- The data exchange stream (MBPS)[b]

In the next section we will give an account of these characteristics for a realized and for a future SMS system.

---

[a] MIPS   Million Instructions per Second
     MFLOPS Million Floating Point Operations per Second
[b] MBPS   Million Bytes per Second

Present and Future SMS Systems

In order to study the architectural aspects of large multiprocessor systems, the SMS 201 with 128 8080-based microcomputer modules and a total memory capacity of 2,5 MByte has been implemented (Figure 2).

Figure 2: SMS 201 Multiprocessor System with 128 Microcomputer Modules

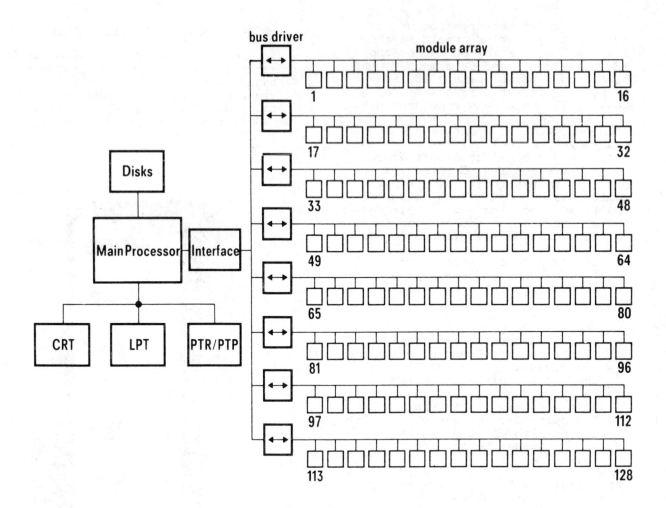

Figure 3: Block Diagram of SMS 201

Figure 3 shows its block diagram:
8 groups of 16 modules each are connected to a minicomputer representing the main processor /12/. The
system, up and running since autumn
1977, provides a performance comparable to larger main frame systems,
except for the limited floating-arith-
metic capabilities of the 8 bit-micro-
processors. But it will be improved
by a factor of about 20 by adding
a dedicated 1-chip arithmetic processing unit (APU) to each module.

Recently a concept for a new, very
powerful system has been designed.
The SMS 3 will provide a performance
enhancement of about 20x - 30x compared to the SMS 201 with APUs.

This is achieved by:

- Extending the module number
- Using more powerful modules
  . Faster components (bit slice
    microprocessors)
  . Greater word length
- Speeding up data exchanges
  . Double-word bus
  . Communication memory with dou-
    ble-word interface
  . Faster bus cycle
  . Special communication proces-
    sor /12/.

The performance characteristics of
the SMS 201 with and without APUs,
and of the SMS 3 are summarized in
Table 1. An average module processor utilization of 80% is assumed.

	SMS 201	SMS 201 / APU	SMS 3
Instruction Stream	32 MIPS$_8$ 0.03 MFLOPS$_{32}$	32 MIPS$_8$ 0.55 MFLOPS$_{32}$	250 MIPS$_{16}$ 18 MFLOPS$_{32}$
Data Exchange Stream	0.1 MBPS	0.1 MBPS	3.5 MBPS

Table 1: Performance Characteristics of SMS Systems[c]

Figure 4 shows a comparison of the instruction stream of sequential, general purpose computers with SMS-type parallel computers. In order to obtain equivalent values for different word lengths, the following conversion has been applied[c]:

$$1 \text{ MIPS} = 1 \text{ MIPS}_{64} = 7 \text{ MIPS}_{16} = 24 \text{ MIPS}_8$$

The SMS 101, an 8 module system /10/ reaches the minicomputer class; the SMS 201 has an instruction stream comparable to present mainframe computers. The SMS 3 will surpass them for many application problems. Further improvements on the parallel processor side will be possible soon by progresses in LSI-technology, whereas further speed-up in sequential processors will be slow due to physical limits /6/.

Using the SMS - Example Weather Forecast

The problem structure of the applications mentioned initially, is the following /11/. Many elements, parts of the whole problem, interact with each other in a fairly simple way. The translation to a parallel processor leads to subprograms for the modules ("elementary tasks"); the real interactions are reproduced by data exchanges between the modules. We want to describe that translation, which means the programming of the SMS, for a weather forecast model. This was been the first application of the SMS 201:

The numerical model of the atmosphere, which is a finite difference approximation to partial differential equations /18/, subdivides the northern hemisphere by a 3-layer grid of 2000 mesh points each. Figure 5 shows the horizontal structure of the prognose model, which has been adapted from a model used by the German Weather Service /17/.

---

[c] The index is the number of bits

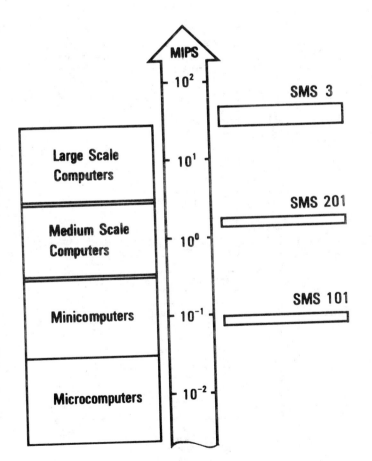

MIPS = Mio Instuctions per Second

Figure 4: Comparison of Instruction Stream

239

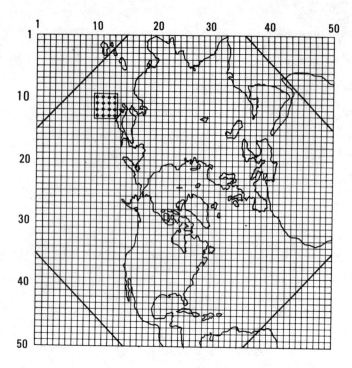

Figure 5: Horizontal Structure of
the Prognose Model

The weather forecasting model is
implemented on the SMS in the following manner. Each module represents a local prognosis block of
3x16 adjacent mesh points. Starting

with the initial values the system
calculates the further development
in time steps of 5 minutes real time.
After each time step the results
of all local areas are distributed
to the other local areas, thus reproducing the real world physical
interactions by data exchanges between the modules.

The data exchange program for the
main processor (or the data exchange
processor) might be generated automatically by a planned generator. When
this tool is available, the user
will only have to supply the interaction grid of each elementary task
to its neighbours and the boundary
conditions of the problem. If the
problem is homogenious, then the
connection characteristic is identical for all tasks, and it is sufficient to specify only the connection characteristic for one task.

Figure 6 shows the flowchart of the
SMS-prognose-program.

The corresponding program for a sequential processor is outlined in
Figure 7. In this case the parallel
tasks are sequentially computed in
a time consuming loop. The frame
of the program, the repetetive sequence of discrete timesteps, is
identical for parallel and sequential processors.

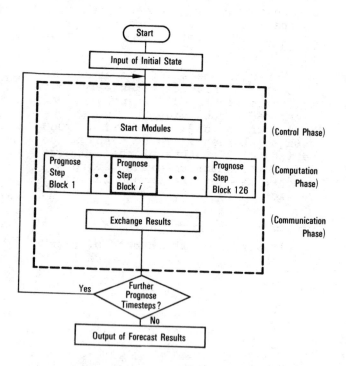

Figure 6: Prognose Program for the
SMS 201

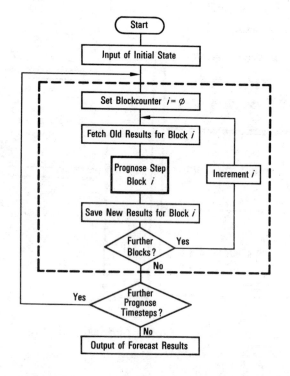

Figure 7: Prognose Program for a
Sequential Computer

The computation time for a real time interval of 24 hours (288 timesteps), measured with the SMS 201, and extrapolated for the SMS 201 with APU and the SMS 3, are summarized in Table 2.

	SMS 201	SMS 201 / APU	SMS 3
Autonomous Computations	73.2 min	4.2 min	8.4 sec
Control Phase + Data Exchanges	3.4 min	3.4 min	5.8 sec
Total :	77 min	7.6 min	14.2 sec

Table 2: Computation Times for a 24 Hours-Prognose

The improvement in processing speed is remarkable. The computation time of the SMS 201 can be speeded up by a factor of 300 with SMS 3, although the share of time needed for control and data exchanges raises from 4,5% to 41%. It is possible to reduce substantially the amount of communication time by more sophisticated interconnection networks, introducing parallelism into the exchange.

At the moment, however, we do not see the necessarity to implement more complicated bus-structures. The reason is, that with faster module-computers the length of the elementary task will tend to increase too. In this way the user can achieve a higher sophistication of his physical model and better accuracy. So the relation of time needed for data exchanges to the time needed for the autonomous computations will become less critical.

Conclusion

The SMS concept is well suited for a large class of applications with extensive numerical calculations. Taking full advantage of the trend of LSI-technology it will provide a considerable improvement in performance. That will allow us to solve problems, which cannot yet be treated fast enough by present computer systems. The utilization, task allocation and programming of the system is possible in a transparent manner.

References

/1/ M.J. Flynn:
Some Computer Organizations and their Effectiveness
IEEE Trans. on Computers, Vol. C-21, No. 9, Sept. 1972, p.948-960

/2/ G.H. Barnes, R.M. Brown, M. Kato, D.J. Kuck, D.L. Slotnick, R.A. Stokes:
The ILLIAC IV Computer
IEEE Trans. on Computers, Vol. C-17, No. 8, Aug. 68, p.746-757

/3/ C.H. Radoy, G.J. Lipovski:
Switched Multiple Instruction, Multiple Data Processing
Proc. 2nd Symposium on Comp. Architecture, Jan. 1975, p.183-187

/4/ G.J. Lipovski:
On a Varistructured Array of Microprocessors
IEEE Trans. on Computers, Vol. C-26, No. 2, Febr. 1977, p.125-138

/5/ G.A. Korn:
Back to Parallel Computation; Proposal for a Completely On-Line Simulation System Using Standard Minicomputers for Low-Cost Multiprocessing
Simulation, Aug. 1972, p. 37-45

/6/ J.W. Wirsching:
Computer of the 1980 s - It is a Network of Microcomputers
Digest of Papers, Compcon Fall 75, 1975, p. 23-26

/7/ S.H. Fuller, D.P. Siewiorek,
R.J. Swan:
Computer Modules: An Architecture
for Large Digital Modules
ACM SIGARCH, Comp.Arch. News,
Vol. 2, No4, Dec. 1973,
p. 231-236

/8/ R.J. Swan, S.H. Fuller, D.P.
Siewiorek:
Cm* - A Modular Multi-Processor
AFIPS Conf. Proc., Vol. 46,
1977 National Computer Conference, p. 637-744

/9/ J.L. Baer:
Multiprocessing Systems
IEEE Trans. on Computers, Vol.
C-25, No. 12, Dec. 1976,
p. 1271-1277

/10/ R. Kober, H. Kopp, Ch. Kuznia:
SMS 101 - A Structured Multi-
microprocessor System with Deadlock Free Operation Scheme
Euromicro Newsletter, 2 (1976),
p. 56-64

/11/ Ch. Kuznia, H. Kopp:
A Model for Process Communi-
cation in Parallel Processor
Systems
Proc. IMACS-GI-Symposium on
Parallel Computers and Parallel
Mathematics, Munich, March 14-16
(1977) p. 339-342

/12/ R. Kober:
A fast Communication Processor
for the SMS Multimicroprocessor System
Proc. Euromicro Symposium on
Microprocessing and Microprogramming, Oct. 1976, Venice,
p. 183-189

/13/ R. Kober:
The Multiprocessor System SMS
201 - Combining 128 Microprocessors to a Powerful Computer
Digest of Papers, Compcon Fall
1977, p. 225-229

/14/ M. Tasto:
Parallel Array Processor for
Digital Image Processing
Optica Acta, Vol. 24, 1977,
No. 4, p. 391-406

/15/ M. Inouye:
The Computer as a Wind Tunnel
Proc. 2nd USA-Japan Comp. Conf.,
1975, p. 405-409

/16/ F.R. Bailey:
Computational Aerodynamics -
ILLIAC IV and Beyond
Digest of Papers, Compcon Spring
1977, p. 8-11

/17/ H. Kopp:
Numerical Weather Forecast with
the Multimicroprocessor
System SMS 201
Proc. IMACS-GI-Symposium on
Parallel Computers and Paral-
lel Mathematics, Munich March
14-16 (1977), p. 265-268

/18/ H.O. Welch:
Numerical Weather Prediction
in the PEPE Parallel Proces-
sor
Proc. Int. Conf. on Parallel
Processing, 1977, p. 186-192

Reprinted from *Proceedings of the 1979 International Conference on Parallel Processing*, 1979, pages 231-238. Copyright © 1979 by The Institute of Electrical and Electronics Engineers, Inc.

A COMPARISON OF THREE TYPES OF MULTIPROCESSOR ALGORITHMS[a]

Harry F. Jordan[1], Maria Scalabrin[2] and Wynne Calvert[1]

[1]Electrical Engineering Department
University of Colorado
Boulder, Colorado 80309

[2]Computer Science Department
Universidade Estadual de Campinas
Brasil

Abstract

In a multiprocessor system with limited communications paths between processors, a heavy communications demand is made by an algorithm requiring input values from all processors in the system. The Finite Element Machine is a special purpose computer designed from 1024 microprocessors communicating by way of explicit word-serial channels. The algorithms for structural analysis using the finite element method which have been proposed for this machine require both maximum and summation over a set of numbers stored one per processor. Three distinct types of sum and maximum algorithm making different use of the communications paths have been formulated and analyzed with respect to execution time. The results give some insight into the best way to use communications paths in a multiprocessor. The study demonstrated the need for a special hardware mechanism to support the global sum and maximum operations in this machine. The design of this hardware unit is also discussed.

Introduction

The Finite Element Machine [1,2] is a special purpose computer architecture developed to support structural analysis using methods based on the theory of finite elements [3]. The machine consists of a large number (1024 is the target design) of microprocessors communicating over a network of parallel "local" channels connecting each processor to a limited number of other processors. The parallel local channels are backed up by a time multiplexed global bus connecting all processors. If a node in a finite element model of a structure is considered to be "connected" to another node when the two correspond to a nonzero stiffness matrix coefficient, then the model forms a graph with the qualitative characteristic that each node connects to only a few others. The Finite Element Machine with processors as nodes and local communications links as edges has the same qualitative characteristic. The idea is to use this qualitative similarity to carry out the solution of finite element model equations in such a way that most of the required interprocessor communications can be performed using the parallel local channels while the time multiplexed bus takes care of the mismatches between the finite element model topology and the topology imposed by the fixed local channels.

The linear equations of the finite element model are solved by iterative methods so that most data interchange between processors is determined by the topology of nonzero elements of the sparse stiffness matrix. In any iterative method, however, a test for convergence must be made which depends on values associated with every node. In particular, a maximum must be computed over 1024 values, one stored in each processor. Rapidly converging iterative methods, such as the conjugate gradient method [4], require not only maximum but also summation over values from all processors. These global computations strain the communications capabilities of a machine tailored to the more limited requirements of iterative updating of values.

This paper takes the architecture of the Finite Element Machine as fixed and proposes three algorithms for performing the global sum and maximum calculations. These algorithms are compared with respect to execution time to measure their suitability for a 1024 processor machine. The fixed machine architecture is then extended by the addition of special hardware to make these computations more efficient.

Description of the Multiprocessor

The Finite Element Machine consists of a large number (~1000) of microprocessors communicating by way of a network of point to point First-In-First-Out (FIFO) communications. The multiprocessor array is not easily characterized as tightly or loosely coupled [5]. The speed and information carrying capacity of the communications network would indicate a tightly coupled system while the lack of shared memory would suggest loose coupling. The communications occur over two separate networks: the local network and the global network. The local network consists of a large number (~8000) of bidirectional unshared connections between two nearest neighbor processors. The global network consists of a single time multiplexed bus connecting all processors. A third interconnecting network is composed of a set of signal flags which are primarily oriented toward processor synchronization. A brief description of the three networks interconnecting the processors is necessary to an understanding of the algorithms to follow. Further details can be found in [2].

The local communications network imposes a fixed interconnection topology on the 16 bit microcomputers making up the array. The current prototyping effort being carried out at NASA

---

[a]This work was partially supported by NASA under grant number NSG 1489.

Langley Research Center will allow investigation of several interconnection patterns. For the purposes of this paper, however, we will consider only a square array of 32 x 32 processors with each processor having a local communications link to each of its eight nearest neighbors. Processors on the boundaries are connected to those on opposite boundaries in the manner of a toroid so that all processors have a full eight neighbors. The global bus simply connects in parallel to all of the processors in the array. Of course this is only true logically; electronically, the bus and its arbitration network form a tree structure. The structure of the signaling flag network parallels that of the global bus. An abbreviated PMS [6] diagram for the processor array is shown in Figure 1.

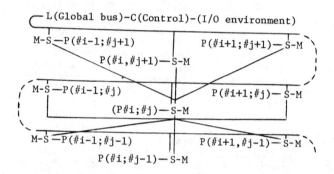

Figure 1: Partial PMS Diagram for the Array

Local communications output is broadcast to all neighbors simultaneously, although neighbors can be selectively disabled from receiving. Information coming in from a neighbor is placed in a hardware FIFO, which the receiving processor may interrogate and empty at its own initiative. Transmission is actually bit serial to conserve hardware but becomes parallel at the processor interfaces. Figure 2 shows a logical block diagram of the local communications interfaces for one processor and lists the primitive operations the processor can perform in connection with these interfaces. The various local neighbors are identified by the eight points of the compass.

The global bus acts as a time multiplexed crosspoint switch, allowing the transmission of one 16 bit word from any source processor to any destination processor. A transaction thus appears on the bus as three items: the source processor number, destination processor number and data word. Since a bus transaction time is short compared to an instruction time a FIFO buffer receives input from the bus. Further, since contention for the bus may delay a transmission, FIFO buffering is also provided for output to the bus. A destination register allows a processor to transmit several successive data words to the same destination without respecifying it. A special processor number serves to identify broadcast data and matches the address of any processor which is enabled for broadcast reception.

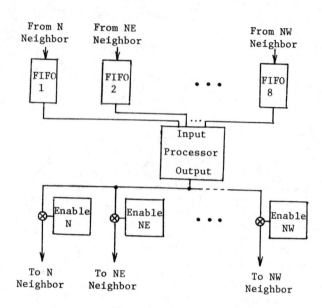

a) Local Communications Interfaces

Operations:

Output (word)	– Broadcast word to all enabled neighbors.
Enable (j)	– Enable neighbor j.
Disable (j)	– Disable neighbor j.
Input (j,word)	– Input word from FIFO j and advance it.
Interrupt enable (j)	– Enable FIFO j non-empty interrupt.
Interrupt disable (j)	– Disable FIFO j non-empty interrupt.

Tests:

Output busy?	– Is any enabled neighbor's FIFO full?
Input ready (j)?	– Is input FIFO j non-empty?

b) Local Communications Primitives

Figure 2: Local Communications for a Single Processor

Figure 3 shows the block diagram and primitive operations for a processor's global bus communications.

The signal flag network consists of eight single bit variables, or flags, per processor. One of these and the corresponding flags in all other processors form the inputs to a network which forms the combinational functions AND and OR over all its inputs. The OR and AND functions are available to each processor and indicate whether the corresponding flag is set in any other processor or in all other processors, respectively. An enable bit allows a flag to be

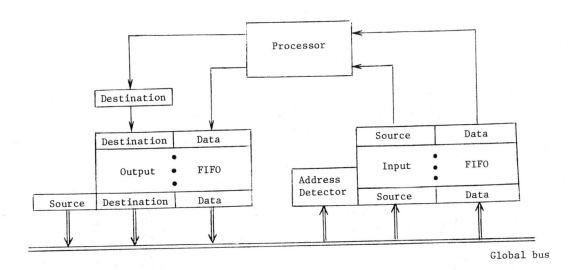

a) Global Communications Interfaces

Operations:

Set destination (i)	- Set destination register to i.
Send word (w)	- Put (Destination, w) into output FIFO.
Set broadcast	- Set destination register to broadcast address.
Read source (s)	- Get source address from head of input FIFO.
Read data (w)	- Get data and advance input FIFO.
Receive broadcast	- Sensitize detector to broadcast address.
Ignore broadcast	- Disable detection of broadcast address.

Tests:

Input ready?	- Is input FIFO nonempty?
Output full?	- Is output FIFO full?

b) Global Communications Primitives

Figure 3: Global Communications for a Single Processor

effectively connected into or isolated from the computational network. There are eight independent and nearly identical networks, one for each of the eight flags available to a processor. Also associated with each flag is a synchronization bit, Sync i, which is set when the AND function becomes true and reset when the OR function becomes false. The only difference between the eight flag networks is that one of them, flag zero, is augmented by a unique selection network used in some algorithms to solve the "multiple hit" problem but not needed below. Whenever a group of enabled processors asynchronously set this flag, one of them will be designated as the "first" to do so. The "first" indicator is thus a separate bit associated with flag zero for each processor. The structure and primitive operations for the signal flag network are shown in Figure 4.

Methods for Performing Array Computations

The finite element method algorithms proposed for the multiprocessor array described above primarily require local computation with input from neighboring processors; but also some calculations involving numbers from all processors in the array are needed. Specifically, the test for convergance in an iterative algorithm requires the computation of $\max_i X_i$ where X_i is a value contained in processor i only and the maximum is taken over all processors. Using the conjugate gradient method to perform the iterative linear equation solution requires the computation of $\sum_i X_i$ where the sum runs over all processors. Again X_i is local to a given processor and in this case it is the product of two local values. The computation performed is

245

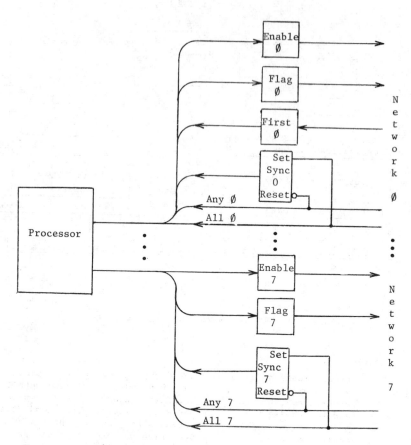

a) Signal Flag Interfaces

Operations:

Connect (k)	– Enable the kth flag.
Disconnect (k)	– Disable the kth flag.
Set (k)	– Set flag k.
Clear (k)	– Clear flag k.

Tests:

Any (k)?	– Is flag k set in any connected processor?
All (k)?	– Is flag k set in all connected processors?
Sync (k)?	– Was All true previously?
First?	– Was this processor's Set (Ø) the "first" one?

b) Signal Flag Primitives

Figure 4: Signal Flag Communications for One Processor

actually a vector inner product but only the summation requires calculation involving the whole array.

Consider then the isolated problem of evaluating $\max_i X_i$ over the entire array of nodal processors. At least three distinct methods of evaluation are possible using different aspects of the three processor communication networks. First all values could be sent over the global bus to a single processor which would compute the maximum sequentially. This would require 1024 times the length of a several instruction loop in a microprocessor of the array. A possibly faster method would be to compute maxima over subgroups of the nodal processors, using the local connection network to transmit information without conflict between groups. These subgroup maxima could then be combined using local or global communications to form the maximum over all processors, perhaps using higher level grouping of subgroup results.

Call the first method using one processor for the maximum calculation the central computation method and call the second method distributed computation.

The third method that presents itself might be called cooperative computation and operates using the network of signal flags. This is a tightly synchronized calculation which uses some signal flags for synchronization but also uses a signal flag to compute the maximum value in a bit serial manner. The computation proceeds roughly as follows (processor synchronization is not mentioned explicitly):

1. All processors connect themselves to a signal flag, say Flag k, by setting the Enable k bit. A counter ℓ is initialized to zero.

2. Each processor with its Enable k bit set sets its signal Flag k to the ℓth bit of X_i

   where the bits are numbered starting with zero at the left.

3. Each processor performs the Any (k) test and records a 1 in the ℓth bit of the maximum if Any (k) is true and a 0 if it is false. If Any (k) is true each processor which still has Enable k set clears it if its Flag k is zero.

4. All processors advance to the next bit of X_i

   by incrementing ℓ. If there are more bits, the loop is repeated beginning at step 2, otherwise step 5 is executed.

5. At this point all processors which still have Enable k set (always at least one) are associated with an X_i which equals the maximum value. All processors have recorded the maximum so that the result of the computation is already distributed.

Many possible versions of the distributed computation of the maximum are possible depending on the way in which the processor array is divided into groups. We considered what is perhaps the simplest of them in which groups of nine processors are formed initially (so far as possible). One processor receives values from each of its eight neighbors and computes the maximum of the nine values to which it has access. These receiving processors then combine subgroup maxima in pairs using the global bus for communications. The pairwise maxima form a binary tree with the final array maximum appearing at the root node. Of course, an array of 1024 processors is not evenly divisible into groups of nine so some of the groups are smaller.

The initial grouping on the array is indicated in Figure 5. In the first phase of the computation the processors marked A merely transmit a value over the local network to a neighbor. The B processors receive and form the group maximum of these values. The three types of B processors, B1, B2 and B3, compute maxima of 9, 6, and 4

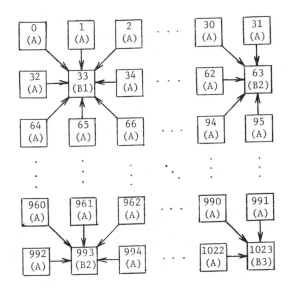

Figure 5: Partioning the Array for Distributed Computation

values respectively. In the second phase of the computation, the 121 B processors are formed into a seven level binary tree with half of the processors remaining at any one level transmitting values over the global bus to another processor and disabling themselves. Thus 61 transmissions will time multiplex the global bus at the first tree level and this number will be successively halved at successive levels. The longest program will be executed by the processor which eventually forms the root of the tree and it is this program which will be used, along with estimates of overhead due to global bus conflicts, to determine the speed of the distributed algorithm.

Comparison of the Methods

The problem is to decide which of the three computational methods (centralized, distributed or cooperative) is most efficient for a 1024 processor version of the finite element machine. To do this, algorithms of each type were formulated and coded. A timing analysis of the code was performed and the overhead due to global bus congestion was estimated and added to the code time. Note that the first two computational methods, centralized and distributed, are also possible ways of calculating $\sum_i X_i$. The cooperative method, using a similar bit serial approach, is possible if one of the signal flag networks is augmented with a parallel counter. This would appear to a processor as an 11 bit port, Count (k), which gives the number of processors having Enable k and Flag k both set. We will take the analysis for Max X_i as indicative and use the results to determine whether the addition of a parallel counter is cost effective for the computation of $\sum_i X_i$.

The algorithms for central, distributed and cooperative calculation of $\text{Max } X_i$ were timed and compared using hardward parameters from the prototype Finite Element Machine desinged at the University of Colorado and under construction at NASA Langley Research Center. The microprocessor used is a Texas Instruments TMS 9900 with an average instruction time of about 6 microseconds. The time for one transmission over the global bus is taken as 0.5 microseconds. The time for the central computation is determined by the algorithm executed by the single central receiver. This algorithm is a straightforward access and combination of 1024 values. The TMS 9900 program required the execution of 9,219 instructions so that the time for evaluating the maximum would be about 55.3 milliseconds. Since a global bus transmission time is shorter than an instruction time, no transmission overhead need be added to this number.

In the specific distributed calculation described above, there are distinct algorithms executed by distinct groups of processors. Some of them compute maxima over values from their eight neighboring processors and themselves, transmit this local maximum and then wait for a broadcast message containing the overall maximum. This corresponds to the section marked Phase 1 in the flowchart of Figure 6. In Phase 2, one of the processors involved in computing the pairwise maxima will receive values at all seven levels of the binary tree and broadcast the final maximum back to all processors. It is not absolutely necessary that the same processor execute both Phase 1 and Phase 2 of the flowchart, but the overall time will be determined by the juxtaposition of these two program segments in any case. The program code amounts to 175 instructions executed from start to finish or about 1050 microseconds. Added to this will be non-overlapped communications time. The first local network transmission requires 20 microseconds. Subsequent local transmissions overlap with instruction execution. Overlap of global bus transmission with computation time is harder to estimate but it is certainly bounded above by the total number of values transmitted, 120, times the bus transmission time. This gives an upper bound of 60 microseconds for a total of 1.13 milliseconds for the distributed algorithm.

The code for the cooperative algorithm follows the flowchart of Figure 7. The explicitly specified synchronization is an example of so-called barrier synchronization in which all processors must reach a given point before any may proceed. Here it serves to assure that all processors have input a bit into the Flag 1 network before the OR of all the bits is tested. With all processors running at the same speed the overhead due to synchronizing waits will be zero and can thus be neglected even if the processors only run at nearly the same speed. The number of instructions executed in this algorithm is 328 for a time of about 1.97 milliseconds.

As expected, the central computation is the clear loser taking 49 times as long as the distributed calculation. Somewhat unexpected, however, is the result that the crude distributed algorithm which we analyzed is almost twice as fast as the cooperative method. This gain comes at the expense of having to load different programs into different groups of processors while in the cooperative method one program serves for all processors. Certainly the comparison indicates that the

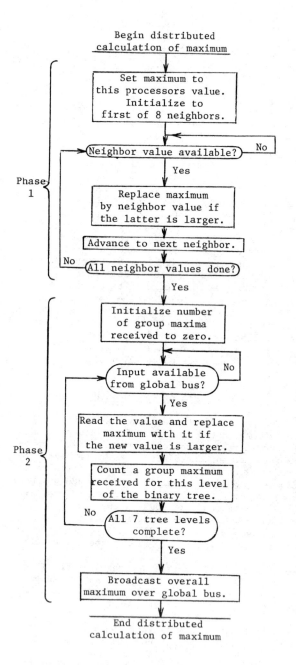

Figure 6: Distributed Calculation of $\text{Max } X_i$

248

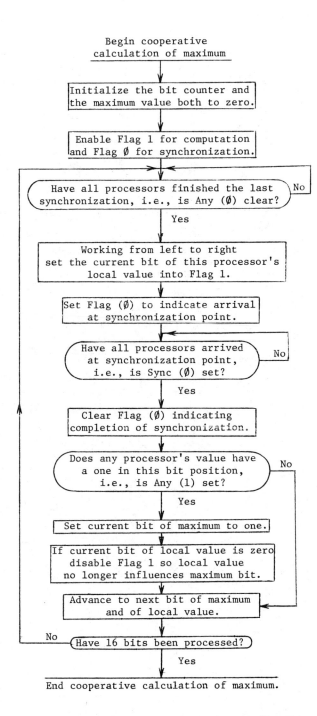

Figure 7: Cooperative Calculation of $\text{Max } X_i$

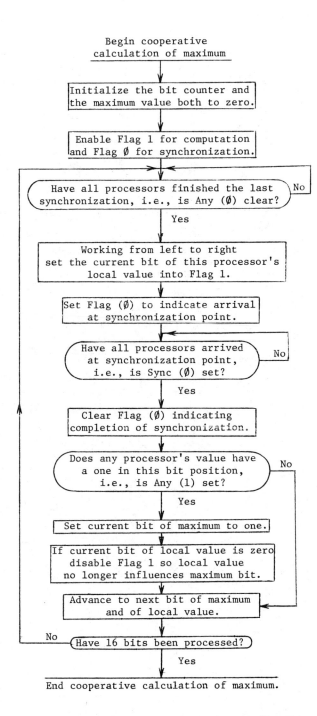

Hardware Support for Global Calculations

As a result of the above analysis a hardware circuit has been included in the finite-element machine to avoid long delays in calculating global sum and global maximum. The configuration of this circuit is a binary tree, in which each tree element accepts an argument pair and passes on the result to the next higher level. The global results, which appear at the apex of the tree, are then broadcast to all the processors. With this configuration, a tree of N levels can serve 2^N processors. For instance, 1024 processors require 10 levels and 1023 tree elements.

The tree elements are serial. Each one accepts two serial arguments and produces a serial result, delayed by one bit period. The sum and maximum functions are calculated alternately, sharing the same tree connections and element circuitry. The entire calculation sequence involves a serial frame of 48 bit periods: 26 for sum, 16 for maximum and 6 unused.

The tree input data consists of a single 16-bit output register at each processor. Both functions are thus calculated from the same data, and they are separately available. The sum requires a double-word input register for the entire result; the maximum requires a single-word register. In both cases, the data are treated as positive, integer values.

The sum-maximum tree is implemented without facilities for process synchronization. Use of the circuit will generally require barrier synchronization, such as that already provided by the signal flags. However, functional synchronization is included, whereby each output register is sampled as a unit. This assures that the results are valid even while different processors are updating their output registers.

The delay for the circuit consists of the tree delay of one bit period for each level, plus the frame delay of 48 bit periods. The delay for 1024 processors, which requires 10 levels in the tree, is thus 58 bit periods. With a bit period of one microsecond, the entire calculation of both sum and maximum is accomplished in 58 microseconds.

Conclusion

The detailed timing analysis for three algorithms for computing $\sum_i X_i$ and $\text{Max}_i X_i$ over all processors in a multiprocessor array has been performed. The three algorithms make distinctly different use of the communication pathways in the machine. The analysis shows that $\text{Max}_i X_i$ can be computed in 55.3 milliseconds by a centralized algorithm, in 1.13 milliseconds by a distributed algorithm and in 1.97 milliseconds by a cooperative algorithm. The distributed algorithm is the most logically complex, requiring about 6 different programs for different groups of processors.

addition of a parallel counter to support cooperative calculation of $\sum_i X_i$ would not be cost effective. On the other hand, the fastest method takes a millisecond, which is quite long with respect to the processor speed so hardware support for both $\text{Max}_i X_i$ and $\sum_i X_i$ is indicated.

As a result of this analysis a proposal to support cooperative calculation of $\sum_i X_i$ with special hardware in the Finite Element Machine was discarded. Instead a complete hardware unit to calculate sum and maximum using a bit serial binary tree organization was designed. The unit can calculate both sum and maximum over the same set of 1024 operands in 58 microseconds.

References

[1] H. Jordan, "A Special Purpose Architecture for Finite Element Analysis," Proc. 1978 International Conference on Parallel Processing, (August, 1978), pp. 263-266.

[2] H.F. Jordan and P.L. Sawyer, "A Multi-microprocessor System for Finite Element Structural Analysis," Trends in Computerized Structural Analysis and Synthesis (A.K. Noor and H.G. McComb, Jr., Eds.), Pergamon Press, (1978), pp. 21-29.

[3] O.C. Zienkiewicz and Y.K. Cheung, Finite Element Method in Structural and Continuum Mechanics, McGraw Hill, (1972).

[4] M.R. Hestenes and E. Stiefel, "Methods of Conjugate Gradients for Solving Linear Systems," J. Res. Nat. Bur. Std., 48, (1952), pp. 409-436.

[5] P.H. Enslow (Ed.), Multiprocessors and Parallel Processing, John Wiley and Sons, (1974).

[6] C.G. Bell and A. Newell, Computer Structures: Readings and Examples, McGraw Hill, (1971).

Reprinted from *Proceedings of the IEEE*, Volume 67, Number 5, May 1979, pages 826–856. Copyright © 1979 by The Institute of Electrical and Electronics Engineers, Inc.

Basics of Cellular Logic with Some Applications in Medical Image Processing

KENDALL PRESTON, JR., FELLOW, IEEE, MICHAEL J. B. DUFF, STEPHANO LEVIALDI, MEMBER, IEEE, PHILIP E. NORGREN, MEMBER, IEEE, AND JUN-ICHIRO TORIWAKI

Abstract—Cellular logic operations (CLO's) are performed digitally to transform an array of data $P(I, J)$ into a new data array $P'(I, J)$. The value of each element in the new array is determined by its value in the original array and the original values of its nearest neighbors. The neighborhood configuration (tessellation) is usually called the "cell"; whence the term "cellular logic." CLO's may be categorized according to the tessellation in which they are embedded and according to the type or types of CLO sequences: sequences which are carried out in a single step; those which iterate the same CLO for many steps; those which repetitively alternate subsequences of CLO strings. The effect of the CLO sequence on the contents of the data array is frequently one of boundary modification. Depending on the CLO sequence(s) utilized, a boundary may be expanded to form the convex hull, or reduced so as to form the convex kernel, skeleton, or residue.

As of 1977, cellular logic computers have become a commercial product in biomedical image processing where they are used in clinical instruments whose purpose is to classify white blood cell images at rates of several thousand per hour. Many other applications are foreseen and, as further examples, preliminary results in automatic X-ray image analysis and tissue image analysis are presented.

I. INTRODUCTION

NEIGHBORHOOD logic (or "cellular logic") is a discipline in the field of computational geometry [1]. Since an image or picture is a two-dimensional topology, cellular logic has applications in image processing. This is the primary concern of this paper. It is worth mentioning, however, that cellular logic is applied one dimensionally in the generation of shif-register sequences [2] and has been treated in three-dimensional studies of what are called "patterns of growth" in the field of cellular automata theory [3].

Cellular logic refers to an operation performed digitally on an array of data $P(I, J)$ which is carried out so as to transform $P(I, J)$ into a new data array $P'(I, J)$ wherein each element in the new array has a value determined only by the corresponding element in the original array along with the values of its nearest neighbors. The nearest neighbor configuration is called the "cell" and operations over arrays of identical cells are called "cellular logic." When one considers the implementa-

Manuscript received September 18, 1978; revised January 26, 1979. This work was supported in part by the Japanese Ministry of Health and Welfare under Grant-in-Aid 52-04 and the Ministry of Education under Grant-in-Aid 285072; U.S. NSF under Grants APR75-08154 and MCS76-09401; U. K. Science Research Council; the Consiglio Nazionale delle Recerche; and the Perkin-Elmer Corporation.

K. Preston, Jr. is with the Department of Electrical Engineering, Carnegie-Mellon University, Pittsburgh, PA 15213.

M. J. B. Duff is with the Department of Physics and Astronomy, University College London, London WCIE 6BT, England.

S. Levialdi is with the Laboratorio di Cibernetica, Consiglio Nazionale delle Recerche, Naples, Italy.

P. E. Norgren is with the Optical Group, Perkin-Elmer Corporation, Norwalk, CT 06856.

J-i. Toriwaki is with the Faculty of Engineering, Nagoya University, Nagoya, Japan.

tion of cellular logic by an array of computers the logic and memory associated with the cell defines a processing element (PE). The array itself is then a cellular automaton (CA).

This paper explores cellular logic by discussing basic cellular logic operators (CLO's) and then illustrates the use of cellular logic in a variety of medical image processing applications. This is particularly timely in that cellular logic computers have become a commercial product in the biomedical image processing field. They are used daily in hematology laboratories for the purpose of recognizing white blood cell images at rates of several thousand pictures per hour.

Cellular logic studies have taken place in several disparate areas: 1) the theoretical analysis of CA's, 2) the investigation of "patterns of growth," 3) the playing of games by computer, and 4) the theoretical and practical analysis of pictures. Although this paper concentrates on item 4), it is important to review some of the associated work connected with items 1)–3).

The original study of CA's was initiated by von Neumann [4], [5] who was particularly interested in CA's where the interconnections of the PE's were to four neighbors only (up, down, left, right). As stated in an essay by Thatcher [6],

> "von Neumann, as the originator of this area of study, was not interested in cellular automata as mathematical objects of study but instead was attempting to find a manageable way of treating in detail the problem of how to make machines reproduce themselves, hoping to shed some light not only on the intrinsic capabilities of machines, but also on the problems of biological self-reproduction."

The work of von Neumann and many other investigators in this field (Thatcher, Moore, Myhill, Ulam, Schrandt, Stein, Holland) [6]–[12] are collected in the book *Essays on Cellular Automata* by Burks [13]. Subsequent to the work reported in this book there has been additional theoretical effort by Banks [14] at M.I.T., Yamada and Amoroso [15] at the University of Pennsylvania and Fort Monmouth, Smith [16]–[19] at Polytechnic Institute of Brooklyn, and Akers [20] at General Electric. Recent work of significance is reported in the IEEE proceedings of a conference on CA [21] and in surveys by Noguchi and Oizumi [22], Nishio [23], and Maruoka [24] in Japan. Still more recent work in the field is that of Rosenfeld and Dyer [25].

II. CELLULAR AUTOMATA

The first large-scale CA was constructed in the early 1960's at Westinghouse, Baltimore, MD, by Slotnick *et al.* [26]. It was called SOLOMON and was a 16×16 computer array. (After building SOLOMON, Slotnick moved to the University

EHO182-6/81/0000/0251 © 1979 IEEE

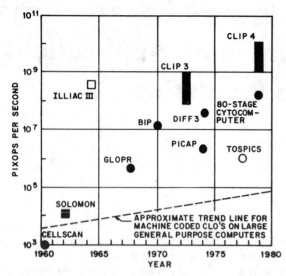

Fig. 1. Pixel operation (pixop) rates for various cellular automata (squares) and cellular logic machines (circles) which are described in the text. Although ILLIAC III was never constructed it was, in concept, a decade ahead of its time. TOSPICS, although not a true cellular automata, is an interesting special case of a new interactive image processing system which executes cellular logic using special purpose hardware and is two orders of magnitude faster than present general purpose computers.

of Illinois where he was involved with the ill-fated ILLIAC IV [27].)

At the same time work involving the processing of bubble chamber photographs both in the United States and United Kingdom led to further work on CA's. McCormick and Narasimhan [28] at the University of Illinois began the design of a pattern-recognition computer which soon became known as ILLIAC III. A few years later Duff *et al.* [29] at University College London began work on a CA consisting of a 20 X 20 array of photodiodes followed by several layers of wired logic for extracting vertices and end-points in processing bubble chamber photographs. The use of signal propagation between cells in the array was applied to evaluating connectivity by Levialdi [30]. This idea was extended by Duff *et al.* [31] in the design of a switchable hardwired diode array. This CA inspired a series of machines called CLIP 1, CLIP 2, CLIP 3, and CLIP 4 which are discussed below.

A. ILLIAC III

The concept of ILLIAC III was a landmark in computer architecture. If construction had been completed, its performance would have exceeded contemporary machines, such as SOLOMON, by several orders of magnitude (see Fig. 1). A general description of ILLIAC III can be found in McCormick [32] where the system is introduced as the first machine capable of processing pictorial information by means of a conceptually new processor called the pattern articulation unit (PAU). The PAU was to be a 32 X 32 by 8-bits three-dimensional structure which could perform "horizontal" (over the 32 X 32 array) CLO operations or "vertical" Boolean operations between PE's belonging to different bit-planes within a 3 X 3 cell. This cell, therefore, was to have included a three-dimensional structure having 9 columns of 8 bits per column. The results of the CLO were to be stored in one of the planes not used during processing by means of an instruction particularly designed for this purpose. (The instruction word for all ILLIAC III commands was to have either three or four 8-bit bytes.)

The main function of the PAU's (of which 25 were meant to be constructed) was to perform local preprocessing so as to produce a labeled graph which could then be extracted as a list structure and syntactically analyzed by what were called taxicrinic units (TU's). The TU's, named after their intended scope, i.e., to "judge the obtained arrangements," would then complete the recognition process. Finally, there was to be an arithmetic unit (AU) and an output complex (OC) designed so as to compute mathematically useful functions (such as three-dimensional reconstruction, statistical analyses, etc.) and to store/display the output from these systems, respectively.

Using 1963 technology an array operation was to have taken 2 μs (propagation across the 32 X 32 array with a delay time of 60 ns/cell). Unfortunately, the entire ILLIAC III was never completed nor have the results of any parallel image processing using the small part of the hardware which was constructed been reported in the literature. The significant fact is to notice that most of the ideas on picture processing using CLO's were suggested by McCormick [33] including the possibility of using both the hexagonal and Cartesian tessellations. In particular it was demonstrated that sequential tracking (for pairing nodes in a graph) can be efficiently achieved by "judicious programming."

B. Cellular Logic Image Processor

Starting from the classical cybernetic approach to vision modeling, Levialdi built some prototype machines to demonstrate the feasibility of feature extraction (as in retinal vision) by means of the simultaneous isotropic propagation of signals from PE's belonging to the input image [30], [34], [35]. In some cases it was found that simulation of such machines was a better approach to the study of the properties of parallel computation on images. An example of this can be seen in the study of problems of connectivity where both a special purpose machine and an algorithm simulation on a sequential computer were compared for the purpose of counting objects [36]. The algorithm operates on a 2 X 2 window and shrinks every 8-connected object into a single isolated element after a number of steps dependent on the longest side of the greatest object [37]. No objects merge or disconnect during this process. Experience gained studying this problem showed the cost advantages and flexibility of simulating parallel algorithms with a sequential computer, although running such algorithms on actual parallel processors gives a better indication of their real effectiveness [38]. Furthermore, the intrinsic architecture of the parallel processor might, in some cases, suggest a different computational approach in solving the same problem.

With the reduction in computer costs brought on by integrated circuit (IC) technology towards the end of the 1960's, University College London started the construction of the Cellular Logic Image Processor (CLIP) family of computers incorporating experience gained in earlier studies by Duff and Levialdi [30], [39], [40]. The CLIP family represents the classic embodiment of von Neuman's original CA.

The basic unit of a CLIP cell (PE) is the two-input binary processor shown in Fig. 2. This PE computes two independent binary outputs, one of which is transmitted to the neighboring cells [41]. The first of the two inputs is the local value of the image element being processed. The second is derived from the outputs of the neighboring cells. In addition to the binary output transmitted to the neighbors, another binary output corresponds to the new image element value to be stored in the cell. In all CLIP machines options are provided for different

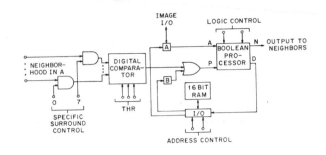

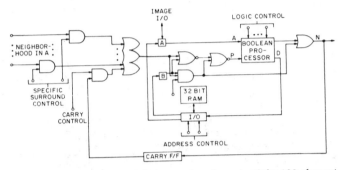

Fig. 2. Block schematics of the processing elements of the 192-element CLIP3 cellular automata and the 9216-element CLIP4 cellular automata. Each processing element has random access memory for storing a multiplicity of pixel values, a neighborhood decoder followed by (in CLIP3 only) a digital comparator, and a general purpose Boolean processor. CLIP4 in addition has arithmetic carry capability.

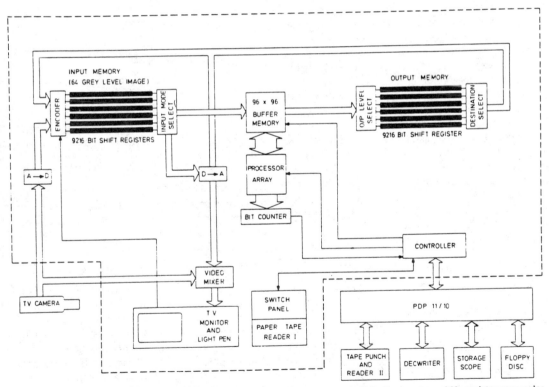

Fig. 3. Block schematics of the entire CLIP4 system including input/output digital converters, shift-register memories, television scanners and display devices, and the control minicomputer.

neighborhoods (4, 6, or 8) as well as for the choice of any required subset of elements belonging to a given neighborhood. Each PE has a storage capacity of from 16 to 32 bits. In CLIP 3, which has been in use since 1973, an elementary operation requires 2 μs, e.g., an operation for contour extraction. Since CLIP 3 is a 16 $\times$ 12 CA, the computation time per pixel operation or "pixop" is 10 ns. The corresponding time for CLIP 4 (a 96 $\times$ 96 array) is 1 ns.

The entire CLIP 4 system is diagrammed in Fig. 3. Images from the video system (camera) pass through an analog–digital converter and encoder and enter six 9216-bit shift registers. Inputs to CLIP 4 are derived from the central area of the video scan. Each pixel is stored as a 6-bit binary word. A number of different modes are provided for selecting data from the full set of gray-scale information available. These are as follows.

1) Threshold Cut: A 6-bit digital comparator is used to threshold the digitized video data so that any pixel value which is greater than (less than) the stored threshold is passed to the array as a binary 1.

2) Level Select: In this mode only those data points having a value identical to the threshold are passed to the array as a binary 1.

3) Bit Select: In order to facilitate rapid transfer of the entire gray-scale picture into array storage, it is possible to select and transfer each of the bit strings individually. Thus in six operations (one for each of the six shift registers) the entire picture can be entered into the array.

4) Control and Programming: The array controller includes a tape reader, from which the program memory is loaded. The program, which includes all necessary input–output (I/O) instructions and register analysis routines, is automatically sequenced by the controller. Certain types of instructions are altered by the state of sense switches on the console and alteration of the states of the switches can be used to control the program sequence. The system is interfaced over the standard PDP Unibus arranged in such a way that the program memory is interfaced to the minicomputer as an extension of core.

The software system for CLIP 4 includes a library of parallel processing routines which can be called in any required sequence by setting an appropriate code on the console sense switches. There are additional programs designed for interactive use with the minicomputer system including programs for compiling, editing, assembling, storage, printing, and various debugging functions. The specific programming language for controlling the action of the PE's on a step-by-step basis consists of a series of load (LD) and process (PR) instructions. LD provides CLIP 4 with the addresses for those 1-bit pixels which are to be used as inputs to the PE as well as the destination address in which the 1-bit result is to be stored. PR indicates the specific neighborhood pattern which is to be gated into each PE and also provides the inputs to the Boolean processor for the purpose of calculating the PE outputs. (In the case of CLIP 3, the PR instruction also provides an input neighborhood threshold value.)

Examples of typical operations are given in the sections below.

III. CELLULAR LOGIC MACHINES

Early investigators of pattern recognition recognized that a two-dimensional parallel processor would eventually become a powerful tool for two-dimensional pattern recognition. Although hardware implementation of two-dimensional processors was out of the question, investigations began in the 1950's by computer simulation of parallel processing by Unger [42], Selfridge [43], Kirsch [45], and Moore [46] and later by Tojo *et al.* [47]–[52]. Most of this work treated binary pictures. Various algorithms for picture processing were introduced heuristically. At that time a systematic investigation of picture processing operations was not performed, but the utility of CLO's in the rapid and simple determination of size, shape, and area of picture components became evident.

The result was that starting in the 1960's, a series of machines was constructed in various laboratories which carried out sequential cellular logic operations by means of special purpose

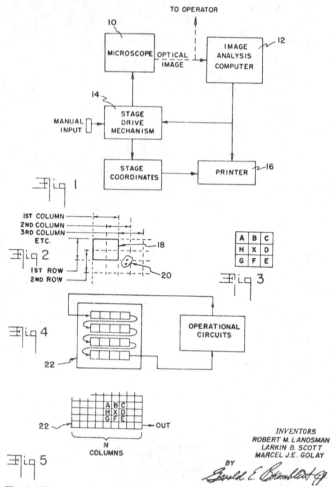

Oct. 26, 1965   R. M. LANDSMAN ETAL   3,214,574

APPARATUS FOR COUNTING BI-NUCLEATE LYMPHOCYTES IN BLOOD

Original Filed Oct. 8, 1959   5 Sheets—Sheet 1

Fig. 4. Figures excerpted from the basic United States patent on cellular logic machines filed in 1959 by M. J. E. Golay, issued in 1965, and assigned to the Perkin-Elmer Corporation.

hardware. These machines were not true CA's in that a single processor (or, at most, a few processors) was used to sequentially operate upon an array of numbers as if these numbers resided in an array of processing elements although, in actuality, they were stored in bulk memory.

A. The CELLSCAN and GLOPR Machines

The first of these machines was built in 1960 by the Navigation Computer Corporation for the Perkin-Elmer Corporation under contract to the University of Rochester. This CLM was called CELLSCAN and has been described both by Preston [52]–[54] and by Izzo and Coles [55] and was the first reduction to practice of the basic cellular logic invention of Golay [56] (see Fig. 4). CELLSCAN stored a binary data field on a continuous 2-track magnetic tape of 19 200 bits and operated as a Turing machine in that it read elements of the field sequentially from the tape and wrote sequentially on the tape elements of a modified 19 200-bit field. The image manipulation logic of CELLSCAN consisted of three control registers, two 60-bit shift registers holding the incoming bits, one 60-bit shift register holding processed bits, and a 9-bit register which operated on a cellular basis (see Fig. 5). The X-bit corresponded to the binary image element being processed. The $A, B, \cdots,$

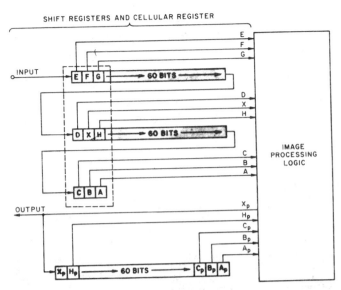

Fig. 5. Block schematic of the image processing logic of CELLSCAN which was the first cellular logic machine built in the United States and was applied to various biomedical image processing problems in 1961-1966. A 63 × 63 1-bit input image flowed through the cellular register (dashed) exactly embodying Golay's patent. Hardwired image processing logic provided only a small number of cellular logic operations (shrinking, inverting, and reduction to residues).

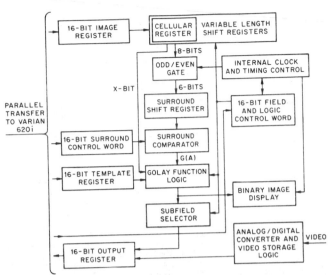

Fig. 6. Block diagram of the GLOPR cellular logic machine built in 1968. Five 16-bit registers were used to transfer image data and control words from a control minicomputer. One of the two control words determined permissible Golay hexagonal neighborhood configurations to be monitored while the other determined subfield order and image size. Two image data registers were used to transfer the A, B, or C data fields while the final register was used for either the D field or the digitized video input.

H bits were the eight immediate neighbors in a square tessellation and were contained in the cellular register. Finally, a 4-bit register was used to hold the A_p, B_p, C_p, and H_p bits which were the processed values corresponding to A, B, C, and H. The shifting action of the registers permitted the image array to "flow" through the cellular register and to be processed in one bit time (the time between appearances of bits at the magnetic tape reading heads). During this operation the control registers were used to perform various counting functions. One control register, called the "timing counter," was used to indicate the start and end of each line in the binary data field. Another register, called the "pass counter," was used to indicate the number of complete cycles of the data field through the cellular register. Programming was carried out from the control console. Only a limited number of CLO's were available: 1) contraction or "shrinking" groups of contiguous bits in the data field, 2) counting isolated bits, i.e., single binary ones surrounded by 8 binary zeros, 3) image complementation or "inversion."

The success of CELLSCAN in the automation of the recognition of images of human white blood cells led to the construction of another and faster CLM the Golay Logic Processor (GLOPR). GLOPR was fabricated by Perkin-Elmer in 1968 [57]. While CELLSCAN was relatively slow (25 ms were required per pixop), GLOPR required only 3 μs and was considerably more flexible. Software options permitted operation in either a 32 × 32, 64 × 64, or 128 × 128 array and performance of essentially all generalized CLO's in the hexagonal tessellation.

The block diagram of the GLOPR computer is shown in Fig. 6. As with CELLSCAN, this computer performs cellular logic on a sequential basis. Integrated circuit shift registers were employed for data storage whose length was electronically variable so as to permit processing data fields in the array sizes mentioned above. The cellular register was arranged in an hexagonal pattern produced by alternately switching the shift register stages selected from line to line. After each shift of

the registers, the 6 bits surrounding the X bit were transferred to a surround shift register which was shifted circularly at 4 MHz. At each shift, the contents of the surround shift register addressed 14 comparators. All possible orientation independent hexagonal patterns were checked. (These 14 patterns, called the "Golay Surrounds," are shown in Fig. 7.)

The GLOPR computer was completely programmable and operated under the control of a minicomputer. The minicomputer was used to pass two 16-bit control words to GLOPR for the purpose of defining the hexagonal patterns to be monitored, the size of the binary data field, the subfield to be selected, and the subfield sequence. In addition to two control word registers, the GLOPR computer contained two additional registers to receive bits from the binary data field stored in the minicomputer and an output register for use in storing the contents of the destination data field. After operating on the entire 16-bits of the data field being addressed, several I/O transfers were initiated so as to store results and obtain more image data from the minicomputer. This added approximately 50 percent overhead to the basic 2-μs computation cycle resulting in an overall allocation of 3 μs for each bit processed. This led to a requirement of 48 ms to process a 128 × 128 data field, 12 ms for 64 × 64, and 3 ms for 32 × 32.

B. Binary Image Processor

The next CLM machine constructed in the United States was the binary image processor (BIP) described by Gray [56]–[60]. BIP is a sequential machine which performs the following computations on two images stored in memory: 1) logical operations on two corresponding picture elements of two images to produce the new value of the corresponding element in the result image, 2) array correlation whose output is the nine correlation counts over a 3 × 3 neighborhood between the two images, and 3) an array analysis of a single image based on a 2 × 2 window. The machine is designed in such a way that the 8 neighborhood is processed in pipeline fashion. Thus BIP can be considered as a nearly parallel 3 × 3 window for specific

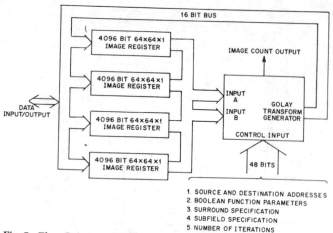

Fig. 7. The Golay transform processor of the diff3 contains four 64 × 64 1-bit image memories interfaced to the transform generator which services 8 pixels and their neighborhoods simultaneously. A full image processing cycle requires 100 µs (25 ns/pixop) and is executed under control of the associated minicomputer.

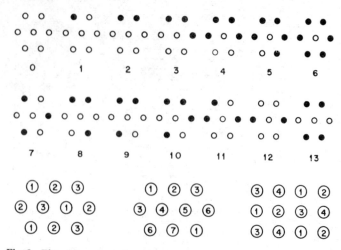

Fig. 8. The 14 orientation-independent Golay neighborhood configurations in the hexagonal tessellation (upper two rows) and subfield assignments for Golay's subfields of 3 and 6 and Preston's Cartesian subfield of 4 (lower row).

binary operations having two inputs and one output. At maximum speed (image correlation mode) the time for one pixop is 20 ns.

Although BIP was primarily designed for binary image processing, it may also operate on gray-valued images and perform arithmetic operations on pairs of arrays by means of a bit-plane representation of the data. As with GLOPR it is considerably faster than a conventional computer in that it may initiate the processing of thousands of data bits by means of one instruction. BIP is part of an overall system for use in alpha numeric data processing and storage called GRAPHIX I made by Information International Incorporated.

C. PICAP

A still more recent machine and the first system to be built outside of the United States is the University of Linkoping PICAP System. PICAP is based on the GLOPR and BIP principles of using special purpose peripherals in conjunction with a general purpose minicomputer. This system has been described by Kruse [61], [62]. The core of the machine is an array processor operating on a 3 × 3 neighborhood having a set of 9 shift registers each 4 bits wide and 4096 bits long capable of storing one picture of 64 × 64 pixels. The basic operation time for obtaining a transformation of a full picture is 2.6 ms. PICAP is, therefore, five times faster than GLOPR but four times slower than BIP. As in GLOPR and BIP, the cellular logic operation is performed by matching the states of each 3 × 3 cell with a given configuration or configurations in order to compute the new value of the picture element. Whereas GLOPR and BIP can process two images simultaneously, PICAP can conduct CLO's on multiple pictures and can store as many as nine images in picture registers. In this mode the states of the elements that are the 3 × 3 neighbors in the former mode will now be the states of the corresponding elements (along the same vertical crossing of all picture planes) of the different operand pictures. Logical operations on binary images may be expanded to arithmetic operations in PICAP on gray-value images with the possibility of iterating a given transformation until a certain register has zero content. PICAP also has the provisions of operating on larger than 3 × 3 neighborhood by using covering procedures.

PICAP uses a minicomputer for controlling what is called

the parallel processing machine (PPM) along with an input image digitizer. The full system includes the minicomputer, the PPM, input devices (flying-spot scanner and 4 telecameras), output devices (2 television monitors), a 512 × 512 picture memory, and a 10-Mbyte disk. The programming of PICAP may be done in Fortran since subroutines in the PICAP code may be used by means of CALL statements.

D. diff3

In the interval 1973–1976 Perkin-Elmer undertook the commercialization of GLOPR and incorporated it in a clinical white blood cell image analyzing machine called "diff3" (see Section VI). Fig. 7 shows a block diagram of the Golay Transform Processor (GTP) which is implemented as part of the diff3. The GTP, although technically structured as a peripheral device to a general purpose computer, is in truth an autonomous processor for manipulating two-dimensional data. In the configuration used in the diff3, the GTP includes four 1-bit image registers each organized as a 64 × 64 bit array connected to the transform generator by a 16-bit bus. As many as two of the four images may be used as inputs, labeled *A* and *B*, to produce a single image output.

Control of the image processor is via a set of control words from a minicomputer. Five separate functions are specified: 1) the binary image register designations (6 bits of control data), 2) the Boolean function specification which supports all possible combinations of data from the *A* and *B* images with the designated Golay surround(s), 3) the surround specification (14 bits, one for each surround), 4) the number of iterations for which a given transform is to be performed (5 bits are used to request from 1 to 63 iterations with an additional bit to specify iteration until the image stabilizes), 5) a subfield specification which, in the diff3, supports subfields of one (i.e., the entire field in parallel) and subfields of three (see Fig. 8). In practice, this control information is passed as three 16-bit words in order to make the transform generator compatible with a 16-bit minicomputer.

Control of the image processor requires three I/O operations to load the registers and at the end of the cycle a separate I/O operation to read back to them. The transform iterations are performed at the rate of 100 µs/cycle (25 ns/pixop). During this time the control computer is free to perform other func-

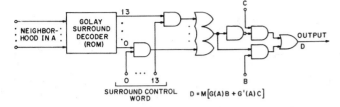

Fig. 9. The 14 Golay neighborhood configurations are simultaneously decoded in diff3 using 8 READ-ONLY MEMORIES operating in parallel whose outputs are used to compute the Golay transform. The full Golay transform processor in diff3 is comprised of 8 of the above processing elements.

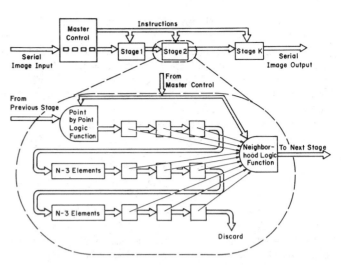

Fig. 10. Block schematic of the pipeline cellular logic machine being constructed by the ERIM. With approximately eighty stages in the pipeline this machine (the "cytocomputer") will have a pixop time of 8 ns.

tions, as the image transform generator operates completely autonomously once the specifications have been provided to it.

The only direct output from the transform generator to the control computer is a result count. This is available at the end of each iteration of a transform and provides a count of all one bits in the image resulting from that transform. Again, this value is provided in a 16-bit register for compatibility with 16-bit minicomputer architectures.

Fig. 9 shows the circuitry in the GTP which is used for detecting surround configurations to produce the so called "Golay function" $G(A)$ of image A. This function is defined as being true at any point in the image where one of the specified surround configurations is present. In order to detect the presence of the Golay surrounds, a ROM containing sixty-four 14-bit words is used. The address lines to the ROM are the 6 bits of the surround being processed from image A. The output for each request is a 14-bit word containing a single binary one at the location corresponding to the surround configuration present on the address lines. These 14-bit words are compared in a set of fourteen "AND" gates with the surround specification. The fourteen results are "ORed" together to produce the Golay function. There are eight such circuits in the configuration of the image processor used in the diff3 so that eight pixels are processed in parallel. These circuits, therefore, must operate at twice the clock rate of the shifting done on the basic 16-bit bus.

The final stage of computing the Golay transform is performed in a set of eight combinational logic circuits. Inputs to this consist of the eight center bits from image A and the center bits from image B. This logic calculates the specified function and outputs the data on a 16-bit bus connecting to the destination image register. Finally, as this data is output, a set of eight counters is used to keep track of the total bit count in the destination image. At the end of the complete transform cycle, the results of these counters are added together to produce the final output count for the entire transformed image.

E. Current Efforts

There are several current CLM programs which are not yet fully described in the literature either in their structural aspects or as to results obtained on specific image processing programs. Several of these projects are outlined briefly below.

1) Cytocomputer: For the past four years the Environmental Research Institute of Michigan (ERIM) has been investigating the use of cellular logic in image analysis as applied to aerial photographs. ERIM is now constructing a CLM, called the "cytocomputer," which is structured in a serial pipeline configuration. Each PE in the pipeline is a fully table-driven CLM

designed to operate on either the 4, 6, or 8 neighborhood. Each PE in the pipeline operates in 650 ns and passes the result of its CLO to a 1024-stage, 4-bit shift register. The cytocomputer now being constructed will consist of approximately 80 stages so that the time per pixop is 8 ns (further increases in speed are possible by simply adding additional stages).

The cytocomputer is interfaced to the MIDAS computer system at ERIM which down-loads both instructions and images to the cytocomputer and receives the result once the pipeline operations are completed. Pictures are entered into the cytocomputer in a line-scanned format and progress through the pipeline at real-time rates. Following an initial delay to fill the pipeline, images can be processed at the same rate at which they are scanned (Fig. 10).

2) The Flexible Processor: Another pipeline machine is the Control Data Corporation (CDC) Flexible Processor. This machine is not designed specifically as a CLM but can be programmed to carry out CLM-like operations. The Flexible Processor was initially designed for use in change detection as applied to synthetic aperture radar imagery [62]. It has also been used for change detection for the purpose of locating lesions in chest radiographs.

Each stage in the Flexible Processor pipeline is a complete central processing unit consisting of a fast arithmetic logic unit and hardware multiplier plus microcoded instructions for certain specialized operations such as calculating the square root. The operation cycle per pixop thus varies considerably depending upon the exact instructions to be executed.

3) The STARAN Parallel Computer: In the early 1970's the Goodyear Aerospace Corporation developed a general-purpose array processor as a high-speed peripheral to a host computer. The primary feature of this processor is the memory array which consists of up to 32 multidimensional access memories each consisting of 256 256-bit words. Many access modes are available to these words thus permitting a machine to address its memory as a $32 \times 256 \times 256$ array.

In addition to the array there is both a control memory and a unit which permits parallel I/O to the host computer.

Although STARAN was not designed specifically for image processing, some results have appeared in the literature [63] which treat this application.

A STARAN at the (NASA) Johnson Space Center is currently in use for a variety of image processing tasks in conjunction with the Large Area Crop Inventory Experiment (LACIE) project. As with the Flexible Processor, it is difficult to make speed comparisons with a true CLM but typical operations mentioned in the literature require a few microseconds per pixop.

4) Distributed Array Processor: Another machine featuring parallelism is the distributed array processor (DAP) which consists of a 32 X 32 array of processing elements. The available memory in each element is 1K (expandable to 2K). Both logic and arithmetic capabilities are provided by means of three 1-bit registers and a 1-bit full adder.

As with STARAN there is an interface to a host computer with a master control unit used to decode instructions (32 bits long) from this machine. Incoming data may be stored with successive bits in successive store locations belonging to each processing element. The speed of operation is based on a cycle time of 200 ns. Typical applications envisaged for DAP are in meteorology, many-body simulation, table look-up, data management, and pattern matching. As an example of computational speed the literature reports that the replacement of every element of a matrix by its modulus takes approximately 1 μs [64].

5) Toshiba Image Processing System: Of particular interest is the Toshiba Image Processing System (TOSPICS) which is specifically designed for high-speed interactive image processing. This machine consists of a host minicomputer, a parallel processor, and image I/O devices. One feature of interest is that the host computer may be bypassed and the data flow from the input device directed through the parallel processor and thence to an output device via intermediate image memories. Although not as fast as the true CLM's described above, TOSPICS is far more flexible in its repetoire of image processing operations.

The input image source is a high-precision flying-spot scanner having 32768 X 32768 addressable points (4096 X 4096 resolution) which generates data at 10 Mbytes/s. This data may be processed in real time by the parallel processor which operates in a pipeline configuration permitting 64 multiplications, 64 additions (or subtractions), and 256 data transfers to be executed in the basic pixop time which 1μs. As can be seen from Fig. 1 TOSPICS is about two orders of magnitude faster than a high-performance general purpose computer installation. The literature [65]–[68] reports applications in remote sensing picture processing, medical image analysis, and character recognition.

6) Floating Point Systems: Finally, we should note the availability of certain high-speed peripherals such as the Floating Point Systems, Inc., AP-120B Array Processor. This machine has been commercially available since 1974. A single instruction can initiate various tasks simultaneously such as a) floating-point addition, b) floating-point multiplication, c) conditional branching, and d) a memory fetch or store. This results in the performance of each one of these tasks in a pipeline fashion in a time of 167 ns. The word length utilized in AP-120B is 64 bits. The machine can be considered as a peripheral to either a large computer or minicomputer which speeds up computational power in those cases where the number of data array transfers are small with respect to the computations required on the arrays. An example of the power of this machine is that it performs a 1024-point Fourier transform in 3 ms.

IV. THEORETICAL BACKGROUND

A cellular automaton (CA) is a regular two-dimensional array of a finite number of identical interconnected processing elements (PE's), each of which is comprised of both logic and storage circuits. Elements in the interior of the array are, normally, connected to their immediate neighbors, whereas edge elements are provided with hardwired special interconnections under program control. Although initially arrays of this kind were proposed to process both numerical and nonnumerical data, in practice such an array is particularly useful when structured data is considered, e.g., a digital image in which the pictorial information is contained in the optical density of the individual picture elements (pixels) and in their spatial relationships (context). There is a one-to-one correspondence between the pixels and the PE's of the CA so that the dimensions of the array of picture elements and of the CA are identical. It is for this reason that CA's have been suggested, designed, and built with various internal structures with the intention of providing general purpose image processing devices (see Section III). The logic structure of each element of the array can be determined by means of an external control signal (which identically controls every element of the array). A CA together with its control unit can be seen as a single instruction multiple data stream (SIMDS) machine [69] and, therefore, as a stored memory computer specially suited for image processing. The value of each pixel is stored in the memory of the corresponding array cell. Two images $\mathfrak{A}$, $\mathfrak{B}$ may be considered to be simultaneously present on the CA; such images are formed by the values of their corresponding pixels which will be called a_{xy} b_{xy}, respectively. The subindices xy stand for the Cartesian coordinates of each pixel within the image so that $\mathfrak{A} = \{a_{xy}\}$, $\mathfrak{B} = \{b_{xy}\}$ for $1 \leqslant x$, $y \leqslant l$ if l is the side of a square CA.

A. The Cellular Logic Array as a Turing Machine

There have been different approaches to the formalization of a CA. Moore [7] defined the CA by means of the quintuple (X, Y, Q, F, β) where X is a set representing the input states; Y the output states; Q the internal states; F the next-state function; β, the mapping of Q into Y. Smith [16]–[19] reduced Moore's notation to the triple (G, d, N) and assumed that the CA is "uniform" which means that each cell has the same neighborhood. In Smith's notation G is the automaton having transition function F; d is the dimension; N is the neighborhood index. Yamada and Amoroso [15] used the quadruple (A, E^d, X, I) where A is the "finite" set of states of each automata in a Euclidean space E of dimension d; X is an n-tuple defining the neighborhood of the cell; I specifies which of the possible transition functions F are feasible in the particular automata considered. Finally, Codd [70] uses the triple (V, v_0, F) to define the automaton. In Codd's notation V (as with A and Q, above) specifies the set of cellular states; v_0 is a specific element of V called the "quiescent state"; F is the transition function from V^t into V^{t+1}, where t is the transition time. It is not easy to choose a formal description of the CA which is at the same time general enough while still possessing features which clearly identify the functions which an array of this kind may implement through adequate programming. Since any finite state machine can always be described in terms of a Turing machine, this approach will be taken here with particular emphasis on the special properties which strictly belong to those CA's in which each cell may be considered as a PE. The internal states of a PE will be called $\mathfrak{s}^t_{xy}$ where the superscript indicates a given instant of time (along a discrete time scale) while the subscript refers to the Cartesian coordinates of the specific PE that is considered within the CA.

The internal state of a PE depends on the values of five independent variables, namely

$$\mathfrak{s}^t_{xy} = \{(a, b, c)_{xy}, w, z,\}^t. \qquad (4.1)$$

The first three variables might differ from element to element whilst the last two are equal for all PE's at any given time and may be considered as instructions. The variable "a" represents the binary value of the pixel of the input image; "b," the value of a corresponding pixel of a second image (which is not necessarily present in every computation); "c," a function of the output values of neighboring PE's (or of a subset of these values) and a given threshold; (w) and (z), considered as the values of the instructions. The CA will change the internal state of all PE's at a given instant of time in a synchronous and deterministic fashion by means of the application of a next-state function F. Moreover, the output state of each PE is obtained after each new state is reached and is described in terms of the values of $\mathcal{O}_{xy} = (a', c')_{xy}$ which are indexed according to the position of the PE within the CA. The variable a' represents the output binary value of the new pixel while the variable c' is the value of the output signal which is sent to all the specified neighboring PE's.

In conclusion, the function of a CA is described in terms of a sequence of internal states $\mathfrak{s}_{xy} = \{\mathfrak{s}^0, \mathfrak{s}^1, \cdots, \mathfrak{s}^t\}_{xy}$ for any general PE with xy coordinates, having as input five variables and producing at the output a state $\mathcal{O}_{xy}$ containing the values of two Boolean variables. Such an operation, independently and simultaneously computed on all the PE's of the CA, will be called a cellular logic operation (CLO) and may be iterated in time. For control purposes the contents of the array may be tested until such contents are empty (or, arbitrarily, full). At this moment the CA may be instructed to stop the computation.

Following this description, the computation of successive CLO's may be represented by the application of the next-state function F at time $t = 0$ on the input states $\mathfrak{s}^0_{xy}$ (for all PE's). Such PE's have output states $\mathcal{O}^0_{xy}$ and, after the CLO is computed, the output states will become $\mathcal{O}^1_{xy}$ (for $t = 1$). The iteration of such a computation on the whole CA will produce $\mathcal{O}^2_{xy}, \mathcal{O}^3_{xy}, \cdots,$ for all successive instants of time during which the CA is in operation. In practice, for $t = 0$, $F \to (\mathfrak{s}^0_{xy}, \mathcal{O}^0_{xy}) \to \mathcal{O}^1_{xy}$ and, for $t = 1$, $F \to (\mathfrak{s}^1_{xy}, \mathcal{O}^1_{xy}) \to \mathcal{O}^2_{xy}$, and so on so that, after t instants of time, $F \to (\mathfrak{s}^t_{xy}, \mathcal{O}^t_{xy}) \to \mathcal{O}^{t+1}_{xy}$.

B. Partitioning the Image Plane

In order to spatially digitize an image, a tessellation is preferred so that a number of similar polygons come together at a point. Letting the number of polygons be n, there are only three geometrically possible values for n (6, 4, 3) which correspond to the hexagonal, orthogonal, and triangular tessellations, respectively. Nonregular tessellations have been discussed by Sklansky [71] and other authors, but are difficult to handle from the point of view of the design of CA hardware.

The choice of the value of n will be influenced by the complexity of the interconnection structure and by the various topological and perceptual consequences of the resulting image representations. Various authors have considered the use of triangular arrays, but this tessellation produces, in some algorithms, a larger computing time and a less satisfactory image representation despite some theoretical interest [72], [73].

Hexagonal arrays have also been investigated since 1963 by McCormick [28] but the most important practical implementation was made after Golay [56] and Preston [74]. The main reason for introducing the hexagonal tessellation is that all elements are equidistant in the Euclidean sense from their six immediate neighbors, while this is not true in the orthogonal tessellation. In an orthogonal array every element has four neighbors at distance one and four neighbors at distance $\sqrt{2}$. In order to avoid the so called "connectivity paradox" [75] connectedness between cells in an orthogonal array may be defined as follows: Two cells are 4-connected if one of them is either a horizontal or a vertical neighbor of the other (any cell of the pair might be chosen since connectivity is a commutative property). Two cells are 8-connected if one of them is either a horizontal, vertical, or diagonal neighbor of the other.

For the representation of line drawings the hexagonal array has three principal directions while the orthogonal array has four, including the diagonal directions. In particular, the vertical straight lines on the orthogonal array seem perceptually more satisfactory than on the hexagonal array since in real scene analysis there is a natural predominancy of vertical structures. This last point appears to be a drawback for the use of the hexagonal tessellation.

A general theory of the geometrical properties of discrete binary images has been developed [76]. Since gray-level images may be thresholded to yield binary images then most results obtained by such a theory can be also used on judiciously thresholded gray-level images. Many features contained in multilevel images sometimes required arithmetical computations and the design of special purpose algorithms for their efficient extraction, regardless of whether the machine is serial or parallel. Moreover, it has been shown in practice that many image processing tasks could not be easily described in terms of the general theory so that, even if parts of the problem could be solved, a solution for the complete problem was still not within reach.

C. The Extended Neighborhood

Most of the theoretical work on cellular automata treat CA's with N^4 (von Neuman neighborhood) or N^8 (Moore neighborhood). This causes no loss of generality because any CA with an arbitrary neighborhood can be shown to be equivalent to the one with N^4 or N^8 with respect to its computing capability [70], [71], [77]. The size of the neighborhood, the number of the machine states, and the computation time (the number of programming steps) required to recognize (to accept or to reject) a given input (image) are in complementary relation in some sense with each other. Thus for a given automaton with the neighborhood $N^n (n \geqslant 9)$, it is possible to synthesize the equivalent automaton with N^4 and N^8 and an increased number of machine states.

In practical applications, on the other hand, the size of the neighborhood is selected considering many factors such as convenience of design and performance evaluation, computing time, the ease of hardware and software implementation. In fact, as is obvious, the fundamental idea of a neighborhood consisting of a fixed number of pixels is completely arbitrary as the decision as to which pixels are "neighbors" depends on the resolution (sampling interval) at which the original image was scanned. Hence, CLO's with different sizes of neighborhoods will be presented in this section. Such CLO's are considered as the subclass of the operations known as linear and nonlinear two-dimensional spatial filters. Thus a brief explanation of the basic properties of the filtering is necessary to help the reader understand how the specific types of CLO's shown in this section have been selected and how they work.

1) Basic Notations and Concepts: Filtering is the operation F deriving the output image $\mathcal{O}^{t+1}$, from the input image $\mathcal{I}^t$ (or the transformation of $\mathcal{I}$ into $\mathcal{O}$) defined by the following equation:

$$F: \mathcal{I} \to \mathcal{O}, \mathcal{O}_{xy}^{t+1} = F(\mathcal{I}_{xy}^t) \quad \mathcal{I}_{xy}^t = \{S_{pq}^t; \ (p,q) \in N_{xy}\} \quad (4.1)$$

where S_{pq}^t is the value of the picture element having coordinates p, q in the neighborhood N_{xy} and F is a multivariate function. (See Fig. 11.) The most common example of N_{xy} is the rectangle

$$R_{xy}^{KL} = \{(p,q); \ x - L1 \leqslant p \leqslant x + L2, y - K1 \leqslant q \leqslant y + K2\}. \quad (4.2)$$

If $L = K = 3$, where $L = L1 + L2 + 1$ and $K = K1 + K2 + 1$, then we have the Moore neighborhood N^8, of the pixel (x, y).

Let the notation $\mathcal{O} = F(\mathcal{I})$ present that $\mathcal{O}$ is the output of the filter F applied to the input picture $\mathcal{I}$. If the function F is linear, the filter is called the linear filter (LF); otherwise, the nonlinear filter. The linear filter $L(W)$ is given as follows:

$$L(W): \mathcal{I}_{xy}^t \to \mathcal{O}_{xy}^{t+1}, \mathcal{O}_{xy}^{t+1} = \sum_{p=x-L1}^{x+L2} \sum_{q=y-K1}^{y+K2} \omega_{p+L1-x+1, \, q+K1-y+1}$$

$$\cdot S_{pq}^t \quad (4.3)$$

where $W = \{\omega_{pq}^{LK}\}$ is called the weight matrix. If all of ω_{pq} are equal to the same constant such as 1 or $1/LK$ we call the filter the uniform weight smoothing filter (UWSF) and represent it by $S[L1, L2; K1, K2]$. Although filters with arbitrary values of the ω_{pq} are not CLO's, we consider that any filter is a CLO where the values of the ω_{pq} are the same or are of only two different values.

2) Difference Filter, Range Filter, and Bridge Filter: When the value of the function F depends on the differences between the values of S_{pq} or between functions of the values of S_{pq}, the filter is called the difference filter (DF).

Two DF's which are of importance are $D_1[L1, L2; K1, K2]$, and $D_2[L1, L2; K1, K2]$ which are defined as follows.

$$D_1[L1, L2; K1, K2]: \mathcal{I} \to \mathcal{O}, \mathcal{O}_{xy}^{t+1} = \mathcal{I}_{x+L2, \, y+K2}^t - \mathcal{I}_{x-L1, \, y-K1}^t,$$

$$D_2[L1, L2; K1, K2]: \mathcal{I} \to \mathcal{O}, \mathcal{O}_{xy}^{t+1} = \mathcal{I}_{x+L2, \, y+K2}^t - 2\mathcal{I}_{xy}^t$$

$$+ \mathcal{I}_{x-L1, \, x-K1}^t. \quad (4.4)$$

In practical cases, $D_1[L1, L2; K1, K2]$ and $D_2[L1, L2; K1, K2]$ are usually applied to the smoothed version of an input image in order to suppress the effect of random noise.

Another important filter is called the range filter $RF[L, K]$ defined as follows [78]:

$$RF[K, L]: \mathcal{I} \to \mathcal{O}, \mathcal{O}_{xy}^{t+1} = \max \{\mathcal{I}_{kl}^t - \mathcal{I}_{mn}^t; (k, l), (m, n)$$

$$\in R_{xy}^{LK}\}$$

$$= \max \{\mathcal{I}_{kl}; (k, l) \in R_{xy}^{LK}\}$$

$$- \min \{\mathcal{I}_{kl}; (k, l) \in R_{xy}^{LK}\}. \quad (4.5)$$

Next, assume that three filters L_1, L_2, and L_3 are given, where

$$\mathcal{O} = L_k(\mathcal{I})\mathcal{O}_{xy}^{t+1} = l_k(\mathcal{I}_{kxy}^t), \mathcal{I}_{kxy}^t = \{S_{pq}^t; (p, q) \in N_{kxy}\},$$

$$k = 1, 2, 3. \quad (4.6)$$

Then the filter L_3 is said to be a serial composition L_1 and L_2

SIMPLE (MOORE) NEIGHBORHOOD

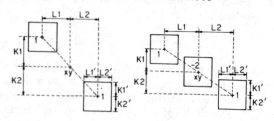

$SD_1[K1', K2'; L1', L2'; K1, K2; L1, L2] \quad SD_2[K1', K2'; L1', L2'; K1, K2; L1, L2]$

EXTENDED NEIGHBORHOOD

Fig. 11. The simple Moore 3 × 3 neighborhood (above) and the extended neighborhoods of Toriwaki (below).

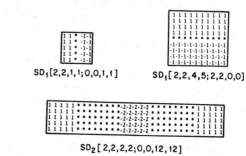

$SD_1[2,2,1,1;0,0,1,1] \qquad SD_1[2,2,4,5;2,2,0,0]$

$SD_2[2,2,2,2;0,0,12,12]$

Fig. 12. Weighting functions for certain typical versions of the linear smoothing difference filter $SD_k[K1', K2'; L1', L2': K1, K2; L1, L2]$, $k = 1, 2$.

[79] and is represented as $L_3 = L_2 \cdot L_1$, if the following relation holds:

$$\mathcal{O} = L_3(\mathcal{I}) = L_2(L_1(\mathcal{I})), \quad \text{for } \mathcal{I} \in P$$

where P is the set of all input pictures. In other words, $L_3 = L_2 \cdot L_1$ means that the sequential application of the filter L_1 followed by the filter L_2 is equivalent to the single filtering by L_3. It can be shown that, given two arbitrary filters L_1 and L_2, there exists the filter L_3 such that $L_3 = L_2 \cdot L_1$. (Note that it does not necessarily follow that $L_3 = L_1 \cdot L_2$.)

It has been found that the serial composition of the smoothing filter and either of the difference filters, which are called the linear smoothing difference filters (LSDF) of the first and the second order, are more important than either filter used alone. They are represented as $SD_1[L1', L2'; K1', K2': L1, L2; K1, K2]$ and $SD_2[L1', L2'; K1', K2': L1, L2; K1, K2]$ and defined as follows [80]:

$$SD_k[L1', L2'; K1', K2': L1, L2; K1, K2]$$

$$= S[L1', L2'; K1', K2']$$

$$\cdot D_k[L1, L2; K1, K2], \quad k = 1, 2. \quad (4.7)$$

The span of the coordinates pq is illustrated in Fig. 11 while the corresponding weight matrices are shown in Fig. 12. $D_2[L1, L2; K1, K2]$ and $SD_2[L1', L2'; K1', K2': L1, L2; K1, K2]$ have been named the bridge filter [80], [81] after their physical interpretation.

D. Propagation

In most cellular automata theory it is assumed that the individual automata (PE's) make their transitions in synchronism at time t. It is also assumed that the set of automata in the array sequence through a series of "configurations" given by $c_0, c_1, \cdots, c_t, \cdots$ in the notation of Codd [70] who calls this sequence a "propagation," and symbolizes it by $\langle c_0 \rangle$. This points to a particularly important use of the CA or CLM in image processing, i.e., using a large set of CLO's to make global changes in the initial image ($\mathcal{I}^0$) for the purpose of feature extraction. Clearly, in order that the propagation of a signal to 2nd, 3rd, $\cdots$, nth nearest neighbors take place, one of the initial inputs must be different from zero. This is a necessary but not sufficient condition in order to send a signal to the PE's neighborhood by means of a suitable F function.

Both directional and omnidirectional propagation can be effected by means of a particular choice of w and z in (4.1). A propagation signal can be stopped by a specific value of the "a" variable in (4.1) or the propagation signal can be made to continue through the PE's if the "a" variable is not contained in the logical expression of F. Finally, a propagation can also be stopped either by ending the CLO computations or when all the available cells have been reached by the propagation signal. Edge PE's can be conditioned so that the propagation may be mirror-like reflected or toroidally continued on the opposite edge. Logical inconsistencies in the truth table for F lead to oscillations of the contents of the CLA.

After each CLO is computed, the new value of the variable a (namely a') will be obtained for each pixel and, depending on the program, a new value of c' will also be obtained. In some cases $c' = a$ and is therefore invariant during a CLO. There are many CLO's which do not produce significant results unless they are applied iteratively until some kind of limit state is reached. Consider, for an example, the following CLO:

$$g_{xy} = \min \{a_{xy}, a_{x-1,\,y}, a_{x,\,y-1}, a_{x+1,\,y}, a_{x,\,y+1}\} + b_{xy}$$

where $\mathcal{A} = \{a_{xy}\}$ and $\mathcal{B} = \{b_{xy}\}$ are two input pictures. Assume that the picture $\mathcal{F} = \{f_{xy}\}$ is given where $f_{ij} \geqslant 0$, and that the picture $\mathcal{G}^{t+1}$ is generated by applying the above operator iteratively, that is

$$\mathcal{G}^{t+1} = \{g_{xy}^{t+1}\}$$

$$g_{xy}^{t+1} = \min \{g_{xy}^t, g_{x-1,\,y}^t, g_{x,\,y-1}^t, g_{x+1,\,y}^t, g_{x,\,y+1}^t\} + f_{xy},$$
$$t = 0, 1, 2, 3, \cdots. \quad (4.8)$$

$$g_{xy}^0 = \begin{cases} M, & \text{if } f_{xy} > 0 \\ 0, & \text{if } f_{xy} = 0 \end{cases} \quad (4.9)$$

where M is a sufficiently large constant.

The sequence of pictures $\{\mathcal{G}^t; t = 0, 1, 2, 3, \cdots\}$ converges to the gray weighted distance transformation (GWDT) [82] first introduced by Levi and Montanari [83]. The number of times that the iteration is required to obtain the limit picture depends on the input picture $\mathcal{F}$ but will always be finite. Application of this CLO once produces no significant result.

E. Arithmetic CLO's

It is possible to combine specific CLO's so that all the basic arithmetic operations may be carried out. A particular set of CLO's may be selected according to the number representation system which has been chosen in the CA so as to implement addition or subtraction, a multiplication, or a division. Three

possible systems may be used for representing numbers within a CA [84]. Some or all of them may be used in most practical machines based on the cellular array concept. Consider the CA as an $l \times l$ array of PE's each having memory which may be represented by a set of 1-bit storage planes ($l \times l \times 1$ fields) $\mathcal{S}$. The first system uses each column of an $\mathcal{S}$ plane to store, in binary form, the number to be represented so that l numbers with l significant bits will be contained in the plane. Negative numbers are stored in two's complement form and empty columns will represent zeros. The second system considers a number of $\mathcal{S}$ planes ($\mathcal{S}_1, \mathcal{S}_2, \mathcal{S}_3, \cdots, \mathcal{S}_k$) each one representing one bit of a number which is binary coded in column form (these columns are perpendicular to the storage planes). According to this scheme l^2 numbers will be stored each one having its least significant bit in plane $\mathcal{S}_1$ and its most significant bit in plane $\mathcal{S}_k$. This system is generally used for the representation of gray-level images where the number of pixels is l^2 and the number of planes required to store N gray levels is $\log_2 N$. This system is known in the literature as the bit-plane system. The last system, which is typically used for displaying histograms, considers that the number of 1-elements present in each column of the CLA (or of an $\mathcal{S}$-plane) directly represents the number in linear form. As in the first system only l numbers may be stored.

It is outside the scope of this paper to explain in detail the way in which all arithmetic operations may be performed. If the first representation (of numbers) is chosen, then a binary column incrementation will be used for counting the number of 1-elements present in each column of the CA (or on the other hand, the bit-plane system is used, a "vertical column" incrementation will take place. If the linear column system is used, then a suitable set of CLO's will inject 1-elements from the bottom row (whenever such elements are present in the corresponding columns) and, in practice, the column will shift upwards each time a 1-element is added. The bottom element corresponds to the least significant bit while the top element (upmost 1-element) will correspond to the maximum significant bit.

A general description of the incrementation (adding a 1) or of the addition (adding any two numbers) and subtraction has been presented by Cordella *et al.* [85]. The specific coding of these algorithms in the language designed for CLIP machines has been described by Duff [84]. Both negative and positive numbers may be entered by means of the use of the topmost element (in a vertical column) in much the same way as the sign is indicated with a "sign bit" in a computer word. Moreover, floating point arithmetic may be implemented by means of two planes which will contain the fractional part and the exponent part of each number. The bit-plane representation is also possible by assigning a plane for each bit of the fractional part and another plane to each bit of the exponent.

V. FUNDAMENTAL SEQUENCES OF CELLULAR LOGIC OPERATIONS

This section is concerned with a description of the fundamental operations (CLO's) which may be performed with the CA in analyzing images. Note that the most complex algorithms implemented on a CA are built by means of a sequence of elementary CLO's which may truly be called general purpose. Their generality stems from the fact that they are all based on a local computation and that although using 1-bit images, they may be employed to process multilevel images by appropriate thresholding operations.

Any computation on a CA may be described by a succession of CLO's which ends after a finite time. The temporal repetition of a given CLO may depend either on the specific program specification (the number of times a certain instruction should be iterated) or on the context (the data contained in the CA) which will stop the iteration when, for instance, elements having particular values (edge elements, contents of an array, etc.) are met during the computation. The total computation which will generate the outcome may always be considered as the result of applying for a certain number of times a sequence of CLO's having fixed local neighborhoods. As is shown below, many properties of the image may be detected by means of a suitable sequence of CLO's.

Below, only the square tessellation will be considered and a 3×3 neighborhood (N^8) will be used for all the CLO's included in the examples. It is hoped that extensions to other neighborhoods will be obvious to the reader. Note that the N^8 CLO can be regarded as isotropic if it is equal in its effect in each of the four array directions. For instance an isotropic CLO edge extractor would be made by the following four configurations:

$$
\begin{array}{ccc}
\begin{matrix} 1 & 1 & 1 \\ 0 & 0 & 0 \\ 0 & 0 & 0 \end{matrix} &
\begin{matrix} 1 & 0 & 0 \\ 1 & 0 & 0 \\ 1 & 0 & 0 \end{matrix} &
\begin{matrix} 0 & 0 & 1 \\ 0 & 0 & 1 \\ 0 & 0 & 1 \end{matrix} &
\begin{matrix} 0 & 0 & 0 \\ 0 & 0 & 0 \\ 1 & 1 & 1 \end{matrix} \\
\text{(a)} & \text{(b)} & \text{(c)} & \text{(d)}
\end{array}
$$

Conversely, if a horizontal edge is to be extracted an anisotropic CLO is required which will be made only by (a) and (d) configurations.

In the following sections, three different types of sequences will be considered: Type I, the unit sequence consisting of a single CLO; Type II, the same CLO repeated a number of times; Type III, the sequence consisting of a string of more than one kind of CLO, which string may itself be repeated. Sequences may be terminated either after a predetermined number of iterations (data independent) or by means of a test based on the contents of an array (data dependent). Point by point Boolean operations (AND, OR, ···) between two images *A* and *B* are examples of Type I. Another example of a Type I CLO is the extraction of the contour of a 1-bit image where the 1-elements of the output image must satisfy the logical condition of having at least one 8-adjacent neighbor belonging to the "background" (the set of 0-elements). An example of a Type II sequence is the extraction of a connected object from a field of many objects when a marker for the object exists. An example of Type III sequence is the extraction of a connected object from a field containing many other objects when no marker exists.

A. Data Independent Operations

Boolean operations between 1-bit images produce obvious results and are not discussed here in detail. However, to assist the reader in understanding further sections of this paper, this section will use these operations to introduce the programming notation use in CLIP4, diff3, the SUPRPIC software CA emulator used at Carnegie-Mellon University, and the AISCR system for chest X-ray analysis supported by Subroutine Library for Image Processing (SLIP) used at Nagoya University [124].

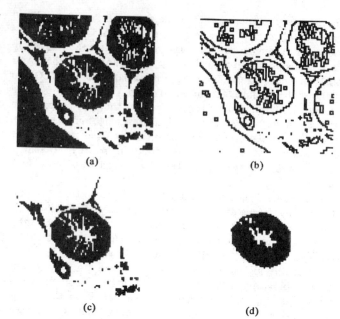

Fig. 13. A 1-bit image (a) whose edge has been marked (b). By propagating the border, edge-connected 1-elements may be removed (c) and by a sizing operation using "shrinking" followed by templating it is possible to locate (and smooth) the largest object in the field (d).

In the CLIP family of computers the logical AND between images $\mathcal{A}$ and $\mathcal{B}$ (yielding the outcome $\mathcal{D}$) is produced by executing the following load and processing instructions:

$$
\begin{aligned}
&\text{LD} \quad \text{A, B, D} \\
&\text{PR} \quad \text{P} \cdot \text{A}
\end{aligned} \tag{5.1}
$$

As in all CLIP commands, LD furnishes the numerical addresses (for the RAM in each PE) while PR provides the *w* and *z* functions (in this case only *w* is used).

The diff3 machine is programmed in Golay Logic Language (GLOL) which is given in full by Preston [57]. The logical AND in GLOL is produced by the teletype command

$$
D = AB \tag{5.2}
$$

In the SUPRIPIC software system the equivalent is

$$
\text{CALL AND (A, B, D)} \tag{5.3}
$$

and in the AISCR-system:

$$
\text{CALL PPMN1I(A, B, D, IE, JE)}
$$

Many other comparisons between these programming languages is given in Table I.

1) Arithmetic Operations: Arithmetic operations, when the data is stored in bit planes, only require the transmission of information stored in perpendicular columns in the CA. Thus these operations are also N^0 Boolean operations. In the same way a thresholding operation is Boolean where, when information stored in a "linear" way (Section IV-E), only those numbers (again stored in perpendicular columns) above a certain value (θ) are made binary 1's while all others become 0's.

2) Labeling or Marking: A type I CLO using N^8, which is widely used for the identification of pixels having certain boundary conditions, established by the values of its neighbors, is called "labeling" (or "marking"). The most frequently used example of labeling is edge detection (Fig. 13), the pro-

TABLE I
PROGRAMS AND PROGRAMMING NOTATION FOR CLIP (UNIVERSITY COLLEGE LONDON), GLOL (COULTER diff3), SUPRPIC (CARNEGIE-MELLON UNIVERSITY), AND AISCR (NAGOYA UNIVERSITY)

| TYPE OF COMMAND | CELLULAR LOGIC SYSTEM (EXECUTION TIMES ARE FOR A 64 X 64 ARRAY) | | | | | | | |
| | CLIP | | diff3 | | SUPRPIC* | | AISCR-V2 AND SLIP** | |
	NOTATION	TIME	NOTATION	TIME	NOTATION	TIME	NOTATION	TIME
COPY	LD A, C, D PR A	8us	D=A	100us	CALL COPY (A. D)	15ms	CALL TRNS11(A, D, IE, JE)	7ms
INVERT	LD A, C, A PR -A	8us	A=A'	100us	CALL INVCOPY (A, A)	15ms	CALL RVRS41(A, A, IE, JE, 1)	7ms
AND	LD A, B, D PR P*A	8us	D=AB	100us	CALL AND(A, B, D)	30ms	CALL PPMX11(A, B, D, IE, JE)	20ms
OR	LD A, B, D PR P+A	8us	D=A+B	100us	CALL OR(A, B, D)	30ms	CALL PPMN11(A, B, D, IE, JE)	20ms
SHRINK (ONE CYCLE)	LD A, C, D PR 0(1-8)A, P+A, S	8us	D=M[G(A)A] 6,,	100us	CALL AUGRED (A, 01. 07. 09. 00) CALL COPY(A. D)	300ms	CALL THIC11(A, IE, JE, 1, IE, 1, JE, 8, 4HTHIN, 1)	35ms***
EXPAND (ONE CYCLE)	LD A, C, D PR 0(1-8)-A, -P*A, S	8us	D=M[G(A)+ G'(A)A]1-5ₙ	100us	CALL INVCOPY (A, A) CALL AUGRED (A, 01. 07. 09. 00) CALL INVCOPY (A. D)	300ms	CALL THIC11(A, IE, JE, 1, IE, 1, JE, 8, 4HTHIC, 1)	35ms***
LABEL (EDGE POINTS)	LD A, C, D	8us	D=M[G'(A)A]6,,	100us	CALL AUGRED (A. 01. 08. 02. 00) CALL COPY (A, D)	300ms	CALL REPL61(A, IE, JE, 1, IE, 1, JE, 0, 1, 5, 8)	30ms***

SHRINK TO RESIDUE OF LARGEST OBJECT	LD A, C, E
	PR A
	REPEAT:
	LD E, C, F
	PR 0(1-8)A, P+A, S
	BR F, (TEST°), FINISH
	LD F, C, E
	PR A
	BR REPEAT
	FINISH:
	
	°TEST FOR EMPTY
		500us (TYPICAL)	DO I/1, 32
			COUNT A, K
			IF K. GT. 1
			A=M[G'(A)A]0-4,,
			ELSE
			STOP
				5ms (TYPICAL)	DATA DEPENDENT CELLULAR LOGIC OPERATORS NOT IMPLEMENTED IN SUPRPIC	N/A	ONLY A SEQUENTIAL ALGORITHM IS IMPLEMENTED.	

THIN	LD A, C, E
	PR 0(128)A, -P*A, S
	LD A, C, F
	PR 0(46)-A, -P*A, S
	LD E, F, G
	PR P*A
	LD A, G, A
	PR -P*A
	LD G, H, H
	PR P+A
	
	THIS SEQUENCE MUST BE REPEATED FOR 7 OTHER NEIGHBOR-HOODS THEN TESTED FOR NO CHANGE
		13ms (TYPICAL)	DO I/1, 32
			A=M[G'(A)A]0-4,,3
			B=M[G(A)+ G'(A)B]11-13,,
			STOP
			(DATA INDEPENDENT SEQUENCE)
				5ms	CALL AUGRED (A, 04. 06. 04. 05)
					CALL COPY (A. B)
					CALL AUGRED (B. 01. 08. 04. 00)
					CALL OR (B. C. C)
					THIS DATA INDEPEN-DENT SEQUENCE IS REPEATED 32 TIMES
						50 sec.	ONLY A SEQUENTIAL ALGORITHM IS IMPLEMENTED	

*INTERDATA 7/32 COMPUTER   **FACOM 230-75 COMPUTER   ***TIME DEPENDS ON THE DATA.

grams for whose execution are given in Table I. In SUPRPIC advantage is taken of the fact that all neighborhoods in the vicinity of an edge have a crossing number CNUM of 2 where CNUM is given by

$$CNUM = \sum_I |N(I) - N(I + 1)| \qquad (5.4)$$

where $N(I)$ are the N^8 neighbor values and I iterates cyclically through the neighborhood, i.e., the quantity $(I + 1) = 1$ when $I = 8$. In the AISCR and SLIP systems two local features, a connectivity number and a coefficient of curvature, are utilized for the same purpose [91]-[93]. SUPRPIC also uses an argument FAC in its CLO call which directly corresponds to the threshold of the digital comparator in CLIP3 (Fig. 2).

Thus the SUPRPIC format for its general purpose CLO is:

$$CALL\ AUGRED\ (A, CYC, FAC, CNUM, MODE) \qquad (5.5)$$

which causes the 1-bit image A to be modified according to its N^8 in a manner defined by FAC and CNUM, while MODE specifies the subfield order [56], and, for Type II operations, CYC specifies the number of iterations. Similarly GLOL employs the notation:

$$D = M[G(A)B + G'(A)C] N1 - N2, CYC, MODE \qquad (5.6)$$

where the arguments include the designation A of the array from which the neighborhood $G(A)$ is to be extracted and with specific neighborhood configurations being designated by the numerics N1 - N2. Three other arrays, B, C, and the destination D are used. The function is executed for a number of cycles given by the argument CYC and the subfield and subfield order is given by the argument MODE. The GLOL command for edge detection is given in Table I.

For CLIP3 the two teletype instructions for a general CLO are

LD   A, B, D

PR   THR (N1 - N2) W, Z, TES EDGE.   (5.7)

The value of the variable c is given by the W portion of each PR instruction. W is computed by each processor as a Boolean function of the values of a and b and the nearest neighbor inputs. The numerics N1 - N2 indicate which neighbor values are to be used in computing c, the value of TES provides the tessellation, and EDGE provides the value of the border pixels. The quantities N1 and N2 can have values in the range 1–8 for the 8-neighborhood; 1–6 for the 6-neighborhood; etc. The argument THR provides the value of the threshold to be used in computing W. The value of the variable which is to be stored in d is given by the Boolean function Z which is a function of the same variable as is W. The CLIP3 commands for edge detection are also given in Table I.

Data independent Type I operations have uses in other applications than edge detection. They have been applied to the classification of line drawings [86] and for use in character recognition [87]. They are commercialized in optical character recognition machines [88], [89]. This use is of particular interest in Japan where more than 3000 Kanji characters as well as about 100 Katakana and Hiragana characters are employed in everyday life. Examples of this kind of Type I CLO's are given in Fig. 14 [88].

3) Shrinking and Expanding: Another fundamental CLO is of Type II (iterative) where all 1-elements belonging to the core of a binary image are labeled with the boundary condition arranged so that:

$$\text{if } \sum A_{xy} = 8, \quad d_{xy} = 1$$

$$\text{otherwise,} \quad d_{xy} = 0. \quad (5.8)$$

This CLO, which is sometimes called "core extraction," considers the core as the set of 1-elements having no 0-elements (background). Such a core is called an 8-core. When this CLO is iterated it, of course, causes a sequence of contractions in connected sets of 1-elements in an image where sets of 1-elements are considered objects on a background of 0-elements. Hence the name "shrinking." Counts of the number of 1-elements after each step in the sequence may be used to form a "feature vector." As is reported in Section VI such feature vectors have been found useful in shape analysis and object identification.

Of course, when the number of 1-elements is reduced, the number of 0-elements is augmented. Thus any "shrinking" operation has as its dual an "expanding" operation. (At Carnegie-Mellon University all such operations are called "augreding" operations to indicate that they form a special class in the analysis of topology.)

Extraction of the 8-core can readily be performed using the CLIP3 by setting the digital comparator to a threshold of 8. Interesting properties are obtained, however, with other thresholds. For example (Fig. 15), when the dual of the initial image is iteratively augred with threshold 4 the pattern stabilizes and the resulting edge elements in the final outcome form a *pseudo-convex hull* of the original objects.

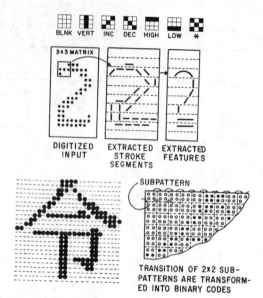

Fig. 14. Encoding Kanji characters and Arabic numerals by means of cellular logic labeling operators. These operators are useful in both text storage and character recognition [88], [139]. (Courtesy Toshiba Electric Company Ltd. and Nippon Electric Company Ltd.)

If threshold 6 is used and also any 1-element with a neighborhood whose CNUM ≥ 4 is retained, the resulting stable pattern is the exoskeleton (Fig. 15).

4) Smoothing: Another well-known operation [90] is known as "smoothing." This, at least for CLIP3, is a Type III operation in that a sequence of alternating CLO's are required. To implement this algorithm, which is often used to reduce noise in the initial 1-bit image produced by thresholding the image, a majority rule is introduced in the N^8 neighborhood so that

$$\text{if } \sum a_{xy} \leqslant 2, \quad d_{xy} = 0$$

$$\text{if } \sum a_{xy} \geqslant 6, \quad d_{xy} = 1$$

$$\text{otherwise,} \quad d_{xy} = a_{xy}. \quad (5.9)$$

In some modifications the central value of the element may also be considered and the total number of pixel values processed in the CLO will amount to 9 for an N^8 neighborhood. An example is given in Fig. 16. Smoothing in a sense combines a shrinking CLO with an expanding CLO. Shrinking and expanding can be combined in a great number of ways. Since both are isotropic operations, they will erase irregularities of shape when alternated. In this case the combined process of shrink-expand CLO's always produces a smoothing effect on the contour of the objects. Many variations on this theme (a number of shrinking CLO's used with a number of expanding CLO's) have been suggested [90], [91]–[93] but all are based on the CLO's defined above.

B. Data Dependent Operations

The operations considered in Section V-A, e.g., edge detection, generation of the exoskeleton, formation of the convex hull and kernel, etc., are basically data *independent* although the number of cycles over which the appropriate CLO's must be taken are data *dependent*. However, if the number of cycles required to reach the limit cycle are exceeded, the outcome is not altered and it is simply found that $\mathfrak{D} = \mathfrak{A}$. In fact a test for $\mathfrak{D} = \mathfrak{A}$ is usually incorporated in most practical

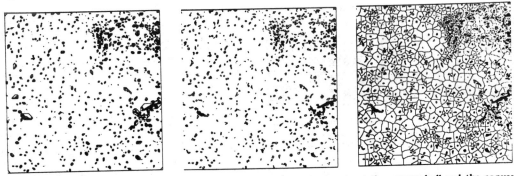

Fig. 15. Augment/reduce (augreding) operations may be used to both extract the convex hull and the convex kernel of objects in a 1-bit image. Also shown is the exoskeleton of the group of objects taken as a whole.

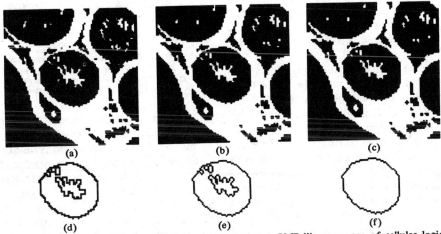

Fig. 16. Three stages (a), (b), (c) of smoothing using a CLIP-like sequence of cellular logic operations using thresholds 2 and 7. (d) is the 8-connected edge of the object shown in Figure 13D, (e) is the 4-connected edge, and (f) is the 8-connected outside edge.

CA's (or CLM's) with a branch to the next sequence of CLO's when this condition is obtained.

There are data dependent operations in neighborhood logic where $\mathfrak{D}$ must be tested for some particular feature(s) and, when this test is met, the sequence *must* be arrested and the next sequence started. Failure to arrest the sequence, unlike the data independent operations, would destroy the information present in the pixel values stored by the PE's (at the value of t when $\mathfrak{D}$ meets the test specified). There are, of course, no Type I data dependent operations. In fact, since each CLO (or groups of identical CLO's) are followed by CLO's used to test for termination of the sequence, all data dependent operations are strictly Type III.

1) Thinning, Templating, and Matched Filtering: Many authors [91]–[100] have developed algorithms which thin elongated objects. Thinning produces stick-like figures from the originals so that their width is reduced to unity. At this point encoding CLO's (Section V-A2) may be employed for use in image recognition. Thinning might be defined as a process that gradually reduces width (until it is unitary) taking care not to disconnect a single object nor to merge two separate objects present in the image (see Fig. 17). In the CLIP family of CA's thinning is performed by the use of a sequence of different CLO's, whereas in diff3 the same CLO is iterated (Table I). Thinning is data dependent, since it must be stopped when the object(s) contained in the array no longer have interior points (core). Thus the termination test is to label (at each t) neighborhoods in $\mathfrak{D}$ exhibiting connectivity (e.g., Golay surrounds 7 through 13) and test to see if the resultant

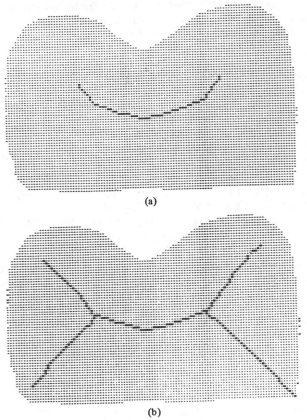

Fig. 17. Typical examples of thinning (a) and skeletonizing (b).

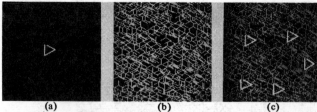

Fig. 18. Illustration of matched filtering using cellular logic operations. (a) is the object to be located, (b) is the 1-bit image data field to be interrogated, and (c) is the result. (Courtesy Environmental Research Institute of Michigan.)

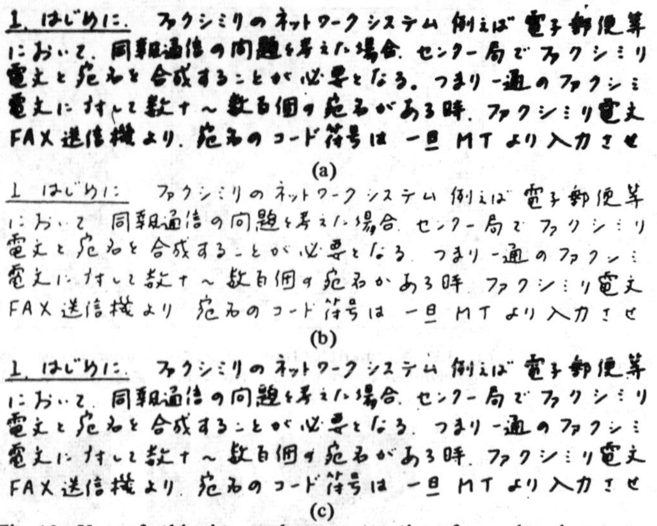

set is identical to $\mathcal{D}$ itself. If so, the sequence is arrested and a branch to the next sequence takes place.

Besides the generation of stick figures for object encoding and recognition, thinning may be employed as a sizing operation. For example, suppose that it is decided to extract the largest, closed connected object in a 1-bit image. In this case thinning is performed until $\mathcal{D} = 0$, i.e., $d_{xy} = 0$, $1 \leqslant x$, $y < l$. At the corresponding value of t, the sequence is terminated. The contents of $\mathcal{C}$ will, of course, be finite ($\mathcal{C}^t = \mathcal{D}^{t+1} \neq 0$. Thus $\mathcal{C}$ contains the value of what is called the "residue" of the object desired. This residue is then employed in a new sequence called "templating" where the residue remains in $\mathcal{C}$ and $\mathcal{B}$ contains the original 1-bit image. Templating augments 1-elements in $\mathcal{C}$ whose neighborhood contains 1-elements in $\mathcal{B}$. Templating itself is data independent although it almost always is preceeded by the data dependent generation of a residue. Templating is also used (without prior residue generation) in removing edge-connected objects. Here the edge itself is considered the residue and is used as $\mathcal{C}$ while, again, $\mathcal{B}$ holds the original image. Examples are given in Fig. 13.

Templating is of interest in the CLIP family because of the rapidity with which it can be carried out. The CLIP machines can be programmed to provide feedback of the N output into the neighborhood input so that templating is a "propagating" function and takes place by "flash through" [41]. Pixop times for CLIP3 when templating are 1 ns and, for CLIP4, 100 ps.

Finally, it should be noted that the class of thinning and templating CLO's have been extended to what are basically matched filtering operations. Preston [74] first introduced the idea of using thinning and templating to sort objects and showed that a field containing two classes of objects (specifically, silhouettes of peripheral blood lymphocyte and neutrophil nuclei) could be divided into two new fields, each containing one class of object only, by this method. Since then Sternberg [101] has carried this idea forward, both analytically and experimentally, as is illustrated in Fig. 18.

2) Skeletonizing: Although formation of the exoskeleton is a data independent operation, formation of the endoskeleton, like thinning, is data dependent since CLO's for termination testing of the data present in $\mathcal{D}$ must in general be interleaved with the primary CLO's. As with the thinned object, the endoskeleton of an object or its features is a useful descriptor in shape recognition. The transformation used to generate the endoskeleton of an object is essentially based on the extraction of all points which are equidistant from at least two points on the edge of the object and/or the assignment of a function to each interior point which is the value of its distance of the edge. (This is the "quench function" of Blum [102], [103].) The interest in this transformation is three-

Fig. 19. Use of thinning and reconstruction for reduced entropy facsimile transmission of text [110], [111]. (a) is the original; (b) is the thinned version ready for transmission; (c) is the reconstructed result. (Courtesy Nippon Electric Company Ltd.)

fold: 1) this transformation is reversible, in the sense that, given the endoskeleton, the original object may be obtained by means of an isotropic expansion of the skeleton a number of times equal to the maximum value of the quench function; 2) an appropriate pruning of branches of the skeleton may be used to produce a smoothed version of the reconstructed object [104]–[106]; 3) a certain storage reduction may be obtained in some cases by means of coding the object using the endoskeleton [107]–[109]. Unfortunately there are many problems to be solved in order to preserve the topological structure of the object when its endoskeleton is extracted.

The endoskeleton may be extracted by means of the sequential application of a series of isotropic masks combined with Boolean operations between partial results obtained during the process. Skeletonizing is data dependent because the termination of the process is determined by the data in the sense that, whenever the object processed at a certain step has no core, the computation stops.

Blum's medial axis transform is not the only transform used for skeletonizing. Equation (4.7) provides the gray-weighted skeletonizing transform of Levi and Montanari [83]. The distance transform [75] of a 1-bit image constitutes a rough approximation to the endoskeleton. Although the result of this transform is not necessarily connected, it is nevertheless reversible. In the distance transform a particular labeling of object elements (1-elements) is applied which assigns to each element of the object a number representing the distance of this element to the background (0-elements). In practice, this transform is implemented by a sequence of CLO's which reduce, at every step, the core of the object until no more core remains. In this example arithmetic CLO's are required in order to update the value given to each element every time a new core is extracted.

Use is presently being made of the endoskeleton in the encoding of Kanji characters for transmission over a digital communications link [110], [111]. After transmission the reversible properties of the endoskeleton are employed to reconstruct the original characters. An example is given in Fig. 19. Other examples of the use of skeletonizing in biomedical image analysis are presented in Section VI.

C. Ancillary Operations

Some fundamental operations in the CA or CLM are image manipulative rather than image analyzing. Some of these operations are described next. They are testing, scrolling, and scanning.

1) Testing: The data dependent termination test is performed in a CA or CLM by checking the value of $\mathfrak{D}$ array. This operation involves the inspection of the whole array contents and might be thought of either as a single parallel test on l^2 PE's or l^2 iterations of a specific CLO testing each PE. The existence of this text implies the implementation of the Fortran IF statement within the execution of a sequence of CLO's. Clearly, the hardware implementation of this function must permit an execution time compatible with the execution time of the individual CLO.

2) Scrolling: This particular CLO belongs to a class of direction oriented CLO's and is exemplified by a process in which the image on the array is moved in any one of the eight possible directions, by means of an iterative shifting procedure. Suppose the image contents are to be shifted rightwards (along the horizontal axis); the condition to be fulfilled by a_{xy} in order that $d_{xy} = 1$ is simply that its left neighbor shall be a 1-element, therefore, this condition is that $a_{x-1, y} = 1$ and at each successive step the image contents of $\mathfrak{C}$ will be right shifted by one PE. A similar operation can be performed along any one of the 8 possible directions contained in the square tessellation. Interestingly, although readily performed on the CLIP family of CA's, scrolling is not possible on the CELLSCAN, GLOPR, or diff3 CLM's (Table I).

3) Scanning: Another fundamental sequence of CLO's is that which automatically extracts from an image all connected objects which are present in the image, one by one. Generally this process is required in order to process each object separately or, in some cases, to decide whether an object should be processed at all. This process may substantially be divided into two parts: 1) the raster scan and 2) object extraction by means of a propagation signal.

To begin the raster scan a 1-element object ("marker") is placed in $\mathfrak{C}$ in its top left corner ($a_{11} = 1$). A sequence of data dependent CLO's will shift this marker rightwise until either an object (present in $\mathfrak{B}$) is detected (on its topmost left element) or until the first row has been completely addressed. The next row will be visited and so on until all objects present in $\mathfrak{C}$ have been detected and all the rows have been scanned. The sequence is essentially a right shifting process which is terminated on the last column, combined with a downwards shifting process which moves the marker from one row to the next one down. If $d_{x+1, y}$ is the element of the processed image which is on the right-hand side of a_{xy} in its N^8 neighborhood, the horizontal movement of the marker may be represented by the following short expressions: if $a_{xy} = 1$, $d_{x+1, y} = 1$ while the vertical movement will be given by: if $a_{xy} = 1$, $d_{x, y+1} = 1$.

When many objects are present in the array, this method proves to be very much faster in execution than alternate methods not using a scanner [112]. As soon as an object is found by the marker ($\mathfrak{D} \neq 0$ where $\mathfrak{D} = \mathfrak{C} \cdot \mathfrak{B}$), templating is used to actually perform the object extraction. Then, by means of a new Boolean operation, this object will be stored in a different array plane ready for further processing. At this point the scanning sequence is reinstituted so that the marker may find another object, if any, or continue until the last bottom rightmost element of the array $\mathfrak{C}$ is reached.

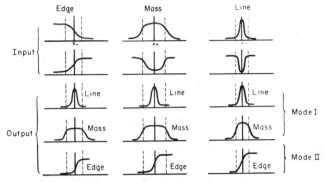

Fig. 20. Examples of the performance of the difference filter in response to the inputs representing idealizations of edge, mass, and line.

VI. APPLICATIONS

Significantly the only widely used commercial CLM (diff3) is employed in automated biomedical image analysis in hospital hematology laboratories. In fact biomedical image analysis has in general has provided the most fertile area for the use of cellular logic. This section presents specific examples taken from investigations of the use of CLO's in the analysis of: 1) medical X-ray images, 2) images of human white blood cells, and 3) images of human liver tissue biopsy sections.

A. Medical X-Ray Analysis

Many component patterns are observed in X-ray images [113]–[118]. In chest X-ray images, for example, the heart, ribs and blood vessels as well as abnormal shadows (tumor lesions, etc.) are significant patterns to be recognized. Usually rather elaborate procedures are required to recognize these component patterns because they exist on a complicated background and often partially overlap each other. The CLO plays an important role in X-ray picture processing procedures. Various types of CLO's have been employed in many practical problems and are illustrated below.

1) Performance of the Difference Filter: Most of the CLO's referred to in subsequent sections are basically various types of the difference filter (DF). These DF's are used to segment the X-ray image into regions of interest (lung, heart, ribs, ⋯). The boundaries between regions may be characterized by three types of pixel value distributions which we call: 1) "edge," 2) "mass," or 3) "line." These are illustrated in Fig. 20 in the form of idealized 1-dimensional profiles.

Since most real boundaries have definite slopes (definite values of the derivative), the "edge" itself is a region with definite width. It is regarded as a transition region from the region of higher density to that of lower density. The "mass" means the whole of the region in which density is almost constant and relatively lower (or higher) than the background. The "line" is a special case of the elongated mass which is very narrow in one direction (ideally one pixel in width). Fig. 20 shows how the DF responds to each of these three types of inputs. It should be noted here that edge, mass, or line can be obtained by suitably selecting the form of the DF. Figure 21 shows a concrete example showing how the outputs of $D_1[0, 0; d/2, d/2]$ and $D_2[0, 0; d, d]$ vary with its parameter d. (A detailed analysis of $D_1[K1, K2; L1, L2]$ and $D_2[K1, K2; L1, L2]$ has been presented in [80].)

The concept of the operational mode of the DF is useful in designing the image processing procedure and in grasping the performance of the proposed procedure. Assuming that the location of the input figure (edge, mass, or line) is represented

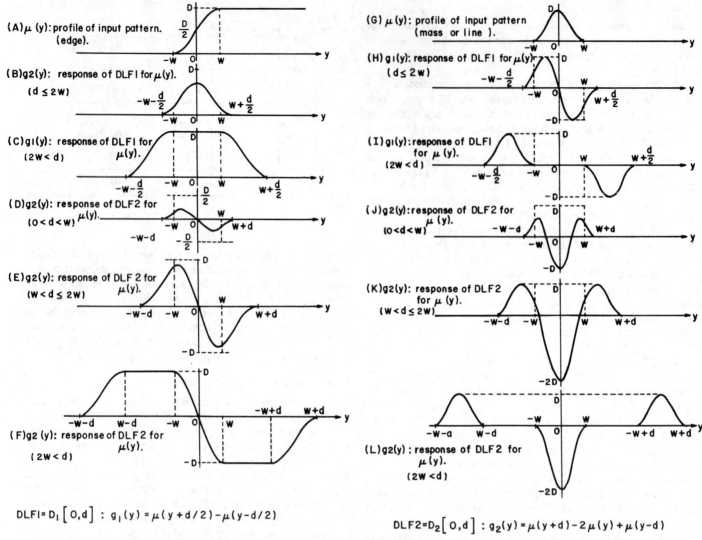

DLF1 = $D_1[0,d]$: $g_1(y) = \mu(y+d/2) - \mu(y-d/2)$

DLF2 = $D_2[0,d]$: $g_2(y) = \mu(y+d) - 2\mu(y) + \mu(y-d)$

Fig. 21. Detailed examples showing the outputs of the $D_1[0, 0; d/2, d/2]$ and $D_2[0, 0; d, d]$ as a function of the parameter d.

by the coordinates of its center (x_0 in Fig. 20 or the origin in Fig. 21), it will be found that the output is either maximum at the location of the input figure or that the output is equal to (or very close to) zero at the same location. In the former case we say that the filter works in the operational Mode I and, in the latter case, operational Mode II. The operational mode is not the feature inherent to each filter, but a property which is dependent on both the filter and the input. Thus a specified filter can work either in Mode I or Mode II. The operational mode of the filter governs the types of operations which will be employed subsequently. In the detection of borders, for example, a DF working in the Mode I should be followed by thresholding and thinning, while a DF working in the Mode II should be followed by thresholding and border following.

2) Global Structure of the X-Ray Image: An outline of the global structure (major component patterns) of the chest X-ray image is illustrated in Fig. 22. All of these component patterns are desired to be recognized in the automated analysis of chest radiographs [114], [120]. Many examples of CLO's applied to the elucidation of these component parts are found in the software system Automated Interpretation System of Chest Roentgenograms—Version 2 (AISCR-V2) [113], [120], [121]. We illustrate the use of that system below. Table II shows all of DF's employed in the above system AISCR-V2.

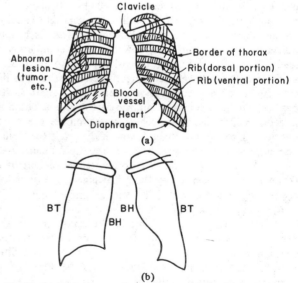

Fig. 22. Skeletal structure of the human chest (a) and important feature points in its idealized outlines (b).

3) Outlining of the Heart and Lung: In general, the outline of the lung and heart, i.e., border of thorax (BT) and border of heart (BH) in Fig. 22, can be distinguished quite clearly by

TABLE II
DIFFERENCE FILTERS USING THE ADJACENT
NEIGHBORHOOD PROGRAMMED IN AISCR-V2
(UNIVERSITY OF NAGOYA)

a_{xy} and A, B, ... , H are density values of a pixel (x, y) and its adjacent neighbors.

D	C	B
E	a_{xy}	A
F	G	H

LINEAR DF

(1) $A-a_{xy}$, $B-a_{xy}$, ..., $G-a_{xy}$, $H-a_{xy}$

(2) A-E, C-G, B-F, D-H $D_1[0, 0, 1, 1]$, $D_1[-1, -1, 0, 0]$, $D_1[-1, -1, 1, 1]$, $D_1[-1, -1, -1, -1]$

(3) $(B+A+H)-(D+E+F)$, $(B+C+D)-(F+G+H)$

(4) $A+E-2a_{xy}$, $B+F-2a_{xy}$, $C+G-2a_{xy}$, $D+H-2a_{xy}$
$D_2[0, 0, 1, 1]$, $D_2[-1, 1, 1, -1]$, $D_2[0, 0, 1, 1]$, $D_2[1, 1, 1, 1]$

(5) $(A+C+E+G)-4a_{xy}$, $(B+D+F+H)-4a_{xy}$ (4-neighbor Laplacian)

(6) $(A+B+C+D+E+F+G+H)-8a_{xy}$ (8-neighbor Laplacian)

NONLINEAR DF

(7) Absolute values of (1) through (6)

(8) $\text{Max}\{A, B, C, D, E, F, G, H, a_{xy}\} - \text{Min}\{A, B, C, D, E, F, G, H, a_{xy}\}$ (RF$[3, 3, 3]$)

(9) $a_{xy} - \text{Min}\{A, B, C, D, E, F, G, H\}$

(10) $\text{Max}\{|A-E|, |C-G|, |B-F|, |D-H|\}$

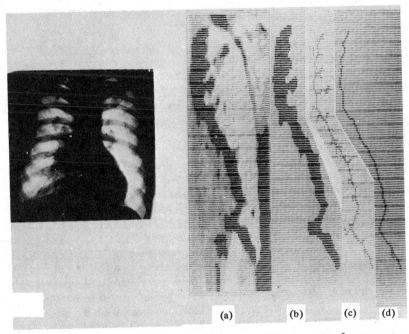

(a) (b) (c) (d)

Fig. 23. A typical chest photofluorogram and the outputs of a sequence of CLOs used in finding the outline of the heart. (a) output of $SD_1[2, 2; 1, 1: 0, 0; 3, 3]$ working in Mode I, (b) result of thresholding, (c) result of skeletonizing and thinning using the Wave Propagation Method, (d) a border obtained by eliminating redundant points.

the human eye, but in actuality the analytical location of these borders is not so clear. Analysis of the borders as drawn by doctors suggests the use of the first-order difference for BH and the second order for BT. In AISCR-V2, $SD_1[2, 2; 1, 1: 0, 0; 1, 1]$ was used for the detection of BH and $SD_2[2, 2; 1, 1: 0, 0; 1, 1] \cdot SD_2[2, 2; 1, 1: 0, 0; 1, 1]$ for BT. Their outputs were processed by thresholding and thinning to obtain the final borders [114]. For thinning, the wave propagation method using the iterative local operator given by equation (4.7) and a special one-step operator with

N^8 was employed [114] to eliminate redundant elements. These procedures are illustrated by Fig. 23. Other methods for finding BH, BT, and the border of the diaphragm have been presented in [115]–[118].

4) Outlining of the Ribs: Rib images are also reasonably clear to the human eye so that recognition of the locations of the ribs seems easy. Investigation of density profiles reveals, however, that the difference between the density value of the rib image and of its neighborhood may often be very small. Furthermore, images of the ventral and dorsal

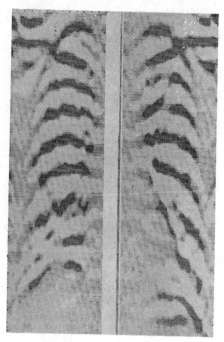

Fig. 24. Output of $SD_2[2, 2; 2, 2: 8, 8; 0, 0]$ working in Mode I for use in detecting rib images as mass patterns in the chest photofluorogram.

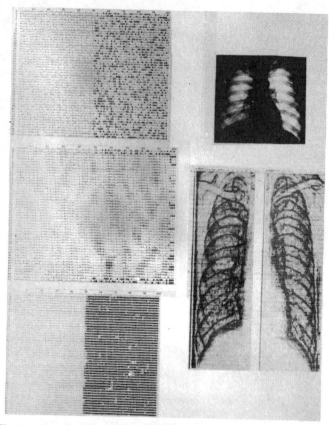

Fig. 25. Examples of the behavior of the range filter. (a) input image consisting of random numbers generated with low and high variance with output (b) using $SD_1[2, 2; 2, 2: 0, 0; 4, 5]$ and (c) for RF[1, 1; 1, 1]. The chest photofluorogram (d) with the result (e) of applying RF[1, 1; 1, 1].

ribs frequently overlap each other. Complex images of blood vessels which also overlap the rib shadows make rib outlining still more difficult.

A complete procedure for the location of rib borders has not been developed in spite of the fact the several procedures have been proposed [113], [118], [122], [123]. The present procedure in AISCR-V2 is composed of three major steps [113]: 1) rough estimation, 2) primitive curve extraction, and 3) refinement by an iterative process. In the first step, $SD_2[2, 2, 2, 2; 8, 8, 0, 0]$ was used which worked in Mode I and provided mass patterns giving the information on shapes and locations of ribs (Fig. 24). It should be noted here that the whole of the rib image is detected instead of its border. Three filters $SD_1[5, 5; 2, 2: -2, -2; -2, -2]$, $SD_1[5, 5: 2, 2: -2, -2; 2, 2]$ and $SD_1[2, 2; 4, 5: -2, -2; 0, 0]$ were used in the second step. They were designed so as to match the shape of the rib border. They worked in Mode I and, when followed by thresholding and thinning, extracted segments of curves giving rib boundaries.

5) Tumor Lesion Detection: Abnormal shadows due to lung cancer and pulmonary tuberculosis, etc., which are observed in chest photofluorograms are often very small compared with the full size of the picture. For example, a circular shadow with a diameter of 1 mm must be detected in an image recorded on 70-mm film. The shapes, sizes, and positions of abnormal shadows are full of variety. Moreover, the variance of grey values inside and outside these shadows is small in many cases (usually from 7 to 10 percent of the background density). Thus borders of shadows may hardly be distinguished visually even by radiologists.

Fortunately, it is allowable in automated prescreening of chest photofluorograms for the extracted positions and sizes of abnormal shadows to be only approximately coincident with those of the shadows pointed out by radiologists. This has led to the procedure previously presented in detail [120], [121], [124]. This procedure contains two major steps: 1)

extraction of suspicious regions (SR's) and 2) test of SR's. The filter $SD_2[2, 2; 2, 2: 0, 0; 12. 12]$ followed by thresholding was used 1) to extract masses from a given input image which are SR's and 2) to examine each SR closely by various tests to eliminate normal shadows. For this step the filter $SD_2[2, 2; 2, 2: K1, K2; L1, L2]$ was again employed where parameters $K1$, $K2$, $L1$, and $L2$ were optimized. All these filters worked in Mode I and detected mass patterns instead of borders.

For tumor lesions observed in standard chest X-ray pictures having relatively clear borders a border detection procedure including calculation of the gradient using $D_1[1, 1; 0, 0]$ and $D_1[0, 0; 1, 1]$ was applied [117]. Fig. 25 shows examples of the range filter (RF) applied to both artificial images and a chest photofluorogram. As can be seen, the RF has characteristics different from DF because of its nonlinearity.

B. Applications in Blood Cell Image Recognition

The visual classification of blood cells is a $2-billion per year industry in the United States alone [125]-[128]. About 1-million cell images are classified per day by hematology technologists using the laboratory microscope to permit visual identification of these objects (Fig. 26). The objects themselves are contained in a thin layer of blood made on a microscope slide and stained with appropriate biochemicals to introduce pH specific color clues. The features used for identification are both spatial (size and shape of nucleus, texture of cytoplasm, etc.) and colorimetric (color of granules, cytoplasm, etc.).

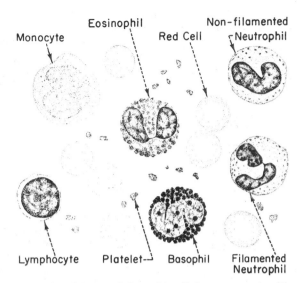

Fig. 26. A stylized image of the major cellular components of human peripheral blood. Six types of white blood cell (leukocyte) are shown along with red blood cells (erythrocytes) and platelets (thrombocytes) [129].

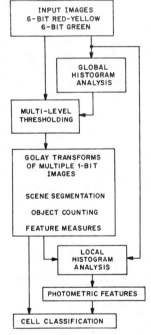

Fig. 27. Flowchart of the sequence of operations carried out in the diff3 in conducting the recognition of a single human while blood cell from its two-color television image.

In 1969 Ingram, Preston, Norgren, and others [129] used the GLOPR CLM connected to an automatic white blood cell locating microscope to perform the first demonstration of fully automated white blood cell classification. This led to the diff3 white blood cell analyzer which is a commercial instrument employed in hematology laboratories whose specifications in comparison with other commercial blood analyzers are given in Table III. The GTP CLM which was designed as part of this commercial instrument has been described in Section III-D. A list of the features extracted by diff3 in processing each blood cell image is given in Table IV [130].

1) Analysis Using diff3: Fig. 27 shows a generalized flowchart of the processes used to make morphological and photometric measurements in the diff3 system. The data source is two (yellow–red and green) digitized fields containing the cells to be analyzed which resides in two gray-level (6-bits per pixel) image memories. The Golay transform processor (GTP) of the diff3's CLM is employed in making all measurements. For the more obviously shape dependent measurements, such as indentations in the nucleus, number of nuclear lobes, nuclear to cytoplasmic ratio, and cell perimeter, the measurements are made directly using sequences of CLO's. In the case of measurements relating to cell constituent transmission (or optical density) for more than one color, the GTP is used indirectly. Since the GTP has identified the cell component parts (nucleus, cytoplasm, etc.), templates for each part are resident in the 1-bit image memories of the GTP just prior to the determination of the average optical density of the pixels which comprise these component parts. Additional memory (out-

TABLE III
CURRENT SPECIFICATIONS ON COMMERCIAL WHITE BLOOD CELL DIFFERENTIAL COUNTING INSTRUMENTS

SYSTEM SOURCE AFFILIATION	ADC 500 J. E. Green Abbott Laboratories	Coulter diff3 G. T. Paul Perkin-Elmer	Hematrak ® M. N. Miller Geometric Data	LARC ® C. H. Rogers Corning
OPTICS				
OBJECTIVE				
Magnification	40	40	40	100
Numerical Aperture	1.0	1.0	1.0	1.3
Type	Planapochromat	Planachromat	Planachromat	Planachromat
Immersion Medium (Index)	Oil (1.518)	Oil	Oil (1.518)	Oil (1.515)
OCULAR				
Magnification	10	12.5	10	10
Type	Highpoint	KPL	KPL	(Adjustable Focus)
ILLUMINATION				
Light Source	150w Zenon	60w Tungsten	CRT	80w Tungsten
Wavelength(s) (nm)	412, 525, 560	510, 580	425, 530, 595	Orange, Blue-Green
Bandwidth(s) (nm)	30, 20, 20	33, 20	50, 50, 75	-
MODULATION TRANSFER FUNCTION	-	-	-	-
SCANNERS				
MECHANICAL				
Slide Magazine Capacity	50	14	20	1
Stage Increments (X,Y,Z) (μm)	8, 8, -	3,3,0.1	350,350,0.25	5,5,0.1
Increment Time (X,Y,Z) (ms)	0.1-0.5, 0.1-0.5, -	1,2,2	70(X,Y)	2,2,3
Total Travel (X,Y,Z) (mm)	≈80, ≈80, 0.1	20,10,0.5	57, 25, 2	60,20,0.25
SEARCH MODE				
Type of Scanner	50 x 50 Diode Array	Linear Diode Array	CRT	Mirror
Scan Lines/Sec.	3,000	1,000	2,000	500
Spot Velocity (μ/ms)	2,500	-	1,200	150
Line Length (μm)	400	200	300	≈ 300
Line Width (μm)	8	3	0.25	≈ 7
Line Spacing (μm)	8	3	2	≈ 5
Coverage (mm² / min.)	600	36	135	45
Focus Method	Dual 128 - Diode Scanner	Not Used	Max. High Video Freq.	Move Objective
Focus Response (sec.)	0.01	N/A	0.04	Real Time
Cell Acquisition Time (sec.)	0.016	0.15	—	0.10
Video Bandwidth	-	75kHz	800kHz	-
IMAGING MODE				
Type of Scanner	Three 50 x 50 Diode Arrays	Plumbicon	CRT	Plumbicon
Pixel Spacing (μm)	0.5	0.4	0.25	0.4
Acquisition Rate (pixels/sec.)	150,000	$2.5 \cdot 10^6$	$3 \cdot 10^6$	-
Acquisition Time (sec.)	0.016	0.02	0.05	-
Format (x pixels, y pixels)	50 x 50	128, 128	128, 96	48, 48
Video Bandwidth	-	1 MHz	800kHz	-
Bits/Pixel	6	6	3	6
IMAGE PROCESSOR				
Type of Computer	Nova-2 and Special	Nova and Special	HP2105 and Special	PDP 8M
Image Memory (words)	2.5K (Special)	16 - 20 k	-	16k
Operating System (words)	12K (Nova)	32 k	20K	-
Measurements Made	8(Red Cell)/8(White Cell)	20(Red Cell)/50(White Cell)	116(Red Cell)/96(White Cell)	8
Measurement Time (ms)	16	500	Real Time	-
Recognition Time (ms)	50	7	30	-
Processing Rate (cells/hr.)	29,000 (Av.) 36,000 (Peak)	3,500 - 4,000 (Av. White) 5,000 - 6,000 (Av. Red)	30,000 (Av.) 40,000 (peak)	5,500 (Av.) 8,000 (peak)
Output	Printed Lab. Ticket; Computer Link	Printed Lab. Ticket; Computer Link Video Display	Printed Lab. Ticket Computer Link Video Display	Printed Lab. Ticket; Computer Interface Video Display

side the GTP) contains the spatially sampled and digitized video image of the blood cell scene. This data is retained in diff3 for repeated reference during the analysis of the scene.

As shown in Fig. 27, the first step in the analysis is to generate global photometric histograms of the scene and use these to derive the thresholding levels that will permit 1-bit image representation of the significant spatial constituents (component parts) of each cell. These 1-bit images are stored in the GTP and serve as input for subsequent image processing and analysis. This processing is vital to all subsequent phases of the image analysis. This is true because simple thresholding does not ordinarily produce 1-bit image constituents which

272

TABLE IV
COLORIMETRIC AND
MORPHOLOGICAL MEASURES
(PARTIAL LIST) MADE ON EACH
WHITE BLOOD CELL BY THE diff3

diff3 SHAPE MEASURES

Dense Nuclear Edge
Dense Fine Structure
Minor Chromatin Clumps
Nuclear Inclusion Area
Minor Nuclear Concavities
Major Nuclear Concavities
Trimmed Area
Trimmed Edge
Area After Shrinking
Edge After Shrinking
Inlets
Accumulated Bridges
Nuclear Lobe Count
Cytoplasm Area
Cytoplasm Inclusion Area
Cytoplasm Granule Count
Cytoplasm Edge
Central Pallor Area
Central Pallor Edge
Area Within Central Pallor

diff3 COLOR MEASURES

Nuclear Color (G, R)
Cytoplasm Color (G, R)
Cytoplasm Granule Color (G, R)
Lowest Transmission (G, R)

relate directly to the true cell components which are used in the morphological description of each specific cell type. A sequence of many CLO's is used to standardize the thresholded scene prior to extraction of morphological pattern features as discussed below.

Fig. 27 also indicates that, besides providing direct morphological information about the cells in the scene under examination, the GTP provides data upon which the local photometric measurements are based. Photometric information about various cell constituents (nucleus, cytoplasm, etc.) is obtained by making gated histograms using the 1-bit cell constituent templates which localize and identify the image constituent whose pixel values are to be histogrammed. It is important to note that these templates are the result of a considerable number of CLO's as discussed above.

The final step in the cell classification procedure is then to combine the morphological pattern features and the photometric pattern features into a pattern vector which is classified by hyperplane partitioning techniques to identify the cell type.

2) Results of Image Processing with diff3: Fig. 28 is a 5 X 9 matrix of pictures representing various stages of processing with the diff3 image processor. Each column relates to a different type of cell and each row represents a different stage of the processing for that particular cell type. The first row shows the gray-level representation of the scene generated by the high-resolution television microscope. The field of view represented is approximately 900 μm^2. Each picture is spatially sampled on a 64 X 64 point grid with each point quantized to 64 levels so as to provide 6 bits of gray-level information. In each case, the leukocyte (white blood cell) to be analyzed is centered in the field with some erythrocytes (red blood cells), and sometimes thrombocytes (platelets), also being present.

The images shown in each row below the gray-level pictures in Fig. 28 are all 1-bit images having the same scale and 64 X 64

format. They illustrate some of the morphological processing steps used to measure cell characteristics. The results of all measurement steps in the entire CLO sequence are not shown. These pictures, however, give a representative sample of some important measurements produced in the process of doing a white cell differential count.

The second row of images shows the 1-bit image extracted from the corresponding gray-level image by thresholding at a transmission level selected so as to separate the background from all cytological constituents in the field. Note that other objects are present in this field along with the white cell. Some of these touch the border of the field while some of them are isolated. In the case of the basophil, for example, a large platelet near the basophil appears joined to the basophil.

The third row shows the step at which the white cell cytoplasm, a significant cellular constituent, has been extracted. The central object in the field (the desired white cell) has been isolated from all other objects. In the case of the basophil, the platelet has been removed. The nucleus and cytoplasm of the cell have been separated.

The nucleus, itself, which is another significant constituent, is shown in the fourth row. Note that, in the case of the monocyte, the nucleus is shown as solid, although simple thresholding would leave internal voids in the nuclear image (see third row). The sequence which produces the filled image of the nucleus uses a CLIP-like propagating function which starts at the image border and is arrested at the outer nuclear edge.

The fifth row shows 1-bit images in which the pseudo-convex-hull of the nucleus has been generated. This operation (along with the generation of partial convex hulls) is useful in measuring concavities of various sizes in the nuclear silhouette.

The sixth row shows the result of reducing the nucleus using a sequence of shrinking operations. The area and perimeter measures of the reduced nucleus have been found, empirically, to be significant in cell identification [131]. The examples of segmented and banded neutrophils shown in Fig. 28 were taken deliberately to illustrate this point. In the upper row they seem to be somewhat equivocal in their morphology. The gray-level image of the segmented neutrophil looks as if it has a continuous nucleus, however, its reduced nucleus shows a significant different as compared to the nucleus of the band.

The seventh row of the figure shows the nuclear skeleton. The number of pixels in the skeleton is used as another morphological measure. The skeleton is then reduced to residues for the purpose of counting the lobes of the nucleus (a meausure useful in determining the age of a white blood cell).

The final two rows of Fig. 28 relate to the 1-bit nuclear image which is created by thresholding at the average nuclear transmission level (see eighth row). In the final row, a labeling CLO has been applied to measure nuclear fine structure using Golay surrounds having a crossing number greater than 2. A count of the pixels labeled provides a measure of nuclear texture which has been found useful in distinguishing small monocytes from large lymphocytes [132].

3) Rate of Operation: The entire sequence used for image analysis in diff3 is about 500 CLO's in length. The GTP in diff3 requires about 300 ms to execute this sequence over the 4096 pixel field employed. Since each pixop is equivalent to at least 20 assembly language instructions in a general purpose computer, the GTP in diff3 is at least equivalent to a 100 MIP (million instructions per second) machine. In fact,

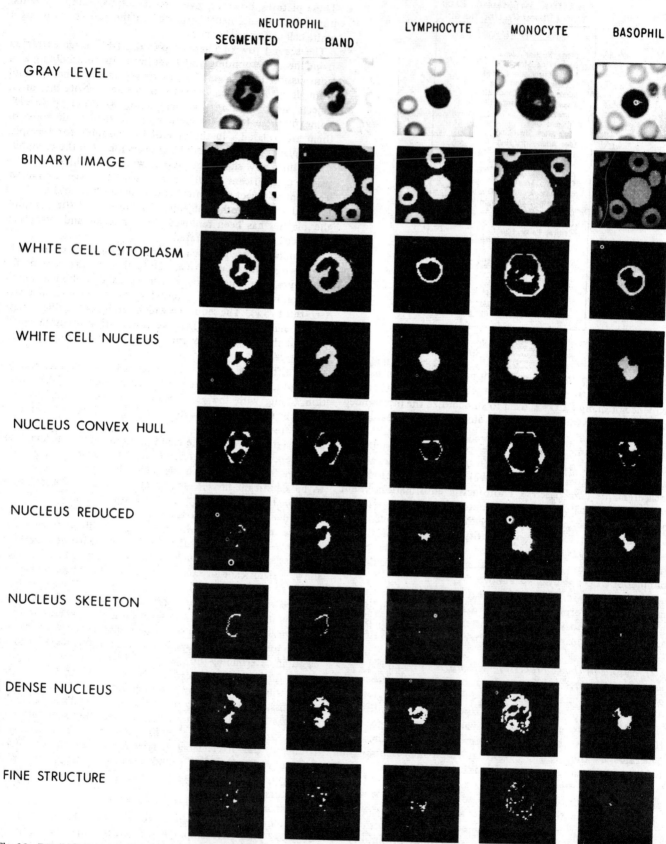

Fig. 28. Detailed pictorial of the major intermediate results obtained by the diff3 sequence of cellular logic operators used for extracting features of the human white blood cell image in the process of generating a white blood cell differential count. Input images (green illumination) are shown in the top row. The lower rows show a multiplicity of 1-bit 64 × 64 images produced at certain stages of a 500-CLO sequence carried out by diff3 in approximately 300 ms.

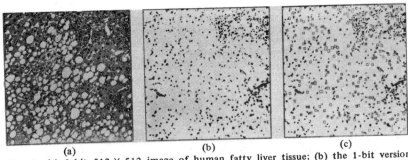

Fig. 29. (a) 2-bit 512 × 512 image of human fatty liver tissue; (b) the 1-bit version produced by thresholding at the mid-range of the probability density function; (c) the output of a sizing operation carried out by a sequence of CLOs for the purpose of labeling small nuclei which are considered indicative of inflammation.

at 25 ns/pixop for many CLO's it is closer to a 1000 MIPS machine.

C. Application to Biopsy Tissue Image Analysis

The examination of the tissue biopsy is as frequently performed in biomedicine as is the examination of the blood smear described in Section VI-B [133]. Visual tissue biopsy examination is done in the hospital pathology laboratory. Unlike blood smear analysis, where there is a great deal of uniformity from input to input, the work of the pathologist is characterized not only by the variety of tissues examined but by also the complexity of the analysis required. The task of the pathologist is comparable in difficulty to that performed by the radiologist in examining the chest X-ray (Section VI-A). This section reports preliminary efforts in applying neighborhood logic to digitized images of diseased liver tissue biopsies for the purpose of computer localization of disease sites (suspicious regions).

1) Liver Tissue Architecture: Tissue biopsies are prepared by sectioning tissue with a microtome which produces a thin (a few micrometers) slice of tissue which is mounted on a microscope slide. As with the blood smear, the tissue slice is stained with certain biochemicals in order to provide information on the chemical composition of tissue constituents (cell nuclei, cytoplasmic granules, connective tissue structure, etc.) by colorimetric labeling. The tissue itself may be drawn from an excised organ (or portion thereof) or from the percutaneous extraction of a tissue core with a biopsy needle. The biopsy needle is hollow and the core which it extracts is approximately 10 mm long and 1 mm in diameter.

Fig. 29(a) is a 2-bit image of a portion (400 × 400 μm) of a slice of a needle biopsy core taken from a fatty human liver. The white regions consist of the cytoplasm of cells that have metabolized fat, the dark regions (or dark regions surrounding small white regions) are the nuclei of the tissue cells. Many types of cells are present, e.g., ordinary liver cells (hepatocytes), various types of white blood cells (leukocytes), red blood cells, plasma cells, epithelial cells, fibroblasts, kupfer cells, etc. Cell by cell identification is difficult even for the trained observer. Major disagreements occur from pathologist to pathologist on certain cell types. In some cases, no identification is possible. Rather, the pathologist ordinarily diagnoses the state of the tissue from its overall architecture. Fig. 30 shows the general diagnosis for the liver tissue shown in Fig. 29(a). In this example, the abnormalities are some fibrosis, some inflammation, and, in the upper right quadrant a severe infection which is indicated by an infiltration (concentration) of leukocytes. The direction taken in the investigation which is reported here was to devise sequences of CLOs

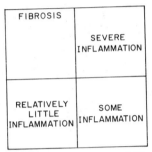

Fig. 30. A block diagram of the table-driven cellular logic operator used in the SUPRPIC software system.

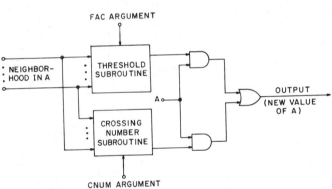

Fig. 31. Diagnostic map of the fatty liver tissue image shown in Fig. 29.

which would extract regions of abnormality. The result (reported in detail below) was the discovery that certain features of the exoskeleton of the cell nuclei (or clusters of cell nuclei) were the most useful indicators of abnormal tissue architecture.

2) Method of Approach: Several sequences of CLO's were designed and tested using as input the 1-bit image obtained from thresholding Fig. 29(a) at a level coincident with the mid-range of its normalized probability distribution function (Fig. 29(b)). These CLO sequences were executed using SUPRPIC (Section V-A).

The logic for the general SUPRPIC CLO is shown in Fig. 31. The output is obtained from ORing the values obtained by ANDing each a_{xy} with two other 1-bit quantities which are obtained by comparing the count of the total number of 1-elements in the N^8 with a threshold (FAC) and the crossing number of the N^8 with a second threshold (CNUM). If the total count of 1-elements exceeds FAC or if the crossing

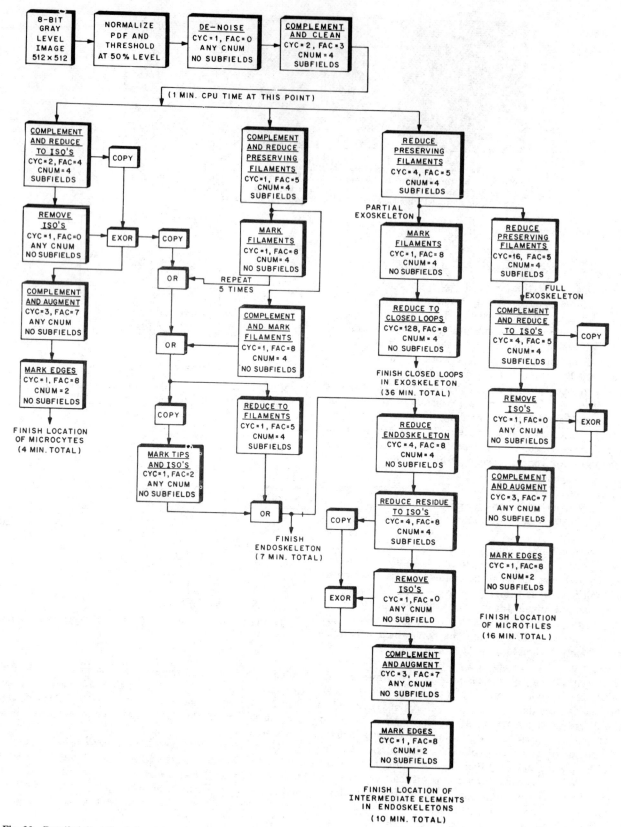

Fig. 32. Detailed flowchart showing all SUPRPIC cellular logic operations carried out in the investigation of the specificity of various sequences in locating regions of pathology in Fig. 29(a).

number is equal to or greater than the threshold CNUM and the value of a_{xy} is a binary 1, then the output of the SUPRPIC CLO (a'_{xy}) is a binary 1.

The SUPRPIC CLO may operate in 3 primary modes:

1) operations without subfields, 2) operation in subfields of 4 (Fig. 7) with a subfield order given by 1-3-4-2, and 3) the same as mode 2 except that residues ($a_{xy} = 1$ and all neighborhood elements zero) are preserved. These modes

are selected by specifying the appropriate arguments in the Fortran call statement.

A flowchart of the CLO sequences investigated is given in Fig. 32. The structure of the sequences and their outcomes are discussed in the section below. They include both the generation of the endoskeleton and the exoskeleton and an analysis of these structures.

3) Discussion of Results: Because abnormal regions in liver tissue biopsies are characterized by an infiltration of leukocytes, which have smaller nuclei than the ordinary hepatocyte, a CLO sequence was designed for sizing the nuclei shown in Fig. 29(b) using a shrinking sequence which preserved residues. Before carrying out this sequence of CLO's, the image was smoothed (denoised) using 1 iteration with FAC = 0 followed by an inversion (1s complement) and two iterations with FAC = 3 and CNUM = 4. After this the image was recomplemented and small cell nuclei were reduced to residues (ISO's) using two iterations with FAC = 4 and CNUM = 4. After this residues were extracted into a separate data field. These residues were transformed into 7 X 7 squares by complementing and augmenting (3 iterations with FAC = 7). The edges of the squares were marked (one iteration with FAC = 8 and CNUM = 2) and ORed with the original image resulting in the Fig. 29(c). As can be seen, the location of the residues (small cell nuclei) was only partly specific to the disease sites. This is due to the fact that there are leukocytes throughout even normal tissue. It was also recognized from this study, however, that since in the region of inflammation the leukocytes occur in clusters, a pure sizing operation was inadequate for the location of clusters of leukocytes.

Next a CLO sequence was designed to permit the location of both small cell nuclei and small clusters of cell nuclei. This sequence first generated the endoskeleton. It consisted of five cycles of a two-step sequence which first performed one iteration with FAC = 5 and CNUM = 4 in subfields for the purpose of skeletonizing and then accumulated the endoskeleton filaments in an auxiliary data field by labeling these filaments (FAC = 8 and CNUM = 4). This result was ORed with the residues obtained from the first CLO sequence and with the set of all pixels whose N^8 characterized ends (tips) of the skeleton branches. Next, intermediate elements in the endoskeleton were located using a sizing operation based on shrinking executed in two stages. During the first stage residues were not preserved (4 iterations using FAC = 8 and CNUM = 4). After that 4 more iterations were performed using subfields and the SUPRPIC mode which preserved residues. The residues were then transformed into squares (as in the sequence for locating small nuclei) and ORed with the original image resulting in the results shown in Fig. 33(b). This result was more specific to the disease sites but still located many regions within the tissue sample which were not inflamed. It had the advantage of successfully marking small clusters of leukocytes in the diseased upper right region of the original image.

Further CLO sequences were designed using the exoskeleton. The exoskeleton was generated by iterating a CLO using FAC = 5 and CNUM = 4 in the subfield mode until $\mathfrak{D} = \mathfrak{C}$. The full exoskeleton (and its complement) are shown in Fig. 34. This figure also shows the result of a sizing operation (using shrinking) which located the small "tiles" enclosed by the filaments of the exoskeleton. These tiles were located using 4 iterations in subfields and preserving residues (FAC =

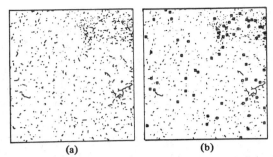

Fig. 33. (a) The endoskeleton of Fig. 29(b) and (b) labeling of intermediate endoskeletal elements.

TABLE V
OPERATION TIMES FOR VARIOUS CELLULAR LOGIC SEQUENCES
FOR ANALYZING IMAGES OF LIVER TISSUE BIOPSIES

CLO SEQUENCES 512 x 512 ARRAY	ESTIMATED COMPUTATION TIME REQUIRED	
	USING SUPRPIC	USING diff3
Location of microcytes	4 min.	100 ms.
Extraction of endoskeleton	7 min.	200 ms.
Location of intermediate elements in endoskeleton	10 min.	350 ms.
Location of microtiles in exoskeleton	16 min.	500 ms.
Extraction of closed loop in partial exoskeleton	36 min.	950 ms.

5 and CNUM = 4). The resultant residues were transformed into small squares (as above) and ORed with the initial image resulting in the various other images displayed in Fig. 34. As can be seen, the location of small tiles is considerably more specific to the sites of tissue abnormality than any of the previously generated features.

Another successful sequence in the analysis of abnormality was to note that, as the exoskeleton was generated, closed loops in the exoskeleton first appeared in regions of abnormality (Fig. 35). By arresting the generation of the exoskeleton (i.e., the partial exoskeleton) after 4 iterations (FAC = 5 and CNUM = 4), closed loops were extracted after 128 cycles (FAC = 8 and CNUM = 4) without subfields. This relatively lengthy sequence culminated in the result shown in Fig. 35 which was judged to be the most successful sequence for extracting regions of abnormality from the particular image under examination.

4) Speed of Operation: Fig. 32 not only furnishes the details of all CLO sequences utilized in investigations of liver tissue image architecture but indicates CPU time required when running SUPRPIC on an Interdata 7/32. Although these times are good for a general purpose computer (approximately 40 μs per pixop) the actual expense of running such an analysis for liver tissue biopsy image analysis would be prohibitive. To determine the improvement in speed possible using a commercial CLM, the CLO sequences were converted into GLOL (Section VI-B) and time estimates made for running them on the diff3. Results are given in Table V.

VII. CONCLUSION

Cellular logic and cellular logic operations (CLO's) have been known and studied since the early work of von Neumann, Kirsch, Golay, and Unger in the 1950's. This early interest

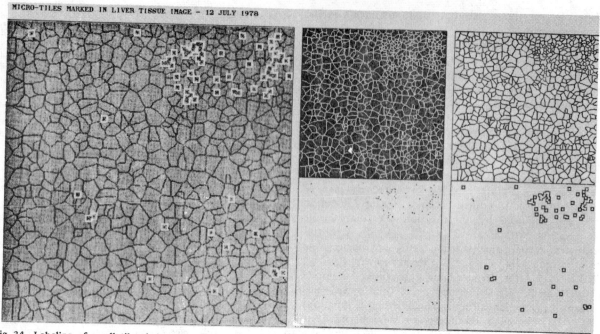

Fig. 34. Labeling of small tiles (microtiles) in the exoskeleton of Fig. 29(b) using a shrinking sequence of CLO's for the purpose of sizing.

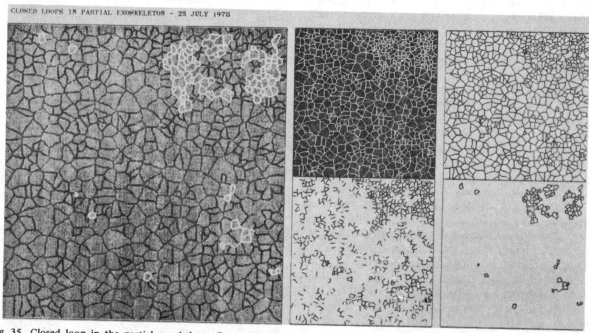

Fig. 35. Closed loop in the partial exoskeleton (lower left insert) are located by a sequence which iteratively removes 1-elements having a crossing number less than 4. The result is a labeling of the fatty liver tissue image which is more specific to sites of inflammation than all other measurements investigated.

in cellular logic was for the most part theoretical. Practical applications, primarily in image analysis, ensued in the 1960's and 1970's. Such applications were frequently realized and implemented using special purpose hardware such as the CLIP series of CA's as well as by such cellular logic machines as CELLSCAN, GLOPR, BIP, and PICAP. Finally, the mid-1970's saw the commercialization of cellular logic image analysis when diff3[1] became a commercial product. The latter machine is applied exclusively in the analysis of white blood cell images and points to biomedicine as the major successful area of application of cellular logic for image processing.

In reviewing the uses of cellular logic and the methodology of its employment in image processing, this paper has shown how CLO's may be categorized according to the tessellation in which they are embedded and according to the type or types of CLO sequences employed. It is found in reviewing most cellular logic algorithms that there are three basic types of sequences: those which are carried out in a single step; those which iterate the same CLO for many steps; those which repetitively alternate subsequences of CLO strings.

[1] A Perkin-Elmer Corporation development now manufactured by Coulter Electronics Company.

The effect of the CLO sequence on the data array which comprises an image is frequently one of boundary modification. Depending on the CLO sequence(s) utilized, a boundary may be expanded to form the convex hull, or reduced so as to form the convex kernel, skeleton, or residue. Many such CLO sequences have been illustrated herein.

The features of an image are extracted, when using CLO sequences, by carrying out image bit counts at strategic points during the execution of one or more CLO sequences. These counts form a measurement vector which is used in image classification. A typical example is in the analysis of the white blood cell image where features related to the size, shape, and texture of both nucleus and cytoplasm are extracted and then used for automatic white blood cell identification. Other medical image processing applications which have been illustrated in this paper are concerned with the determination of the structure of the thorax as presented in the chest radiograph and in the quantitation of tissue architecture as presented in microscope images of tissue biopsies. Further illustrations are provided in character recognition and in character encoding for reduced entropy facsimile transmission of text.

In all the applications of cellular logic are growing rapidly and its use is being facilitated by the rapidly decreasing cost of large scale integrated circuitry. It is hoped that the purpose of this paper, which is to codify, generalize, and clarify cellular logic operations, will be realized in assisting the reader to understand this particular form of image processing and pattern-recognition logic.

ACKNOWLEDGMENT

Particular appreciation goes to L. Cordella and the staff of the Cybernetics Laboratory, Naples, Italy, to T. J. Fountain and the members of the Image Processing Group, University College London, to O. Greunke and F. Senk of the Perkin-Elmer Corporation, to N. Wald, J. M. Herron, L. Davis, and S. England of the Biomedical Image Processing Unit of the University of Pittsburgh, and to T. Fukumura and N. Honda of Nagoya University, Y. Inagari of Mie University, and to the members of the Pattern Recognition Group in Nagoya University. Finally the assistance of Claire A. Haluska, Department of Electrical Engineering, Carnegie-Mellon University, is acknowledged in typing the manuscript as well as the assistance of G. B. Arnold, E. G. Beggs, V. B. Platek, and Mary N. Adams in preparing the line drawings and photographic illustrations.

REFERENCES

[1] M. L. Minsky and S. Papert, *Perceptrons, Introduction to Computational Geometry.* Cambridge, MA: M.I.T. Press, 1970.

[2] S. W. Golomb, *Shift Register Sequences.* San Francisco, CA: Holden Day, 1967.

[3] R. G. Schrandt and S. M. Ulam, "On recursively defined geometrical objects and patterns of growth," in *Essays on Cellular Automata*, A. W. Burks, Ed. Urbana, IL: Univ. Illinois Press, 1970, p. 232.

[4] J. von Neumann, "The general logical theory of automata," in *Cerebral Mechanisms in Behavior—The Hixon Symposium*, L. A. Jeffress, Ed. New York: Wiley, 1951.

[5] ——, *Theory of Self-Reproducing Automata*, A. W. Burks, Ed. Urbana, IL: Univ. Illinois Press, 1966.

[6] J. W. Thatcher, "Universality in the von Neumann cellular model," in *Essays on Cellular Automata*, A. W. Burks, Ed. Urbana, IL: Univ. Illinois Press, 1970, p. 132.

[7] E. F. Moore, "Machine models of self-reproduction," in *Essays on Cellular Automata*, A. W. Burks, Ed. Urbana, IL: Univ. Illinois Press, 1970, p. 187.

[8] J. Myhill, "The abstract theory of self-reproduction," in *Essays on Cellular Automata*, A. W. Burks, Ed. Urbana, IL: Univ. Illinois Press, 1970, p. 206.

[9] S. M. Ulam, "On some mathematical problems connected with patterns of growth of figures," in *Essays on Cellular Automata*. Urbana, IL: Univ. Illinois Press, 1970, p. 219.

[10] R. G. Schrandt and S. M. Ulam, "On patterns of growth of figures in two dimensions," *Nat. Amer. Math. Soc.*, vol. 7, pp. 642-651, 1960.

[11] P. R. Stein and S. M. Ulam, "Nonlinear transformation studies on electronic computers," in *Essays on Cellular Automata*. Urbana, IL: Univ. Illinois Press, 1970, p. 244.

[12] J. H. Holland, "Iterative circuit computers," in *Essays on Cellular Automata*. Urbana, IL: Univ. Illinois Press, 1970, p. 277.

[13] A. W. Burks, Ed., *Essays on Cellular Automata*. Urbana, IL: Univ. Illinois Press, 1970.

[14] E. R. Banks, "Universality in cellular automata," in *Proc. 11th SWAT*, pp. 194-215, 1970.

[15] H. Yamada and S. M. Amoroso, "Structural and behavioral equivalences of tessellation automata," *Inform. Contr.*, vol. 18, pp. 1-31, 1971.

[16] A. R. Smith, III, "Cellular automata and formal languages," in *Proc. 11th SWAT*, pp. 216-224, 1970.

[17] ——, "Two-dimensional formal languages and pattern recognition by cellular automata," in *Proc. 12th SWAT*, pp. 144-152, 1971.

[18] ——, "Cellular automata complexity trade-offs," *Inform. Contr.*, vol. 18, pp. 466-482, 1971.

[19] ——, "Simple computation-universal cellular spaces," *J. Assoc. Comput. Mach.*, vol. 18, pp. 339-353, 1971.

[20] S. B. Akers, Jr., "A rectangular logic array," *IEEE Trans. Comput.*, vol. C-21, pp. 848-857, Aug. 1972.

[21] *Proc. Int. Symp. Uniformly Structured Automata and Logic* (IEEE 75 CH1052-6C), 1975.

[22] S. Noguchi and J. Oizumi, "A survey of cellular logic," *J. Inst. Electron. Commun. Eng. Jap.*, vol. 54, no. 2, pp. 206-220, 1971.

[23] H. Nishio, "A classified bibliography on cellular automata theory—With focus on recent Japanese references," in *Proc. IEEE Int. Symp. Uniformly Structured Automata and Logic*, pp. 206-214, 1975.

[24] A. Maruoka: "Cellular automata," *J. Inst. Electron. Commun. Eng. Jap.*, vol. 61, no. 10, pp. 1073-1083, 1978.

[25] A. Rosenfeld and C. R. Dyer, "Cellular pyramids for image analysis," Dep. Computer Science, Univ. Maryland, College Park, Tech. Reps. 544 and 596, 1977.

[26] D. L. Slotnick, W. C. Borck, and R. C. McReynolds, "The SOLOMON computer," in *Proc. Western Joint Computer Conf.*, pp. 87-107, 1962.

[27] H. Falk, "What went wrong V—Reaching for a gigaflop," *IEEE Spectrum*, vol. 13, no. 10, pp. 65-69, 1976.

[28] B. H. McCormick, "The Illinois pattern recognition computer—ILLIAC III," *IEEE Trans. Electron. Commun.*, vol. EC-12, pp. 791-813, 1963.

[29] M. J. B. Duff, B. M. Jones, and L. J. Townsend, "Parallel processing pattern recognition system UCPR1," *Nucl. Instrum. Meth.*, vol. 52, p. 284, 1967.

[30] S. Levialdi, "CLOPAN: A closedness pattern analyzer," in *Proc. Inst. Elec. Eng.*, vol. 115n, no. 6, pp. 879-880, 1968.

[31] M. J. B. Duff, "A cellular logic array for image processing," *Pat. Recog.*, vol. 5, pp. 229-247, 1973.

[32] B. H. McCormick, W. J. Watson, and R. T. Borovec, "The pattern articulation unit of ILLIAC III: Homogeneous Boolean functions in the iterative array," Dep. Computer Science, Univ. Illinois, Urbana, Rep. 253, 1968.

[33] B. H. McCormick, "Advances in the development of image processing hardware," in *Image Processing in Biological Science*, D. M. Ramsey, Ed. Berkeley, CA: Univ. California Press, 1968, p. 149.

[34] S. Levialdi, "Parallel pattern processing," *IEEE Trans. Syst., Man, Cybern.*, vol. SMC-1, pp. 292-296, 1971.

[35] ——, "Parallel pattern processing," *IEEE Trans. Syst. Man, Cybern.*, vol. SMC-1, no. 3, pp. 292-296, 1971.

[36] ——, "Parallel counting of binary patterns," *Electron. Letts.*, vol. 6, no. 25, pp. 798-800, 1970.

[37] ——, "On shrinking of binary patterns," *Commun. ACM*, vol. 15, no. 1, pp. 7-10, 1972.

[38] L. Cordella, M. J. B. Duff, and S. Levialdi, "Comparing sequential and parallel processing of pictures," in *Proc. 3rd IJCPR*, pp. 703-707, 1976.

[39] S. Levialdi, "Incremental ratio by parallel logic," *Electron. Lett.*, vol. 13, no. 12, p. 554, 1967.

[40] M. J. B. Duff, "Cellular logic and its significance in pattern recognition," in *AGARD Conf. Proc. no. 94 on Artificial Intelligence*, vol. 25, pp. 1-13, 1971.

[41] ——, "Geometrical analysis of image parts," in *Digital Image Processing and Analysis*, J. C. Simon and A. Rosenfeld, Eds. Leyden, The Netherlands: Noordhoff, 1977, p. 101.

[42] S. H. Unger, "Pattern recognition and detection," *Proc. IRE*, vol. 47, p. 1737, 1959.

[43] O. Selfridge, "Pattern recognition in modern Computers," in *Proc. WJCC*, pp. 94–97, 1955.

[44] R. A. Kirsch, "Experiments in processing pictorial information with a digital computer." in *Proc. EJCC*, p. 221, 1957.

[45] G. A. Moore, "Applications of computers to the quantitative analysis of microstructures," NBS Rep. 9428, Oct. 1966.

[46] A. Tojo, "Note on spatial pattern recognition with the iterative circuit information processing system," *Bull. Electrotech. Lab.*, vol. 30, no. 11, pp. 937–945, 1966.

[47] ——, "Pattern description with a highly parallel information processing system—I," *Bull. Electrotech. Lab.*, vol. 31, no. 8, pp. 930–946, 1967.

[48] ——, "Pattern description with a highly parallel information processing unit—IV—Generalized discussion on template matrix matching operation," *Bull. Electrotech. Lab.*, vol. 31, no. 12, pp. 1294–1301, 1967.

[49] ——, "Pattern description with a highly parallel information processing unit—V—Distance functions and minimum path connections," *Bull. Electrotech. Lab.*, vol. 32, no. 9, pp. 1930–1942, 1968.

[50] A. Tojo, T. Yamaguchi, and H. Aoyama, "Pattern description with highly parallel information unit—VI—Construction and simulation of this system," *Bull. Electrotech. Lab.*, vol. 33, no. 5, pp. 479–505, 1969.

[51] A. Tojo and T. Yamaguchi, "Highly parallel information processing system for graphical data processing and associative processing," *J. Inform. Proc. Soc. Jap.*, vol. 11, no. 2, pp. 70–78, 1970.

[52] K. Preston, Jr., "The Cellscan system—A leukocyte pattern analyzer," in *Proc. WJCC*, p. 173, 1961.

[53] M. Ingram, P. E. Norgren, and K. Preston, Jr., "Automatic differentiation of white blood cells," in *Image Processing in Biological Science*, D. M. Ramsey, Ed. Berkeley, CA: Univ. California Press, 1968, p. 97.

[54] K. Preston, Jr., "Applications of cellular logic to biomedical image processing," in *Computer Techniques in Biomedical Engineering*. New York: Auerbach, 1973, p. 295.

[55] N. F. Izzo and W. Coles, "Blood cell scanner identifies rare cells," *Electronics*, vol. 35, no. 52, Apr. 1962.

[56] M. J. E. Golay, "Hexagonal parallel pattern transformations," *IEEE Trans. Comput.*, vol. C-18, pp. 733–740, 1969.

[57] K. Preston, Jr. and P. E. Norgren, "Interactive image processor speeds pattern recognition," *Electronics*, vol. 45, p. 89, 1972.

[58] S. B. Gray, "Local properties of binary images in two dimensions," *IEEE Trans. Comput.*, vol. C-20, p. 551, 1971.

[59] ——, "The binary image processor and its applications," Information International Inc., Rep. 90365-5C, Jan. 1972.

[60] B. Kruse, "A parallel picture processing machine," *IEEE Trans. Comput.*, vol. C-22, p. 1075, 1973.

[61] ——, "Design and implementation of a picture processor," Univ. Linkoping, Linkoping, Sweden, Studies Sci. and Tech. Dissertations No. 13, ISBN 91-7372-141-7, 1977.

[62] G. R. Allen, L. O. Bonrud, J. J. Cosgrove, and R. M. Stone, "The design and use of special purpose processors for the machine processing of remotely sensed data," LARS Tech. Rpt., Purdue Univ., 1973.

[63] D. Rohrbacher and J. L. Potter, "Image processing with the STARAN parallel computer," *Computer*, vol. 10, no. 8, pp. 54–59, 1972.

[64] P. M. Flanders, D. H. Hunt, S. F. Reddaway, and D. Parkinson, "Efficient high speed computing with the distributed array processor," in *Proc. Symp. High Speed Computer and Algorithm Organization* (University of Illinois, Urbana), 1977.

[65] H. Asada, "An interactive system for image processing—TOSPICS." Inst. Electronics Commun. Eng., PRL75-51, pp. 19–30, 1975.

[66] T. Kondou, "Image processing software system—TOSPICS EXEC," in *Proc. 6th Image Tech. Conf.*, p. 61, 1975.

[67] K-i. Mori, H. Shinoda, and H. Asada, "Toshiba pattern information cognition system—TOSPICS," *Toshiba Rev.*, vol. 107, pp. 3–5, 1977.

[68] ——, "Design of local parallel pattern processor for image processing," in *Proc. Nat. Computer Conf.*, 1978.

[69] M. J. Flynn, "Some computer organizations and their effectiveness," *IEEE Trans. Comput.*, vol. C-21, pp. 948–960, 1972.

[70] E. F. Codd, *Cellular Automata*. New York: Academic Press, 1968.

[71] J. Sklansky, "A theory of nonuniformly digitized binary pictures," *IEEE Trans. Syst. Man, Cyber.*, vol. SMC-6, no. 9, pp. 637–647, 1976.

[72] E. S. Deutsch, "Thinning algorithms on rectangular, hexagonal and triangular arrays," Computer Science Center, Univ. Maryland, College Park, Tech. Rep. 70-115, 1970.

[73] C. T. Zahn, "Region boundaries on a triangular grid," in *Proc. 2nd IJCPR*, p. 136, 1974.

[74] K. Preston, Jr., "Feature extraction by Golay hexagonal pattern transforms," *IEEE Trans. Comput.*, vol. C-20, pp. 1007–1014, 1971.

[75] A. Rosenfeld, "Connectivity in digital pictures," *J. Assoc. Comput. Mach.*, vol. 17, pp. 146–160, 1970.

[76] A. Rosenfeld and A. C. Kak, "Digital topology," Maryland Computer Science Center, Univ. Maryland, College Park, Tech. Rep. 77-542, 1977.

[77] S. N. Cole, "Real-time computation by *n*-dimensional iterative arrays of finite-state machines," *IEEE Trans. Comput.*, vol. C-18, no. 4, pp. 349–365, 1969.

[78] Y. Suenaga, J-i. Toriwaki, and T. Fukumura, "Range filters for processing continuous tone pictures and their applications," *Syst. Comput. Contr.*, vol. 5, no. 3, pp. 16–24, 1974.

[79] S. Yokoi, J-i. Toriwaki, and T. Fukumura, "Theoretical analysis of parallel processing of pictures using algebraic properties of picture operations," in *Proc. 3rd IJCPR*, p. 723, 1976.

[80] Y. Suenaga, J-i. Toriwaki, and T. Fukumura, "Fundamental study of difference filters for processing of continuous tone pictures," *Trans. Inst. Electronics Commun. Eng. Jap.*, vol. 57D, no. 3, pp. 119–126, 1974.

[81] J-i. Toriwaki, Y. Suenaga, T. Negoro, and T. Fukumura, "Pattern recognition of chest X-ray images," *Proc. 1st IJCPR*, p. 125, 1973.

[82] S. Yokoi, J-i. Toriwaki, and T. Fukumura, "Properties of gray weighted distance transformation and decomposition of operations," Tech. Group Pattern Recognition Learning, Inst. Electron. Commun. Eng., Japan, Rep. PRL 76-29, 1976.

[83] G. Levi and U. Montanari, "Grey weighted skeleton," *Inform. Contr.*, vol. 17, no. 1, pp. 62–91, 1970.

[84] M. J. B. Duff, "Arithmetic operations in CLIP3," Image Proc., Univ. College London, Group Rep. 75/5, 1975.

[85] L. Cordella, M. J. B. Duff, and S. Levialdi, "Thresholding: A challenge for parallel processing," *Comput. Graph. Image Process.*, vol. 6, pp. 207–220, 1977.

[86] T. Negoro, J-i. Toriwaki, and T. Fukumura, "A method for classification of point elements in line-drawing patterns," *Trans. J. Inst. Electron. Commun. Eng. Jap.*, vol. 55-D, no. 11, pp. 762–763, 1972.

[87] S. Yamamoto, M. Yasuda, K. Miyamoto, and M. Tsutsumi, "Design of hand-written numeral recognizer," *Trans. Inst. Electron. Commun. Eng.*, vol. 53-C, no. 10, pp. 691–698, 1970.

[88] H. Genchi, K. Mori, S. Watanabe, and S. Katsuragi, "Recognition of handwritten numerical characters for automatic letter sorting," *Proc. IEEE*, vol. 56, no. 8, pp. 1292–1301, 1968.

[89] N. Nakayama, C. Nago, and H. Takebe, "High performance optical character reader, OCR-W (Type BOP-200)," *Toshiba Rev.*, vol. 30, no. 4, pp. 341–344, 1975.

[90] S. Yamada and J. P. Fornango, "Experimental results for local filtering of digitized pictures," Dep. Computer Science, Univ. Illinois, Urbana, Rpt. 184, 1965.

[91] S. Yokoi, J-i Toriwaki, and T. Fukumura, "Topological properties in digitized binary pictures," *Trans Inst. Electron. Commun. Eng. Jap.*, vol. 56-D, no. 11, pp. 662–669, Nov. 1973.

[92] ——, "An analysis of topological properties of digitized binary pictures using local features," *Comput. Graph. Image Proc.*, vol. 4, pp. 63–73, 1975.

[93] J. Toriwaki and T. Fukumura, "Extraction of structural information from digitized grey pictures," *Comput. Graph. Image Proc.*, vol. 7, pp. 30–51, 1978.

[94] R. Stefanelli and A. Rosenfeld, "Some parallel thinning algorithms for digital pictures," *J. Assoc. Comput. Mach.*, vol. 18, pp. 255–264, 1971.

[95] E. S. Deutsch, "Thinning algorithms on rectangular arrays," Computer Science Cent., Univ. Maryland, College Park, Tech. Rep. 70-115, 1970.

[96] P. Saraga, "Thinning operators," Mullard Res. Labs., Tech. Note 1294, 1974.

[97] E. S. Deutsch, "Comments on a line thinning scheme," *Brit. Comput. J.*, vol. 12, no. 4, p. 142, 1969.

[98] ——, "On some preprocessing techniques for character recognition," in *Computer Processing in Communications*. New York: Brooklyn Polytech. Press, 1969, pp. 221–234.

[99] G. L. Shelton and L. P. Horowitz, "Pattern recognition preprocessing techniques," U.S. Patent 3 339 179, 1967.

[100] C. J. Hilditch, "Linear skeletons from square cupboards," in *Machine Intelligence*, vol. 4, B. Meltzer and D. Michie, Eds. New York: American Elsevier, 1969, pp. 403–420.

[101] S. Sternberg, Environmental Res. Inst. Michigan (ERIM), personal communication.

[102] H. Blum, "A transformation for extracting new descriptors of shape," in *Models for the Perception of Speech and Visual Form*, W. Wathen-Dunn, Ed. Cambridge, MA: M.I.T. Press, 1967, pp. 362–380.

[103] C. Mott-Smith, "Medial axis transforms," in *Picture Processing and Psychopictorics*, B. S. Lipkin and A. Rosenfeld, Eds. New York: Academic Press, 1970, pp. 267–283.

[104] K. Shikand, J-i. Toriwaki, and T. Fukumura, "A wave propagation method—A method of conversion of grey pictures into line figures," *Trans. Inst. Electron. Commun. Eng. Jap.*, vol. 55-D, no. 10, pp. 668–675, 1972.

[105] J-i. Toriwaki, K. Shikano, and T. Fukumura, "Properties of wave propagation method for conversion of grey pictures into line figures," *J. Inform. Process. Soc. Jap.*, vol. 14, no. 7, pp. 474–481, 1973.

[106] K. Shikano, J-i. Toriwaki, and T. Fukumura, "Modified algorithms of wave propagation method for processing of multilevel pictures," *Trans. Electron. Commun. Eng. Jap.*, vol. 56-D, no. 9, pp. 515–522, 1973.

[107] S. Mori, T. Mori, K. Yamamoto, M. Yamada, and T. Saito, "Recognition of handprinted characters," in *Proc. 2nd IJCPR*, pp. 233–237, 1974.

[108] T. Mori, S. Mori, K. Yamamoto, H. Yamada, T. Saito, and K. Nakata, "Recognition of handprinted and alphanumeric and special characters," *Trans. Inst. Electron. Commun. Eng. Jap.*, vol. 58-D, no. 6, pp. 414–421, 1976.

[109] T. Mori, "Fundamental research with respect to feature extraction for handprinted character recognition," *Res. Electrotech. Lab.*, no. 762, June 1976.

[110] S. Mizuno, T. Usubuchi, K. Iinuma, and T. Ishiguro, "Efficient facsimile data reduction using thinning process," *Tech. Group Commun. Syst.*, Rep. CS77-38, July 1977.

[111] T. Usubuchi, S. Mizuno, and K. Iinuma, "Entropy reduction of facsimile pictures by a thinning process," in *Abstracts of Presentation, 1977 Picture Coding Symp.* (Tokyo, Japan, August 1977), pp. 55–56, 1977.

[112] M. J. B. Duff and D. M. Watson, "CLIP3: A cellular logic image processor," in *New Concepts and Technologies in Parallel Information Processing*, E. R. Caianiello, Ed. The Netherlands: Noordhoff, Leyden, 1975, pp. 75–86.

[113] J-i. Toriwaki, Y. Suenaga, T. Negoro, and T. Fukumura, "Pattern recognition of chest X-ray images," *Comput. Graph. Image Process.*, vol. 2, no. 3/4, pp. 252–271, Dec. 1973.

[114] J-i. Toriwaki and T. Fukumura, "Pattern recognition of chest photofluorograms—Recognition and feature extraction of the heart shadow," *Syst. Comput. Contr.*, vol. 5, no. 6, pp. 99–106, 1974.

[115] P. P. Tsiang, C. A. Harlow, G. S. Lodwick, and S. J. Dwyer, III, "Computer analysis of chest radiographs using size and shape descriptors," Dep. Electrical Engineering, Univ. Missouri, Columbia, Tech. Rep. IAL-TR 39-74, 1974.

[116] K. S. Fu, Y. P. Chien, and E. Persoon, "Computer systems for the analysis of chest X-ray," School of Electrical Engineering, Purdue Univ., Lafayette, IN, AARL-Memo no. 12, 1975.

[117] D. H. Ballard, "Hierarchic recognition of tumors in chest radiographs," School of Engineering, Univ. California, Irvine, Tech. Rep. 74-4, 1974.

[118] H. Wechsler and J. Sklansky, "Finding the rib cage in chest radiographs," *Pattern Recog.*, vol. 9, no. 1, pp. 21–30, 1977.

[119] J. Toriwaki, J. Hasegawa, and T. Fukumura, "Recognition of vessel shadows for automated measurements and classification system of chest photofluorograms," in *Proc. Symp. Computer Aided Diagnosis of Medical Images*, pp. 1–8, 1976.

[120] J. Toriwaki, Y. Suenaga, T. Negoro, and T. Fukumura, "Pattern recognition of chest X-ray images," in *Proc. 1st IJCPR*, 1973, pp. 125–137.

[121] Y. Suenaga, J. Toriwaki, and T. Fukumura, "Pattern recognition of chest photofluorograms—Recognition of abnormal shadows in lung," *Syst. Comput. Contrls.*, vol. 5, no. 3, pp. 35–43, 1974.

[122] J. Sklansky, "Boundary detection in medical radiographs," in *Digital Processing of Biomedical Images*, K. Preston, Jr. and M. Onoe, Eds. New York: Plenum Press, 1976, pp. 309–322.

[123] E. Persoon, "A new edge detection algorithm and its applications in picture processing," *Comput. Graph. Image Process.*, vol. 5, pp. 425–446, 1976.

[124] J. Toriwaki, M. Koshimizu, and T. Fukumura, "MINISCR-V2—The software system for automated interpretation of chest photofluorograms," in *Digital Processing of Biomedical Images*, K. Preston, Jr. and M. Onoe, Eds. New York: Plenum Press, 1976, pp. 357–384.

[125] M. Levine, "Automated differentials: Geometric Data's HEMATRACK^{tm}," *Amer. J. Med. Technol.*, vol. 40, p. 462, 1974.

[126] D. A. Cotter and B. H. Sage, "Performance of the LARC^{tm} classifier in clinical laboratories," *J. Histochem. Cytochem.*, vol. 24, no. 1, pp. 202–210, 1976.

[127] K. Preston, Jr., "Clinical use of automated microscopes for cell analysis," in *Digital Processing of Biomedical Images*, K. Preston, Jr. and M. Onoe, Eds. New York: Plenum Press, 1976, pp. 47–58.

[128] J. E. Green, "Parallel processing in a pattern recognition based image processing system: The Abbott ADC-500^{tm} differential counter," in *Proc. 1978 IEEE Computer Soc. Conf. Pattern Recognition Image Process.*, pp. 492–498, 1978.

[129] M. Ingram and K. Preston, Jr., "Automatic analysis of blood cells," *Sci. Amer.*, vol. 223, no. 5, pp. 72–82, 1970.

[130] *Perkin-Elmer diff3 System Users Manual*, Norwalk, CT, Nov. 1976.

[131] K. Preston, Jr., "Use of the Golay logic processor in pattern recognition studies using hexagonal neighborhood logic," in *Computers and Automata*. New York: Polytechnic Press, 1972, pp. 609–624.

[132] K. Preston, Jr., and J. R. Carvalko, "On determining optimum simple Golay marking transformations for binary image processing," *IEEE Trans. Electronic Comput.*, vol. C-21, p. 1430, 1972.

[133] Clinical Laboratory Study, Chicago Hospital Council, Chicago, IL, 1965.

Reprinted from *Computer*, Volume 12, Number 3, March 1979,
pages 28-37. Copyright © 1979 by The Institute of Electrical
and Electronics Engineers, Inc.

*Relational data base machines using head-per-track
disk technology or its electronic equivalent can move
processing logic closer to the data, providing simplified
storage organizations for large-scale applications.*

Relational Data Base Machines

Diane C.P. Smith
John Miles Smith

University of New Mexico*

The potential of special-purpose hardware, particularly intelligent secondary storage devices, holds special appeal to the implementers of relational data base management systems. The relational model,[8] however, is structurally and behaviorally far removed from the storage organization and primitive operators of existing hardware. This means that the implementer must construct multiple levels of sophisticated software to produce an efficient system. The development of VLSI technology for chip design and innovations in mass storage technology suggest that this gap can be narrowed, easing the problem of providing efficient support for high-level, user-oriented data base management systems.

The designs proposed for relational DBMS support have been investigated and developed to very different degrees. Some have been specified for only a partial set of DBMS functions; some have been simulated while others have been prototyped. The depth of coverage in this survey reflects these differences and also the availability of published documentation. Because of variations in the design objectives and in the detail of specifications, no attempt is made to contrast critically the expected performance.

The relational model

The relational model is based on the notion that objects can be modeled as *n*-ary relations. For example, a "supplier" can be thought of as a relationship among such attributes as "supplier number" (S#), "supplier name" (SN) and "supplier location"

(SLOC). Such relations can be pictured as unordered tables with nonredundant rows.

Figure 1 shows a relational model of a simplified inventory data base. Individual rows in the PART table correspond to individual types of parts in the inventory. Because rows are required to be nonredundant within a relation, each row can be named uniquely by a subset of its attributes. For example, in Figure 1 either S# or SN can be used to name a row uniquely, while S# and P# must be used together to identify a row of the SUPPLY table. Such sets of attributes are called the *key* of the relation. If a subset of the attributes in one relation is the key of a second relation, we can interpret the first relation as a relationship between its remaining attributes and the second relation. In Figure 1 S# and P# are the keys of the SUPPLIER and PART relations, respectively. Thus SUPPLY is a relationship between these two objects and quantity (Q). Such keys in SUPPLY are called *foreign keys*. They are used to support relationships between different objects in the data base and queries over such relationships.

Modeling data in a relational structure lends itself to the development of high-level query languages. Rather than implementing a query by programming a traversal from record instance (row) to record instance, operators in the relational languages apply to the tables as a whole. Since the traversal strategy must be determined by the language processor, less programming expertise is required of data base users.

Several styles of relational query language have been developed. One of these, Relational Algebra,[9] has received the most attention as a candidate for hardware support. Relational Algebra consists of a set of operators which can be applied to relations to create new relations. These operators can be composed to form expressions. A typical set of relational

---

*Work on this paper was undertaken while the authors were at the University of Utah.

operators is specified in Figure 2. Sample queries using these operators are described in Figure 3. Of these operators, SELECT and JOIN appear to have the most potential for hardware implementation. SELECT is of interest if the parallelism that it exhibits can be exploited by appropriate hardware. JOIN is of intertest because it is a very expensive operation to implement in software on conventional hardware. It requires a large amount of cross checking between rows of different relations. Greater efficiency could be achieved by more parallelism in the cross checking or by an optimized sort of the rows delivered to a software JOIN from the different relations.

The tabular layout, the use of foreign keys (as opposed to physical pointers), and the high level of the associated query languages all contribute to the user orientation of relational models. However, these same features make successful implementation dependent on layers of very sophisticated software. With more direct support by the underlying hardware, it will be easier to build these convenient DBMSs.

Hardware advances and their potential for DBMS applications

Two recent developments in hardware technology show particular promise for providing direct support for the relational features itemized: the very-large-scale integration of logic on chips and the development of electronic rotating store based on CCD and magnetic-bubble technology. The capability of placing sophisticated and specialized logic on very inexpensive chips means that the logic can be easily replicated and distributed over data. Thus functions such as searching and sorting (on which the operators JOIN and SELECT are based) can be moved from the CPU to storage, thereby reducing the data-transfer costs and decreasing processing time because of increased parallelism.

The most effective distribution associates logic with small amounts of data. This maximizes the amount of parallel processing, thereby minimizing

---

PROJECT relation (column list)

The effect of PROJECTing a relation on a set of columns is to produce a new relation with only the columns named in the column list.

SELECT relation (selection condition)
Selection condition: a Boolean expression defined over the columns of relation. The expression can consist of membership tests ($\in$) on the value of a column in the relation and of comparison tests ($=, \neq, <, >, \leq, \geq$) between columns and constants or computer values.

The effect of SELECTing from a relation is a new relation with only the rows from the original relation that satisfy the selection condition.

JOIN relation1 (joining condition) relation2
Joining condition: a Boolean expression of comparisons ($=, \neq, <, >, \leq, \geq$) between columns in relation1 and relation2.

The effect of JOINing two relations is a new relation consisting of all column headers from the two joined relations and rows formed by concatenating rows from relation1 with rows from relation2 where the values in the rows satisfy the joining condition.

UNION relation1 (column-pair list) relation2
Column-pair list: a list of pairs consisting of a column name from relation1 and a column name from relation2.

The effect of UNIONing two relations is a relation consisting of all the rows of both relation1 and relation2 with any duplicates removed and the columns ordered in the sequence given in the column-pair list.

INTERSECT relation1 (column-pair list) relation2

The result of INTERSECTing two relations is a new relation consisting of only those rows appearing in both relations.

DIFFERENCE relation1 (column-pair list) relation2

The effect of differencing two relations is a new relation consisting of rows that are in relation1 and not in relation2.

Figure 2. Definitions of a set of relational operators.

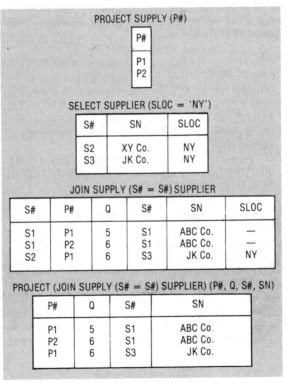

Figure 3. Sample queries over the inventory data base of Figure 1, using the relational operators defined in Figure 2.

SUPPLY

S#	P#	Q
S1	P1	5
S1	P2	6
S3	P1	6

SUPPLIER

S#	SN	SLOC
S1	ABC Co.	—
S2	XY Co.	NY
S3	JK Co.	NY

PART

P#	PD
P1	CAM
P2	GEAR

Figure 1. A simplified relational data base for keeping inventories.

total execution time. Logic can be distributed over data in any of three ways: (1) by integrating both the logic and data on a single VLSI chip, (2) by associating the logic with the read/write mechanism of a track or loop of rotating memory, and (3) by configurating distributed microprocessor-based architectures. Starting with the first approach, each subsequent approach supports broader levels of parallelism.

The first approach holds little promise for data base applications, since MOS storage is too expensive for the large amounts of data typically involved. The second and third approaches, however, have been used to develop select, join, and sort machines for data base applications. We will survey data base-oriented machines based on these approaches and then consider how each of these machines supports the relational features discussed above.

The possibility of associating logic with the read/write heads of rotating storage devices* was recognized in the 1970's when Slotnick[33] proposed adding compare logic to magnetic disks and drums. Parker,[30] Parhami,[29] and Healy[15] refined this idea further. More recently Su,[10, 12, 38, 39, 41] Ozkarahan,[26-28, 32] and Lin[21, 22] investigated designs tailored to data base requirements, while Edelberg,[14] Chang,[6] Chen,[7] and Todd[40] developed designs to exploit the new CCD and bubble technologies.

CASSM—the Content Addressable Segment Sequential Memory of Lipovski and Su et al.—was one of the first data base-oriented designs. It was generalized to support network and hierarchical data bases as well as relational models. CASSM was implemented on fixed-head floppy disks as a standalone data base computer. As such it was provided with a full programming language interface[38] consisting of statements to:

(1) create and modify data bases (CREATE, AUGMENT, DESTROY, and RENAME);
(2) operate on the individual rows of a relation (OUTPUT, DELETE, INSERT, UPDATE, MARK, and MATCH);
(3) identify the relation in which rows are to be processed (IN); and
(4) control which rows are to be processed (IF-THEN-ELSE—a selection statement, DO, FOR-EACH, and BEGIN-END).

A second cellular logic machine has been prototyped that was oriented directly toward the relational model. RAP—the Relational Associative Processor of Ozkarahan et al.—was constructed using CCD shift registers. It is also a stand-alone data base computer with a full programming language interface similar to that of CASSM.

The remaining cellular logic machine studies that we consider have resulted in designs but not implementations. They are of interest, however,

because they either concentrate on solutions to important problems common to all cellular logic technology or attempt a unique exploitation of a particular hardware technology. RARES—the Rotating Associative Relational Store of Lin et al.—was designed as a backend processor. It interfaces with a comprehensive optimization strategy[34] for distributing the execution of relational queries between concurrent processors and a backend selection-and-sort machine. The design concentrates on optimizing the throughput of selected or sorted rows. Edelbert et al.'s Intelligent Memory was also designed as a backend machine for performing sorts, selections, and updating. This design, however, was developed to exploit the CCD and bubble technologies using a loop configuration for the memory cells. Chang's design, on the other hand, exploits a major/minor loop architecture for a bubble memory; Todd's design is based on a lattice architecture. The Chang machine was designed as a stand-alone data base computer and the Todd machine as a query processor. Chen's design is concerned only with supporting efficient sorting.

The idea of basing the design of data base hardware on a network of microprocessors dedicated to specific data base functions was first developed by Madnick in a system called INFOPLEX.[24] It organizes a memory and microprocessor hierarchy to exploit the parallelism inherent in concurrent accesses to a data base. The Database Computer[4, 5, 16] is a more extensive design that incorporates such important but neglected features as access control. The DBC has dedicated processors for access control, query and update interpretation, directory processing, etc. Similar to both INFOPLEX and DBC is the design for a distributed data base machine proposed by Stonebraker.[35] It uses conventional micro/mini computers to off-load data base functions from a central host computer. Both the DBC and INFOPLEX[18] support conventional access methods such as directories as well as associative head-per-track processors. They were designed to support any of the existing data base models—the network and hierarchic as well as the relational.

We will devote most of our attention in this paper to the impact of the new VLSI, bubble, and CCD chip technologies on the design of relational data base hardware. However, it is important to note that the exploitation of these advances is not the only route possible in developing relational hardware. New approaches to the overall design of a central processor architecture can provide a better base for building relational systems. One project, the LEECH machine[25] being built in Glasgow, is a special-purpose processor for vector-mode processing of relation rows piped from mass memory. A second project is the Content-Addressed File Store (CAFS)[3] being developed at ICL in Stevenage. It positions a special search processor and random-access bit-addressable memory between rotating storage device and a general-purpose processor. The JOIN algorithims of these two machines are described in the section on search and join features.

---

*The overall architecture of logic-per-track devices (also called cellular logic devices) is discussed by Su.[37] Only those features that directly support the relational data model are discussed in this paper.

Relational data representations

One expected benefit of moving processing logic closer to the data is that it will be possible to simplify the storage organization of the data. Currently, providing efficient access in a relational data base requires sophisticated address structures based on pointer chains, hashing algorithms, and directories.[2,36] These access structures require the capabilities of skilled system programmers for implementation and add to the space overhead of the data base. The designers of the data base machines described above have produced more simplified representations. These representations permit viewing the data in tabular (or close to tabular) form, but they differ greatly in organization and its impact on performance.

One effect of the difference in organization is a difference in storage utilization. In designing a representation, decisions must be made on how a relation and its columns are identified and how and where rows are marked to indicate interest for further processing. For example, a column value can be labeled with the column name, delimited by special characters, or stored in a fixed position. Space can be reserved in the data storage area for marks, or special marking memories can be provided. How these decisions are made determines the cost in space of storing a relation.

A result of moving selection logic to data on rotating storage is that only selected rows need be output for reporting purposes or for further processing. However, if many rows have been selected, two or more of them may contend for the output channel. In such cases only one row can be output; the others must wait for subsequent revolutions of the device. The storage representation chosen can impact the amount of contention possible. The proposed representations and the mechanisms they use to handle marking and contention are examined below.

CASSM. In CASSM, data is laid out along the track or loop of the rotating storage device in variable-length blocks. Each block, which can contain one or more rows of a relation, is treated as a sequence of 40-bit words. Thirty-two bits can be used to store either a delimiter, a column-value pair, a character string, or (to support non-relational applications) pointers and instructions. The remaining

bits are used as a tag to identify word content, as mark bits, and for internal processing. CASSM stores a relation as a two-level tree. The first level (0) corresponds to the entire relation and is represented by a delimiter word giving the relation name and the level number. The relation rows are stored following this delimiter in the format illustrated in Figure 4.

A row delimiter preceding each row gives the relation name and the level number (1). One word is then used for each non-null value in the row. From the word's 32-bit data field, 16 bits are used to encode the column name and 16 bits to encode the value. Expanded names and values are stored separately, using the character-string format. Since encoding space is needed for column names but none is wasted for null values, storage effectiveness depends on the relation's null-value ratio.

CASSM uses auxiliary storage to mark rows of relation and to support its strategy for rewriting a track. When CASSM simultaneously selects more than one row for output, it uses an output arbiter to output one of them and marks the remaining rows for output on subsequent revolutions. CASSM uses a bit-addressable RAM associated with each track for this. To rewrite a track, CASSM uses two physical tracks per logical track. Data is read from the first, analyzed and written to the second, then rewritten to the first with all desired modifications.[19]

RAP. Like CASSM, RAP lays its data along the tracks of its storage device, but the similarity ends there; RAP uses a fixed-length representation for the rows of a relation. This length can vary from relation to relation, but within a relation all rows must use the same amount of storage. Only one type of relation can be stored on a given track. Within a track rows are stored one per block, and the end of each block is marked by a delimiter. RAP's track format is illustrated in Figure 5.

The beginning of a track has a special track marker, followed by two "header blocks." The first block gives the name of the relation stored on the track, and the second gives the column names in the order in which they will appear in the row representations. The blocks following these header blocks contain rows of the relation. The row blocks contain the concatenated values of the row in the order given by the second header block. These concatenated values are

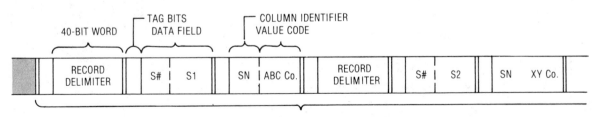

Figure 4. CASSM data organization.

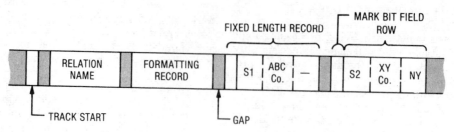

Figure 5. RAP data organization.

preceded by a string of mark bits. All names and values on the track are encoded as 32, 16, or 8-bit strings, each preceded by a 2-bit code indicating its length.

Like CASSM, RAP uses an output arbiter to select a single row for output when two or more are contending. However, RAP uses the mark bits preceding each row to indicate which rows must be output on subsequent revolutions. To rewrite a row (e.g., to place a mark) RAP uses two heads per track: a read head connected by a buffer to a write head. The length of this buffer determines the maximum size of a block, since it must hold an entire row. A row is read by the read head, processed in the buffer, and then rewritten with any necessary changes back to the track.

RARES. RARES uses a very different organization from CASSM and RAP. It lays out relation rows across tracks (along the radius of a disk) in byte-parallel fashion: the first byte of a value is placed on a track; the second byte of the value is placed in the same position on the adjacent track, and so on. The decision to use a byte-parallel rather than a bit-parallel organization was based on the speed of the logic available to process a row laid out along a

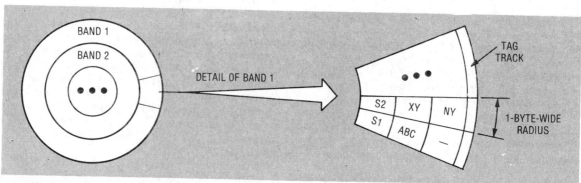

Figure 6. RARES data organization.

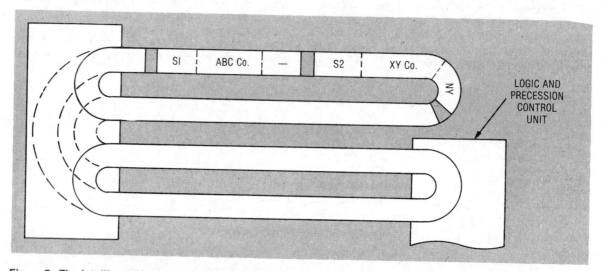

Figure 7. The Intelligent Memory's data organization.

radius, given the rotation time of the disk. Each set of tracks used to store a relation in this fashion is called a band. The number of tracks in the band may vary; the size of the band is determined by the width of a row. Relations with wide rows may use more than one radius to store a row. This format, called an orthogonal layout, is illustrated in Figure 6.

The orthogonal layout means that fewer rows can come into contention for output. However, some contention is still possible, so RARES also need an output arbiter. It uses a fast memory, called a response store, associated with each band to mark rows to be output on subsequent device revolutions. Since RARES was developed only as a query support facility, storage requirements for row rewriting were not specified.

Representations for electronic disk-based designs. The Intelligent Memory assumes a loop-configured CCD or bubble memory. It can store either a single record per loop for a CCD memory or multiple records per loop for a bubble memory. The loops are linked in a chain by logic which can either connect two or more loops to make a single larger loop or interchange two loops. The first option allows the device to be configured for different-sized relations. The second is used to support sorting (see the section on sorting). Rows are laid out along the loops as in the CASSM and RAP designs, but the format of a row in a loop has not been specified. The Intelligent Memory can be programmed to accommodate the format of either RAP or CASSM. Figure 7 illustrates a multiple row per loop configuration of the Intelligent Memory with a RAP record format.

Chang's major/minor loop machine assumes a bubble-chip configuration with a series of minor bubble loops joined by a major loop to accomplish reading and writing. He assumes that a single relation type will be stored on a chip. If the minor loops are thought of as tracks on a conventional magnetic disk, the organization proposed is similar to that of RARES. Rows are laid out across the minor loops, one column per minor loop. Wide relations can be accommodated by using as many chips as necessary. Different lengths for values of different columns may use more than one minor loop for a column. Since loops can be processed individually on bubble chips, this layout permits a column of a relation to be processed individually. Figure 8 illustrates this organization. An off-chip processing unit is associated with each chip, as are off-chip marker loops.

The lattice configuration of a bubble memory assumed by Todd is somewhat similar to that of the Intelligent Memory, although loops are linked by switches in a lattice instead of just a chain. This configuration implies different processing algorithms but a similar relation organization (see Figure 9).

The search and join features

The most important feature of the relational machines is their ability to select at the device level.

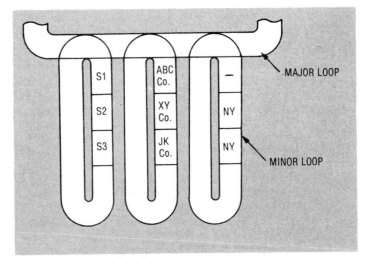

Figure 8. Chang's Major/Minor Loop Machine.

In all of the designs discussed above, this is accomplished by associating comparison logic with the read and write heads for each track or loop. The storage representation used in each design, however, determines the complexity of the comparison logic and the number of revolutions needed to complete the selection operation. Further, the decision to implement some form of the join operation in hardware can affect the design of the comparison logic.

The trend in designing associative hardware to implement the join operation has been to concentrate on a form called the *implicit join*. This join does not create a new relation from the two original relations; rather, the values of the join columns in one relation are used to select rows in the second relation that have those same values in their join columns. Only RARES, LEECH, and CAFS, all of which are intend-

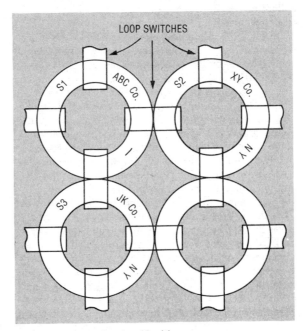

Figure 9. Todd's Lattice Machine.

ed to interface with conventional frontend computers, consider the problem of full joins. Their algorithms are based on these frontend processors. They do not provide a totally hardware-supported join.

CASSM. To perform a Boolean select, CASSM uses one Instruction Control and Rewrite module per track, special fields in the delimiter word preceding each row, and a RAM for marking selected rows. The ICR module can perform integer arithmetic, logical operations involving AND, OR and NOT, data field (32-bit) and subfield searches, and arithmetic functions such as SUM, COUNT, MAX, MIN, and FIRST. The data portion of a delimiter word for a row contains, in addition to the name of the relation and its level number, a 6-bit stack called the B-stack and two 1-bit fields called the S bit and the Q bit, respectively. These are used for storing temporary search results and for defining the context of searches.

We can see how a Boolean select is implemented by considering a specific query. (We will ignore the name and value decoding steps.) A query to select from the relation SUPPLY all rows with P# = P1 and Q > 5 would be executed on CASSM as follows: in the first revolution of the memory all SUPPLY rows are identified as the context of the select by marking the delimiter's S bit for all rows named SUPPLY and at level 1. In the second revolution the Q bits of the delimiters for these rows are set. Then a match is performed in the next revolution against the pair words in each row to locate those containing a pair $<$P#, P1$>$. If such a pair word is found, a mark is pushed on the B-stack in the delimiter for that row. In the next revolution a match is performed against the pair words in each previously selected row to locate those rows containing a pair $<$Q, X$>$ where X > 5. If such a pair word is found, a 1 is ORed to the top of the B-stack for the row. If the result of this is 1 then the collection bit, in the tags of the desired pair words of that row, is set.

In CASSM, all marks to the fields of delimiter words (the B-stack or the S and Q bits) are made using the RAM available to the logic associated with each read head/write head pair. For each delimiter word in the data base it is assumed that there is a bit reserved in the RAM. If a delimiter is to be marked, its RAM bit is marked. On the next revolution, when the delimiter word is reached, the mark is placed in it before it reaches the rest of the processing logic for consideration by the next CASSM instruction. The RAM is also the main mechanism used to support the implicit join operation in CASSM.

The implicit join of two relations is executed in CASSM by transforming the values of the join columns from the selected rows in one relation to marks in the RAM, where each value is assumed to have a corresponding bit. This may take several revolutions to complete, since more than one track may be trying to mark the same bit (e.g., in joining SUPPLY and PART on P#, if the S1 and S3 rows of SUPPLY are on different tracks, the logic associated with each track will try to mark the P1 bit). Next the rows of the second relation are matched on their join columns

against the values in the RAM and are marked if the match succeeds. Again, contention in accessing the RAM can occur and will cost additional revolutions. The number of revolutions needed to compute the implicit join depends on the amount of contention that occurs at these two times.

RAP. To perform a Boolean select, RAP transmits the search criteria to all tracks simultaneously. If a row satisfies the criteria, it is read out as soon as the output channel is available. The matching is accomplished by circulating each row as it is read through a buffer designed to hold an entire row. The logic associated with each buffer consists of a fixed number k of comparators which operate in parallel. Thus, up to k terms of the Boolean select can be evaluated in a revolution. The results of these k independent evaluations are combined through hardware Boolean operations to complete the evaluation.

If a selected row needs additional Boolean terms of the select condition evaluated, it must be marked. In RAP, such marks are stored in the string of mark bits preceding the values of each row and must be placed there before the row is written back onto the track. In subsequent revolutions the mark bit field is used in computing the remainder of the match. This mechanism is also used to handle rows contending for output.

RAP uses three commands to perform implicit join. The first, the "cross mark command," takes the join column values of one relation and uses them as a disjunctive select condition for the second relation. Since RAP has k comparators per track, k values from the first relation can be checked against the second relation in each pass. Thus the number of revolutions needed is the number of rows selected from the first relation divided by k. The "get first mark" command is used to perform an implicit join between a relation and itself. The "cross condition mark" command is used to do repeated implicit joins.

RARES. Because RARES lays rows along radii of a disk rather than along tracks, its method for performing selection differs from those of CASSM and RAP. Instead of needing search logic for each track, RARES only needs search logic for each band. But because bands may vary in width, special logic is needed to reassign the search logic to a new set of adjacent tracks whenever a band's width is redefined; RARE's designers use a type of "barrel switch."[22] As a radius of a band (containing a complete or partial row of the relation being searched) comes under the read head, it is passed through a shift register where it can be processed by the search logic. If the match is successful but further matches are required on the row, a mark is placed in the response store associated with the search logic for the band. The access point to this store is automatically advanced as each new row is read. If the match is successful and complete, the search logic waits for a signal from the output artiber. If the signal so indicates, the row is read to the output buffer; otherwise it is marked for output on subsequent revolutions. In RARES the amount of contention depends heavily on the width of a band, a parameter that is under user control.

RARES performs a Boolean select by matching a single term per revolution in a way similar to CASSM's. Within one revolution a radius of a row is selected for matching. The comparison logic matches the radius against a search operand. If previous matches have been performed on the row to which the radius belongs, the response store will contain a bit that indicates the accumulated result of these matches. The hardware combines the current result with this accumulated result. No algorithms or special operations for computing implicit joins are specified in the RARES design. It was intended to support a query optimization approach that divides the processing load between RARES and one or more general-purpose processors. In this approach, full joins (wherein rows are physically concatenated) can be computed by the general-purpose processors exploiting RARES's ability to output rows in specific sort orders.

Search and join in electronic disk-based designs. The Intelligent Memory, with its storage layout similar to that of RAP, performs select in the following manner: the location of a column to be searched, the value to be matched, and the comparison relation ($=$, $<$ or $>$) to be used are broadcast to the logic associated with each loop. There is an upper bound on the size of the search key, which means that if the column being matched is wider than this limit more than one revolution will be needed to complete the match. However, several Boolean terms can be matched if they can be treated as a concatenated string of width less than or equal to the limit, e.g., a conjunction of equality matches. If a match is made, a tag bit is written back into the loop for the row. If it is known that only a single row is selected, the Intelligent Memory moves it up by interconnecting loops, cycling the rows through them until the selected row reaches the output port. If more than one row is selected, an arbiter selects the loops to be cycled through the memory to the output port in an appropriate order.

Chang's major/minor loop machine, with its data organization similar to that of RARES, uses a somewhat different selection mechanism. Associated with each chip is a 1-bit comparator. This is sufficient, since the major loop delivers a bit at a time from a column value, and general, since it performs matches of any length. When a selected row is to be marked for additional processing, the mark is placed in an off-chip marker loop. This marker loop's length is equal to that of the minor loops and is synchronized with them.

In Todd's bubble lattice design, the chips are used as queues connecting microprocessors that implement the relational operators. The major emphasis of the design is on algorithms for moving rows through such chips, not on the designs of the selection and join algorithms executed by the microprocessors.

The LEECH machine and CAFS. To implement full joins, the LEECH machine first processes all rows of each relation being joined to produce a bit map of their join values. It combines these bit maps to produce a single filter for selecting the rows needed for the join, then passes the relations through this filter. The selected rows are processed by conventional algorithms to produce the concatenated rows of the full join. This algorithm is most effective when few rows are selected from each relation.

CAFS processes only one relation to produce a filter in its bit-addressable memory. The filter can be produced in two ways. In the first, the possible values of the join columns are encoded by associating each with a unique address in the bit memory, which holds 64,000 bits. This encoding is then used to encode the join columns in the relations. To compute the join the bit memory is cleared and rows from one relation are scanned. Each row that is to participate in the final join is used to set a bit in the bit memory (the bit addressed by the value in the encoded column). These rows are sent to a general-purpose processor to be held for completing the join, then the second relation is passed by the filter. Those rows whose encoded columns address set bits are sent to the general-purpose processor to complete the join. The second method uses hashing from uncoded join columns to set and test the filter bits.

The sort feature

The notion of order is not part of the relational model, yet it is important to relational processing at two levels. First, the output reports generated by queries often require that rows be delivered in a specific sort order; second, full joins may be computed efficiently by processing rows from each relation sorted on their respective join columns. Only the designs of RARES, the Intelligent Memory, and the Chen machine have been oriented toward performing sorts. However, the techniques developed for these machines can be generalized for use on other data base machine architectures.

RARES. The RARES design is oriented toward sorting in two ways. Its orthogonal data organization permits it to maintain existing sort orders efficiently, and a sort algorithm has been designed to exploit its associative search capability. This algorithm can also be used with many of the other data organizations. Because data is stored across tracks in RARES rather than along them, an existing sort order can be maintained if only a single band is being processed at a time; there will be no contention for output, so as a row is selected it can be output in the existing sort order if the output buffer is not full. Only then must processing be continued (from the same row) on subsequent revolutions. To achieve this in organizations that lay data in sorted order along tracks, processing must be restricted to one track per revolution, slowing the processing.

RARES' sort algorithm[23] is based on the use of buckets and a histogram. First, a histogram is built to determine the distribution of values in the sort columns. Intervals containing an appropriate number of rows, determined by the number that can be sorted by a general-purpose processor in one revolution, are established. The sort then uses those intervals to retrieve rows with values falling in a given interval. These rows are sorted by the general-purpose processor, taking one revolution per interval.

Bubble-memory-based sorts. The sort algorithm designed for the Intelligent Memory is called the gyro sort. It assumes the existence, in the Intelligent Memory, of a special piece of logic associated with each loop called the precessor control circuit. This circuit, controlling circulation within a loop, contains a data buffer that holds one row, which can be compared to a row in an adjacent buffer and exchanged with it. This capability is used to sort rows across (but not within) loops, and to make it possible to sort the rows in the memory so that all the rows in one loop are less than or equal to (or greater than) all the rows in its adjacent loop. Loops of rows are then output to another processor and sorted using a conventional algorithm.

Another sorting technology based on a lattice architecture, like the one described by Todd, is that of Chen et al.[7] It uses a lattice arrangement two loops wide and as deep as needed (the depth should equal the number of rows to be sorted). Rows enter the lattice at the top, go down one side, come up the other, and exit. As each row enters, it is split in half. As rows hit the bottom of the sorter, they either remain there, if rows with lower (higher) values of sort columns

follow them, or are shipped up to be compared with rows coming down the lattice. A four-row example of this algorithm is illustrated in Figure 10.

Applicability and availability

The designs for relational data base machines discussed here were mainly based on head-per-track disk technology or its electronic equivalents. Current projections indicate that such devices will remain at least an order of magnitude more expensive than movable-head disks well into the 1980's. Thus in very-large-scale data base applications, these designs will be too costly to use for storing the entire data base, and their most likely use will be as staging devices. The data will reside in conventional mass memory and only needed portions will be paged into the data base machine.

The machines discussed in this survey were selected because they form a well-documented and representative selection of the designs being investigated. The availability of such machines will depend on corroborating research and critical comparisons of the different configurations. Such work is being carried out by a number of projects. Anderson and Kain[1] have built and are testing a CCD-based machine for relational querying. Copeland[11] is concentrating on problems of more complicated matching capabilities at Tektronics. Rohmer and Tusera[31] are initiating a project at IRIA in France. Leilich et al.[20] are investigating a design for a movable-head

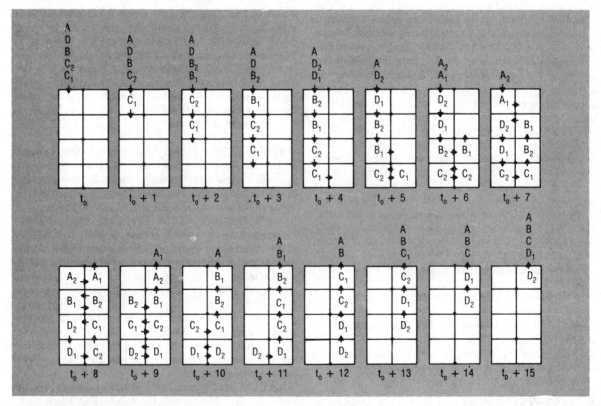

Figure 10. Chen's rebound sort.

disk at the University of Braunschweig in Germany. Dewitt[13] is studying inter-query concurrency by means of a cross-point switch-connected set of microprocessors and CCD memory cells. Jino and Liu[17] are investigating sort and merge algorithms for bubble memories at the University of Illinois. In addition to these prototyping efforts, Langdon[19] has made a detailed comparison between the RAP and CASSM designs.

Despite this progress, many questions remain before these designs can move from prototype to product. In particular, issues of reliability and recovery must be solved. ■

References

1. Anderson, G. A., and R. Y. Kain, "A Content-Addressed Memory Designed for Data Base Applications." *Proc. 1976 International Conf. Parallel Processing*, 1976, pp. 191-195.

2. Astrahan, M. M. et al. "System R: Relational Approach to Database Management," *ACM Trans. Database Syst.* Vol. 1, No. 2, June 1976, pp. 97-137.

3. Babb, E., "Implementing a Relational Database by Means of Specialized Hardware," *ACM Trans. on Database Systems,*" Vol. 4, No. 1, Mar. 1979.

4. Banerjee, J., and D. K. Hsiao, "DBC—A Database Computer for Very Large Databases," *IEEE Trans. on Computers,*" Vol. C-28, No. 3, 1979.

5. Baum, R. I., J. Banerjee, and D. K. Hsiao, "Concepts and Capabilities," *ACM Trans. on Database Systems,* Vol. 3, No. 4, Dec. 1978, pp. 347-384.

6. Chang, H. "On Bubble Memories and Relational Data Base," *Proc. 4th International Conf. Very large Data Bases*, West Berlin, 1978, pp. 207-229.

7. Chen, T. C., V. W. Lum, and C. Tung, "The Rebound Sorter: An Efficient Sort Engine for Large Files," *Proc. 4th International Conf. Very Large Date Bases*, West Berlin, 1978, pp. 312-315.

8. Codd, E. F., "A Relational Model of Data for Large Shared Data Banks," *ACM*, Vol. 13, No. 6, June 1970, pp. 377-387.

9. Codd, E. F., "Relational Completeness of Date Base Sublanguages," *Courant Computer Science Symposia 6: Data Base Systems*, Prentice-Hall, Englewood Cliff, N. J., May 1971, pp. 65-98.

10. Copeland, G. P., "A Cellular System for Non-Numeric Processing," Tech. Rep. No. 1, Proj. CASSM, U. of Florida, Gainesville, Fla., 1974 (also available as PhD thesis, University Microfilms, Ann Arbor, Mich.).

11. Copeland, G. P., "String Storage and Searching for Data Base Applications: Requirements and Strategy for Implementation," Tektronix, Beaverton, Ore., 1978.

12. Copeland, G. P., G. J. Lipovski, and S. Y. W. Su, "The Architecture of CASSM: A Cellular System for Non-Numeric Processing, *Proc. 1st Annual Symposium on Computer Architecture*, Dec. 1973, pp. 121-128.

13. Dewitt, D. J., "DIRECT—A Multiprocessor Organization for Supporting Relational Data Base Management Systems," *The 5th Annual Symposium on Computer Architecture*, April 1978, pp. 182-189.

14. Edelberg, M. and L. R. Schissler, "Intelligent Memory," *Proc. 1976 NCC*, Vol. 45, AFIPS Press, Montvale, N. J., pp. 393-400.

15. Healy, L. D., K. L. Doty and G. J. Lipovski, "The Architecture of a Context-Addressed Segment Sequential Storage," *Proc. 1972 FJCC*, Vol. 41, Pt. II, AFIPS Press, Montvale, N.J., pp. 691-701.

16. Hsiao, D. K., K. Kanan, and D. S. Kerr, "Structure Memory Designs for a Database Computer," *Proc. ACM 1977*, Dec. 1977, pp. 343-350.

17. Jino, M. and J. W. S. Liu, "Intelligent Magnetic Bubble Memories," *The 5th Annual Symposium on Computer Architecture,*" April 1978, pp. 166-174.

18. Kerr, D. S., "Data Base machines Utilizing Very Large Content-Addressable blocks and Special Structural Information Processors" (this issue).

19. Langdon, G. G., Jr., "A Note on Associative Processors for Date Management," *ACM Trans. Database Syst.*, Vol. 3, No. 2, June 1978, pp. 148-158.

20. Leilich, H. O. G. Stiege, and H. Ch. Zeidler, "A Search Processor for Data Base Mangement Systems," *Proc. 4th International Conf. Very Large Data Bases*, West Berlin, 1978, pp. 280-287.

21. Lin, C. S., D. C. P. Smith, and J. M. Smith, "The Design of a Rotating Associative Memory for Relational Database Applications," *ACM Trans. Database Syst.*, Vol. 1, No. 1, Mar. 1976, pp. 53-65.

22. Lin, C. S., "The Design of a Rotating Associative Relational Store," MS Thesis, University of Utah, 1976.

23. Lin, C. S., "Sorting With Associtive Secondary Storage Devices," *Proc. 1977 NCC*, AFIPS Press, Montvale, N. J., pp. 691-695.

24. Madnick, S. E., "INFOPLEX—Hierarchical Decomposition of a Large Information Management System Using a Microprocessor Complex," *Proc. 1975 NCC*, Vol. 44, AFIPS Press, Montvale, N. J., pp. 581-586.

25. McGregor, D. R., R. G. Thomson, and W. N. Dawson, "High Performance for Database Systems," *Systems for Large Databases*, North-Holland Publishing Co., 1976, pp. 103-116.

26. Ozkarahan, E. A., "An Associative Processor for Relational Databases—RAP," PhD Thesis, U. of Toronto, Toronto, Ont., Jan. 1976.

27. Ozkarahan, E. A., S. A. Schuster, and K. C. Smith, "RAP—An Associative Processor for Data Base Management," *Proc. 1975 NCC*, Vol. 45, AFIPS Press, Montvale, N. J., pp. 379-387.

28. Ozkarahan, E. A. and K. C. Sevcik, "Analysis of Architectural Features for Enhancing the Performance of a Database Machine," *ACM Trans. Database Syst.* 2, Vol. 4, Dec. 1977, pp. 297-316.

29. Parhami, B., "A Highly Parallel Computer System for Information Retrieval," *Proc. 1972 FJCC*, Vol. 41, Pt. II, AFIPS Press, Montvale, N. J., pp. 681-690.

30. Parker, J. L., "A Logic Per Track Device," *Proc. IFIP Cong. 1971*, North-Holland Pub. Co., Amsterdam, pp. TA4-146-TA4-150.

31. Rahmer, J., and D. Tusera, "Special Purpose Micro-programs and Micromachines for High Speed Information Retrieval," IRIA-Laboria, 78150 Le Chesnay, France.

32. Schuster, S. A., E. A. Ozkarahan, and K. C. Smith, "A Virtual Memory System for a Relational Associative Processor," *Proc. 1976 NCC,* Vol. 45, AFIPS Press, Montvale, N. J., pp. 855-862.

33. Slotnick, D. L., "Logic per Track Devices," *Advances in Computers,* Vol. 10, J. Tou, ed., Academic Press, New York, 1970, pp. 291-296.

34. Smith, J. M. and P. Y. Chang, "Optimizing the Performance of a Relational Algebra Data Base Interface," *CACM,* Vol. 18, No. 10, Oct. 1975, pp. 568-579.

35. Stonebraker, M., "A Distributed Data Base Machine," Electronics Research Laboratory, UC Berkeley Memorandum No. UCB/ERL M78/23.

36. Stonebraker, M. R., E. Wong, and P. Kreps, "The Design and Implementation of INGRES," *ACM Trans. Database Syst.,* Vol. 1, No. 3, Sept. 1976, pp. 189-222.

37. Su. S. Y. W., "On Logic-per-Track Devices: Concept and Applications " (this issue).

38. Su. S. Y. W. and A. Emam, "CASDAL: CASSM's Data Language," *ACM Trans. Database Syst.,* Vol. 3, No. 1, Mar. 1978, pp. 57-91.

39. Su. S. Y. W. and G. J. Lipovski, "CASSM: A Cellular System for Very Large Data Bases," *Proc. Conf. Very Large Data Bases,* Framingham, Mass., Sept. 1975, pp. 456-472.

40. Todd, Stephen, "Hardware Design for High Level Databases," IBM United Kingdom Scientific Centre, peterlee, TN 49, 12 pp.

41. Watson, J. K., G. J. Lipovski, and Su, S. Y. W., "A Multiple-Head Disk System for Fast Context Addressing for Large Data Bases," Workshop in Computer Architecture for Non-Numeric Processing, Dallas, Tex., 1974.

Diane C. P. Smith and **John Miles Smith** will be joining the Department of Computing and Information Sciences of the University of New Mexico as associate professors in August 1979. Previously with the Computer Science Department at the University of Utah, they are currently on leave at the Computer Corporation of America. Their research interests include data base design, data models, data base machines, and distributed data base management.

A member of the ACM, John Smith received his MS and PhD from the University of Pennsylvania. Diane Smith is a member of the ACM, the IEEE Computer Society, and Sigma Xi, and is vice-chairman of the ACM Special Interest Group on the Management of Data. She received her PhD from the University of Pennsylvania.

COMPUTER

7. Parallel Programming Languages

We present papers discussing languages for parallel programming in this chapter. Perrott's paper illustrates a recently designed Pascal-based language for array and pipelined computers. A FORTRAN-based language for array and pipeline computers is described in the paper by Paul and Wilson (1978).

The next two papers are about language constructs for multiprocessor programming. The first, Hansen's paper on concurrent Pascal describes fairly widely used constructs to achieve synchronization between concurrent processes. Simple synchronization primitives like these are important. Performing synchronization in its more general form, by making use of store and fetch as indivisible operations, leads to complex segments of code (Dijkstra, 1968), and higher-level synchronization can be implemented in terms of these primitives. The second paper on multiprocessor language constructs, by Hoare, is presented because of the elegance of the constructs described there and because similar constructs are used in the Ada programming language (Ichbiah *et al.*, 1979). Among the many other parallel language constructs, we should mention monitors (Hoare, 1974) and path expressions (Campbell and Habermann, 1974).

The last paper in this section, by Ackerman, describes dataflow languages and relates them to applicative languages.

EHO182-6/81/0000/0293 © 1981 IEEE

A Language for Array and Vector Processors

R. H. PERROTT

NASA/Ames Research Center

The scientific community has consistently demanded from computing machines an increase in the number of instructions executed per second. The latest increase has been achieved by duplication of arithmetic units for an array processor and the pipelining of functional units for vector processors. The high level programming languages for such machines have not benefited from the advances which have been made in programming language design and implementation techniques.

A high level language is described in this paper which is appropriate for both array and vector processors and is defined without reference to the hardware of either type of machine. The syntax enables the parallel nature of a problem to be expressed in a form which can be readily exploited by these machines. This is achieved by using the data declarations to indicate the maximum extent of parallel processing and then to manipulate this, or a lesser extent, in the course of program execution. It was found to be possible to modify many of the structured programming and data structuring concepts for this type of parallel environment and to maintain the benefits of compile time and run time checking. Several special constructs and operators are also defined.

The language offers to the large scale scientific computing community many of the advances which have been made in software engineering techniques while it exploits the architectural advances which have been made.

Key Words and Phrases: array processing, vector processing, parallel data structures, parallel control structures

CR Categories: 4.20

1. INTRODUCTION

During the last two decades, the design and development of several generations of computers have given rise to increased processing speeds; the more recent advances in the number of operations performed per second have been obtained by a revolution in computer architecture rather than by component technology. Examples of this revolution are the duplication of arithmetic units for array processors such as the Illiac IV [1] and the Phoenix [2], and the pipelining of functional units for vector processors such as the Star-100 [3] and the Cray-1 [10].

Permission to copy without fee all or part of this material is granted provided that the copies are not made or distributed for direct commercial advantage, the ACM copyright notice and the title of the publication and its date appear, and notice is given that copying is by permission of the Association for Computing Machinery. To copy otherwise, or to republish, requires a fee and/or specific permission.

This work was done while the author was on leave of absence from The Queen's University of Belfast and was with the Institute for Advanced Computation, NASA/Ames Research Center, Moffett Field, CA 94035.

Author's address: Department of Computer Science, The Queen's University, Belfast BT7 1NN, Northern Ireland.

© 1979 ACM 0164-0925/79/1000-0177 $00.75

Reprinted with permission from *ACM Transactions on Programming Languages and Systems* Volume 1, Number 2, October 1979, pages 177-195. Copyright © 1979 by the Association for Computing Machinery, Inc.

R. H. Perrott

These types of computer are based on a form of parallel or lockstep processing which does not have the synchronization problems of a conventional multiprocessor system. These machines are widely used in large scale scientific computations, particularly for grid or mesh type problems where regularity of processing the data is the dominant problem characteristic; they form the baseline architecture for this paper. Hence asynchronous parallel configurations such as C.mmp [15] are excluded from consideration.

Unfortunately, there has not been a comparable investment of either research funds or effort into the development of programming languages or software production tools to utilize these technological and architectural advances. Most of the high level languages currently used to program these parallel computers are extensions of languages which were specifically designed, many years ago, for sequential machine architectures, e.g., extended Fortran for the Star-100 [11], CFT for the Cray-1 [10], and IVTRAN [8], CFD [12] (Fortran-like languages), and Glypnir [7] (an Algol-like language) for the Illiac IV. SL/1 [6] is one of the few languages that has tried to bring some of the benefits of structured programming to one of these machines, namely, the Star-100.

The gap between the hardware and software development for these machines has been apparent in many of the projects attempted, e.g., some conversions of important production codes to the Illiac IV were terminated due to software problems [5, 13]. Also the size and the complexity of the projects that programmers are being asked to implement have increased with the available processing power and are now almost beyond the features and capabilities of the programming languages being used to tackle them.

More specifically, to construct and to increase the efficiency of a program, the user either has to be aware of the machine instruction set or of the method of detection of parallelism used by the compiler. In addition, the organization of the transfer of data to and from the backing store can require the use of low level primitives; the transfer can critically affect the performance of a program. Hence the challenge to the language designer is to devise a language which provides the programmer with sufficient tools to enable the construction of efficient algorithms and at the same time effectively utilize the hardware.

The language described in this paper is an attempt to redress the technology imbalance: to develop a high level language whose features exploit the advanced architecture of these parallel machines and incorporate the new software engineering approaches that are necessary in writing algorithms in this parallel environment. The language is called Actus.

The new language enables the specification of parallelism directly. The features are appropriate for both array and vector processors and they are defined without reference to the hardware of either type of machine; the algorithmic and data constructs are of sufficient generality and structure to make efficient use of the parallel computational resources. This could facilitate codes developed on one parallel architecture being moved to another parallel architecture without undue loss of efficiency. The language features of Actus are described using a notation similar to that of the language Pascal [14]. (A possible implementation is also suggested by using a Pascal P-compiler [9]; such an approach is currently being pursued at the Institute for Advanced Computation for one of the parallel computers, namely, the Illiac IV.)

ACM Transactions on Programming Languages and Systems, Vol. 1, No. 2, October 1979.

295

It is therefore hoped that this type of parallel computer can benefit from some of the advances of structured programming and software engineering which are, as yet, not widely disseminated throughout the scientific community and that this, in turn, will mean reduced software production costs, with the improved quality, reliability, and adaptability that have been realized for sequential machines.

2. DESIGN APPROACH

There have been two main approaches to the design of a high level language for a vector or an array processor which are reflected in the existing languages for these machines, namely, either

(i) the user writes a program in a conventional sequential programming language and the compiler tries to detect the inherent parallelism of the program, or
(ii) the parallel nature of the computer is readily apparent in the syntax of the language.

Examples of the first philosophy are IVTRAN for the Illiac IV and CFT for the Cray-1. Such languages try to extract the parallelism within sequential Fortran DO loops. The disadvantages of this approach are that the extraction of the parallelism is somewhat limited and inefficient in the code generated; and often the user has to restructure the program to benefit from the parallelism of the machine.

Examples of the second approach are CFD and Glypnir for the Illiac IV. CFD is an extension of Fortran which reflects in the syntax that the Illiac IV has 64 processors. The user then has to size the data structures of the problem to this natural length of the machine. This can add significantly to the complexity of a program, again causing the user to restructure the program.

Another example is Star Fortran. To access the parallel capability of the Star, the programmer must explicitly encode hardware instructions in separate subroutine calls (one call for each instruction). This effectively turns the extended Fortran into a higher level assembler language.

Another disadvantage in using these existing languages is that normally the two-level memory hierarchy is not a natural part of the language abstraction. For example, in the situation where the database under consideration is so large that it will not fit into the available main store, the user must, employing very basic facilities, organize the transfer of data between the extended memory and the fast processing store. Since the management of the memory hierarchy is often the critical factor in the overall performance of a program, the user must therefore code the most crucial aspect of the program in the most primitive syntax.

The approach adopted in the language reported here is that the language should enable the expression of parallelism in a manner which is suitable for the problem and can be easily exploited by these parallel machines. This will enable the compiler to generate efficient object code in a rapid and straightforward manner without resorting to a complex detection mechanism for the inherent parallelism. Another advantage is that programming with a parallel syntax produces algorithms of greater efficiency, i.e., a user does not have to size the data structures of the problem but can adopt a straightforward and natural notation to suit the problem.

ACM Transactions on Programming Languages and Systems, Vol. 1, No. 2, October 1979.

Thus the current programming situation for these parallel computers is such that the user is forced both to construct a solution to a problem using a language which does not provide the most appropriate abstraction mechanisms and to take account of the particular hardware characteristics of the machine.

3. LANGUAGE CRITERIA

The design of the language involved an extensive study of the problem areas in which such computers are used, consultations with programmers who had used such machines for many years, and a survey of the users of the Illiac IV over the years that it had been operational. The survey responders included users of both types of language as represented by the pair CFD/Glypnir and IVTRAN. The main points were

(i) parallel computations were difficult to express in or adapt to the syntax of the language if they were not based on a factor of 64, i.e., the number of processing elements available,

(ii) manipulation of the status of processing elements was cumbersome; frequently data structures were increased in size to avoid status manipulation,

(iii) the lack of suitable control structures caused complexity of programming and at times required the introduction of machine code; machine code was also introduced to increase efficiency,

(iv) selecting an arbitrary group of array elements was difficult,

(v) manipulation of part words required machine code,

(vi) detailed knowledge of the layout of the data on the backing store and in the main store is required; also the facilities for specifying the transfer of data were primitive and required careful programming,

(vii) debugging and tracing facilities were lacking.

The purpose of the study, the consultations, and the survey were designed to determine the frequency of use of certain features and to identify what new features were required. In this way the relevant abstractions for large scale scientific problems could be formed along with their representation and rules for manipulation. This, in turn, led to the introduction of new data structures, language constructs, and operators. In effect, the new features were involved with manipulation of the extent of parallel processing, while the normal structured programming concepts were modified to enable representation and manipulation of the data in parallel.

The following criteria were adopted for the design of a language for the current parallel computers:

(i) the idiosyncrasies of the hardware should be hidden from the user as much as possible,

(ii) the user should be able to express the parallelism of the problem directly,

(iii) the user should be able to think in terms of a varying rather than a fixed extent of parallel processing,

(iv) control of the parallel processing should be possible both explicitly and through the data, as applicable,

(v) the user should be able to indicate the minimum working set size of the database (in those cases where the database is larger than the size of the fast memory).

The implementation of the language should provide compile and run time checks plus tracing facilities to assist with the debugging and testing of programs. Since lockstep parallel computers were developed as a means of performing the same operation on independent data sets in parallel, in Actus the data declarations indicate the maximum extent of parallelism. The extent of parallelism is defined for an array processor as the number of processors that can logically compute upon a particular data at the same time (this can be less than, equal to, or greater than the actual number of processors); for a vector processor it is the length of the data structure presented to the processor for computation.

Hence each data declaration has associated with it a maximum extent of parallelism; the language statements or constructs can then adjust this maximum (or a lesser) extent of parallelism in the course of program execution. In this way it is possible to express directly in the syntax the parallel nature of an algorithm which is appropriate for both vector and array processors.

The extent of parallelism can be regarded as representing a second programming dimension which can be adjusted in the course of program execution; the first dimension is that represented in a sequential programming language, namely, the successive execution of statements.

4. DATA TYPES

The examination of the problem area indicated that in addition to sequential data types a parallel data structure was required in which it was possible

(i) to associate parallel processing with any of the dimensions of the structure,
(ii) to enable accessing of a two- (or higher) dimensional structure other than by rows or columns, in parallel, and
(iii) to enable the combination of neighboring elements of a parallel structure.

To further facilitate the assignment and modification of the extent of parallelism, parallel constants and index sets, respectively, were introduced.

The language supports standard, enumerated, subrange types, and structured types such as the array and record (without the variant part) as defined in the language Pascal [4]. In addition, standard short integer and short real types requiring half the storage of their corresponding full word types were introduced (if supported by the hardware). All such variables are referred to as scalar variables.

The array declaration is used to indicate the maximum extent of parallelism for the data; in principle, the syntax can support any number of dimensions, but the examples are restricted to three, or fewer.

A scalar array is represented as

$$\textbf{var } scalara\text{: } \textbf{array } [1..m, 1..n] \textbf{ of } integer;$$

i.e., *scalara* contains $m \times n$ (predefined) integer numbers. The lower indices are restricted to 1 for convenience. The maximum extent of parallelism is introduced

by replacing one (and only one) pair of sequential dots ".." by a parallel pair
".":

$$\textbf{var } para: \textbf{array } [1:m, 1..n] \textbf{ of } real;$$

indicates an array *para* of $m \times n$ real numbers for which the maximum extent of parallelism is m. The array *para* can be manipulated m elements at a time since it has been declared as a parallel variable with that extent of parallelism. The array is thus the main data structure to indicate variables which can be manipulated in parallel.

This means of representing the extent of parallel processing had a major influence on the design of the language. Previous to its discovery, special reserved words had been used to indicate parallel variables, for example, row-vector or column-vector prefixes. This, in turn, required the introduction of new control structures to facilitate the manipulation of parallel variables, for example, a **where** construct to select various elements of a row or column vector.

However, the rearrangement of one pair of dots in the data declaration considerably simplified and reduced the number of control structures. As can be seen in a later section, it is possible to use the same control structures for both scalar and parallel variables provided an extent of parallelism is associated with the parallel variables.

More specifically, in the declaration

$$\textbf{var } a: \textbf{array } [1:4, 1..5] \textbf{ of } integer;$$

the parallel dots in the first index indicate that up to four elements of a can be processed in parallel; the elements are selected one from each row and the second index selects the particular column (which can be the same or different for each row; see Section 4.2).

Thus $a[1:4, 2]$ is equivalent to referencing in parallel

$$a[1, 2]\ a[2, 2]\ a[3, 2]\ a[4, 2],$$

and $a[2:3, 1]$ is equivalent to referencing in parallel $a[2, 1]\ a[3, 1]$. Hence, the parallel dots indicate the index which is to be processed in parallel, that is, spread across the processors in an array processor or stored contiguously in a vector processor. The user can now indicate the index of an array with which the parallel processing is associated. Each time a parallel variable is used in a statement, it can have an extent of parallelism less than or equal to its maximum (or declared) extent of parallelism. In this way it is possible in the program text to indicate directly a parallel variable and to easily distinguish between parallel variables and scalar variables, e.g., other arrays or variables.

Binary operators can be applied to parallel variables if the extent of parallelism is the same for both operands or if one of the operands is a scalar variable or constant.

During the design of the language the possibility of having two or more pairs of parallel dots in a declaration was considered, e.g.,

$$pp: \textbf{array } [1:m, 1:n] \textbf{ of } real;$$

This would indicate that the array *pp* was intended to be manipulated in parallel by both its first and its second indices, i.e., m elements at a time and also n

ACM Transactions on Programming Languages and Systems, Vol. 1, No. 2, October 1979.

299

elements at a time either separately or concurrently in the course of program execution. On an array processor, to increase its efficiency, this would require that the data either be transposed during the calculation or skewed when being arranged in the stores. It was decided to restrict the parallelism to one dimension until more experience was gained in the use and the implementation of the language.

Thus the data declarations of Actus allow a flexible choice of index limits for each dimension of an array and enable the user to decide which dimension can be accessed in parallel. Such flexibility is absent in other languages such as CFD and Glypnir, where only the first dimension can be manipulated in parallel and then only with a fixed extent of parallelism, i.e., 64.

4.1 Parallel Constants

In addition to the definition of scalar constants, identifiers can be defined to represent a sequence of integer numbers; they are used to assign values to parallel variables with an extent of parallelism equal to the number of values. The form of a parallel constant is

$$\textbf{const } identifier = start: (increment) \ finish;$$

where the values of *start*, *increment*, and *finish* must be integers and the sequence is

$$start, \ start + increment, \ start + 2*increment, \ldots, finish.$$

If the increment is unity, it may be omitted, e.g.,

$$\textbf{const } n = 50; \ seq = 1{:}n; \ oddseq = 1{:}(2)31;$$

Parallel constants can be used to assign values to parallel variables, for example, *seq* with an extent of parallelism 50 and *oddseq* with an extent 16.

4.2 Independent Indexing

One-dimensional parallel integer arrays can be used for independent indexing in a two- (or higher) dimensional parallel variable, thus enabling other parts of an array other than a row or column to be accessed. This is achieved by assigning appropriate values to a one-dimensional array and then using it as an index of a parallel variable. The extent of parallelism for both the indexing and the indexed array must be the same. For example,

$$\begin{aligned}
&\textbf{const} \quad diagonal = 1{:}100; \\
&\textbf{var} \qquad diag: \textbf{array } [1{:}100] \textbf{ of } integer; \\
&\qquad\qquad para: \textbf{array } [1{:}100, \ 1\,..\,100] \textbf{ of } real;
\end{aligned}$$

then $diag[1{:}100] := diagonal$ assigns element i of the array *diag* the value i, and $para[1{:}100, \ diag[1{:}100]]$ accesses the diagonal elements of the array *para*. Hence any selection of elements of an array can be accessed as determined by the indexing array. Such a mechanism is necessary when it is required to access the off-diagonal elements of an array, for example.

4.3 Index Sets

The extent of parallelism can be changed each time a parallel variable is referenced; this is done by explicitly changing the extent of parallelism or by using an "index set" which identifies the data elements that are to be altered. The members of an index set are (ordered) integer values, each of which identifies a particular element of a data type that can be accessed in parallel.

An index set is defined with the data declarations and takes the form

$$\textbf{index } indx = i{:}j;$$

where i and j are constant integer values such that $i <= j$. The elements i to j inclusive will be accessed whenever the index identifier $indx$ is used as a parallel array index. For example, with the declarations

$$\textbf{var}\quad para{:} \textbf{ array } [1{:}m, 1..n] \textbf{ of } real;$$
$$\textbf{index } interior = 2{:}m - 1;$$

$interior$ can be used as the first index of the array $para$ to access column elements other than the boundary elements.

Specific elements can be excluded from an index set definition by using a comma to indicate a break in the range. Also, if there is regularity in the required parallel index, this can be defined in an index set by inserting the increment in parentheses between the two terminal values. For example,

$$\textbf{index } outerstrips = 1{:}10, 91{:}100;$$
$$odd = 1{:}(2)99;$$
$$even = 2{:}(2)100;$$

would enable the manipulation of various parts of an array with an extent of parallelism 1 to 100 (at least).

The advantages of using index sets are that

(i) statements become more readable since they use the identifier name, and
(ii) the extent of parallelism involved can be evaluated before the statement is encountered (and thus may permit greater efficiency in execution).

Hence an index set indicates an extent of parallelism which is less than or equal to the declared extent of parallelism of the variable being accessed.

Index set identifiers cannot be redefined, but they can be operated upon by union (+), intersection (*), and difference (−) in order to facilitate computation on various parts of a parallel structure. The complement (−) gives the other members of the declared extent of parallelism.

4.4 Alignment of Data

In order to enable the movement of data between elements of the same or different parallel variables, two primitive data alignment operators are included in the language. These are

(i) the **shift** operator which causes movement of the data within the range of the declared extent of parallelism, and
(ii) the **rotate** operator which causes the data to be shifted circularly with respect to the extent of parallelism.

The general form of the parallel index using these binary operators is

$$eop \quad \text{alignment operator} \quad distance$$

where *eop* is either an explicit definition of the extent of parallelism or an index set, and *distance* is a positive or negative integer expression.

The indices of the data to be moved (the source indices) are *eop* + *distance* and the destination indices are *eop*. Hence if *distance* is positive, it causes data to be moved from right to left, while if it is negative, it causes data to be moved from left to right. For example, using

$$\textbf{var} \quad parb: \textbf{array } [1:100] \textbf{ of } integer;$$
$$\textbf{index } first50 = 1:50;$$

then *parb*[*first50*] + *parb*[*first50* **shift** 1] causes elements 1 to 50 of *parb* to be added to elements 2 to 51, respectively, in parallel, while

$$parb[\,first50] + parb[\,first50\textbf{ rotate} - 1]$$

causes element 1 to be added to 50, and elements 2 to 50 to be added to 1 to 49, respectively, in parallel.

To avoid any ambiguities in the application of alignment operators, all the indices involved in a statement are evaluated and the data values determined before the statement is executed. In this way alignment operations which indicate or try to access nonexistent (out of range) elements can be trapped.

In the other parallel languages there is no direct equivalent of index sets or the shift operator; the rotate operator is the main intercommunication mechanism. There are no formal parallel constants either, but a DATA statement can be used in CFD for assignment to particular variables; a reserved constant PEN which contains the values 0 to 63 can be used in Glypnir. A restricted form of independent indexing is available in both languages, i.e., along a nonparallel dimension. Once again the parallelism is in terms of 64 simultaneous operations.

5. STATEMENTS

In conjunction with the choice of data structures (and operators), the rules for their manipulation in the course of program execution were also formed. It was found that to construct algorithms for these parallel machines, many of the capabilities which are required in a sequential environment such as assignment, selection, iteration, procedure, and function abstractions are necessary. The essential difference is that in the new environment such manipulations must be performed in parallel. After many attempts, this was found to be possible by taking the syntax and semantics for sequential constructs and expanding them to include the extent of parallelism. This enables the manipulation of the extent of parallelism by means of the data; additional features were required to enable direct manipulation of the extent of parallelism.

A single extent of parallelism can be associated with each simple or structured statement of the language which involves one, or more than one, parallel variable; this must be less than or equal to the declared extent of parallelism for the parallel variables involved. Hence, during program execution, the smallest unit for which the extent of parallelism can be defined is the single assignment statement; this does not exclude the use of scalar and parallel variables in the same statement but facilitates testing, data alignment, etc., of the parallel variables; for example, it avoids the ambiguity involved in the multiplication of two

ACM Transactions on Programming Languages and Systems, Vol. 1, No. 2, October 1979.

302

parallel variables with different extents of parallelism. Thus the indices, including any alignments, are determined for each statement before execution and if they are found to be incompatible this gives rise to an error.

In those situations where the extent of parallelism will not change for several statements, the **within** construct can be used to define it. In addition, structured statements such as the **if, case, while,** and **for** constructs can define the extent of parallelism for the statements which they are applied to (if they involve parallel variables). These constructs are collectively referred to as extent-setting constructs; in effect, they represent an extension of program-structuring constructs to the lockstep parallel environment.

5.1 The Within Construct

In order to avoid repeatedly indicating the extent of parallelism for a series of assignment statements in which the extent will not change, the **within** construct has been introduced. This, in turn, will avoid a calculation of the extent of parallelism for each of the statements individually. It takes the form

within specifier do statement

where "specifier" is either an index set identifier or an explicit extent of parallelism. The specifier defines the extent of parallelism for the "statement," and the sharp symbol ♯ is used to indicate the extent of parallelism. For example, consider the following code fragment:

```
var    a, b: array [0:100] of integer;
       i, j, incr: integer;
begin
       ...;    (* represents other statements *)
       i := 20; j := 45; incr := 4;
       within i:j do
       begin
         a[#] := b[#] + incr;
         b[#] := b[# shift 1]
       end;
       ...;
end
```

The sharp abbreviation symbol represents the extent of parallelism defined by the specifier, i.e., the ordered integer set i to j inclusive.

This construct will avoid a calculation of the extent of parallelism until another extent-setting construct is encountered or the construct is exited. If another extent-setting construct is encountered, the current extent of parallelism is stacked and the new extent evaluated and applied; when the new construct is exited, the original extent of parallelism is unstacked and it is then applied to the rest of the statements. This is the rule which governs the nesting of all extent-setting constructs.

The **within** construct also serves another purpose when it is embedded in a loop; the specifier can consist of variables which are changed each time through the loop, thus, for example, enabling the examination of various subgrids within a larger grid.

It is appropriate at this point to digress from the presentation of the language in order to mention briefly the implementation of the extent of parallelism. This

ACM Transactions on Programming Languages and Systems, Vol. 1, No. 2, October 1979.

digression is intended to give the reader an appreciation of the central role of this concept both for the language and for the various parallel architectures.

On the Illiac IV, such a concept can be implemented by setting the "mode" bits; one mode bit is associated with each processing element and the status of the bit determines whether that processing element will execute instructions or not. At present, the user must, in CFD and Glypnir, manipulate these bits directly. On the Star-100, the extent of parallelism can be represented by the control vector which determines which elements of a data structure are to be operated upon. At present, in Star Fortran, the user invokes a subroutine call to set the control vector. On the Cray-1, there is a vector mask register which can be used to exclude a data element from execution; at present in CFT, the user has no means of setting this register.

5.2 Structured Statements

To allow for those situations where selection or repetition is concerned, the structured programming concepts of **if**, **case**, **while**, and **for** were expanded to enable the test or loop variables to contain parallel as well as scalar variables. In the latter case, the extent of parallelism for any of the constructs' statements involving parallel variables must be explicitly defined or must be inherited from an enclosing extent-setting construct. If parallel variables are involved in the test or loop variables, then their extent of parallelism must be the same. The extent of parallelism for the construct's statements is determined from these parallel variables and the sharp abbreviation symbol used to represent the appropriate extent of parallelism in the statements. Further illustration of these constructs using parallel variables is now considered.

(a) *Selective Statements.* Selective statements are used to spread the extent of parallelism between two or more execution paths, as determined by a test expression in the **if** or **case** constructs.

If a test expression involves parallel variables, the test is evaluated for each indicated element of the variables and if it is found to be true then the appropriate statements of the construct are applied to that element, e.g.,

$$\textbf{if } a[0:49] > b[0:49] \textbf{ then } a[\#] := a[\#] - 1$$

In this example, 50 elements of a are tested to see which are greater than the corresponding elements of b; those elements that are greater are decremented by 1.

If the test involves data alignment, a base on which to align must be clearly indicated in the test variables, so that there is no ambiguity in the extent of parallelism of the statements, e.g.,

$$\textbf{if } a[10:90] < a[10:90 \textbf{ shift} - 1] \textbf{ then } a[\#] := a[\#] + 1$$
$$\textbf{else } a[\#] := a[\#] - 1$$

Those elements of a in the range 10 to 90 which are less than their left neighbor have their values incremented by 1 and the remaining elements are decremented by 1.

The connectors **and** (conjunction), **or** (disjunction), **not** (negation) plus the "parallel" quantifiers **any** and **all** can be used in a test. The latter two are used to apply a test across an extent of parallelism, i.e., if at least one element obeys the test or if all the elements obey the test, respectively. Since these parallel quantifiers reduce to a single value for the test, they are governed by the rule for a scalar test, that is, the extent of parallelism must be explicitly defined or inherited from an enclosing extent-setting construct. For example,

$$\textbf{if any } (a[40{:}70] > 0) \textbf{ then } a[40{:}70] := a[40{:}70] - 1$$

if one (or more) of the elements 40 to 70 of a are positive, then all the elements 40 to 70 of a will have one subtracted and

$$\textbf{if all } (a[2{:}29] > b[2{:}29]) \textbf{ then } b[2{:}29] := 0$$
$$\textbf{else } a[2{:}29] := 0$$

if all the elements 2 to 29 of b are less than their corresponding elements in a, then the elements 2 to 29 of b are put to zero; otherwise, the elements 2 to 29 of a are put to zero.

The **case** construct has also been expanded to allow parallel variables in the labeled statements and a parallel variable as the selector variable. In the latter situation each element of the selector variable selects a labeled statement as determined by the value of that element; this causes the extent of parallelism to be distributed among the labeled statements which are then successively executed. For example,

```
type groundcover = (ocean, ice, snow, desert, frost):
  var surface: array [1:50] of groundcover;
      . . . ;
      case surface [1:50] of
        ocean: statement1;
        snow, frost, ice: statement2;
        desert: statement3
      end;
      . . . ;
```

The sharp abbreviation must be used to represent the extent of parallelism for each of the "statements" since they are determined by the current values of the selector variable *surface*. The possible values of *surface* are represented by the labels and the current values determine which statements are applied to that element. The extent of parallelism is thus spread among the labeled statements so that each element is associated with one of the statements only.

(b) *Repetitive Statements.* There are two types of repetitive statements, depending upon whether the number of times the statement is to be executed is known before the statement is encountered or whether the number is dependent on conditions generated by the statement.

(i) The first case is for an unknown number of times. This is achieved by using the **while** construct. As with the selection constructs, the test can include parallel or scalar variables or both. The extent of parallelism for the test variables must be the same and the result of its evaluation determines the extent of parallelism for the statements, which is represented by the sharp symbol. For example, in the statement

$$\textbf{while } a[1{:}50] < b[1{:}50] \textbf{ do } a[\#] := a[\#] + 1$$

the sharp symbol identifies those elements of a which are less than their corresponding element in b on each occasion that the comparison of elements is performed; only those elements of a have their value increased by 1. Hence the sharp symbol represents a nonincreasing number of elements as a result of successive executions of the test. Execution terminates when all the elements of a are greater than or equal to their corresponding element in b.

The parallel quantifiers **any** and **all** can be used with parallel test variables in which case the extent of parallelism must be explicitly defined in the statements of the construct (as with a test which involves scalar variables only). For example, in the situation

$$\textbf{while any } (a[1:50] < b[1:50]) \textbf{ do } a[1:50] := a[1:50] + 1$$

all the elements of a are incremented by 1 until none of the elements of a are less than their corresponding element in b.

(ii) The second type of repetition is for a known number of times and is indicated by the **for** construct, e.g.,

$$\textbf{for } control := start \textbf{ to } finish \textbf{ do } statement.$$

The multiplication of an $m \times n$ matrix aa by a vector w of length n can be formed as follows:

```
const  m = 200; n = 100;
var    aa: array [1:m, 1 .. n] of real;
       w: array [1 .. n] of real;
       u: array [1:m] of real;
       i: integer;
begin
       u[1:m] := 0.0;
       for i := 1 to n do
          u[1:m] := u[1:m] + aa[1:m, i] * w[i]
end
```

A **by** clause has been introduced for those situations where a constant increment other than unity is required, e.g.,

$$\textbf{for } control := start \textbf{ by } increment \textbf{ to } finish \textbf{ do } statement.$$

The *control*, *start*, and *finish* variables can be either scalar or parallel variables and can be used with either a scalar or parallel constant increment; the extent of parallelism must be the same for all parallel entities. This extent is then represented by the sharp abbreviation in the statements of the **for** construct. As with independent indexing a one-dimensional parallel integer array is used as the parallel loop index enabling a different fixed number of iterations to be applied to each element of a parallel array. For example,

```
const  seq = (1:50);
var    i:   array [1:50] of integer;
       aa:  array [1:50, 1 .. 100] of real;
       . . . ;
       for i[1:50] := seq by 2 to 100 do
       aa[#, i[#]] := aa[#, i[#]] + 1.0;
       . . . ;
```

In this example the parallel index i is initialized with the values 1 to 50. After each execution, all the values are increased by 2 until they reach 100. Hence the extent of parallelism decreases as the number of times the statements are executed increases.

5.3 Functions and Procedures

Functions and procedures can be declared using the data declarations and statements previously defined; the maximum extent of parallelism of all variables must be known at compile time. The Pascal scope rules for procedures and functions apply; hence local variables cannot have their extent of parallelism altered by a function or procedure call.

The formal parameter list for both functions and procedures was expanded to allow for parameters which are parallel variables. The actual parameters can then be either of the same extent of parallelism or a section of the same extent of a larger parallel variable. Only procedures and functions involving scalar variables may be parameters.

In the case of a function either a scalar or parallel variable can be returned as a result of its execution; the extent of parallelism can be different from that of the parameter(s). Procedures can be used to return one or more results which can be either scalar or parallel variables or a mixture of both.

In addition, several standard functions have been defined which perform frequently required operations; they can be divided in two classes:

(i) those which can be applied to each element of a parallel variable e.g., the cosine function;
(ii) those which yield a single result using several elements of a parallel variable, e.g., the sum function which adds the elements of the parallel variable which is its argument.

5.4 Examples

Two examples are now considered to illustrate further the use of some of the above features.

(i) The first example represents the main loop in a Gauss–Jacobi solution of Poisson's equation and in particular illustrates the use of an index set and an operand alignment operator.

The basis of the method is that each interior point of a rectangular grid aa is updated using its adjacent neighbors at the north, south, east, and west positions. This is achieved in turn for each column in parallel and the process is repeated until successive values for all the points differ by a required tolerance *epsilon*. The values used to calculate the new values are those obtained as a result of the previous calculation.

```
const   epsilon = 0.1; m = 64; n = 64;
var     aa, bb: array [1:m, 1 .. n] of real;
            test: boolean;
              j: integer;
index   interior = (2:m − 1);
begin
        test := true; for j := 2 to n − 1 do bb[1:m, j] := 0.0;
        bb[1:m, 1] := aa[1:m, 1];
```

ACM Transactions on Programming Languages and Systems, Vol. 1, No. 2, October 1979.

307

```
        bb[1:m, n] := aa[1:m, n];
        while test do
        begin
          test := false;
          for j := 2 to n − 1 do
          begin
          test := test or any (abs(bb[interior, j] − aa[interior, j]) > epsilon);
          bb[interior, j] := aa[interior, j];
          aa[interior, j] := (bb[interior, j − 1] + aa[interior, j + 1]
             + aa[interior shift − 1, j] + aa[interior shift + 1, j])/4.0
          end   (* for j *)
        end   (* while *)
  end.    (* program *)
```

(ii) The second example transposes an $n \times n$ matrix in the fast processing store and illustrates the use of the **within** construct and independent indexing.

The algorithm works by moving n elements of the array aa to their new positions in the array bb in parallel. The n elements are selected by diagonals and are moved to their reflected positions about the main diagonal. The n old and n new positions are determined by the indexing arrays i and j, respectively. *Note*: An in-place transpose can be performed which requires less storage.

```
  const  n = 200; diagonal = (0:n);
  var    aa, bb  : array [0:n, 0 . . n] of real;
               i, j: array [0:n] of integer;
               k: 0 . . n;
  begin
        within 0:n do
        begin
            i[#] := diagonal; j[#]:= diagonal;   (* initially the main diagonal *)
            for k := 0 to n do
            begin
                bb[#, j[#]] := aa[# rotate − k, i[#]];
                i[#] := i[# rotate + 1];
                j[#] := j[# rotate − 1]
            end   (* k *)
        end   (* within *)
  end,    (* program *)
```

(* the index $i[\#]$ selects two off diagonals in aa, an upper and a lower off diagonal; their corresponding positions in the transposed matrix bb are indicated by $j[\#]$. The other indices of aa and bb indicate the row coordinates of these diagonals*)

The examples illustrate how an extent of parallelism is associated with each data declaration and subsequently manipulated by the statements.

6. AUTOMATIC BUFFERING

The current parallel computers are often required to handle large databases which cannot be held in the fast store; the backing store is used to hold the database and the programmer has to ensure that the data are brought into the fast store in units which can be easily stored and manipulated (in the Star-100 this process is handled by a virtual memory). In order to avoid the considerable latency delays associated with the backing store, some form of buffering is necessary.

ACM Transactions on Programming Languages and Systems, Vol. 1, No. 2, October 1979.

To automate the management of the memory, it is important to determine either from the user or by the compiler the size of the working set; the working set is the minimum amount of the database required to be resident in the fast store so that processing can continue without excessive interruptions. On the basis of such information, the fast store can be divided into buffers and processing can be overlapped with backing store transfers. Thus the compiler rather than the user is responsible for the organization of data transfers.

The data declaration is used to indicate such information; for example, consider the array

$$\textbf{var } aaa: \textbf{array}[1:m, 1 .. n, 1 .. p] \textbf{ of } integer;$$

If the product of the dimensions $m \times n \times p$ is such that it is not possible to hold the array aaa in the fast store, then the user should, employing his knowledge of the use of aaa, indicate the minimum working set size. This can be achieved by appending a positive integer to the index that changes most slowly in the course of the calculation. For example, the declaration

$$\textbf{var } aaa: \textbf{array}[1:m, 1 .. n(3), 1 .. p] \textbf{ of } integer;$$

indicates that the user wishes to sweep through the database in the third index direction and requires three columns of the second index when making an update; the minimum working set size is $m \times 3 \times p$ (in the case of the Star-100 this information can be used to determine the page transfer size or to pack data on a page). Hence a small change in the syntax will guide the automatic allocation of temporary storage in the fast store. For example, single, double, or multiple buffering can be used to divide up the fast store to obtain an overlap of processing and data fetching based on the working set size for the database.

A program can be tested using a smaller database and a small syntax change in the data declaration is all that is required to move to a larger database. For example, in the Gauss–Jacobi solution of the last section, if the size of the database is too large, only the declaration of aa and bb should be changed to help with the movement of the data, e.g.,

$$aa, bb: \textbf{array}[1:m, 1 .. n(5)] \textbf{ of } real;$$

7. IMPLEMENTATION

The features of Actus have been described using a syntax similar to that of Pascal; this was due, in part, to a plan to use an existing Pascal compiler for its implementation.

Since it has been possible to express the constructs of Actus in sequential Pascal, it is therefore possible to build a preprocessor for Actus programs. This will enable the debugging of Actus programs at an installation which does not have a parallel machine of this type but does have a Pascal compiler. After debugging, such programs could be sent to an installation which does have a parallel machine of this type, by means of the ARPA network, for example.

In this way a wider range of potential users can be given the opportunity of being involved with existing parallel machines. This could also promote the exportability of codes developed on one parallel processor to another. Such a preprocessor is currently being constructed in Pascal.

ACM Transactions on Programming Languages and Systems, Vol. 1, No. 2, October 1979.

309

A frequently used procedure for the implementation of a high level language for current parallel computers is to use an auxiliary computer to perform the compilation of the programs. A similar approach has been adopted for the implementation of Actus on the Illiac IV.

More specifically, a Pascal P-compiler is being used in the creation of the Actus compiler. This P-compiler is being modified and enhanced with the new features to form an Actus P-compiler which also generates code for a hypothetical stack computer. Since this code is machine independent, the Actus P-compiler can be used as a basis for the implementation of Actus on other parallel machines.

Using a Pascal compiler as the host compiler should significantly reduce the implementation time. Also, many of the implementation decisions, e.g., the parameter passing mechanism, are already decided and proven in practice, and compatible with the extensions. Finally, all the compile time and run time checking facilities of Pascal are inherited and they can be expanded to check the new language features also.

Preliminary results of the implementation indicate that the features of Actus can be mapped onto the instruction set of the Illiac IV. The extent-setting patterns that will arise due to the control structures can be implemented by means of the mode bits, where the status of each of the 64 mode bits determines whether its corresponding processing element is active or not. This, in turn, determines whether a particular element of a parallel array is to be acted upon or not. The Illiac IV has sufficient registers to handle the nesting of a number of extent-setting constructs.

The layout of the data in the main store to face the processing power, i.e., the processing elements, requires that some base point be chosen so that parallel variables have the same indices aligned opposite the same processing elements. For example, if processing element zero is chosen as index base point 1, then all indices which are an incremental distance of 64 (either positive or negative) should be placed in the store of processing element zero, and similarly for all the other processing elements (1 to 63).

Thus an array with a parallel index range greater than 64 will be stored in consecutive rows with all multiples of 64 in the same processing element's store. The processing of such arrays will require repeated application of the processing elements to the number of rows involved, with allowance being made for the end conditions.

For example, in the assignment statement $a[1:n] := 0$ where $n > 64$, this will require (n **div** 64) applications of the 64 processing elements to the consecutive rows plus (n **mod** 64) processing elements active in another application of the processing elements (n not a multiple of 64). A nonuniform extent of parallelism $a[\#] := 0$ will require the status of the processing elements to be enabled and disabled accordingly.

Intercommunication between parallel arrays using the alignment operators requires that extra storage is set aside whenever the index range is greater than 64; this temporary storage is governed by the distance the data is to be moved. It is required to ensure that the updating of the end of one row with the beginning of another (or vice versa) is done properly.

The control unit of the Illiac IV, which has no floating point arithmetic capability, can be used to manipulate the data stack in the course of program execution.

These are the features of Actus which are currently being implemented in the first phase of the compiler for the Illiac IV at the Institute for Advanced Computation.

8. SUMMARY

The objective of the research reported here was to design a high level language which is appropriate for both vector and array parallel computers, and at the same time to reflect many of the advances which have been made in the design and implementation of high level languages in general. The language is therefore unsuitable for other types of parallel processors, such as multiprocessor configurations.

The first objective was achieved by introducing the concept of the extent of parallelism, whose maximum size is defined in the data declarations and subsequently manipulated (in parallel) either in part or in total by the statements and constructs of the language. Using this concept, it was found to be possible to adopt a unified approach for both types of computers. The second objective was achieved by modifying existing data and program structuring constructs of Pascal to accommodate the special demands of a parallel environment.

The advantage of the language is that a problem's parallel nature is expressed directly in the syntax of the language which, in turn, makes efficient use of the machine's computational resources. The user, therefore, does not have to get involved with the hardware of these machines or the compiler dependencies of the languages; this involvement has been necessary when using current or previous languages for such machines. Thus the language brings the benefits of program and data structuring to the large scale scientific computation area and still maintains the advantages of compile time and run time checking.

ACKNOWLEDGMENTS

The author wishes to thank the staff of the Institute for Advanced Computation for the help he received in the course of this work. In particular, D. Stevenson's continual penetrating questions and knowledge of the architecture of these parallel computers were of invaluable assistance. The author would also like to thank the referees for their careful reading of the manuscript and for a number of suggested improvements.

REFERENCES

1. BARNES, G.H., BROWN, R.M., KATO, M., KUCK, D.J., SLOTNICK, D.L., AND STOKES, R.Q. The ILLIAC IV computer. *IEEE Trans. Comptr. C-17* (Aug. 1968), 746–757.
2. FEIERBACH, G.F., AND STEVENSON, D.K. The Phoenix array processor. Proc. 17th Annu. Tech. Symp., June 1978, pp. 3–10.
3. HOLLAND, S.A., AND PURCELL, C.J. The CDC Star-100: a large scale network oriented computer system. Proc. 1971 IEEE Conf., Sept. 1971, pp. 55–65.
4. JENSEN, K., AND WIRTH, N. Pascal: user manual and report. *Lecture Notes in Computer Science, Vol. 18.* Springer-Verlag, Berlin, 1974.
5. KISKI, T. Tensor/ILLIAC IV project. Rep. UCRL-51467, Lawrence Livermore Lab., U. of California, 1973.

ACM Transactions on Programming Languages and Systems, Vol. 1, No. 2, October 1979.

311

6. KNIGHT, J. The SL/1 programming manual. NASA Langley Res. Ctr., March 1978.
7. LAWRIE, D.H., LAYMAN, T., BAER, D., AND RANDAL, J.M. Glypnir—a programming language for ILLIAC IV. *Comm. ACM 18*, 3 (March 1975), 157–164.
8. MILLSTEIN, R.E. Control structure in ILLIAC IV FORTRAN. *Comm. ACM 16*, 10 (Oct. 1973), 622–627.
9. NORI, K.V., AMMANN, U., JENSEN, K., AND NÄGELI, H. The Pascal (P) compiler: implementation notes. Institut für Informatik, Eidgenössische Technische Hochschule, Zürich, 1975.
10. RUSSELL, R.M. The Cray-1 computer system. *Comm. ACM 21*, 1 (Jan. 1978), 63–72.
11. Star programming manual. Control Data Corp., 1976.
12. STEVENS, K. CFD—a FORTRAN-like language for the ILLIAC IV. Sigplan Notices (March 1975), 72–80.
13. STEVENSON, D.K. Programming the ILLIAC IV. Tech. Rep., Dep. Comptr. Sci., Carnegie-Mellon U., 1975.
14. WIRTH, N. The programming language PASCAL. *Acta Informatica 1* (1971), 35–63.
15. WULF, W.A., AND BELL, C.G. C.mmp—a multi-mini processor. Proc. AFIPS 1972 Fall Joint Computer Conf., 1972, pp. 765–777.

Received August 1978; revised February 1979

ACM Transactions on Programming Languages and Systems, Vol. 1, No. 2, October 1979.

312

The Programming Language Concurrent Pascal

PER BRINCH HANSEN

Abstract—The paper describes a new programming language for structured programming of computer operating systems. It extends the sequential programming language Pascal with concurrent programming tools called processes and monitors. Section I explains these concepts informally by means of pictures illustrating a hierarchical design of a simple spooling system. Section II uses the same example to introduce the language notation. The main contribution of Concurrent Pascal is to extend the monitor concept with an explicit hierarchy of access rights to shared data structures that can be stated in the program text and checked by a compiler.

Index Terms—Abstract data types, access rights, classes, concurrent processes, concurrent programming languages, hierarchical operating systems, monitors, scheduling, structured multiprogramming.

I. THE PURPOSE OF CONCURRENT PASCAL

A. Background

SINCE 1972 I have been working on a new programming language for structured programming of computer operating systems. This language is called Concurrent Pascal. It extends the sequential programming language Pascal with concurrent programming tools called processes and monitors [1]–[3].

This is an informal description of Concurrent Pascal. It uses examples, pictures, and words to bring out the creative aspects of new programming concepts without getting into their finer details. I plan to define these concepts precisely and introduce a notation for them in later papers. This form of presentation may be imprecise from a formal point of view, but is perhaps more effective from a human point of view.

B. Processes

We will study concurrent processes inside an operating system and look at one small problem only: how can large amounts of data be transmitted from one process to another by means of a buffer stored on a disk?

Fig. 1 shows this little system and its three components: a process that produces data, a process that consumes data, and a disk buffer that connects them.

The circles are *system components* and the arrows are the *access rights* of these components. They show that both processes can use the buffer (but they do not show that data flows from the producer to the consumer). This kind of picture is an *access graph*.

Manuscript received February 1, 1975. This project is supported by the National Science Foundation under Grant DCR74-17331.
The author is with the Department of Information Science, California Institute of Technology, Pasadena, Calif. 91125.

EHO182-6/81/0000/0313 © 1975 IEEE

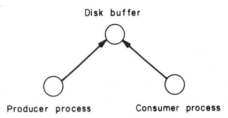

Fig. 1. Process communication.

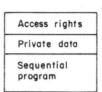

Fig. 2. Process.

The next picture shows a process component in more detail (Fig. 2).

A *process* consists of a *private data* structure and a *sequential program* that can operate on the data. One process cannot operate on the private data of another process. But concurrent processes can share certain data structures (such as a disk buffer). The *access rights* of a process mention the shared data it can operate on.

C. Monitors

A disk buffer is a data structure shared by two concurrent processes. The details of how such a buffer is constructed are irrelevant to its users. All the processes need to know is that they can *send* and *receive* data through it. If they try to operate on the buffer in any other way it is probably either a programming mistake or an example of tricky programming. In both cases, one would like a compiler to detect such misuse of a shared data structure.

To make this possible, we must introduce a language construct that will enable a programmer to tell a compiler how a shared data structure can be used by processes. This kind of system component is called a monitor. A monitor can synchronize concurrent processes and transmit data between them. It can also control the order in which competing processes use shared, physical resources. Fig. 3 shows a monitor in detail.

A *monitor* defines a *shared data* structure and all the operations processes can perform on it. These synchronizing operations are called *monitor procedures*. A monitor also defines an *initial operation* that will be executed when its data structure is created.

Reprinted from *IEEE Transactions on Software Engineering*, Volume SE-1, Number 2, June 1975, pages 199-207. Copyright © by The Institute of Electrical and Electronics Engineers, Inc.

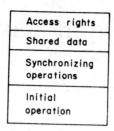

Fig. 3. Monitor.

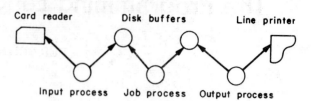

Fig. 4. Spooling system.

We can define a *disk buffer* as a monitor. Within this monitor there will be shared variables that define the location and length of the buffer on the disk. There will also be two monitor procedures, *send* and *receive*. The initial operation will make sure that the buffer starts as an empty one.

Processes cannot operate directly on shared data. They can only call monitor procedures that have access to shared data. A monitor procedure is executed as part of a calling process (just like any other procedure).

If concurrent processes simultaneously call monitor procedures that operate on the same shared data these procedures must be executed strictly one at a time. Otherwise, the results of monitor calls will be unpredictable. This means that the machine must be able to delay processes for short periods of time until it is their turn to execute monitor procedures. We will not be concerned about how this is done, but will just notice that a monitor procedure has *exclusive access* to shared data while it is being executed.

So the (virtual) machine on which concurrent programs run will handle *short-term scheduling* of simultaneous monitor calls. But the programmer must also be able to delay processes for longer periods of time if their requests for data and other resources cannot be satisfied immediately. If, for example, a process tries to receive data from an empty disk buffer it must be delayed until another process sends more data.

Concurrent Pascal includes a simple data type, called a *queue*, that can be used by monitor procedures to control *medium-term scheduling* of processes. A monitor can either *delay* a calling process in a queue or *continue* another process that is waiting in a queue. It is not important here to understand how these queues work except for the following essential rule: a process only has exclusive access to shared data as long as it continues to execute statements within a monitor procedure. As soon as a process is delayed in a queue it loses its exclusive access until another process calls the same monitor and wakes it up again. (Without this rule, it would be impossible for other processes to enter a monitor and let waiting processes continue their execution.)

Although the disk buffer example does not show this yet, monitor procedures should also be able to call procedures defined within other monitors. Otherwise, the language will not be very useful for hierarchical design. In the case of a disk buffer, one of these other monitors could perhaps define simple input/output operations on the disk. So a monitor can also have *access rights* to other system components (see Fig. 3).

D. System Design

A process executes a sequential program—it is an active component. A monitor is just a collection of procedures that do nothing until they are called by processes—it is a passive component. But there are strong similarities between a process and a monitor: both define a data structure (private or shared) and the meaningful operations on it. The main difference between processes and monitors is the way they are scheduled for execution.

It seems natural therefore to regard processes and monitors as *abstract data types* defined in terms of the operations one can perform on them. If a compiler can check that these operations are the only ones carried out on the data structures, then we may be able to build very reliable, concurrent programs in which *controlled access* to data and physical resources is guaranteed before these programs are put into operation. We have then to some extent solved the *resource protection* problem in the cheapest possible manner (without hardware mechanisms and run time overhead).

So we will define processes and monitors as data types and make it possible to use several instances of the same component type in a system. We can, for example, use two disk buffers to build a *spooling system* with an input process, a job process, and an output process (Fig. 4). I will distinguish between definitions and instances of components by calling them *system types* and *system components*. Access graphs (such as Fig. 4) will always show system components (not system types).

Peripheral devices are considered to be monitors implemented in hardware. They can only be accessed by a single procedure *io* that delays the calling process until an input/output operation is completed. Interrupts are handled by the virtual machine on which processes run.

To make the programming language useful for stepwise system design it should permit the division of a system type, such as a disk buffer, into smaller system types. One of these other system types should give a disk buffer access to the disk. We will call this system type a *virtual disk*. It gives a disk buffer the illusion that it has its own private disk. A virtual disk hides the details of disk input/output from the rest of the system and makes the disk look like a data structure (an array of disk pages). The only operations on this data structure are *read* and *write* a page.

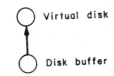

Fig. 5.   Buffer refinement.

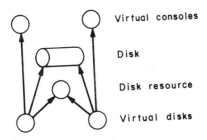

Fig. 6.   Decomposition of virtual disks.

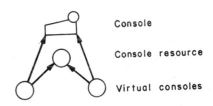

Fig. 7.   Decomposition of virtual consoles.

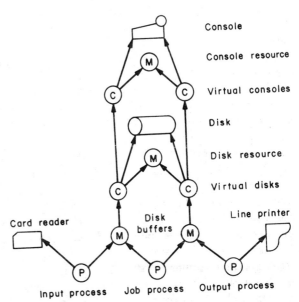

Fig. 8.   Hierarchical system structure.

Each virtual disk is only used by a single disk buffer (Fig. 5). A system component that cannot be called simultaneously by several other components will be called a *class*. A class defines a data structure and the possible operations on it (just like a monitor). The exclusive access of class procedures to class variables can be guaranteed completely at compile time. The virtual machine does not have to schedule simultaneous calls of class procedures at run time, because such calls cannot occur. This makes class calls considerably faster than monitor calls.

The spooling system includes two virtual disks but only one real disk. So we need a single *disk resource* monitor to control the order in which competing processes use the disk (Fig. 6). This monitor defines two procedures, *request* and *release* access, to be called by a virtual disk before and after each disk transfer.

It would seem simpler to replace the virtual disks and the disk resource by a single monitor that has exclusive access to the disk and does the input/output. This would certainly guarantee that processes use the disk one at a time. But this would be done according to the built-in short-term scheduling policy of monitor calls.

Now to make a virtual machine efficient, one must use a very simple short-term scheduling rule (such as first come, first served) [2]. If the disk has a moving access head this is about the worst possible algorithm one can use for disk transfers. It is vital that the language make it possible for the programmer to write a medium-term scheduling algorithm that will minimize disk head movements [3]. The data type *queue* mentioned earlier makes it possible to implement arbitrary scheduling rules within a monitor.

The difficulty is that while a monitor is performing an input/output operation it is impossible for other processes to enter the same monitor and join the disk queue. They will automatically be delayed by the short-term scheduler and only allowed to enter the monitor one at a time after each disk transfer. This will, of course, make the attempt

to control disk scheduling within the monitor illusory. To give the programmer complete control of disk scheduling, processes should be able to enter the disk queue during disk transfers. Since *arrival* and *service* in the disk queueing system potentially are simultaneous operations they must be handled by different system components, as shown in Fig. 6.

If the disk fails persistently during input/output this should be reported on an operator's console. Fig. 6 shows two instances of a class type, called a *virtual console*. They give the virtual disks the illusion that they have their own private consoles.

The virtual consoles get exclusive access to a single, real console by calling a *console resource* monitor (Fig. 7). Notice that we now have a standard technique for dealing with virtual devices.

If we put all these system components together, we get a complete picture of a simple spooling system (Fig. 8). Classes, monitors, and processes are marked C, M, and P.

E. Scope Rules

Some years ago I was part of a team that built a multiprogramming system in which processes can appear and disappear dynamically [4]. In practice, this system was used mostly to set up a fixed configuration of processes. Dynamic process deletion will certainly complicate the semantics and implementation of a programming language considerably. And since it appears to be unnecessary for a large class of real-time applications, it seems wise to exclude it altogether. So an operating system written in Concurrent Pascal will consist of a fixed number of processes, monitors, and classes. These components and their data structures will exist forever after system initialization. An operating system can, however, be extended by recompilation. It remains to be seen whether this restriction will simplify or complicate operating system design. But the poor quality of most existing operating systems clearly demonstrates an urgent need for simpler approaches.

In existing programming languages the data structures of processes, monitors, and classes would be called "global data." This term would be misleading in Concurrent Pascal where each data structure can be accessed by a single component only. It seems more appropriate to call them *permanent data structures*.

I have argued elsewhere that the most dangerous aspect of concurrent programming is the possibility of *time-dependent programming errors* that are impossible to locate by program testing ("lurking bugs") [2], [5], [6]. If we are going to depend on real-time programming systems in our daily lives, we must be able to find such obscure errors before the systems are put into operation.

Fortunately, a compiler can detect many of these errors if processes and monitors are represented by a structured notation in a high-level programming language. In addition, we must exclude low-level machine features (registers, addresses, and interrupts) from the language and let a virtual machine control them. If we want real-time systems to be highly reliable, we must stop programming them in assembly language. (The use of hardware protection mechanisms is merely an expensive, inadequate way of making arbitrary machine language programs behave almost as predictably as compiled programs.)

A Concurrent Pascal compiler will check that the private data of a process only are accessed by that process. It will also check that the data structure of a class or monitor only is accessed by its procedures.

Fig. 8 shows that *access rights* within an operating system normally are not tree structured. Instead they form a directed graph. This partly explains why the traditional scope rules of block-structured languages are inconvenient for concurrent programming (and for sequential programming as well). In Concurrent Pascal one can state the access rights of components in the program text and have them checked by a compiler.

Since the execution of a monitor procedure will delay the execution of further calls of the same monitor, we must prevent a monitor from calling itself recursively. Otherwise, processes can become *deadlocked*. So the compiler will check that the access rights of system components are hierarchically ordered (or, if you like, that there are no cycles in the access graph).

The *hierarchical ordering* of system components has vital consequences for system design and testing [7].

A hierarchical operating system will be tested component by component, bottom up (but could, of course, be conceived top down or by iteration). When an incomplete operating system has been shown to work correctly (by proof or testing), a compiler can ensure that this part of the system will continue to work correctly when new untested program components are added on top of it. Programming errors within new components cannot cause old components to fail because old components do not call new components, and new components only call old components through well-defined procedures that have already been tested.

(Strictly speaking, a compiler can only check that single monitor calls are made correctly; it cannot check sequences of monitor calls, for example whether a resource is always reserved before it is released. So one can only hope for compile time assurance of *partial correctness*.)

Several other reasons besides program correctness make a hierarchical structure attractive:

1) a hierarchical operating system can be studied in a stepwise manner as a sequence of *abstract machines* simulated by programs [8];

2) a partial ordering of process interactions permits one to use *mathematical induction* to prove certain overall properties of the system (such as the absence of deadlocks) [2];

3) *efficient resource utilization* can be achieved by ordering the program components according to the speed of the physical resources they control (with the fastest resources being controlled at the bottom of the system) [8];

4) a hierarchical system designed according to the previous criteria is often *nearly decomposable* from an analytical point of view. This means that one can develop stochastic models of its dynamic behavior in a stepwise manner [9].

F. Final Remarks

It seems most natural to represent a hierarchical system structure, such as Fig. 8, by a two-dimensional picture. But when we write a concurrent program we must somehow represent these access rules by linear text. This limitation of written language tends to obscure the simplicity of the original structure. That is why I have tried to explain the purpose of Concurrent Pascal by means of pictures instead of language notation.

The class concept is a restricted form of the class concept of Simula 67 [10]. Dijkstra suggested the idea of monitors [8]. The first structured language notation for monitors was proposed in [2], and illustrated by examples in [3]. The queue variables needed by monitors for process scheduling were suggested in [5] and modified in [3].

The main contribution of Concurrent Pascal is to extend monitors with explicit access rights that can be checked at compile time. Concurrent Pascal has been implemented at Caltech for the PDP 11/45 computer. Our system uses sequential Pascal as a job control and user programming language.

II. THE USE OF CONCURRENT PASCAL

A. Introduction

In Section I the concepts of Concurrent Pascal were explained informally by means of pictures of a hierarchical spooling system. I will now use the same example to introduce the language notation of Concurrent Pascal. The presentation is still informal. I am neither trying to define the language precisely nor to develop a working system. This will be done in other papers. I am just trying to show the flavor of the language.

B. Processes

We will now program the system components in Fig. 8 one at a time from top to bottom (but we could just as well do it bottom up).

Although we only need one *input process*, we may as well define it as a general system type of which several copies may exist:

```
type inputprocess =
process(buffer: diskbuffer);
var block: page;
cycle
    readcards(block);
    buffer.send(block);
end
```

An input process has access to a *buffer* of type diskbuffer (to be defined later). The process has a private variable *block* of type page. The data type page is declared elsewhere as an array of characters:

$$\text{type page} = \text{array } (.1..512.) \text{ of char}$$

A process type defines a *sequential program*—in this case, an endless cycle that inputs a block from a card reader and sends it through the buffer to another process. We will ignore the details of card reader input.

The *send* operation on the buffer is called as follows (using the block as a parameter):

$$\text{buffer.send(block)}$$

The next component type we will define is a *job process*:

```
type jobprocess =
process(input, output: diskbuffer);
var block: page;
cycle
    input.receive(block);
    update(block);
    output.send(block);
end
```

A job process has access to two disk buffers called *input* and *output*. It receives blocks from one buffer, updates them, and sends them through the other buffer. The details of updating can be ignored here.

Finally, we need an *output process* that can receive data from a disk buffer and output them on a line printer:

```
type outputprocess =
process(buffer: diskbuffer);
var block: page;
cycle
    buffer.receive(block);
    printlines(block);
end
```

The following shows a declaration of the main system components:

```
var buffer1, buffer2: diskbuffer;
    reader: inputprocess;
    master: jobprocess;
    writer: outputprocess;
```

There is an input process, called the *reader*, a job process, called the *master*, and an output process, called the *writer*. Then there are two disk buffers, *buffer1* and *buffer2*, that connect them.

Later I will explain how a disk buffer is defined and initialized. If we assume that the disk buffers already have been initialized, we can initialize the input process as follows:

$$\text{init reader(buffer1)}$$

The *init* statement allocates space for the *private variables* of the reader process and starts its execution as a sequential process with access to buffer1.

The *access rights* of a process to other system components, such as buffer1, are also called its *parameters*. A process can only be initialized once. After initialization, the parameters and private variables of a process exist forever. They are called *permanent variables*.

The init statement can be used to start concurrent execution of several processes and define their access rights. As an example, the statement

$$\text{init reader(buffer1), master(buffer1, buffer2),} \\ \text{writer(buffer2)}$$

starts concurrent execution of the reader process (with access to buffer1), the master process (with access to both buffers), and the writer process (with access to buffer2).

A process can only access its own parameters and private variables. The latter are not accessible to other system components. Compare this with the more liberal scope rules of block-structured languages in which a program block can access not only its own parameters and local variables, but also those declared in outer blocks. In Concurrent Pascal, all variables accessible to a system component are declared within its type definition. This access rule and the init statement make it possible for a programmer to state access rights explicitly and have them checked by a compiler. They also make it possible to study a system type as a self-contained program unit.

Although the programming examples do not show this, one can also define constants, data types, and procedures within a process. These objects can only be used within the process type.

317

C. Monitors

The *disk buffer* is a monitor type:

```
type diskbuffer =
monitor(consoleaccess, diskaccess: resource;
    base, limit: integer);

    var disk: virtualdisk; sender, receiver: queue;
        head, tail, length: integer;

    procedure entry send(block: page);
    begin
        if length = limit then delay(sender);
        disk.write(base + tail, block);
        tail:= (tail + 1) mod limit;
        length:= length + 1;
        continue(receiver);
    end;

    procedure entry receive(var block: page);
    begin
        if length = 0 then delay(receiver);
        disk.read(base + head, block);
        head:= (head + 1) mod limit;
        length:= length − 1;
        continue(sender);
    end;

    begin "initial statement"
        init disk(consoleaccess, diskaccess);
        head:= 0; tail:= 0; length:= 0;
    end
```

A disk buffer has access to two other components, *consoleaccess* and *diskaccess*, of type resource (to be defined later). It also has access to two integer constants defining the *base* address and *limit* of the buffer on the disk.

The monitor declares a set of *shared variables:* the *disk* is declared as a variable of type virtualdisk. Two variables of type queue are used to delay the *sender* and *receiver* processes until the buffer becomes nonfull and nonempty. Three integers define the relative addresses of the *head* and *tail* elements of the buffer and its current *length*.

The monitor defines two *monitor procedures*, send and receive. They are marked with the word *entry* to distinguish them from local procedures used within the monitor (there are none of these in this example).

Receive returns a page to the calling process. If the buffer is empty, the calling process is *delayed* in the receiver queue until another process sends a page through the buffer. The receive procedure will then read and remove a page from the head of the disk buffer by calling a *read* operation defined within the virtual disk type:

$$disk.read(base + head, block)$$

Finally, the receive procedure will *continue* the execution of a sending process (if the latter is waiting in the sender queue).

Send is similar to receive.

The queuing mechanism will be explained in detail in the next section.

The *initial statement* of a disk buffer initializes its virtual disk with access to the console and disk resources. It also sets the buffer length to zero. (Notice, that a disk buffer does not use its access rights to the console and disk, but only passes them on to a virtual disk declared within it.)

The following shows a declaration of two system components of type resource and two integers defining the base and limit of a disk buffer:

```
var consoleaccess, diskaccess: resource;
    base, limit: integer;
    buffer: diskbuffer;
```

If we assume that these variables already have been initialized, we can initialize a disk buffer as follows:

```
init buffer(consoleaccess, diskaccess, base, limit)
```

The *init* statement allocates storage for the parameters and shared variables of the disk buffer and executes its initial statement.

A monitor can only be initialized once. After initialization, the parameters and shared variables of a monitor exist forever. They are called *permanent variables*. The parameters and local variables of a monitor procedure, however, exist only while it is being executed. They are called *temporary variables*.

A monitor procedure can only access its own temporary and permanent variables. These variables are not accessible to other system components. Other components can, however, call procedure entries within a monitor. While a monitor procedure is being executed, it has *exclusive access* to the permanent variables of the monitor. If concurrent processes try to call procedures within the same monitor simultaneously, these procedures will be executed strictly one at a time.

Only monitors and constants can be permanent parameters of processes and monitors. This rule ensures that processes only communicate by means of monitors.

It is possible to define constants, data types, and local procedures within monitors (and processes). The local procedures of a system type can only be called within the system type. To prevent *deadlock* of monitor calls and ensure that access rights are hierarchical the following rules are enforced: a procedure must be declared before it can be called; procedure definitions cannot be nested and cannot call themselves; a system type cannot call its own procedure entries.

The absence of recursion makes it possible for a compiler to determine the store requirements of all system components. This and the use of permanent components make it possible to use *fixed store allocation* on a computer that does not support paging.

Since system components are permanent they must be declared as permanent variables of other components.

D. Queues

A monitor procedure can delay a calling process for any length of time by executing a *delay* operation on a queue variable. Only one process at a time can wait in a queue. When a calling process is delayed by a monitor procedure it loses its exclusive access to the monitor variables until another process calls the same monitor and executes a continue operation on the queue in which the process is waiting.

The *continue* operation makes the calling process return from its monitor call. If any process is waiting in the selected queue, it will immediately resume the execution of the monitor procedure that delayed it. After being resumed, the process again has exclusive access to the permanent variables of the monitor.

Other variants of process queues (called "events" and "conditions") are proposed in [3], [5]. They are multi-process queues that use different (but fixed) scheduling rules. We do not yet know from experience which kind of queue will be the most convenient one for operating system design. A single-process queue is the simplest tool that gives the programmer complete control of the scheduling of individual processes. Later, I will show how multi-process queues can be built from single-process queues.

A queue must be declared as a permanent variable within a monitor type.

E. Classes

Every disk buffer has its own virtual disk. A virtual disk is defined as a class type:

```
type virtualdisk =
class(consoleaccess, diskaccess: resource);

var terminal: virtualconsole; peripheral: disk;

procedure entry read(pageno: integer; var block: page);
var error: boolean;
begin
  repeat
    diskaccess.request;
    peripheral.read(pageno, block, error);
    diskaccess.release;
    if error then terminal.write('disk failure');
  until not error;
end;

procedure entry write(pageno: integer; block: page);
begin "similar to read" end;

begin "initial statement"
  init terminal(consoleaccess), peripheral;
end
```

A virtual disk has access to a console resource and a disk resource. Its permanent variables define a virtual console and a disk. A process can access its virtual disk by means of *read* and *write* procedures. These procedure entries *request* and *release* exclusive access to the real disk before and after each block transfer. If the real disk fails, the virtual disk calls its virtual console to report the error.

The *initial statement* of a virtual disk initializes its virtual console and the real disk.

Section II-C shows an example of how a virtual disk is declared and initialized (within a disk buffer).

A class can only be initialized once. After initialization, its parameters and private variables exist forever. A class procedure can only access its own temporary and permanent variables. These cannot be accessed by other components.

A class is a system component that cannot be called simultaneously by several other components. This is guaranteed by the following rule: a class must be declared as a permanent variable within a system type; a class can be passed as a permanent parameter to another class (but not to a process or monitor). So a chain of nested class calls can only be started by a single process or monitor. Consequently, it is not necessary to schedule simultaneous class calls at run time—they cannot occur.

F. Input/Output

The real *disk* is controlled by a class

$$\text{type disk} = \text{class}$$

with two procedure entries

```
read(pageno, block, error)
write(pageno, block, error)
```

The class uses a standard procedure

```
io(block, param, device)
```

to transfer a block to or from the disk device. The io parameter is a record

```
var param: record
    operation: iooperation;
    result: ioresult;
    pageno: integer
  end
```

that defines an input/output operation, its result, and a page number on the disk. The calling process is delayed until an io operation has been completed.

A *virtual console* is also defined as a class

```
type virtualconsole =
class(access: resource);
var terminal: console;
```

It can be accessed by read and write operations that are similar to each other:

```
procedure entry read(var text: line);
begin
  access.request;
  terminal.read(text);
  access.release;
end
```

The real *console* is controlled by a class that is similar to the disk class.

G. Multiprocess Scheduling

Access to the console and disk is controlled by two monitors of type *resource*. To simplify the presentation, I will assume that competing processes are served in first-come, first-served order. (A much better disk scheduling algorithm is defined in [3]. It can be programmed in Concurrent Pascal as well, but involves more details than the present one.)

We will define a multiprocess queue as an array of single-process queues

type multiqueue = array (.0..$q$length-1.) of queue

where $q$length is an upper bound on the number of concurrent processes in the system.

A first-come, first-served scheduler is now straightforward to program:

```
type resource =
monitor

var free: Boolean; q: multiqueue;
  head, tail, length: integer;

procedure entry request;
var arrival: integer;
begin
  if free then free:= false else
  begin
    arrival:= tail;
    tail:= (tail + 1) mod qlength;
    length:= length + 1;
    delay(q(.arrival.));
  end;
end;

procedure entry release;
var departure: integer;
begin
  if length = 0 then free:= true else
  begin
    departure:= head;
    head:= (head + 1) mod qlength;
    length:= length - 1;
    continue(q(.departure.));
  end;
end;

begin "initial statement"
  free:= true; length:= 0;
  head:= 0; tail:= 0;
end
```

H. Initial Process

Finally, we will put all these components together into a concurrent program. A Concurrent Pascal program consists of nested definitions of system types. The outermost system type is an anonymous process, called the initial process. An instance of this process is created during system loading. It initializes the other system components.

The initial process defines system types and instances of them. It executes statements that initialize these system components. In our example, the initial process can be sketched as follows (ignoring the problem of how base addresses and limits of disk buffers are defined):

```
type
  resource = monitor···end;
  console = class···end;
  virtualconsole =
    class(access: resource);···end;
  disk = class···end;
  virtualdisk =
    class(consoleaccess, diskaccess: resource);···end;
  diskbuffer =
    monitor(consoleaccess, diskaccess: resource;
      base, limit: integer);···end;
  inputprocess =
    process(buffer: diskbuffer);···end;
  jobprocess =
    process(input, output: diskbuffer);···end;
  outputprocess =
    process(buffer: diskbuffer);···end;
var
  consoleaccess, diskaccess: resource;
  buffer1, buffer2: diskbuffer;
  reader: inputprocess;
  master: jobprocess;
  writer: outputprocess;
begin
  init consoleaccess, diskaccess,
    buffer1(consoleaccess, diskaccess, base1, limit1),
    buffer2(consoleaccess, diskaccess, base2, limit2),
    reader(buffer1),
    master(buffer1, buffer2),
    writer(buffer2);
end.
```

When the execution of a process (such as the initial process) terminates, its private variables continue to exist. This is necessary because these variables may have been passed as permanent parameters to other system components.

ACKNOWLEDGMENT

It is a pleasure to acknowledge the immense value of a continuous exchange of ideas with C. A. R. Hoare on structured multiprogramming. I also thank my students L. Medina and R. Varela for their helpful comments on this paper.

REFERENCES

[1] N. Wirth, "The programming language Pascal," *Acta Informatica*, vol. 1, no. 1, pp. 35–63, 1971.
[2] P. Brinch Hansen, *Operation System Principles*. Englewood Cliffs, N. J.: Prentice-Hall, July 1973.
[3] C. A. R. Hoare, "Monitors: An operating system structuring concept," *Commun. Ass. Comput. Mach.*, vol. 17, pp. 549–557, Oct. 1974.
[4] P. Brinch Hansen, "The nucleus of a multiprogramming

system," *Commun. Ass. Comput. Mach.*, vol. 13, pp. 238–250, Apr. 1970.

[5] ——, "Structured multiprogramming," *Commun. Ass. Comput. Mach.*, vol. 15, pp. 574–578, July 1972.

[6] ——, "Concurrent programming concepts," *Ass. Comput. Mach. Comput. Rev.*, vol. 5, pp. 223–245, Dec. 1974.

[7] ——, "A programming methodology for operating system design," in *1974 Proc. IFIP Congr.* Stockholm, Sweden: North-Holland, Aug. 1974, pp. 394–397.

[8] E. W. Dijkstra, "Hierarchical ordering of sequential processes," *Acta Informatica*, vol. 1, no. 2, pp. 115–138, 1971.

[9] H. A. Simon, "The architecture of complexity," in *Proc. Amer. Philosophical Society*, vol. 106, no. 6, 1962, pp. 468–482.

[10] O.-J. Dahl and C. A. R. Hoare, "Hierarchical program structures," in *Structured Programming*, O.-J. Dahl, E. W. Dijkstra, and C. A. R. Hoare. New York: Academic, 1972.

Per Brinch Hansen was born in Copenhagen, Denmark, on November 13, 1938. He received the M.S. degree in electronic engineering from the Technical University of Denmark, Copenhagen, in 1963. Afterwards he joined the Danish computer manufacturer, Regnecentralen, as a systems programmer and designer. In 1967 he became head of the department at Regnecentralen which developed the architecture of the RC 4000 computer and its multiprogramming system. From 1970 to 1972 he visited Carnegie-Mellon University, Pittsburgh, Pa., where he wrote the book *Operating System Principles* (Englewood Cliffs, N. J., Prentice-Hall, July 1973). This book contains the first proposal of the *monitor concept* on which the programming language Concurrent Pascal is based. In 1972 he became Associate Professor of Computer Science at the California Institute of Technology, Pasadena. He has been a consultant to Burroughs Corporation, Control Data Corporation, Jet Propulsion Laboratory, Philips, and Varian Data Machines. His main research interests are computer architecture and programming methodology.

Dr. Brinch Hansen is a member of the Working Group 2.3 on Programming Methodology sponsored by the International Federation for Information Processing.

Reprinted with permission from Communications of ACM,
Volume 21, Number 8, August 1978, pages 666-677. Copyright
© 1978 by the Association for Computing Machinery, Inc.

Programming   S. L. Graham, R. L. Rivest
Techniques   Editors

Communicating Sequential Processes

C.A.R. Hoare
The Queen's University
Belfast, Northern Ireland

This paper suggests that input and output are basic
primitives of programming and that parallel
composition of communicating sequential processes is a
fundamental program structuring method. When
combined with a development of Dijkstra's guarded
command, these concepts are surprisingly versatile.
Their use is illustrated by sample solutions of a variety
of familiar programming exercises.

Key Words and Phrases: programming,
programming languages, programming primitives,
program structures, parallel programming, concurrency,
input, output, guarded commands, nondeterminacy,
coroutines, procedures, multiple entries, multiple exits,
classes, data representations, recursion, conditional
critical regions, monitors, iterative arrays
CR Categories: 4.20, 4.22, 4.32

1. Introduction

Among the primitive concepts of computer programming, and of the high level languages in which programs
are expressed, the action of assignment is familiar and
well understood. In fact, any change of the internal state
of a machine executing a program can be modeled as an
assignment of a new value to some variable part of that
machine. However, the operations of input and output,
which affect the external environment of a machine, are
not nearly so well understood. They are often added to
a programming language only as an afterthought.

Among the structuring methods for computer pro-

General permission to make fair use in teaching or research of all
or part of this material is granted to individual readers and to nonprofit
libraries acting for them provided that ACM's copyright notice is given
and that reference is made to the publication, to its date of issue, and
to the fact that reprinting privileges were granted by permission of the
Association for Computing Machinery. To otherwise reprint a figure,
table, other substantial excerpt, or the entire work requires specific
permission as does republication, or systematic or multiple reproduc-
tion.
This research was supported by a Senior Fellowship of the Science
Research Council.
Author's present address: Programming Research Group, 45, Ban-
bury Road, Oxford, England.
© 1978 ACM 0001-0782/78/0800-0666 $00.75

grams, three basic constructs have received widespread
recognition and use: A repetitive construct (e.g. the **while**
loop), an alternative construct (e.g. the conditional
if..then..else), and normal sequential program composition (often denoted by a semicolon). Less agreement has
been reached about the design of other important program structures, and many suggestions have been made:
Subroutines (Fortran), procedures (Algol 60 [15]), entries
(PL/I), coroutines (UNIX [17]), classes (SIMULA 67 [5]),
processes and monitors (Concurrent Pascal [2]), clusters
(CLU [13]), forms (ALPHARD [19]), actors (Hewitt [1]).

The traditional stored program digital computer has
been designed primarily for deterministic execution of a
single sequential program. Where the desire for greater
speed has led to the introduction of parallelism, every
attempt has been made to disguise this fact from the
programmer, either by hardware itself (as in the multiple
function units of the CDC 6600) or by the software (as
in an I/O control package, or a multiprogrammed operating system). However, developments of processor
technology suggest that a multiprocessor machine, constructed from a number of similar self-contained processors (each with its own store), may become more
powerful, capacious, reliable, and economical than a
machine which is disguised as a monoprocessor.

In order to use such a machine effectively on a single
task, the component processors must be able to communicate and to synchronize with each other. Many
methods of achieving this have been proposed. A widely
adopted method of communication is by inspection and
updating of a common store (as in Algol 68 [18], PL/I,
and many machine codes). However, this can create
severe problems in the construction of correct programs
and it may lead to expense (e.g. crossbar switches) and
unreliability (e.g. glitches) in some technologies of hardware implementation. A greater variety of methods has
been proposed for synchronization: semaphores [6],
events (PL/I), conditional critical regions [10], monitors
and queues (Concurrent Pascal [2]), and path expressions
[3]. Most of these are demonstrably adequate for their
purpose, but there is no widely recognized criterion for
choosing between them.

This paper makes an ambitious attempt to find a
single simple solution to all these problems. The essential
proposals are:
(1) Dijkstra's guarded commands [8] are adopted (with
a slight change of notation) as sequential control structures, and as the sole means of introducing and controlling nondeterminism.
(2) A parallel command, based on Dijkstra's *parbegin*
[6], specifies concurrent execution of its constituent sequential commands (processes). All the processes start
simultaneously, and the parallel command ends only
when they are all finished. They may not communicate
with each other by updating global variables.
(3) Simple forms of input and output command are
introduced. They are used for communication between
concurrent processes.

(4) Such communication occurs when one process names another as destination for output *and* the second process names the first as source for input. In this case, the value to be output is copied from the first process to the second. There is *no* automatic buffering: In general, an input or output command is delayed until the other process is ready with the corresponding output or input. Such delay is invisible to the delayed process.

(5) Input commands may appear in guards. A guarded command with an input guard is selected for execution only if and when the source named in the input command is ready to execute the corresponding output command. If several input guards of a set of alternatives have ready destinations, only one is selected and the others have *no* effect; but the choice between them is arbitrary. In an efficient implementation, an output command which has been ready for a long time should be favored; but the definition of a language cannot specify this since the relative speed of execution of the processes is undefined.

(6) A repetitive command may have input guards. If all the sources named by them have terminated, then the repetitive command also terminates.

(7) A simple pattern-matching feature, similar to that of [16], is used to discriminate the structure of an input message, and to access its components in a secure fashion. This feature is used to inhibit input of messages that do not match the specified pattern.

The programs expressed in the proposed language are intended to be implementable both by a conventional machine with a single main store, and by a fixed network of processors connected by input/output channels (although very different optimizations are appropriate in the different cases). It is consequently a rather static language: The text of a program determines a fixed upper bound on the number of processes operating concurrently; there is no recursion and no facility for process-valued variables. In other respects also, the language has been stripped to the barest minimum necessary for explanation of its more novel features.

The concept of a communicating sequential process is shown in Sections 3–5 to provide a method of expressing solutions to many simple programming exercises which have previously been employed to illustrate the use of various proposed programming language features. This suggests that the process may constitute a synthesis of a number of familiar and new programming ideas. The reader is invited to skip the examples which do not interest him.

However, this paper also ignores many serious problems. The most serious is that it fails to suggest any proof method to assist in the development and verification of correct programs. Secondly, it pays no attention to the problems of efficient implementation, which may be particularly serious on a traditional sequential computer. It is probable that a solution to these problems will require (1) imposition of restrictions in the use of the proposed features; (2) reintroduction of distinctive no-

tations for the most common and useful special cases; (3) development of automatic optimization techniques; and (4) the design of appropriate hardware.

Thus the concepts and notations introduced in this paper (although described in the next section in the form of a programming language fragment) should not be regarded as suitable for use as a programming language, either for abstract or for concrete programming. They are at best only a partial solution to the problems tackled. Further discussion of these and other points will be found in Section 7.

2. Concepts and Notations

The style of the following description is borrowed from Algol 60 [15]. Types, declarations, and expressions have not been treated; in the examples, a Pascal-like notation [20] has usually been adopted. The curly braces { } have been introduced into BNF to denote none or more repetitions of the enclosed material. (Sentences in parentheses refer to an implementation: they are not strictly part of a language definition.)

```
<command> ::= <simple command>|<structured command>
<simple command> ::= <null command>|<assignment command>
    |<input command>|<output command>
<structured command> ::= <alternative command>
    |<repetitive command>|<parallel command>
<null command> ::= skip
<command list> ::= {<declaration>; |<command>;} <command>
```

A command specifies the behavior of a device executing the command. It may succeed or fail. Execution of a simple command, if successful, may have an effect on the internal state of the executing device (in the case of assignment), or on its external environment (in the case of output), or on both (in the case of input). Execution of a structured command involves execution of some or all of its constituent commands, and if any of these fail, so does the structured command. (In this case, whenever possible, an implementation should provide some kind of comprehensible error diagnostic message.)

A null command has no effect and never fails.

A command list specifies sequential execution of its constituent commands in the order written. Each declaration introduces a fresh variable with a scope which extends from its declaration to the end of the command list.

2.1 Parallel Commands

```
<parallel command> ::= [<process>{||<process>}]
<process> ::= <process label> <command list>
<process label> ::= <empty>|<identifier> ::
    |<identifier>(<label subscript>{,<label subscript>}) ::
<label subscript> ::= <integer constant>|<range>
<integer constant> ::= <numeral>|<bound variable>
<bound variable> ::= <identifier>
<range> ::= <bound variable>:<lower bound>..<upper bound>
<lower bound> ::= <integer constant>
<upper bound> ::= <integer constant>
```

Each process of a parallel command must be *disjoint* from every other process of the command, in the sense that it does not mention any variable which occurs as a target variable (see Sections 2.2 and 2.3) in any other process.

A process label without subscripts, or one whose label subscripts are all integer constants, serves as a name for the command list to which it is prefixed; its scope extends over the whole of the parallel command. A process whose label subscripts include one or more ranges stands for a series of processes, each with the same label and command list, except that each has a different combination of values substituted for the bound variables. These values range between the lower bound and the upper bound inclusive. For example, $X(i:1..n) :: CL$ stands for

$$X(1) :: CL_1 || X(2) :: CL_2 ||...|| X(n) :: CL_n$$

where each CL_j is formed from CL by replacing every occurrence of the bound variable i by the numeral j. After all such expansions, each process label in a parallel command must occur only once and the processes must be well formed and disjoint.

A parallel command specifies concurrent execution of its constituent processes. They all start simultaneously and the parallel command terminates successfully only if and when they have all successfully terminated. The relative speed with which they are executed is arbitrary.

Examples:

(1) [cardreader?cardimage||lineprinter!lineimage]

Performs the two constituent commands in parallel, and terminates only when both operations are complete. The time taken may be as low as the longer of the times taken by each constituent process, i.e. the sum of its computing, waiting, and transfer times.

(2) [west :: DISASSEMBLE||X :: SQUASH||east :: ASSEMBLE]

The three processes have the names "west," "X," and "east." The capitalized words stand for command lists which will be defined in later examples.

(3) [room :: ROOM||fork(i:0..4) :: FORK||phil(i:0..4) :: PHIL]

There are eleven processes. The behavior of "room" is specified by the command list ROOM. The behavior of the five processes fork(0), fork(1), fork(2), fork(3), fork(4), is specified by the command list FORK, within which the bound variable i indicates the identity of the particular fork. Similar remarks apply to the five processes PHIL.

2.2 Assignment Commands

<assignment command> ::= <target variable> := <expression>
<expression> ::= <simple expression>|<structured expression>
<structured expression> ::= <constructor>(<expression list>)
<constructor> ::= <identifier>|<empty>
<expression list> ::= <empty>|<expression>{,<expression>}
<target variable> ::= <simple variable>|<structured target>
<structured target> ::= <constructor>(<target variable list>)
<target variable list> ::= <empty>|<target variable>
    {,<target variable>}

An expression denotes a value which is computed by an executing device by application of its constituent operators to the specified operands. The value of an expression is undefined if any of these operations are undefined. The value denoted by a simple expression may be simple or structured. The value denoted by a structured expression is structured; its constructor is that of the expression, and its components are the list of values denoted by the constituent expressions of the expression list.

An assignment command specifies evaluation of its expression, and assignment of the denoted value to the target variable. A simple target variable may have assigned to it a simple or a structured value. A structured target variable may have assigned to it a structured value, with the same constructor. The effect of such assignment is to assign to each constituent simpler variable of the structured target the value of the corresponding component of the structured value. Consequently, the value denoted by the target variable, if evaluated *after* a successful assignment, is the same as the value denoted by the expression, as evaluated *before* the assignment.

An assignment fails if the value of its expression is undefined, or if that value does not *match* the target variable, in the following sense: A *simple* target variable matches any value of its type. A *structured* target variable matches a structured value, provided that: (1) they have the same constructor, (2) the target variable list is the same length as the list of components of the value, (3) each target variable of the list matches the corresponding component of the value list. A structured value with no components is known as a "signal."

Examples:

(1) $x := x + 1$	the value of x after the assignment is the same as the value of $x + 1$ before.
(2) $(x, y) := (y, x)$	exchanges the values of x and y.
(3) $x := cons(left, right)$	constructs a structured value and assigns it to x.
(4) $cons(left, right) := x$	fails if x does not have the form $cons(y, z)$; but if it does, then y is assigned to left, and z is assigned to right.
(5) $insert(n) := insert(2*x + 1)$	equivalent to $n := 2*x + 1$.
(6) $c := P()$	assigns to c a "signal" with constructor P, and no components.
(7) $P() := c$	fails if the value of c is not P(); otherwise has no effect.
(8) $insert(n) := has(n)$	fails, due to mismatch.

Note: Successful execution of both (3) and (4) ensures the truth of the postcondition $x = cons(left, right)$; but (3) does so by changing x and (4) does so by changing left and right. Example (4) will fail if there is *no* value of left and right which satisfies the postcondition.

2.3 Input and Output Commands

<input command> ::= <source>?<target variable>
<output command> ::= <destination>!<expression>
<source> ::= <process name>

<destination> := <process name>
<process name> ::= <identifier>|<identifier>(<subscripts>)
<subscripts> := <integer expression>{,<integer expression>}

Input and output commands specify communication between two concurrently operating sequential processes. Such a process may be implemented in hardware as a special-purpose device (e.g. cardreader or lineprinter), or its behavior may be specified by one of the constituent processes of a parallel command. Communication occurs between two processes of a parallel command whenever (1) an input command in one process specifies as its source the process name of the other process; (2) an output command in the other process specifies as its destination the process name of the first process; and (3) the target variable of the input command matches the value denoted by the expression of the output command. On these conditions, the input and output commands are said to *correspond*. Commands which correspond are executed simultaneously, and their combined effect is to assign the value of the expression of the output command to the target variable of the input command.

An input command fails if its source is terminated. An output command fails if its destination is terminated or if its expression is undefined.

(The requirement of synchronization of input and output commands means that an implementation will have to delay whichever of the two commands happens to be ready first. The delay is ended when the corresponding command in the other process is also ready, or when the other process terminates. In the latter case the first command fails. It is also possible that the delay will never be ended, for example, if a group of processes are attempting communication but none of their input and output commands correspond with each other. This form of failure is known as a deadlock.)

Examples:

(1) cardreader?cardimage — from cardreader, read a card and assign its value (an array of characters) to the variable cardimage

(2) lineprinter!lineimage — to lineprinter, send the value of lineimage for printing

(3) $X?(x, y)$ — from process named X, input a pair of values and assign them to x and y

(4) DIV!($3*a + b$, 13) — to process DIV, output the two specified values.

Note: If a process named DIV issues command (3), and a process named X issues command (4), these are executed simultaneously, and have the same effect as the assignment: $(x, y) := (3*a + b, 13)$ ($\equiv x := 3*a + b; y := 13$).

(5) console(i)?c — from the ith element of an array of consoles, input a value and assign it to c

(6) console($j - 1$)!"A" — to the $(j - 1)$th console, output character "A"

(7) $X(i)?V( )$ — from the ith of an array of processes X, input a signal $V( )$; refuse to input any other signal

(8) sem!P( ) — to sem output a signal P( )

2.4 Alternative and Repetitive Commands

<repetitive command> ::=*<alternative command>
<alternative command> := [<guarded command>
    {◻<guarded command>}]
<guarded command> := <guard> → <command list>
    |(<range>{,<range>})<guard> → <command list>
<guard> := <guard list>|<guard list>;<input command>
    |<input command>
        <guard list> := <guard element>{;<guard element>}
<guard element> := <boolean expression>|<declaration>

A guarded command with one or more ranges stands for a series of guarded commands, each with the same guard and command list, except that each has a different combination of values substituted for the bound variables. The values range between the lower bound and upper bound inclusive. For example, $(i:1..n)G → CL$ stands for

$$G_1 → CL_1 ◻ G_2 → CL_2 ◻ ... ◻ G_n → CL_n$$

where each $G_j → CL_j$ is formed from $G → CL$ by replacing every occurrence of the bound variable i by the numeral j.

A guarded command is executed only if and when the execution of its guard does not fail. First its guard is executed and then its command list. A guard is executed by execution of its constituent elements from left to right. A Boolean expression is evaluated: If it denotes false, the guard fails; but an expression that denotes true has no effect. A declaration introduces a fresh variable with a scope that extends from the declaration to the end of the guarded command. An input command at the end of a guard is executed only if and when a corresponding output command is executed. (An implementation may test whether a guard fails simply by trying to execute it, and discontinuing execution if and when it fails. This is valid because such a discontinued execution has no effect on the state of the executing device.)

An alternative command specifies execution of exactly one of its constituent guarded commands. Consequently, if all guards fail, the alternative command fails. Otherwise an arbitrary one with successfully executable guard is selected and executed. (An implementation should take advantage of its freedom of selection to ensure efficient execution and good response. For example, when input commands appear as guards, the command which corresponds to the earliest ready and matching output command should in general be preferred; and certainly, no executable and ready output command should be passed over unreasonably often.)

A repetitive command specifies as many iterations as possible of its constituent alternative command. Consequently, when all guards fail, the repetitive command terminates with no effect. Otherwise, the alternative command is executed once and then the whole repetitive command is executed again. (Consider a repetitive command when all its true guard lists end in an input guard. Such a command may have to be delayed until either (1) an output command corresponding to one of the input guards becomes ready, or (2) all the sources named by the input guards have terminated. In case (2), the repetitive command terminates. If neither event ever occurs, the process fails (in deadlock.)

Examples:

(1) $[x \geq y \rightarrow m := x \,[]\, y \geq x \rightarrow m := y]$

If $x \geq y$, assign x to m; if $y \geq x$ assign y to m; if both $x \geq y$ and $y \geq x$, either assignment can be executed.

(2) $i := 0; *[i < size; content(i) \neq n \rightarrow i := i + 1]$

The repetitive command scans the elements content(i), for $i = 0, 1, \ldots$, until either $i \geq size$, or a value equal to n is found.

(3) $*[c\text{:character; west}?c \rightarrow \text{east}!c]$

This reads all the characters output by west, and outputs them one by one to east. The repetition terminates when the process west terminates.

(4) $*[(i:1..10)\text{continue}(i); \text{console}(i)?c \rightarrow X!(i, c); \text{console}(i)!\text{ack}();$
$\quad \text{continue}(i) := (c \neq \text{sign off})]$

This command inputs repeatedly from any of ten consoles, provided that the corresponding element of the Boolean array continue is true. The bound variable i identifies the originating console. Its value, together with the character just input, is output to X, and an acknowledgment signal is sent back to the originating console. If the character indicated "sign off," continue(i) is set false, to prevent further input from that console. The repetitive command terminates when all ten elements of continue are false. (An implementation should ensure that no console which is ready to provide input will be ignored unreasonably often.)

(5) $*[n\text{:integer; } X?\text{insert}(n) \rightarrow \text{INSERT}$
$\quad []n\text{:integer; } X?\text{has}(n) \rightarrow \text{SEARCH}; X!(i < size)$
$\quad]$

(Here, and elsewhere, capitalized words INSERT and SEARCH stand as abbreviations for program text defined separately.)

On each iteration this command accepts from X *either* (a) a request to "insert(n)," (followed by INSERT) *or* (b) a question "has(n)," to which it outputs an answer back to X. The choice between (a) and (b) is made by the next output command in X. The repetitive command terminates when X does. If X sends a nonmatching message, deadlock will result.

(6) $*[X?V() \rightarrow val := val + 1$
$\quad []val > 0; Y?P() \rightarrow val := val - 1$
$\quad]$

On each iteration, accept *either* a V() signal from X and increment val, *or* a P() signal from Y, and decrement val. But the second alternative cannot be selected unless val is positive (after which val will remain invariantly nonnegative). (When val > 0, the choice depends on the relative speeds of X and Y, and is not determined.) The repetitive command will terminate when both X and Y are terminated, or when X is terminated and val ≤ 0.

3. Coroutines

In parallel programming coroutines appear as a more fundamental program structure than subroutines, which can be regarded as a special case (treated in the next section).

3.1 COPY
Problem: Write a process X to copy characters output by process west to process east.
Solution:

$X :: *[c\text{:character; west}?c \rightarrow \text{east}!c]$

Notes: (1) When west terminates, the input "west?c" will fail, causing termination of the repetitive command, and of process X. Any subsequent input command from east will fail. (2) Process X acts as a single-character buffer between west and east. It permits west to work on production of the next character, before east is ready to input the previous one.

3.2 SQUASH
Problem: Adapt the previous program to replace every pair of consecutive asterisks "**" by an upward arrow "↑". Assume that the final character input is not an asterisk.
Solution:

$X :: *[c\text{:character; west}?c \rightarrow$
$\quad [c \neq \text{asterisk} \rightarrow \text{east}!c$
$\quad []c = \text{asterisk} \rightarrow \text{west}?c;$
$\qquad [c \neq \text{asterisk} \rightarrow \text{east}!\text{asterisk; east}!c$
$\qquad []c = \text{asterisk} \rightarrow \text{east}!\text{upward arrow}$
$\quad]]\quad]$

Notes: (1) Since west does not end with asterisk, the second "west?c" will not fail. (2) As an exercise, adapt this process to deal sensibly with input which ends with an odd number of asterisks.

3.3 DISASSEMBLE
Problem: to read cards from a cardfile and output to process X the stream of characters they contain. An extra space should be inserted at the end of each card.
Solution:

$*[\text{cardimage:(1..80)character; cardfile}?\text{cardimage} \rightarrow$
$\quad i\text{:integer; } i := 1;$
$\quad *[i \leq 80 \rightarrow X!\text{cardimage}(i); i := i + 1]$
$\quad X!\text{space}$
$]$

Notes: (1) "(1..80)character" declares an array of 80 characters, with subscripts ranging between 1 and 80. (2) The repetitive command terminates when the cardfile process terminates.

3.4 ASSEMBLE
Problem: To read a stream of characters from process X and print them in lines of 125 characters on a lineprinter. The last line should be completed with spaces if necessary.

327 Communications   August 1978
of   Volume 21
the ACM   Number 8

Solution:

```
lineimage:(1..125)character;
i:integer; i := 1;
*[c:character; X?c →
    lineimage(i) := c;
    [i ≤ 124 → i := i + 1
    []i = 125 → lineprinter!lineimage; i := 1
]   ];
[i = 1 → skip
[]i > 1 → *[i ≤ 125 → lineimage(i) := space; i := i + 1];
    lineprinter!lineimage
]
```

Note: (1) When X terminates, so will the first repetitive command of this process. The last line will then be printed, if it has any characters.

3.5 Reformat
Problem: Read a sequence of cards of 80 characters each, and print the characters on a lineprinter at 125 characters per line. Every card should be followed by an extra space, and the last line should be completed with spaces if necessary.
Solution:

```
[west::DISASSEMBLE||X::COPY||east::ASSEMBLE]
```

Notes: (1) The capitalized names stand for program text defined in previous sections. (2) The parallel command is designed to terminate after the cardfile has terminated. (3) This elementary problem is difficult to solve elegantly without coroutines.

3.6 Conway's Problem [4]
Problem: Adapt the above program to replace every pair of consecutive asterisks by an upward arrow.
Solution:

```
[west::DISASSEMBLE||X::SQUASH||east::ASSEMBLE]
```

4. Subroutines and Data Representations

A conventional nonrecursive subroutine can be readily implemented as a coroutine, provided that (1) its parameters are called "by value" and "by result," and (2) it is disjoint from its calling program. Like a Fortran subroutine, a coroutine may retain the values of local variables (*own* variables, in Algol terms) and it may use input commands to achieve the effect of "multiple entry points" in a safer way than PL/I. Thus a coroutine can be used like a SIMULA class instance as a concrete representation for abstract data.

A coroutine acting as a subroutine is a process operating concurrently with its user process in a parallel command: [subr::SUBROUTINE||X::USER]. The SUBROUTINE will contain (or consist of) a repetitive command: *[X?(value params) → ... ; X!(result params)], where ... computes the results from the values input. The subroutine will terminate when its user does. The USER will call the subroutine by a pair of commands: subr!(arguments);

... ; subr?(results). Any commands between these two will be executed concurrently with the subroutine.

A multiple-entry subroutine, acting as a representation for data [11], will also contain a repetitive command which represents each entry by an alternative input to a structured target with the entry name as constructor. For example,

```
*[X?entry1(value params) → ...
[]X?entry2(value params) → ...
]
```

The calling process X will determine which of the alternatives is activated on each repetition. When X terminates, so does this repetitive command. A similar technique in the user program can achieve the effect of multiple exits.

A recursive subroutine can be simulated by an array of processes, one for each level of recursion. The user process is level zero. Each activation communicates its parameters and results with its predecessor and calls its successor if necessary:

```
[recsub(0)::USER||recsub(i:1..reclimit)::RECSUB].
```

The user will call the first element of

```
recsub: recsub(1)!(arguments); ... ; recsub(1)?(results);.
```

The imposition of a fixed upper bound on recursion depth is necessitated by the "static" design of the language.

This clumsy simulation of recursion would be even more clumsy for a mutually recursive algorithm. It would not be recommended for conventional programming; it may be more suitable for an array of microprocessors for which the fixed upper bound is also realistic.

In this section, we assume each subroutine is used only by a *single* user process (which may, of course, itself contain parallel commands).

4.1 Function: Division With Remainder
Problem: Construct a process to represent a function-type subroutine, which accepts a positive dividend and divisor, and returns their integer quotient and remainder. Efficiency is of no concern.
Solution:

```
[DIV::*[x,y:integer; X?(x,y) →
    quot,rem:integer;quot := 0; rem := x;
    *[rem ≥ y → rem := rem − y; quot := quot + 1];
    X!(quot,rem)
    ]
||X::USER
]
```

4.2 Recursion: Factorial
Problem: Compute a factorial by the recursive method, to a given limit.
Solution:

```
[fac(i:1..limit)::
*[n:integer;fac(i − 1)?n →
    [n = 0 → fac(i − 1)!1
```

```
  []n > 0 → fac(i + 1)!n − 1;
    r:integer;fac(i + 1)?r;fac(i − 1)!(n * r)
  ]]
||fac(0)::USER
]
```

Note: This unrealistic example introduces the technique of the "iterative array" which will be used to a better effect in later examples.

4.3 Data Representation: Small Set of Integers [11]

Problem: To represent a set of not more than 100 integers as a process, S, which accepts two kinds of instruction from its calling process X: (1) S!insert(n), insert the integer n in the set, and (2) S!has(n); ... ; S?b, b is set true if n is in the set, and false otherwise. The initial value of the set is empty.

Solution:

```
S::
content:(0..99)integer; size:integer; size := 0;
*[n:integer; X?has(n) → SEARCH; X!(i < size)
[]n:integer; X?insert(n) → SEARCH;
    [i < size → skip
    []i = size; size < 100 →
      content (size) := n; size := size + 1
]   ]
```

where SEARCH is an abbreviation for:

```
i:integer; i := 0;
*[i < size; content(i) ≠ n → i := i + 1]
```

Notes: (1) The alternative command with guard "size < 100" will fail if an attempt is made to insert more than 100 elements. (2) The activity of insertion will in general take place concurrently with the calling process. However, any subsequent instruction to S will be delayed until the previous insertion is complete.

4.4 Scanning a Set

Problem: Extend the solution to 4.3 by providing a fast method for scanning all members of the set without changing the value of the set. The user program will contain a repetitive command of the form:

```
  S!scan( ); more:boolean; more := true;
*[more;x:integer; S?next(x) → ... deal with x ....
[]more; S?noneleft( ) → more := false
]
```

where S!scan( ) sets the representation into a scanning mode. The repetitive command serves as a **for** statement, inputting the successive members of x from the set and inspecting them until finally the representation sends a signal that there are no members left. The body of the repetitive command is *not* permitted to communicate with S in any way.

Solution: Add a third guarded command to the outer repetitive command of S:

```
... []X?scan( ) → i:integer; i := 0;
            *[i < size → X!next(content(i)); i := i + 1];
            X!noneleft( )
```

4.5 Recursive Data Representation: Small Set of Integers

Problem: Same as above, but an array of processes is to be used to achieve a high degree of parallelism. Each process should contain at most one number. When it contains no number, it should answer "false" to all inquiries about membership. On the first insertion, it changes to a second phase of behavior, in which it deals with instructions from its predecessor, passing some of them on to its successor. The calling process will be named S(0). For efficiency, the set should be sorted, i.e. the ith process should contain the ith largest number.

Solution:

```
S(i:1..100)::
*[n:integer; S(i − 1)?has(n) → S(0)!false
[]n:integer; S(i − 1)?insert(n) →
    *[m:integer; S(i − 1)?has(m) →
      [m ≤ n → S(0)!(m = n)
      []m > n → S(i + 1)!has(m)
      ]
    []m:integer; S(i − 1)?insert(m) →
      [m < n → S(i + 1)!insert(n); n := m
      []m = n → skip
      []m > n → S(i + 1)!insert(m)
      ] ] ]
```

Notes: (1) The user process S(0) inquires whether n is a member by the commands S(1)!has(n); ... ; [(i:1..100)S(i)? b → skip]. The appropriate process will respond to the input command by the output command in line 2 or line 5. This trick avoids passing the answer back "up the chain." (2) Many insertion operations can proceed in parallel, yet any subsequent "has" operation will be performed correctly. (3) All repetitive commands and all processes of the array will terminate after the user process S(0) terminates.

4.6 Multiple Exits: Remove the Least Member

Exercise: Extend the above solution to respond to a command to yield the least member of the set and to remove it from the set. The user program will invoke the facility by a pair of commands:

```
S(1)!least( ); [x:integer;S(1)? x → ... deal with x ...
             []S(1)?noneleft( ) → ...
             ]
```

or, if he wishes to scan and empty the set, he may write:

```
S(1)!least( );more:boolean; more := true;
          *[more; x:integer; S(1)?x → ... deal with x ... ; S(1)!least( )
          []more; S(1)?noneleft( ) → more := false
          ]
```

Hint: Introduce a Boolean variable, b, initialized to true, and prefix this to all the guards of the inner loop. After responding to a !least( ) command from its predecessor, each process returns its contained value n, asks its successor for its least, and stores the response in n. But if the successor returns "noneleft( )," b is set false and the inner loop terminates. The process therefore returns to its initial state (solution due to David Gries).

5. Monitors and Scheduling

This section shows how a monitor can be regarded as a single process which communicates with more than one user process. However, each user process must have a different name (e.g. producer, consumer) or a different subscript (e.g. $X(i)$) and each communication with a user must identify its source or destination uniquely.

Consequently, when a monitor is prepared to communicate with *any* of its user processes (i.e. whichever of them calls first) it will use a guarded command with a range. For example: $*[(i:1..100)X(i)?(\text{value parameters}) \rightarrow ... ; X(i)!(\text{results})]$. Here, the bound variable i is used to send the results back to the calling process. If the monitor is not prepared to accept input from some particular user (e.g. $X(j)$) on a given occasion, the input command may be preceded by a Boolean guard. For example, two successive inputs from the same process are inhibited by $j = 0$; $*[(i:1..100)i \neq j; X(i)?(\text{values}) \rightarrow ... ; j := i]$. Any attempted output from $X(j)$ will be delayed until a subsequent iteration, after the output of some other process $X(i)$ has been accepted and dealt with.

Similarly, conditions can be used to delay acceptance of inputs which would violate scheduling constraints—postponing them until some later occasion when some other process has brought the monitor into a state in which the input can validly be accepted. This technique is similar to a conditional critical region [10] and it obviates the need for special synchronizing variables such as events, queues, or conditions. However, the absence of these special facilities certainly makes it more difficult or less efficient to solve problems involving priorities—for example, the scheduling of head movement on a disk.

5.1 Bounded Buffer

Problem: Construct a buffering process X to smooth variations in the speed of output of portions by a producer process and input by a consumer process. The consumer contains pairs of commands $X!more( )$; $X?p$, and the producer contains commands of the form $X!p$. The buffer should contain up to ten portions.
Solution:

```
X::
buffer:(0..9) portion;
in,out:integer; in := 0; out := 0;
comment 0 ≤ out ≤ in ≤ out + 10;
  *[in < out + 10; producer?buffer(in mod 10) → in := in + 1
  []out < in; consumer?more( ) → consumer!buffer(out mod 10);
    out := out + 1
  ]
```

Notes: (1) When out < in < out + 10, the selection of the alternative in the repetitive command will depend on whether the producer produces before the consumer consumes, or vice versa. (2) When out = in, the buffer is empty and the second alternative cannot be selected even if the consumer is ready with its command $X!more( )$.

However, after the producer has produced its next portion, the consumer's request can be granted on the next iteration. (3) Similar remarks apply to the producer, when in = out + 10. (4) X is designed to terminate when out = in and the producer has terminated.

5.2 Integer Semaphore
Problem: To implement an integer semaphore, S, shared among an array $X(i:1..100)$ of client processes. Each process may increment the semaphore by $S!V( )$ or decrement it by $S!P( )$, but the latter command must be delayed if the value of the semaphore is not positive.
Solution:

```
S::val:integer; val := 0;
  *[(i:1..100)X(i)?V( ) → val := val + 1
  [](i:1..100)val > 0; X(i)?P( ) → val := val − 1
  ]
```

Notes: (1) In this process, no use is made of knowledge of the subscript i of the calling process. (2) The semaphore terminates only when all hundred processes of the process array X have terminated.

5.3 Dining Philosophers (Problem due to E.W. Dijkstra)
Problem: Five philosophers spend their lives thinking and eating. The philosophers share a common dining room where there is a circular table surrounded by five chairs, each belonging to one philosopher. In the center of the table there is a large bowl of spaghetti, and the table is laid with five forks (see Figure 1). On feeling hungry, a philosopher enters the dining room, sits in his own chair, and picks up the fork on the left of his place. Unfortunately, the spaghetti is so tangled that he needs to pick up and use the fork on his right as well. When he has finished, he puts down both forks, and leaves the room. The room should keep a count of the number of philosophers in it.

Fig. 1.

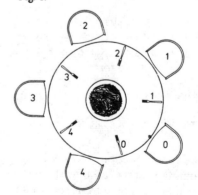

Solution: The behavior of the ith philosopher may be described as follows:

```
PHIL = *[... during ith lifetime ... →
    THINK;
    room!enter( );
    fork(i)!pickup( ); fork((i + 1) mod 5)!pickup( );
    EAT;
    fork(i)!putdown( ); fork((i + 1) mod 5)!putdown( );
    room!exit( )
    ]
```

Communications
of
the ACM

August 1978
Volume 21
Number 8

The fate of the *i*th fork is to be picked up and put down by a philosopher sitting on either side of it

```
FORK =
  *[phil(i)?pickup( ) → phil(i)?putdown( )
  []phil((i − 1)mod 5)?pickup( ) → phil((i − 1) mod 5)?putdown( )
  ]
```

The story of the room may be simply told:

```
ROOM = occupancy:integer; occupancy := 0;
  *[(i:0..4)phil(i)?enter( ) → occupancy := occupancy + 1
  [](i:0..4)phil(i)?exit( ) → occupancy := occupancy − 1
  ]
```

All these components operate in parallel:

```
[room::ROOM||fork(i:0..4)::FORK||phil(i:0..4)::PHIL].
```

Notes: (1) The solution given above does not prevent all five philosophers from entering the room, each picking up his left fork, and starving to death because he cannot pick up his right fork. (2) Exercise: Adapt the above program to avert this sad possibility. Hint: Prevent more than four philosophers from entering the room. (Solution due to E. W. Dijkstra).

6. Miscellaneous

This section contains further examples of the use of communicating sequential processes for the solution of some less familiar problems; a parallel version of the sieve of Eratosthenes, and the design of an iterative array. The proposed solutions are even more speculative than those of the previous sections, and in the second example, even the question of termination is ignored.

6.1 Prime Numbers: The Sieve of Eratosthenes [14]
Problem: To print in ascending order all primes less than 10000. Use an array of processes, SIEVE, in which each process inputs a prime from its predecessor and prints it. The process then inputs an ascending stream of numbers from its predecessor and passes them on to its successor, suppressing any that are multiples of the original prime. Solution:

```
[SIEVE(i:1..100)::
  p,mp:integer;
  SIEVE(i − 1)?p;
  print!p;
  mp := p; comment mp is a multiple of p;
  *[m:integer; SIEVE(i − 1)?m →
      *[m > mp → mp := mp + p];
      [m = mp → skip
      []m < mp → SIEVE(i + 1)!m
  ]  ]
||SIEVE(0)::print!2; n:integer; n := 3;
      *[n < 10000 → SIEVE(1)!n; n := n + 2]
||SIEVE(101)::*[n:integer;SIEVE(100)?n → print!n]
||print::*[(i:0..101) n:integer; SIEVE(i)?n → ...]
]
```

Note: (1) This beautiful solution was contributed by David Gries. (2) It is algorithmically similar to the program developed in [7, pp. 27–32].

6.2 An Iterative Array: Matrix Multiplication
Problem: A square matrix A of order 3 is given. Three streams are to be input, each stream representing a column of an array IN. Three streams are to be output, each representing a column of the product matrix IN $\times$ A. After an initial delay, the results are to be produced at the same rate as the input is consumed. Consequently, a high degree of parallelism is required. The solution should take the form shown in Figure 2. Each of the nine nonborder nodes inputs a vector component from the west and a partial sum from the north. Each node outputs the vector component to its east, and an updated partial sum to the south. The input data is produced by the west border nodes, and the desired results are consumed by south border nodes. The north border is a constant source of zeros and the east border is just a sink. No provision need be made for termination nor for changing the values of the array A.

Fig. 2.

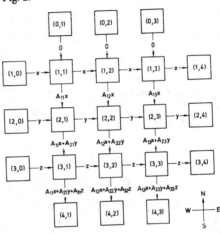

Solution: There are twenty-one nodes, in five groups, comprising the central square and the four borders:

```
[M(i:1..3,0)::WEST
||M(0,j:1..3)::NORTH
||M(i:1..3,4)::EAST
||M(4,j:1..3)::SOUTH
||M(i:1..3,j:1..3)::CENTER
]
```

The WEST and SOUTH borders are processes of the user program; the remaining processes are:

```
NORTH = *[true → M(1,j)!0]
EAST = *[x:real; M(i,3)?x → skip]
CENTER = *[x:real; M(i,j − 1)?x →
      M(i, j + 1)!x; sum:real;
      M(i − 1, j)?sum; M(i + 1,j)!(A(i, j)*x + sum)
  ]
```

7. Discussion

A design for a programming language must necessarily involve a number of decisions which seem to be fairly arbitrary. The discussion of this section is intended to explain some of the underlying motivation and to mention some unresolved questions.

7.1 Notations

I have chosen single-character notations (e.g. !,?) to express the primitive concepts, rather than the more traditional boldface or underlined English words. As a result, the examples have an APL-like brevity, which some readers find distasteful. My excuse is that (in contrast to APL) there are only a very few primitive concepts and that it is standard practice of mathematics (and also good coding practice) to denote common primitive concepts by brief notations (e.g. $+, \times$). When read aloud, these are replaced by words (e.g. plus, times).

Some readers have suggested the use of assignment notation for input and output:

<target variable> := <source>
<destination> := <expression>

I find this suggestion misleading: it is better to regard input and output as distinct primitives, justifying distinct notations.

I have used the same pair of brackets ([...]) to bracket all program structures, instead of the more familiar variety of brackets (**if..fi**, **begin..end**, **case...esac**, etc.). In this I follow normal mathematical practice, but I must also confess to a distaste for the pronunciation of words like **fi**, **od**, or **esac**.

I am dissatisfied with the fact that my notation gives the same syntax for a structured expression and a subscripted variable. Perhaps tags should be distinguished from other identifiers by a special symbol (say #).

I was tempted to introduce an abbreviation for combined declaration and input, e.g. $X?(n:integer)$ for $n:integer; X?n$.

7.2 Explicit Naming

My design insists that every input or output command must name its source or destination explicitly. This makes it inconvenient to write a library of processes which can be included in subsequent programs, independent of the process names used in that program. A partial solution to this problem is to allow one process (the *main* process) of a parallel command to have an empty label, and to allow the other processes in the command to use the empty process name as source or destination of input or output.

For construction of large programs, some more general technique will also be necessary. This should at least permit substitution of program text for names defined elsewhere—a technique which has been used informally throughout this paper. The Cobol COPY verb also permits a substitution for formal parameters within the copied text. But whatever facility is introduced, I would recommend the following principle: Every program, after assembly with its library routines, should be printable as a text expressed wholly in the language, and it is this

printed text which should describe the execution of the program, independent of which parts were drawn from a library.

Since I did not intend to design a complete language, I have ignored the problem of libraries in order to concentrate on the essential semantic concepts of the program which is actually executed.

7.3 Port Names

An alternative to explicit naming of source and destination would be to name a *port* through which communication is to take place. The port names would be local to the processes, and the manner in which pairs of ports are to be connected by channels could be declared in the head of a parallel command.

This is an attractive alternative which could be designed to introduce a useful degree of syntactically checkable redundancy. But it is semantically equivalent to the present proposal, provided that each port is connected to exactly one other port in another process. In this case each channel can be identified with a tag, together with the name of the process at the other end. Since I wish to concentrate on semantics, I preferred in this paper to use the simplest and most direct notation, and to avoid raising questions about the possibility of connecting more than two ports by a single channel.

7.4 Automatic Buffering

As an alternative to synchronization of input and output, it is often proposed that an outputting process should be allowed to proceed even when the inputting process is not yet ready to accept the output. An implementation would be expected automatically to interpose a chain of buffers to hold output messages that have not yet been input.

I have deliberately rejected this alternative, for two reasons: (1) It is less realistic to implement in multiple disjoint processors, and (2) when buffering is required on a particular channel, it can readily be specified using the given primitives. Of course, it could be argued equally well that synchronization can be specified when required by using a pair of buffered input and output commands.

7.5 Unbounded Process Activation

The notation for an array of processes permits the same program text (like an Algol recursive procedure) to have many simultaneous "activations"; however, the exact number must be specified in advance. In a conventional single-processor implementation, this can lead to inconvenience and wastefulness, similar to the fixed-length array of Fortran. It would therefore be attractive to allow a process array with no a priori bound on the number of elements; and to specify that the exact number of elements required for a particular execution of the program should be determined dynamically, like the maximum depth of recursion of an Algol procedure or the number of iterations of a repetitive command.

However, it is a good principle that every actual run of a program with unbounded arrays should be identical to the run of some program with all its arrays bounded in advance. Thus the unbounded program should be defined as the "limit" (in some sense) of a series of bounded programs with increasing bounds. I have chosen to concentrate on the semantics of the bounded case—which is necessary anyway and which is more realistic for implementation on multiple microprocessors.

7.6 Fairness

Consider the parallel command:

$$[X:: Y!\text{stop}(\ )\ ||\ Y::\text{continue:boolean; continue} := \text{true};$$
$$*[\text{continue}; X?\text{stop}(\ ) \rightarrow \text{continue} := \text{false}$$
$$[]\text{continue} \rightarrow n := n + 1$$
$$]$$
$$].$$

If the implementation always prefers the second alternative in the repetitive command of Y, it is said to be *unfair*, because although the output command in X could have been executed on an infinite number of occasions, it is in fact always passed over.

The question arises: Should a programming language definition specify that an implementation must be *fair*? Here, I am fairly sure that the answer is NO. Otherwise, the implementation would be obliged to successfully complete the example program shown above, in spite of the fact that its nondeterminism is unbounded. I would therefore suggest that it is the programmer's responsibility to prove that his program terminates correctly—without relying on the assumption of fairness in the implementation. Thus the program shown above is incorrect, since its termination cannot be proved.

Nevertheless, I suggest that an efficient implementation should try to be reasonably fair and should ensure that an output command is not delayed unreasonably often after it first becomes executable. But a proof of correctness must not rely on this property of an efficient implementation. Consider the following analogy with a sequential program: An efficient implementation of an alternative command will tend to favor the alternative which can be most efficiently executed, but the programmer must ensure that the logical correctness of his program does not depend on this property of his implementation.

This method of avoiding the problem of fairness does not apply to programs such as operating systems which are intended to run forever because in this case termination proofs are not relevant. But I wonder whether it is ever advisable to write or to execute such programs. Even an operating system should be designed to bring itself to an orderly conclusion reasonably soon after it inputs a message instructing it to do so. Otherwise, the *only* way to stop it is to "crash" it.

7.7 Functional Coroutines

It is interesting to compare the processes described here with those proposed in [12]; the differences are most striking. There, coroutines are strictly deterministic: No choice is given between alternative sources of input. The output commands are automatically buffered to any required degree. The output of one process can be automatically fanned out to any number of processes (including itself!) which can consume it at differing rates. Finally, the processes there are designed to run forever, whereas my proposed parallel command is normally intended to terminate. The design in [12] is based on an elegant theory which permits proof of the properties of programs. These differences are not accidental—they seem to be natural consequences of the difference between the more abstract applicative (or functional) approach to programming and the more machine-oriented imperative (or procedural) approach, which is taken by communicating sequential processes.

7.8 Output Guards

Since input commands may appear in guards, it seems more symmetric to permit output commands as well. This would allow an obvious and useful simplification in some of the example programs, for example, in the bounded buffer (5.1). Perhaps a more convincing reason would be to ensure that the externally visible effect and behavior of every parallel command can be modeled by some sequential command. In order to model the parallel command

$$Z :: [X!2\ ||\ Y!3]$$

we need to be able to write the sequential alternative command:

$$Z :: [X!2 \rightarrow Y!3\ []\ Y!3 \rightarrow X!2]$$

Note that this *cannot* be done by the command

$$Z :: [\text{true} \rightarrow X!2; Y!3\ []\text{true} \rightarrow Y!3; X!2]$$

which can fail if the process Z happens to choose the first alternative, but the processes Y and X are synchronized with each other in such a way that Y must input from Z before X does, e.g.

$$Y :: Z?y; X!\text{go}(\ )$$
$$||X :: Y?\text{go}(\ ); Z?x$$

7.9 Restriction: Repetitive Command With Input Guard

In proposing an unfamiliar programming language feature, it seems wiser at first to specify a highly restrictive version rather than to propose extensions—especially when the language feature claims to be primitive. For example, it is clear that the multidimensional process array is not primitive, since it can readily be constructed in a language which permits only single-dimensional arrays. But I have a rather more serious misgiving about the repetitive command with input guards.

The automatic termination of a repetitive command on termination of the sources of all its input guards is an extremely powerful and convenient feature but it also involves some subtlety of specification to ensure that it is implementable; and it is certainly not primitive, since the required effect can be achieved (with considerable inconvenience) by explicit exchange of "end()" signals. For example, the subroutine DIV(4.1) could be rewritten:

```
[DIV :: continue:boolean; continue := true;
 *[continue; X?end() → continue := false
 []continue; x,y:integer; X?(x,y) → ... ; X!(quot,rem)
||X :: USER PROG; DIV!end()
 ]
```

Other examples would be even more inconvenient.

But the dangers of convenient facilities are notorious. For example, the repetitive commands with input guards may tempt the programmer to write them without making adequate plans for their termination; and if it turns out that the automatic termination is unsatisfactory, reprogramming for explicit termination will involve severe changes, affecting even the interfaces between the processes.

8. Conclusion

This paper has suggested that input, output, and concurrency should be regarded as primitives of programming, which underlie many familiar and less familiar programming concepts. However, it would be unjustified to conclude that these primitives can wholly replace the other concepts in a programming language. Where a more elaborate construction (such as a procedure or a monitor) is frequently useful, has properties which are more simply provable, and can also be implemented more efficiently than the general case, there is a strong reason for including in a programming language a special notation for that construction. The fact that the construction can be defined in terms of simpler underlying primitives is a useful guarantee that its inclusion is logically consistent with the remainder of the language.

Acknowledgments. The research reported in this paper has been encouraged and supported by a Senior Fellowship of the Science Research Council of Great Britain. The technical inspiration was due to Edsger W. Dijkstra [9], and the paper has been improved in presentation and content by valuable and painstaking advice from D. Gries, D. Q. M. Fay, Edsger W. Dijkstra, N. Wirth, Robert Milne, M. K. Harper, and its referees. The role of IFIP W.G.2.3 as a forum for presentation and discussion is acknowledged with pleasure and gratitude.

Received March 1977; revised August 1977

References
1. Atkinson, R., and Hewitt, C. Synchronisation in actor systems. Working Paper 83, M.I.T., Cambridge, Mass., Nov. 1976.
2. Brinch Hansen, P. The programming language Concurrent Pascal. *IEEE Trans. Software Eng. 1,* 2 (June 1975), 199–207.
3. Campbell, R.H., and Habermann, A.N. The specification of process synchronisation by path expressions. *Lecture Notes in Computer Science 16,* Springer, 1974, pp. 89–102.
4. Conway, M.E. Design of a separable transition-diagram compiler. *Comm. ACM 6,* 7 (July 1963), 396–408.
5. Dahl, O-J., et al. SIMULA 67, common base language. Norwegian Computing Centre, Forskningveien, Oslo, 1967.
6. Dijkstra, E.W. Co-operating sequential processes. In *Programming Languages,* F. Genuys, Ed., Academic Press, New York, 1968, pp. 43–112.
7. Dijkstra, E.W. Notes on structured programming. In *Structured Programming,* Academic Press, New York 1972, pp. 1–82.
8. Dijkstra, E.W. Guarded commands, nondeterminacy, and formal derivation of programs. *Comm. ACM 18,* 8 (Aug. 1975), 453–457.
9. Dijkstra, E.W. Verbal communication, Marktoberdorf, Aug. 1975.
10. Hoare, C.A.R. Towards a theory of parallel programming. In *Operating Systems Techniques,* Academic Press, New York, 1972, pp. 61–71.
11. Hoare, C.A.R. Proof of correctness of data representations. *Acta Informatica 1,* 4 (1972), 271–281.
12. Kahn, G. The semantics of a simple language for parallel programming. In *Proc. IFIP Congress 74,* North Holland, 1974.
13. Liskov, B.H. A note on CLU. Computation Structures Group Memo. 112, M.I.T., Cambridge, Mass, 1974.
14. McIlroy, M.D. Coroutines. Bell Laboratories, Murray Hill, N.J., 1968.
15. Naur, P., Ed. Report on the algorithmic language ALGOL 60. *Comm. ACM 3,* 5 (May 1960), 299–314.
16. Reynolds, J.C. COGENT. ANL-7022, Argonne Nat. Lab., Argonne, Ill., 1965.
17. Thompson, K. The UNIX command language. In *Structured Programming,* Infotech, Nicholson House, Maidenhead, England, 1976, pp. 375–384.
18. van Wijngaarden, A. Ed. Report on the algorithmic language ALGOL 68. *Numer. Math. 14* (1969), 79–218.
19. Wulf, W.A., London, R.L., and Shaw, M. Abstraction and verification in ALPHARD. Dept. of Comptr. Sci., Carnegie-Mellon U., Pittsburgh, Pa., June 1976.
20. Wirth, N. The programming language PASCAL. *Acta Informatica 1,* 1 (1971), 35–63.

Reprinted with permission from *Proceedings of the National Computer Conference*, Volume 48, 1979, pages 1087-1095. Copyright © 1979 by AFIPS Press.

Data flow languages

by WILLIAM B. ACKERMAN

Massachusetts Institute of Technology
Cambridge, Massachusetts

INTRODUCTION

There are several computer system architectures which have the goal of exploiting parallelism—multiprocessors, vector machines and array processors. For each of these architectures there have been attempts to design compilers to optimize programs written in conventional languages (e.g. "vectorizing" compilers for the FORTRAN language). There have also been new language designs to facilitate using these systems, such as Concurrent PASCAL for multiprocessors,[6] and languages that utilize the features of such systems directly, such as GLYPNIR for the Illiac IV array processor[19] and various "vectorizing" dialects of FORTRAN. These languages almost always make the multiprocessor, vector, or array properties of the computer visible to the programmer—that is, they are actually vehicles whereby the programmer helps the compiler uncover parallelism. Many of these languages or dialects are "unnatural" in that they closely reflect the behavior of the system for which they were designed, rather than reflecting the way programmers think about problem solutions.

Data flow computers also have the goal of taking advantage of parallelism. As will be seen below, the parallelism in a data flow computer is both microscopic (much more so than in a multiprocessor) and all-encompassing (much more so than in a vector processor). Like the other forms of parallel computer, data flow computers are best programmed in special languages. In fact, their need for such languages is stronger—most data flow designs would be extremely inefficient if programmed in conventional languages such as FORTRAN or PL/I. However, languages suitable for data flow computers can be very elegant. The language properties that a data flow computer requires are beneficial in their own right, and are very similar to some of the properties that are known to facilitate understandable and maintainable software, such as the absence of undisciplined control structures and module interactions. In fact, languages having many of these properties have been in existence since long before data flow computers were conceived. The principal property of a language suitable for data flow is *freedom from side effects*, which will be described below. The (pure) LISP language[20] is the best known example of a language without side effects. The connection between freedom from side effects and efficient parallel computation has been known for over ten years.[25]

To see why data flow computers require languages free of side effects, we must examine the nature of data flow computation and the nature of side-effects. A detailed description of the mechanism of data flow computers is beyond the scope of this paper. The interested reader is referred to References 2, 12, 15, 21, 22, 23.

There are three "data flow" languages that will be discussed in this paper. VAL[1] and ID[3] were developed by the data flow projects at the Massachusetts Institute of Technology and the University of California at Irvine, respectively. LUCID[4] was developed for program verification, not for programming data flow computers. It nevertheless is a suitable language for data flow computation.

Let us begin by examining a simple sequence of assignment statements written in a conventional programming language such as FORTRAN:

```
1   P=X+Y
2   Q=P/Y
3   R=X*P
4   S=R−Q
5   T=R*P
6   RESULT=S/T
```

A straightforward analysis of this program will show that many of these instructions can be executed concurrently, as long as certain constraints are met. These constraints can be represented by a graph (see Figure 1) in which nodes represent instructions and an arrow from one instruction to another means that the second may not be executed until the first has completed. So the permissible computation sequences include, among others:

```
(1,3,5,2,4,6)
(1,2,3,5,4,6)
(1, [2 and 3 simultaneously], [4 and 5 simultaneously], 6)
```

This type of analysis (commonly called data flow analysis, a term which long predates data flow computers) is frequently performed in two situations—at run-time in the arithmetic processing units of high performance conventional computers such as the IBM 360/91, and at compile time in optimizing compilers. In optimizing compilers, data

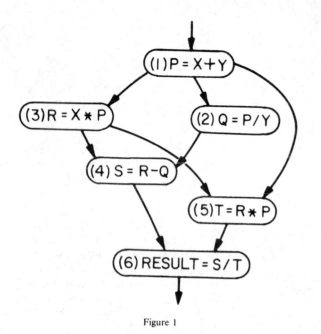

Figure 1

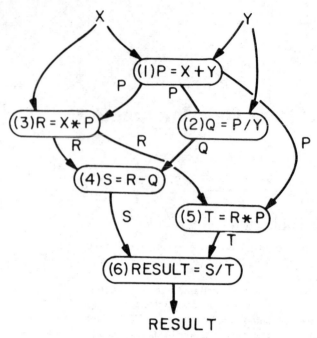

RESULT

Figure 2

flow analysis yields improved utilization of temporary memory locations. For example, on a computer with high-speed general purpose or floating point registers, this program can be compiled to use the registers instead of core memory for P, Q, R, S and T, if it can be determined that they will not be used again. (This determination is very difficult, principally because of GO TOs, which is one of the reasons why it is very difficult to write optimizing compilers for languages such as FORTRAN.)

In the graph representation, an instruction can be executed as soon as all the instructions with arrows pointing into it have completed. On a multiprocessor system, we could allocate a processor for each instruction, with appropriate instructions (such as semaphore operations[13]) to enforce the sequencing constraints, but execution would be hopelessly inefficient because the parallelism of this example is far too "fine grained" for a multiprocessor. The overhead in the process scheduling and in the *wait* and *signal* instructions would be many times greater than the execution time of the arithmetic operations. A data flow computer, on the other hand, is designed to execute algorithms with such a fine grain of parallelism efficiently. In these machines, parallelism is exploited at the level of individual instructions, as in the previous example, and at all coarser levels as well; in most programs there are typically many parts, often far removed from each other, at which computation may proceed simultaneously.

To exploit parallelism at all levels, the instruction sequencing constraints must be deducible from the program itself. Let us refer again to the previous program to see how this may be done.

The sequencing constraints in Figure 1 are given by arrows. It is not difficult to see that these arrows coincide with data transmission from one instruction to its successor through variables. In fact, the graph could be redrawn with the arrows labeled by the variables that they represent, as in Figure 2.

In a data flow computer, the machine level program is represented essentially in this form—a graph with pointers between nodes, the pointers representing both the flow of data and the sequencing constraints. Each instruction is kept in a hardware device (an extremely simple "processor") that is capable of "firing" or executing an instruction when all of the necessary data values have arrived, and sending the result to the processors that hold destination instructions.*

The programming language for a data flow computer must therefore satisfy two criteria:

1. It must be possible to deduce the data dependencies of the program operations.
2. The sequencing constraints must always be exactly the same as the data dependencies, so that the instruction firing rule can be based simply on the availability of data.**

There are two general properties of a language which make it possible to meet these criteria: locality of effect and freedom from side effects.

---

* Although the language concepts presented in this paper assume that the computer exploits parallelism at a microscopic level, not all "data flow" or "data driven" computers do so. Designs of data flow computers that exploit parallelism only at the subroutine level may be found in References 10 and 24.

** Not all designs for data flow computers accept the second of these criteria or its consequences. The LAU language [9] is intended for execution on a data flow computer, but it was designed to support data base updating and retrieval, so it has side effects on certain operations. The sequencing of these operations must therefore be constrained by means other than data dependencies, and so it does not satisfy the second criterion. The extra constraints in LAU are specified by path expressions [7] written into the source program.

LOCALITY OF EFFECT

Locality of effect means that instructions do not have unnecessary far-reaching data dependencies. For example, the FORTRAN program fragment given previously appears to use variables P, Q, R, S and T only as temporaries. A similar program fragment appearing elsewhere in the program might use the same temporaries for some unrelated computation. The logic of the program might be such that the two fragments could be executed concurrently were it not for this overuse of names. (Unfortunately, many conventional languages encourage this style of programming.) Any attempt to execute the program fragments concurrently would be impossible because of the apparent data dependencies arising from overuse of these temporaries, unless the compiler can deduce that the conflict is not real and remove it by using different sets of temporaries.

In languages such as FORTRAN and PL/I, this is not so easy to determine. A reference to a variable in one part of the program does not necessarily imply dependence on the value computed in another part—the variable might be overwritten before it is next read. Careful analysis is required to determine whether a variable is actually transmitting data or is "dead." This analysis is made much more difficult if unrestricted GO TOs or other undisciplined control structures are allowed.

The problem can be simplified by making every variable have a definite "scope," or region of the program in which it is active, and carefully restricting the entry to and exit from the blocks that constitute scopes. It is also helpful to deny procedures access to any data items that are not transmitted as arguments, though this is not really necessary if global variables are avoided and procedure definitions are carefully "block structured" as in PASCAL.

SIDE EFFECTS

Freedom from side effects is a necessary property to ensure that the data dependencies are the same as the sequencing constraints. It is much more difficult to achieve than locality of effect. This is because locality only requires superficial restrictions on the language, whereas freedom from side effects requires fundamental changes in the way the language's "virtual machine" processes data.

Side effects come in many forms—the most well known examples are procedures that modify variables in the calling program, as in the following PASCAL example:

```
procedure GETRS(X, Y : real);    (* RS is declared in
begin RS:=X*X+Y*Y              an outer block *)
end;
```

Absence of global or "common" variables and careful control of the scopes of variables make it possible for a compiler to prohibit this sort of thing, but a data flow computer imposes much stricter prohibitions against side effects—a procedure may not even modify its own arguments. In fact, in a sense nothing may ever be modified at all.

To determine what kind of prohibitions against side effects are needed to achieve concurrent computation, we must examine programs that manipulate structured data such as arrays or records, since the problem does not arise when only simple data values are used.

Consider the following procedure which modifies its arguments by a conventional "call by reference" mechanism. SORT2 is a procedure to sort two elements, J and J+1, of array A into ascending order by exchanging them if necessary.

```
procedure SORT2(var A : array[1. .10] of real;
    J : integer);
var T : real;
begin if A[J]>A[J+1] then begin
            T:=A[J];
            A[J]:=A[J+1];
            A[J+1]:=T;
            end
end;
(1)    SORT2(AA, J);
(2)    SORT2(AA, K);
(3)    P:=AA[L];
```

Statements 1 and 2 might interfere with each other and with Statement 3. Since the values of J, K, and L are not known to the compiler, it must assume that the statements will conflict, and execute them in the exact order specified. Any attempt at parallel execution might result in the incorrect results, depending on J, K, L, and unpredictable fluctuations in timing.

A phenomenon known as "aliasing" makes the problem even more difficult. This occurs when different formal parameters to a procedure refer to the same actual parameter, that is, they are "aliases" of each other:

```
procedure SORTREAD(var A, B : array[1. .10] of real;
    I, J : integer);
begin SORT2(A, I);  (* SORT2 is defined above *)
    RESULT:=B[J];
end;
```

In this program it would appear that, since A and B are different arrays, the invocation of SORT2 and the reference to B[J] could proceed concurrently. However, if this were part of a larger program and SORTREAD were invoked in the statement

```
SORTREAD(Q,Q,M,N);
```

the arrays A and B would actually be the same. Languages such as FORTRAN and PL/I, in which external procedures are not available to the compiler when the calling program is being compiled, make the problem harder still. Facilities for manipulating data structures by pointers, such as the "pointer" data type in PL/I and the record manipulating operations of PASCAL make it possible for all of these problems to arise without using procedures.

Even if procedures and pointers are not used, the sequencing constraints may be far from clear, as in

(1) A[J]:=3;
(2) X:=A[K];

If the convention is made that any statement modifying any element of an array constitutes a "writing" of the array, then Statement 1 clearly passes array A to Statement 2. But then a statement such as the assignment in

for J:=1 to 10 do
    A[J+1]:=A[J]+1;

depends on itself!

The inescapable conclusion is that, if arrays and records exist as global objects in a memory and are manipulated by statements and passed as procedure parameters, it is virtually impossible to tell, when an array element is modified, what effects that modification may have elsewhere in the program.

One way to solve some of these problems is to use "call by value" instead of the more common "call by reference." This solves the aliasing problem and the problem of procedures modifying their arguments. In a "call by value" scheme, a procedure copies its arguments (even if they are arrays). This way it can never modify the actual argument in the calling program. Call by reference has traditionally been used instead of call by value because it is a more natural way of thinking about computation (and is more efficient) on von Neumann computers.

APPLICATIVE LANGUAGES

For data flow languages, a scheme is used which goes far beyond call by value: all arrays are *values* rather than *objects*, and are treated as such at all times, not just when being passed as procedure arguments. Arrays are not modified by subscripted assignment statements such as

A[J]:=S;

Instead, they are processed by *operators* which create new array values. The simplest operator to perform the nearest equivalent of modifying an array takes three arguments—an array, an index, and a new data value. The result of the operation is a new array, containing the given data value at

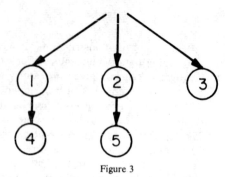

Figure 3

the given index, and the same data as the original array at all other indices.

In the VAL language,[1] the syntax for this elementary operator is

A[J:S]

In the ID language,[3] it is

A+[J]S

This operation *does not modify* its argument. Hence, in this VAL program:

(1) B:=A[J:S];
(2) C:=A[K:T];
(3) P:=A[L];
(4) Q:=B[M];
(5) R:=C[N];

Statements 1 and 2 do not interfere with each other or with array A. Statement 3 may be executed immediately, whether 1 and/or 2 have completed or not, since they would have no effect on Statement 3 anyway. Statement 4 can be executed as soon as Statement 1 completes, whether Statement 2 has completed or not. The sequencing constraints are shown in Figure 3.

Note that this situation is similar to the one in the simple FORTRAN example of the first section. The sequencing constraints are exactly the same as the data dependencies, which is the property we seek for data flow.

An operator-based handling of arrays and records automatically accomplishes call by value. As in a call by value scheme, a routine such as SORT2 would not accomplish its purpose. SORT2 must return the new array as its value. It could be written in VAL (omitting type declarations) as:

```
function SORT2(A, J)
    if A[J]<A[J+1] then A
        else (A[J:A[J+1]])[J+1:A[J]]    % No temporary needed during this
    end                                  % exchange because A is not modified.
end
```

Note that the array construction operator may be composed with itself and with other operators in the same way as arithmetic operators.

In conventional languages, procedures do most, if not all, of their work through side effects—a procedure might be designed to alter dozens of variables in the calling program.

Functions, on the other hand, are typically limited to returning a single value, which typically may not be an array or record. To make functions as powerful and flexible as procedures in conventional languages, applicative languages often allow functions to return several values, or entire records or arrays, or both. If a function returns several values, its call can be used in a "multiple assignment" such as

X,Y,Z:=FUNC(P,Q,R) % FUNC returns 3 values

Treating arrays and records as values instead of objects is perhaps the most profound difference in the way people must think when writing programs in data flow languages instead of conventional languages. The customary view is of arrays as objects residing in static locations of memory, and being manipulated by statements that are executed in some sequence. As we have seen, this view is incompatible with detection of parallelism among the statements. The correct view for data flow is of arrays and records as values manipulated by operations just as simple values (integers, reals) are. Then the parallelism among the operators can be deduced from the data dependencies just as for simple values.

The value-oriented approach to arrays is confusing to some at first, but it need not be. An integer array should be thought of as a string of integers, just as an integer can be thought of as a string of digits. If J has the value 31416, the statement

K:=J−400;

leaves K equal to 31016; no programmer would expect the value of J to be affected. If A is an array with elements [3,1,4,1,6], the statement

B:=A[3:0];

is completely analogous; it leaves B with elements [3,1,0,1,6] and of course does not change A.

Languages which do all processing by means of operators applied to values are called *applicative* languages, and are thus the natural languages for data flow computation. The earliest well known applicative language implemented on a computer is LISP.[20] (It is applicative only if RPLACA, RPLACD, and all other functions with side effects are avoided; this subset of the language is often called "pure" LISP.) The connection between applicative languages and the detection of parallelism has been reproted by Tesler and Enea[25] and by Friedman and Wise.[14] The development of LISP and other applicative languages, and the Tesler/Enea paper, all predate the data flow computer concept by several years. The concept of computation by applicative evaluation of expressions goes back to the invention of the lambda calculus in 1941.[8]

EFFICIENCY CONSIDERATIONS IN APPLICATIVE LANGUAGES

Applicative languages have recently given rise to controversy concerning their time efficiency in practical situations.

It is claimed that many algorithms cannot be executed as efficiently in applicative languages as in conventional statement-oriented languages. The issue is only one of exploiting parallelism, not any fundamental limitation in the computing power of applicative systems. This is because any program written for a conventional von Neumann computer can be rewritten in an applicative language by treating the entire memory space as one array. Statements that manipulate the memory then become operations on that array. The array must be passed from each operation to the next, so execution in such an applicative system must be strictly sequential—no parallelism can be exploited. However, in the original program written in a conventional language, a knowledgeable programmer might be able to explicitly specify parallelism, making the program run more efficiently than in the applicative system.

Consider the conventional program

(1) A[J]:=S
(2) A[K]:=T;
(3) P:=A[M];
(4) Q:=A[N];

If the programmer knows that the set of indices for the array A can be divided into two disjoint sets, with J and M in one set and K and N in the other, then Statements 1 and 2 could be executed simultaneously, 3 would only need to follow 1, and 4 would only need to follow 2. If the programmer has the ability to control parallelism explicitly (say, by semaphores, monitors, or path expressions), he could specify exactly those constraints. This is not possible in a data flow language without some additional mechanism. However, the problem can often be avoided by dividing the array into separate parts, manipulating them separately, and combining them only when necessary. For example, suppose array A1 contains only those elements that J and M are known to index, and A2 contains those that K and N index. Then

B1:=A1[J:S];
B2:=A2[K:T];
P:=B1[M];
Q:=B2[N];

exploits the parallelism exactly. There are other ways of overcoming the tendency for arrays to limit parallelism, which will be discussed later. The question of how to exploit parallelism in applicative languages for a wide variety of programming problems is an active area of research.

DEFINITIONAL LANGUAGES AND THE SINGLE ASSIGNMENT RULE

Having accepted an applicative programming style and a value-oriented rather than object-oriented execution model, we next examine the implications of this style upon the meaning of assignment statements.

Except in iterations, (which will be discussed later), an assignment statement has no effect except to provide a value and bind that value to the name appearing on its left hand side. The result of the assignment is accessible only in subsequent expressions in which that name appears. If the language uses blocks in which all variables are local to the block for which they are declared, the places where a variable is used can be determined by inspection. If the expression on the right hand side of an assignment is substituted for the variable on the left hand side in all places where that variable appears within its scope, the resultant program will be completely equivalent.

```
S:=X+Y;
D:=3*S;          is equivalent to  D:=3*(X+Y);
E:=S/2+F(S);                        E:=(X+Y)/2+F(X+Y);
```

(The program on the left is clearly more efficient, requiring only two additions instead of four. We are not proposing that the substitution be made in practice.)

Now this situation is the same as a system of mathematical equations. If a system of equations contains "S=X+Y", it is clear that "3*S" and "3*(X+Y)" are equivalent. Hence the statement

```
S:=X+Y;
```

means the same thing in the program that the equation "S=X+Y" means in a system of equations, namely that, in the scope of these variables, S is the sum of X and Y. The correspondence can be thought of as holding for all time; it is not necessary to think of the statements as being executed at particular instants. (In fact, perhaps the word "variable" is an inappropriate term.) Of course, the addition of X and Y to form S must take place before any of the operations that use S can be performed, but the programmer doesn't need to be directly concerned with this.

Hence the statement S:=X+Y should be thought of as a *definition*, not an assignment. Languages which use this interpretation of assignments are called *definitional languages* as opposed to conventional *imperative languages*. Such languages are well suited to program verification because the assertions one makes in proving correctness are exactly the same as the definitions appearing in the program itself. In conventional languages one must follow the flow of control to determine *where* in the program text assertions such as "S=X+Y" are true, because the variables S, X, and Y can be changed many times. Assertions must therefore be associated with points in the program.

In a definitional language the situation is extremely simple: If a program block contains the statement

```
S:=X+Y;
```

then the assertion S=X+Y is true. Of course, care must be taken to prevent circular definitions such as

```
X:=Y;
Y:=X+3;
```

We can either have the compiler allow definitions to ap-

pear in any order as long as there is some consistent order, or we can require them to appear in a consistent order. A consistent order is one in which no name is referred to (on the right hand side of a definition) before it is defined. This condition is easily checked by a compiler. So the actual proof rule is: If a program block contains the statement

```
S:=X+Y;
```

and the program compiles correctly, then S=X+Y is true. Strictly speaking, it is only true in the statements after the one defining S, but, since S does not appear in any earlier statements, the assertion can be treated as being true throughout the block.

The power of definitional languages for program verification is well known outside of the data flow field. LUCID[4] is an example of an applicative definitional language designed expressly for ease of program verification.

There is a problem that could ruin the elegance of definitional languages—multiple definition of the same name. Definitional languages almost invariably obey the *single assignment rule*: A name may appear on the left hand side of an assignment (definition) only once within its scope. The single assignment rule prevents program constructs which imply mathematical abominations, such as

```
J:=J+1;
```

Since the appearance of J on the right hand side precedes the definition of J, it implies an inconsistent statement sequencing that the compiler would diagnose. The prevention of such abominations is of course necessary if the definitions in the program are to be carried directly into assertions used in proving correctness, because the assertion "J=J+1" is absurd.

It is not actually necessary that a data flow language conform to the single assignment rule. A data flow language with multiple assignments could be designed in which the scope of a variable extends only from its definition to the next definition of the same variable. The next definition in effect introduces a new variable that simply happens to have the same name. A program written in such a way can be easily transformed into one obeying the single assignment rule: simply choose a new name for any redefined variable, and change all subsequent references to the new name. However, the advantages of single assignment languages, namely, clarity and ease of verification, generally outweigh the "convenience" of re-using the same name.

ITERATIONS

There remains one area in which statements such as

```
I:=I-1;
```

or

```
A:=A[J:X+Y];
```

seem to be necessary, explicitly or implicitly, in conventional languages, and that is in iterations. The technique of renaming variables to make a program conform to the single assignment rule only works for straight-line programs: If a statement appears in a loop, renaming its variables will not preserve the programmer's intentions. For example:

for I: = 1 to 10 do	cannot be	for I: = 1 to 10 do
J: = J + 1;	transformed to	J1: = J + 1;

If the language allows general GO TOs, with the resulting possibility of complex and unstructured loops, the problem is indeed difficult. However, data flow languages generally have no GO TO statement, and require loops to be created only by specific program structures such as the "while. . .do. . ." and similar statements found in PL/I and PASCAL. This makes the problem easy to solve, and makes it possible to give iterations a very simple and straightforward meaning.

To develop the data flow equivalent of a "while. . .do. . ." type of iteration, we must consider what the "do" part of such a structure contains. Since there are no side effects, the only state information in an iteration is the bindings of the loop variables, and the only activity that can take place is the redefinition of those variables through functional operators. An iteration therefore consists of

1. Definitions of the initial values of the loop variables.
2. A predicate to determine whether, for any given values of the loop variables, the loop is to terminate or to cycle again.
3. If it is to terminate, some expression giving the value(s) to be returned. These values typically depend on the current values of the loop variables.
4. If it is to cycle again, some expressions giving the new values to be assigned to the loop variables. These also typically depend on the current values of the loop variables.

An iteration to compute the factorial of N could be written (omitting type declarations) in VAL as follows:

```
for I, J:=N, 1;          % Give loop variables I and
                         % J initial
                         % values N and 1
                         % respectively. I will
                         % count downward. J will
                         % keep
                         % accumulated product.
do if I=0                % Decide whether to
                         % terminate.
   then J                % Yes, final result is current
                         % J.
   else iter I, J:=I-1, J*I;
                         % No, compute new values
                         % of I and J,
                         % and cycle again.
end
```

It could be written in ID as follows:

```
initial I←N; J←1
while I≠0 do
    new I←I-1;
    new J←J*I;
return J
```

Its representation in LUCID is similar to that in ID.

Although the values of the loop variables do change, they change only between one iteration cycle and the next. The single assignment rule, with its prohibition against things like "I=I-1" is still in force within any one cycle. All redefinitions take place precisely at the boundary between iteration cycles (though they need not actually occur simultaneously). This is enforced in VAL by allowing redefinitions only after the word *iter*, which is the command to begin a new iteration cycle. In ID and LUCID, the "new" values become the "current" values at the boundary between cycles.

Since the single assignment rule is obeyed, and names have single values, within any one iteration cycle the mathematical simplicity of assertions about values still exists. The assertions typically take the form

"In any cycle, S=X+Y"

Assertions used in proving correctness of an iteration are usually proved inductively. Because assertions take such a simple form, such proofs are usually simpler than in conventional languages. For example, the assertion

$I \geq 0$ and $J*(I!) = N!$

is used to prove correctness of the previous program. The basis of the induction is that it is true for the initial values I=N and J=1. (We assume $N \geq 0$.) The induction step is that, if another cycle is started with the values I-1 and J*I, they will obey the assertion, that is,

$I-1 \geq 0$ and $(J*I)*((I-1)!) = N!$

which is clearly true if we observe that a new cycle will only be started if I>0 and hence $I-1 \geq 0$.

ERRORS AND EXCEPTIONAL CONDITIONS

Locality of effect requires that errors such as arithmetic overflow be handled by *error values* rather than by program interruptions or manipulation of global status flags. If an error occurs in an operation, that fact must be transmitted to the destinations of that operation and nowhere else. This can be easily accomplished by enlarging the set of values to include error values such as overflow, underflow, or zero-divide.

If the intention is to abort the computation when an error occurs, this can be achieved by making the error values *propagate*—if an argument to an arithmetic operation is an error, the result is an error. When an error propagates to the end of an iteration body, that iteration always terminates rather than cycling again. In this way the entire computation will come to a stop quickly, yielding an error value as the result. If the computer keeps a record of every error generation and propagation, that record will provide a detailed trace of when and where the error occurred, and what iterations and procedures were active.

If the intention is to correct an error when it occurs (perhaps keeping a list of such errors in some array), that can be accomplished through operations that test for errors. For example, a program to set Z to the quotient of X and Y, or to zero if an error occurs, could be written in VAL as follows:

    ZZ:=X/Y;
    Z:=if is_error(ZZ) then 0 else ZZ end;

METHODS OF OBTAINING MAXIMUM PARALLELISM

To achieve the greatest parallelism, it is necessary that computations not be performed sequentially unless necessary. The iteration constructs described previously imply a sequential execution of the various cycles. If the values of the iteration variables in one cycle depend on those of the previous cycles (as they do in the factorial example given previously), nothing can be done about it, although a data flow computer can often execute *part* of a cycle before the previous one has completed. If the values in one cycle do *not* depend on those of the previous cycles, the cycles can be performed in parallel. In VAL this is accomplished with a *forall* program construct which does not allow one cycle to depend on the others, and directs the computer to perform all cycles simultaneously. In ID the same effect is achieved automatically by tagging the values of the iteration variables with their cycle number, and allowing them to be processed out of sequence, or simultaneously, whenever they do not depend on each other.

Another potential "bottleneck" in data flow computation is the requirement that all elements of an array be computed before any element of that array may be accessed. If function "F" creates an array value by filling the array one element at a time, and then passes the array to "G," which reads the elements one at a time, G cannot begin until F completes. In many instances this delay is unnecessary, and various techniques have been proposed for eliminating it without departing from the principle that the sequencing constraints are exactly the data dependencies. One method, mentioned in the fifth section, is to explicitly divide the array into pieces, or use separate data items instead of an array. This method is quite general, but it requires specific calculation by the programmer of which parts of the array are needed at which time.

Streams

A method of overcoming the array bottleneck is the use of "streams."[3,11,26] A stream may be thought of as an array

that is fragmented in time and is processed one element at a time.

In the previous example of F creating an array one element at a time and passing it to G, a stream would be the natural way to do this. G would receive each element as soon as F created it, so G would be processing the Nth element while F computes the $N+1^{st}$, resulting in parallel "pipelined" computation of F and G.

The constraint that stream elements be created and consumed in strict sequence may be enforced by placing some restrictions on the source program to prevent "random access." A program to manipulate streams may be written in a recursive style,[11,26] in which a stream is treated like a list in LISP, or in an iterative style[3] in which the rebinding of an iteration variable denoting a stream causes that stream to advance to the next element. Either method enforces the sequencing constraint if certain rules are followed regarding the permissible recursions or iterations.

When streams are viewed not as temporally separated arrays but as sequences of data items, functions that process streams have a few interesting and useful properties that pure mathematical functions do not have: they can emit more (or fewer) outputs than their inputs, and they can exhibit "memory" from one element to another. This makes stream functions suitable for "on-line" applications such as updating a data base. Stream functions are also useful for operations normally performed by coroutines, such as a function to remove all ⟨newline⟩ characters from its input, or insert a ⟨newline⟩ after every 80 characters. A stream function is equivalent to a coroutine that communicates by transmission and reception of data values. A data flow program using streams is a network of parallel communicating coroutines, a computational model that has been of some theoretical interest in the last few years.[16-18]

Streams and input/output operations

Streams form a natural mechanism for handling input and output. By treating the sequence of characters read in from an external medium as a stream, it is possible for a program to operate on the data as it is read in. The program can generate an output stream, which is printed as it is produced.

CONCLUSION

There have recently been calls for the abandonment of the traditional "von Neumann" computer architecture as a good way of realizing the enormous potential of VLSI technology.[5] There has also been widespread recognition that proper language design is essential if the high cost of software is to be brought under control, and that most existing languages are seriously deficient in this area.

Fortunately, the implications of these trends for language design are similar—languages must avoid an execution model (the "von Neumann" model) that involves a global memory whose state is manipulated by sequential execution of commands. Such a global memory makes realization of the potential of VLSI technology difficult because it creates a ''bottleneck'' between the computer's control unit and the memory. Languages that use a global memory in their execution model also exacerbate the software problem by allowing program modules to interact with each other in ways that are difficult to understand, rather than through simple transmission of argument and result values. Future language designs based on concepts of applicative programming should be able to help control the high cost of software and to meet the needs of future computer designs.

REFERENCES

1. Ackerman, W. B., and J. B. Dennis, ''VAL—A Value-Oriented Algorithmic Language: Preliminary Reference Manual,'' Computation Structures Group, Laboratory for Computer Science, MIT, Cambridge, Massachusetts.
2. Arvind, and K. P. Gostelow, *Dataflow Computer Architecture: Research and Goals*, Department of Information and Computer Science (TR 113), University of California-Irvine, Irvine, California, February 1978.
3. Arvind, K. P. Gostelow and W. Plouffe, *The (Preliminary) Id Report*, Department of Information and Computer Science (TR 114), University of California-Irvine, Irvine, California, May 1978.
4. Ashcroft, E. A., and W. W. Wadge, ''Lucid, a Nonprocedural Language with Iteration,'' *Communications of the ACM*, Vol. 20, No. 7, July 1977, pp. 519-526.
5. Backus, J., ''Can Programming Be Liberated from the von Neumann Style? A Functional Style and Its Algebra of Programs,'' *Communications of the ACM* Vol. 21, No. 8, August 1978, pp. 613-641.
6. Brinch-Hansen, P., ''The Programming Language Concurrent Pascal,'' *IEEE Transactions on Software Engineering*, Vol. SE-1, No. 2, June 1975, pp. 199-207.
7. Campbell, R. H., ''Path Expressions: A Technique for Specifying Process Synchronization,'' Department of Computer Science (Report UIUCDCS-R-77-863), University of Illinois at Urbana-Champaign, Urbana, Ill., 1977.
8. Church, A., ''The Calculi of Lambda-Conversion,'' *Annals of Mathematical Studies*, Vol. 6, Princeton University Press, 1951.
9. Comte, D., G. Durrieu, O. Gelly, A. Plas and J. C. Syre, ''Parallelism, Control and Synchronization Expressions in a Single Assignment Language,'' *SIGPLAN Notices*, Vol. 13, No. 1, January 1978, pp. 25-33.
10. Davis, A. L., ''The Architecture and System Method of DDM1: A Recursively Structured Data Driven Machine,'' *Proceedings of the Fifth Annual Symposium on Computer Architecture, Computer Architecture News*, Vol. 6, No. 7, April 1978, pp. 210-215.
11. Dennis, J. B., ''A Language Design for Structured Concurrency,'' *Design and Implementation of Programming Languages: Proceedings of a DoD-Sponsored Workshop* (J. H. Williams and D. A. Fisher, Eds.), *Lecture Notes in Computer Science*, Vol. 54, October 1976. Also, Computation Structures Group, Note 28-1, February 1977, Laboratory for Computer Science, MIT, Cambridge, Massachusetts.
12. Dennis, J. B., D. P. Misunas and C. K. C. Leung, ''A Highly Parallel Processor Using a Data Flow Machine Language,'' Computation Structures Group, Memo 134, Laboratory for Computer Science, MIT, Cambridge, Massachusetts, January 1977. To appear in *IEEE Transactions on Computers*.
13. Dijkstra, E. W., ''Cooperating Sequential Processes,'' *Programming Languages* (F. Genuys, Ed.), Academic Press, New York, New York, 1968.
14. Friedman, D. P., and D. S. Wise, ''The Impact of Applicative Programming on Multiprocessing,'' *Proceedings of the 1976 International Conference on Parallel Processing* (P. H. Enslow, Ed.), August 1976, pp. 263-272.
15. Gurd, J., I. Watson and J. Glauert, ''A Multilayered Data Flow Computer Architecture,'' Department of Computer Science, University of Manchester, Manchester, England, July 1978.
16. Hoare, C. A. R., ''Communicating Sequential Processes,'' *Communications of the ACM*, Vol. 21, No. 8, August 1978, pp. 666-677.
17. Kahn, G., ''The Semantics of a Simple Language for Parallel Programming,'' *Information Processing 74: Proceedings of the IFIP Congress 74* (J. L. Rosenfeld, Ed.), 1974, pp. 471-475.
18. Kahn, G., and D. MacQueen, ''Coroutines and Networks of Parallel Processes,'' *Information Processing 77: Proceedings of IFIP Congress 77* (B. Gilchrist, Ed.), August 1977, pp. 993-998.
19. Lawrie, D. H., ''GLYPNIR Programming Manual,'' ILLIAC IV Document no. 232, Department of Computer Science, University of Illinois at Urbana-Champaign, Urbana, Ill., August 1970.
20. McCarthy, J., et. al., ''LISP 1.5 Programmer's Manual,'' MIT Press, 1966.
21. Miranker, G. S., ''Implementation of Procedures on a Class of Data Flow Procedures,'' *Proceedings of the 1977 International Conference on Parallel Processing* (J. L. Baer, Ed.), August 1977, pp. 77-86.
22. Patil, S. S., R. M. Keller and G. Lindstrom, ''An Architecture for a Loosely-Coupled Parallel Processor (Draft),'' Department of Computer Science (UUCS-78-105), University of Utah, Salt Lake City, Utah, July 1978.
23. Plas, A., D. Comte, O. Gelly, and J. C. Syre, ''LAU System Architecture: A Parallel Data Driven Processor Based on Single Assignment,'' *Proceedings of the 1976 International Conference on Parallel Processing* (P. H. Enslow, Ed.), August 1976, pp. 293-302.
24. Rumbaugh, J. E., ''A Data Flow Multiprocessor,'' *IEEE Transactions on Computers*, Vol. C-26, No. 2, February 1977, pp. 138-146.
25. Tesler, L. G., and H. J. Enea, ''A Language Design for Concurrent Processes,'' *Proceedings of the AFIPS Conference*, Vol. 32, 1968, pp. 403-408.
26. Weng, K.-S., *Stream-Oriented Computation in Recursive Data Flow Schemas*, Laboratory for Computer Science (TM-68), MIT, Cambridge, Massachusetts, October 1975.

8. Parallelism Extraction

Two approaches to programming parallel processors come to mind immediately. Either the programmer can specify the parallelism explicitly using, for example, one of the languages described in Chapter 7, or a compiler can extract parallelism from sequential programs. The latter approach is considered in the three papers in this chapter. (A compiler which extracts parallelism is actually an optimizing compiler for a parallel processor.)

First, the paper by Kuck *et al.* extracts parallelism by utilizing several methods to speed up programs. The results of the study show that, at least theoretically, a large amount of parallelism can be extracted from programs. A description of the more recent work in this area at the University of Illinois can be found in another paper by Kuck *et al.* (1980). The second paper in this chapter, by Hibbard *et al.*, describes a compiler for Cm* that extracts a low degree of parallelism from programs. (Multiprocessor compiler techniques to extract a high degree of parallelism can be found in Padua *et al.* (1980). Finally, the paper by Dongarra compares the performance of a few optimizing compilers for the CRAY-1 with hand coding.

EHO182-6/81/0000/0345 © 1981 IEEE

Reprinted from *Computer*, Volume 7, Number 1, January 1974, pages 37-46. Copyright © 1974 by The Institute of Electrical and Electronics Engineers, Inc.

Tvtorial

Measurements of Parallelism in Ordinary FORTRAN Programs

David J. Kuck
Paul P. Budnik
Shyh-Ching Chen
Duncan H. Lawrie
Ross A. Towle
Richard E. Strebendt

Department of Computer Science
University of Illinois

Edward W. Davis, Jr.

Goodyear Aerospace Corporation

Joseph Han

Chung Shan Institute of Science and Technology
Hsien-Tien, Taipei, Taiwan

Paul W. Kraska

Control Data Corporation

Yoichi Muraoka

Nippon Telephone and Telegraph Corporation
Tokyo, Japan

Introduction

In the folklore of computer architecture there has been much speculation about the effectiveness of various machines in performing various computations. While it is easy to design a machine (or part of a machine) and study its effectiveness on this algorithm or that, it is rather difficult to make general effectiveness statements about classes of algorithms and machines. We are attempting to move in this direction, and this paper contains experimental measurements of a rather wide class of algorithms. Such measurements should be helpful in establishing some parameters of machine organization.

In the past, the organization of algorithms and programming for multioperation machines has been approached in many ways, including new programming languages, new numerical methods, and a variety of schemes for analyzing programs to exploit some particular kind of simultaneous processing. The latter have included both hardware and software devices[5,15,27,32,33,35,37]. Multiprogramming often formed an important part of these studies. Apparently none of them tried to extract from one program as many simultaneously executable operations as possible. (See Baer, "A Survey of Some Theoretical Aspects of Multiprocessing"[3] for a comprehensive survey of many related results.)

This paper contains little detail about machine organization—we merely sketch some gross simplifying assumptions.

Then we outline the organization of our program analyzer and discuss its improvements over an earlier version[23]. A set of 86 FORTRAN decks totalling over 4000 cards has been analyzed, and these are described in general terms. Then we present a number of tables and graphs summarizing our experiments. These include the possible speedup and number of processors required for the programs analyzed. Finally, we give some interpretations of these results. Our conclusion is that some of the folklore has been in error, at least with respect to the kinds of programs measured.

Goals, Assumptions, and Definitions

We are attempting to determine, for computational algorithms, a set of parameters and their values which would be useful in computer system design. A direct way of doing this is to analyze a large set of existing programs. We have chosen to analyze FORTRAN programs because of their wide availability and because their analysis is about as difficult as any high level language would be. A language with explicit array operations, for example, would be easier to analyze but would restrict our analysis to array-type algorithms. Finally, we are attempting to show that a very wide class of algorithms can be found to possess a good deal of parallelism. The programs analyzed in many cases have no DO loops at all, for example, and most decks have less than 40 cards.

On several counts, the experiments reported here are a substantial improvement over those reported in Kuck *et al*[23] First, we have analyzed more than four times as many programs. These have been drawn from a wide variety of sources, as described below, and represent a wide variety of applications including a number of non-numerically oriented ones. Second, in an attempt to study the sensitivity of the

Acknowledgment. We gratefully acknowledge the contribution of C. Cartegini, W. Hackmann, J. Claggett, D. Romine, W. Tao, and D. Wills, who provided programming assistance. This research was supported by the National Science Foundation, Grant No. GJ-36936 and by NASA, Contract No. NAS2-6724.

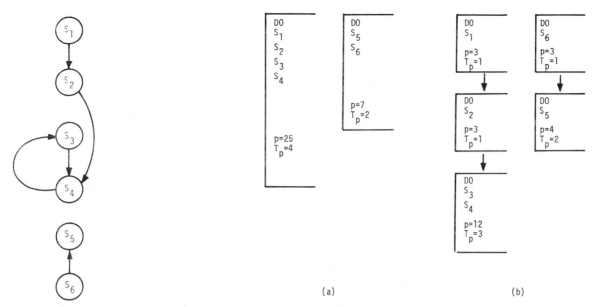

Figure 1. Dependence Graph

Figure 2. Decomposition of DO loop: (a) Vertical scheme, (b) Horizontal scheme

analysis to memory assumptions, we have made two sets of runs as described later (see Table 3). Third, we have made several improvements to the analyzer itself. These include a new method of handling DO loops, which we call the vertical scheme, and a new way of treating IF statements within DO loops. These are discussed later in this paper.

In order to interpret the results of our analysis, we must make a number of assumptions about machine organization. These cannot be discussed in any detail here, but most of them are backed by detailed study (see references). Some are, of course, idealizations which we would not expect to hold in a real machine. Thus the results would be degraded to some extent. On the other hand, since our analyzer is still crude in several respects, we might expect these degradations to be offset by better speedups due to an improved analyzer.

We ignore I/O operations on the assumption that they do not exist in FORTRAN. We also ignore control unit timing, assuming that instructions are always available for execution as required and are never held up by a control unit. We assume the availability of an arbitrary number of processors, all of them capable of executing any of the four arithmetic operations (but not necessarily all the same one) at any time. Each of the arithmetic operations is assumed to take the same amount of time, which we will call *unit time.*

Two nonstandard kinds of processing are assumed. To evaluate the supplied FORTRAN functions we rely on a fast scheme proposed in De Lugish[13]. This allows SIN(X), LOG(X), etc., to be evaluated in no more than a few multiply times. We also assume a many-way jump processor. Given predicate values corresponding to a tree of IF statements, this processor determines in unit time which program statement is the successor to the statement at the top of the tree. With up to 8 levels in such a tree, the gate count for the logic is modest[11,12].

We assume the existence of an instantaneously operating alignment network which serves to transmit data from memory to memory, from processor to processor, and between memories and processors. Based on studies of the requirements of real programs, some relatively inexpensive alignment networks have been designed[22,25]. We assume that the memory can be cycled in unit time and that there are never any accessing conflicts in the memory. In Lawrie[25], and Budnik and Kuck[7], memories are shown that allow the

accessing of most common array partitions without conflict. Hence, we believe that for a properly designed system, accessing and alignment conflicts can be a minor concern and that under conditions of steady state data flow, good system performance could be expected. For more discussion see Kuck, "Multioperation Machine Computational Complexity"[21].

Let the *parallel computation time* T_p be the time measured in unit times required to perform some calculations using p independent processors. The *speedup* over a uniprocessor is defined as $S_p = T_1/T_p$, where T_1 is the serial computation time, and *efficiency* is defined as $E_p = T_1/pT_p \leq 1$, which may be regarded as the quotient of S_p and the maximum possible speedup p. As explained in Kuck *et al*[23], computation time may be saved with the sacrifice of performing extra operations. For example, a(b+cde) requires four operations and $T_p = 4$, whereas ab + acde requires five operations and $T_p = 3$. If O_p is the number of operations executed in performing some computation using p processors, then we call R_p the *operation redundancy* and let $R_p = O_p/O_1 \geq 1$, where $O_1 = T_1$. Note that our definition of efficiency E_p is quite conservative since utilization of processors by redundant operations does not improve efficiency. *Utilization* is defined as $U_p = O_p/pT_p \leq 1$ where O_p is the number of operations which could have been performed. Using R_p, we can rewrite U_p as $U_p = R_pO_1/pT_p = R_pT_1/pT_p$, and by the definition of E_p we have $U_p = R_pE_p$. Thus, if an observer notices that all p processors are computing all of the time he may correctly conclude that the utilization is 1, but he may not conclude that the efficiency is 1 since the redundancy may be greater than 1.

Analysis Techniques

The analyzer accepts a FORTRAN program as input and breaks it into blocks of assignment statements, DO loop blocks, and IF tree blocks. During analysis each block is analyzed independently of the others and $\tilde{T}_1$, $\tilde{T}_p$, $\tilde{p}$, and $\tilde{O}_p$ are found for each block. Next, we find all traces through the program according to the IF and GOTO statements. We accumulate $\tilde{T}_1$, $\tilde{T}_p$, and $\tilde{O}_p$ for each block in each trace to give T_1, T_p, and O_p. The maximum $\tilde{p}$ found in any block in each trace becomes p. R_p, E_p, S_p, and U_p are calculated for each trace.

COMPUTER

A *block of assignment statements* (BAS) is a sequence of assignment statements with no intervening statements of any kind. Statements in a BAS can be made independent of each other by a process called *forward substitution*. For example, A = B + C; R = A + D by forward substitution becomes A = B + C; R = B + C + D. By using the laws of associativity, commutativity, and distributivity as in Muraoka[30] and Han[16], we find the parallel parse tree for each statement. The algorithm of Hu[17] is applied to this forest of trees to give $\tilde{p}$. $\tilde{T}_p$ is the maximum height of the individual trees and $\tilde{O}_p$ is the sum of the operations in the forest. This collection of techniques is called *tree height reduction*.

An *IF tree block* is a section of a FORTRAN program where the ratio of IF statements to assignment statements is larger than some predetermined threshold. An IF tree block is transformed into (1) a BAS consisting of every set of assignment statements associated with each path through the decision tree, (2) a BAS consisting of the relational expressions of the IF statements which have been converted to assignment statements [i.e., X ⩾ Y is converted to B = SIN (X-Y)], and (3) a decision tree into which the IF statements are mapped. The tree-height reduction algorithm is then applied to (1) and (2) combined. Davis[11] shows how to evaluate an eight-level decision tree in unit time. Thus a dual purpose is served: speedup is increased by increasing the size of the BAS through combination of the smaller BAS's between IF statements, and a number of decision points in a program are reduced to a single multiple decision point which can be evaluated in parallel. The complete IF tree algorithm is described in Davis[11,12].

There are two types of parallelism in DO loop blocks which can be found most often in programs. First, the statement

$$DO \ I \ I = 1,3$$
$$1 \ A(I) = A(I+1) + B(I) + C(I) * D(I)$$

can be executed on a parallel machine in such a way that three statements, A(1) = A(2) + B(1) + C(1) * D(1), A(2) = A(3) + B(2) + C(2) * D(2) and A(3) = A(4) + B(3) + C(3) * D(3) are computed simultaneously by three different processors. Thus, we reduce the computation time from $T_1 = 9$ to $T_p = 3$. This type of parallelism (array operations) we will call Type-1 parallelism. If we apply tree-height reduction algorithms to each of these three statements, we can further reduce the computation time to 2 for a six-processor machine.

The second type of parallelism lies in statements such as

(i) DO 1 I = 1,5   (ii) DO 1 I = 1,5
     1 P = P + A(I)   1 A(I) = A(I-1) + B(I)

which both have a recurrence relation between the output and input variables. In example (ii), if we repeatedly substitute the left-hand side into the right-hand side and apply the tree-height reduction algorithms to each resultant statement, we can execute all five statements in parallel—e.g., A(1) = A(0) + B(1), A(2) = A(0) + B(1) + B(2), ..., A(5) = A(0) + B(1) + B(2) + B(3) + B(4) + B(5). This will decrease the computation time from 5 to 3. For a single variable recurrence relation as in example (i), we can use the same techniques and compute only the last output P = P + A(1) + A(2) ... + A(5) in 3 unit steps instead of 5. We will call this type of parallelism Type-0 parallelism.

In order to exploit these parallelisms in DO loops, an algorithm described in Kuck *et al*[23], called the *horizontal scheme*, can be used to transform the original loop into an equivalent set of small loops in which these potential parallelisms will be more obvious. A modification of that algorithm called the *vertical scheme* has now been implemented. These schemes are illustrated with the following example:

$$DO \ S_6 \ I = 1, 3, 1$$

S_1	$T(I) = G(I) + M$
S_2	$G(I) = T(I) + D(I)$
S_3	$E(I) = F(I-1) + B(I)$
S_4	$F(I) = E(I) + G(I)$
S_5	$H(I) = A(I-1) + H(I-1)$
S_6	$A(I) = C(I) + N$

Space limitations prevent a description of the details of the implementation[20,23], and therefore only the essential parts of the vertical scheme are presented:

a) Find the dependence graph among statements (Figure 1). In the dependence graph each node represents a statement; a path from S_i to S_j indicates that an input variable of S_j during certain iterations has been updated by S_i during the same or an earlier iteration, according to the original execution order.

b) Separate the dependence graph into completely disconnected subgraphs, and arrange each subgraph as a DO loop in parallel as shown in Figure 2(a).

c) Apply the forward substitution technique to each subloop and the tree-height reduction algorithms to all resultant statements.

After this, the statements can be computed in parallel. The required $\tilde{p}$ and $\tilde{T}_p$ for each subloop resulting from use of the vertical and horizontal schemes are shown in Figure 2.

For this example, both schemes give us a nice speedup: $T_1 = 18$, $T_p = 6$ for the horizontal scheme and $T_p = 4$ for the vertical scheme. The latter has a better speedup but uses more processors. Note also that the total number of processors listed in Figure 2—12 for the horizontal scheme and 32 for the vertical scheme—can be further reduced by Hu's algorithm[16,17] without increasing the number of steps. This can be accomplished provided that some of the subtrees formed by the resultant statements are not completely filled—which is usually the case in most programs.

The basic difference between these two schemes is that the horizontal scheme tends to facilitate the extraction of Type-1 parallelism while the vertical scheme helps to find Type-0 parallelism. At present, we do not have a general method of determining, *a priori*, which scheme will give a better result for a particular DO loop. Although many cases yield the same result using either scheme, in some cases a higher speedup (with or without lower efficiency of the use of processors) can be achieved using one scheme or the other.

When there are more than a few IF and GOTO statements, they increase the number of possible paths through a DO loop and complicate the task of finding the dependence graph. We find all possible paths and then analyze each path separately. We call this strategy *DO path*. Thus, when p, O_p, etc., are being calculated for an entire program we treat each path through DO loop separately rather than combining the numbers for each DO loop path into one set of numbers that describe the DO loop as a whole as was done in Kuck *et al*[23].

Description of Analyzed Programs

A total of 86 FORTRAN programs with a total of 4115 statements was collected from various sources for this set of experiments. They have been divided into 7 classes: JAN, GPSS, DYS, NUME, TIME, EIS, and MISC. JAN is a subset of the programs described in Kuck *et al*[23], and came from

Conte[10], IBM[18], Lyness[26], and the University of Illinois subroutine library. GPSS contains the FORTRAN equivalents of the GPSS (General Purpose Simulation System) assembler listings[11] of 22 commonly-used blocks. The DYSTAL (Dynamic Storage Allocation Language in FORTRAN[34]) library provided the programs in DYS. NUME contains standard numerical analysis programs from Astill et al[2], Carnahan[8], and other sources. TIME is several time series programs from Simpson[36]. EIS is several programs from EISPACK (Eigensystem Package) which are FORTRAN versions of the eigenvalue programs in Wilkinson Reinsh[38]. Waste paper baskets provided elementary Computer Science student programs, civil engineering programs, and Boolean synthesis programs. These, together with programs from Kunzi et al[24], and Nakagawa and Lai[31] make up MISC. Table 1 and Figures 3 and 4 describe the 86 programs analyzed.

Results

The analyzer determines values of T_1, T_p, p, E_p, S_p, O_p, R_p, and U_p for each trace in a program. Each program was analyzed separately using both the horizontal and vertical schemes of DO loop analysis. The results of vertical or horizontal analysis were then used depending on which scheme gave better results for a particular program. The values of T_1, T_p, etc. for each trace were then averaged to determine an overall value for a program $\overline{T}_1$, $\overline{T}_p$, etc. Thus, we assume that each trace is equally likely, an assumption required by the absence of any dynamic program information. We feel this assumption yields conservative values, since the more likely traces—which are probably large and contain more parallelism—are given equal weight with shorter, special case

Table 1. Characteristics of Analyzed Programs

	JAN	GPSS	DYS	NUME	TIME	EIS	MISC
Av. No. BAS Outside DO	12.2	16.7	8.5	5.4	8.4	1.13	5.0
Av. No. BAS Inside DO	3.7	0.3	2.5	4.3	3.5	6.6	4.4
Av. No. DO Loops	1.8	0.3	1.5	1.9	3.1	1.5	2.4
Av. No. Nested DOs	1.0	0.0	0.5	1.2	0.4	2.8	0.6
Av. No. IFs	6.9	11.3	4.9	3.4	4.1	3.0	3.6
Av. No. IF Trees	1.5	1.9	1.3	0.8	1.5	0.0	0.8
Av. No. Traces	75.5	36.1	21.4	29.7	12.1	5.5	24.6
Av. No. Statements	72.5	61.9	44.9	33.4	45.0	32.2	32.8
Total No. Programs	12	22	10	10	8	8	16

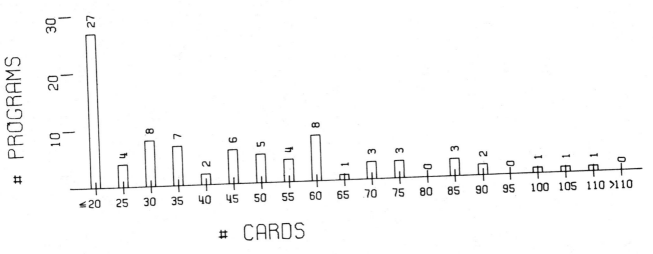

Figure 3. Number of programs versus number of cards in program.

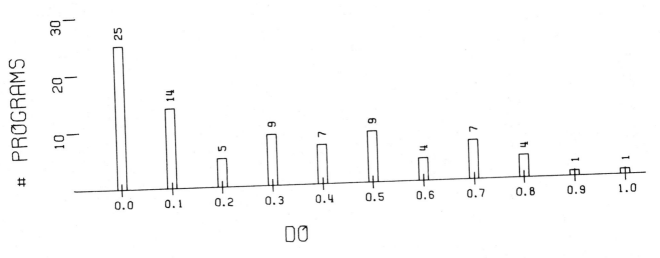

Figure 4. Number of programs versus fraction DO loop.

traces. Figures 5–9 are histograms showing $\bar{T}_1$, $\bar{T}_p$, $\bar{E}_p$, $\bar{S}_p$, $\bar{U}_p$, respectively, versus the number of programs.

The overall program values $\bar{T}_1$, $\bar{T}_p$, etc., are averaged to obtain ensemble values $\hat{T}_1$, $\hat{T}_p$, etc., for groups of related programs (see Table 1). Table 2 shows these ensemble values for each group of programs as well as for all programs combined. As we can see, for a collection of ordinary programs we can expect speedups on the order of 10 using an average of 37 processors with an average efficiency of 35%. The use of averages in these circumstances is open to some criticism, but we feel it is acceptable in view of the facts that the data are well distributed and the final averages are reasonably consistent—e.g., $\hat{p}\hat{E}_p \simeq \hat{S}_p$. Such anomalies as $\hat{T}_1/\hat{T}_p \geqslant \hat{S}_p$ can be attributed to occasional large T_p values in our raw data.

At this time we should stress several points about our source programs. First, four programs were discarded because they contained nonlinear recurrence relations and caused analysis difficulties. Their inclusion would have perturbed the results in a minor way—e.g., speedup would be low for these four. One was discarded because T_1 was so large that it affected the final averages too strongly ($\bar{T}_1 = 10,953$). Second, all the programs were small (see Table 1). Third, the number of loop iterations was 10 or less for all but one of the programs (where it was 20) whose data are shown in Table 2. Higher speedups, efficiencies, etc.,

would be expected using a more realistic number of iterations (see Figures 10–12). Finally, we have employed no multiprogramming—e.g., we do not account for the fact that more than one program can be executed simultaneously, (c.f. Davis[11]). In general, multiprogramming would of course allow the use of more processors.

For the results shown in Figures 5–12 and Table 2, the analyzer accounts for memory stores but not for any memory fetches. The effect of accounting for fetches is shown

Table 2. Average Measured Values for Seven Program Groups and for all Programs Combined

	$\hat{T}_1$	$\hat{T}_p$	$\hat{p}$	$\hat{E}_p$	$\hat{S}_p$	$\hat{O}_p$	$\hat{R}_p$	$\hat{U}_p$
JAN	357	48	62	.37	12.1	654	2.3	.43
GPSS	30	12	14	.30	3.2	67	2.5	.54
DYS	224	146	19	.47	4.9	1969	2.4	.47
NUME	654	77	51	.35	20.7	676	1.2	.38
TIME	174	22	23	.42	7.1	207	1.5	.46
EIS	896	208	82	.32	22.6	2292	2.8	.34
MISC	274	32	39	.32	8.4	486	2.1	.41
ALL	310	63	37	.35	9.8	739	2.2	.45

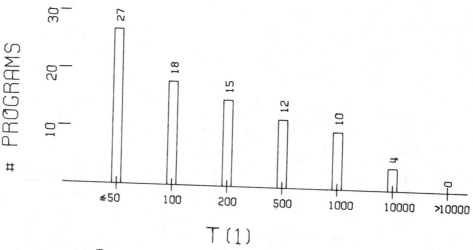

Figure 5. Number of programs versus $\bar{T}_1$

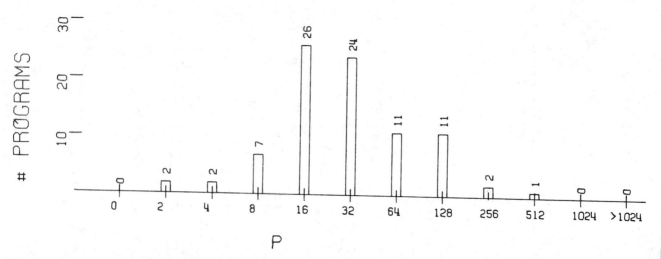

Figure 6. Number of programs versus $\bar{p}$.

in Table 3, which lists the ensemble values for 65 programs run with and without memory fetches. As we can see, accounting for memory fetches improves our results. In reality, a lookahead control unit and overlapped processing and memory cycling would perhaps result in numbers somewhere between these values.

Finally, Figures 10–12 show $\hat{S}_p$ versus $\hat{T}_1$, $\hat{p}$ versus $\hat{T}_1$ and $\hat{S}_p$ versus $\hat{p}$, respectively, for each ensemble JAN, GPSS, etc., as well as for all programs. Additionally, we took the programs in JAN, GPSS, NUME, TIME, and EIS, which had DO loops with a variable limit (about 30% of the programs), and set the DO loop limits to 10. The resulting program values were averaged with all other programs in these groups and the final average plotted in Figures 10–12. The analyses were repeated using DO limits of 20, 30, and 40, and the resulting averages plotted as before.

Conclusions

Our experiments lead us to conclude that multioperation machines could be quite effective in most ordinary FORTRAN computations. Figure 12 shows that even the simplest sets of programs (GPSS, for example, has almost no DO loops) could be effectively executed using 16 processors. The overall average (ALL in Figure 12) as shown in Table 3 is 35 processors when all DO loop limits are set to 10 or less. As the programs become more complex, 128 or

Table 3. Comparison of Averaged Measured Values With and Without Memory Fetches

	Without Memory Fetches	With Memory Fetches
$\hat{T}_1$	678	967
$\hat{T}_p$	148	164
$\hat{p}$	35	35
$\hat{E}_p$	.33	.41
$\hat{S}_p$	9.2	11.1
$\hat{O}_p$	1212	1443
$\hat{R}_p$	2.4	1.9
$\hat{U}_p$	.45	.44

more processors would be effective in executing our programs. Note that for all of our studies, $T_1 \leq 10,0000$ so most of the programs would be classed as short jobs in a typical computer center. In all cases, the average efficiency for each group of programs was no less than 30%. While we have not analyzed any decks with more than 100 cards, we would expect extrapolations of our results to hold. In fact, we obtained some decks by breaking larger ones at convenient points.

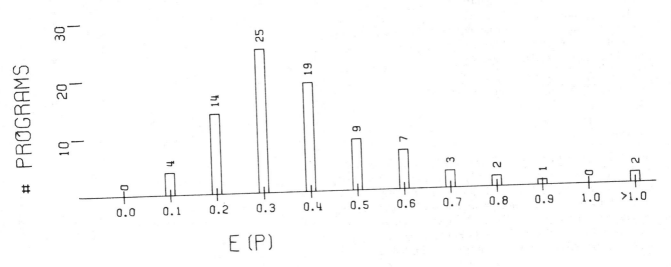

Figure 7. Number of programs versus $\bar{E}_p$

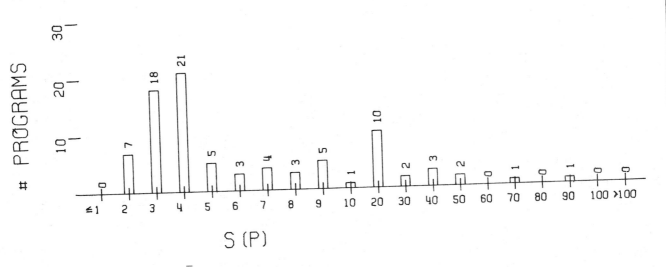

Figure 8. Number of programs versus $\bar{S}_p$

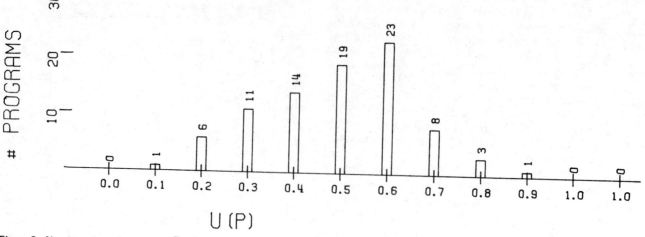

Figure 9. Number of programs versus $\bar{U}_p$

These numbers should be contrasted with current computer organizations. Presently, two to four simultaneous operation general purpose machines are quite common. Pipeline, parallel and associative machines which perform 8 to 64 simultaneous operations are emerging, but these are largely intended for special purpose use. Thus, we feel that our numbers indicate the possibility of perhaps an order of magnitude speedup increase over the current situation. Next we contrast our numbers with two commonly held beliefs about machine organization.

Let us assume that for $0 \leqslant \beta_k \leqslant 1$, $(1-\beta_k)$ of the serial execution time of a given program uses p processors, while β_k of it must be performed on $k \leqslant p$ processors. Then we may write (assuming $O_1 = O_k + O_p$):

$$T_p = \frac{\beta_k T_1}{k} + (1-\beta_k)\frac{T_1}{p}, \text{ and } E_p = \frac{T_1}{\frac{p}{k}\beta_k T_1 + (1-\beta_k)T_1} = \frac{1}{1+\beta_k(\frac{p}{k}-1)}.$$

For example, if $k = 1$, $p = 33$, and $\beta_1 = 1/16$, then we have $E_{33} = 1/3$. This means that to achieve $E_{33} = 1/3$, 15/16 of T_1 must be executed using all 33 processors, while only 1/16 of T_1 may use a single processor. While $E_{33} = 1/3$ is typical of our results (see Figure 7), it would be extremely surprising to learn that 15/16 of T_1 could be executed using fully 33 processors. This kind of observation led Amdahl[1]

and others[9,35] to conclude that computers capable of executing a large number of simultaneous operations would not be reasonably efficient—or, to paraphrase them, "Ordinary programs have too much serial code to be executed efficiently on a multioperation processor."

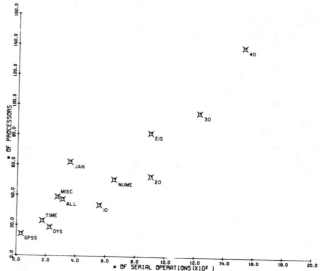

Figure 11. $\hat{p}$ versus $\hat{T}_1$

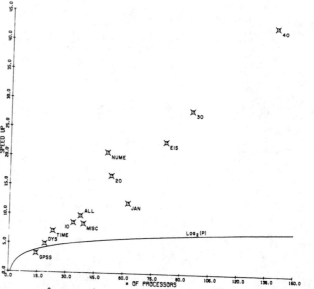

Figure 10. $\hat{S}_p$ versus $\hat{T}_1$

Figure 12. $\hat{S}_p$ versus $\hat{p}$

Such arguments have an invalidating flaw, however, in that they assume k = 1 in the above efficiency expression. Evidently no one who repeated this argument ever considered the obvious fact that k will generally assume many integer values in the course of executing most programs. Thus, the expression for E_p given above must be generalized to allow all values of k up to some maximum.

The technique used in our experiments for computing E_p is such a generalization. For some execution trace through a program, at each time step i, some number of processors k(i) will be required. If the maximum number of processors required on any step is p, we compute the efficiency for any trace as

$$E_p = \frac{\sum_{i=1}^{T_p} k(i)}{pR_pT_p} \text{, assuming p processors are available.}$$

Apparently no previous attempt to quantify the parameters discussed above has been successful for a wide class of programs. Besides Kuck et al[23] the only other published results are by Baer and Estrin[4], who report on five programs.

Another commonly-held opinion, which has been mentioned by Minsky[29], is that speedup S_p is proportional to $\log_2 \cdot p$. Flynn[14] further discusses this, assuming that all the operations simultaneously executed are identical. This may be interpreted to hold 1) over many programs of different characteristics, 2) for one fixed program with a varying number of processors, or 3) for one program with varying DO loop limits. That the above is false under interpretation 1 for our analysis is obvious from Figure 12. Similarly, it is false under interpretation 2 as the number of processors is varied between 1 and some number as plotted in Figure 12. As p is increased still farther, the speedup and efficiency may be regarded as constant or the speedup may be increased at a decreasing rate together with a decreasing efficiency. Eventually, as p becomes arbitrarily large, the speedup becomes constant and in some region the curve may appear logarithmic. Under interpretation 3, there are many possibilities—programs with multiply nested DO loops may have speedups which grow much faster than linearly, and programs without DO loops of course do not change at all.

Abstractly, it seems of more interest to relate speedup to T_1 than to p. Based on our data, we offer the following observation:

For many ordinary FORTRAN programs (with $T_1 \leqslant 10,000$), we can find p such that

1)

$$T_p = a\log_2 T_1 \text{ for } 2 \leqslant a \leqslant 10.$$

and 2)

$$p \leqslant \frac{T_1}{.6 \log_2 T_1},$$

such that 3)

$$S_p \geqslant \frac{T_1}{10 \log_2 T_1} \text{ and } E_p \geqslant .3 .$$

The average a value in our experiments was about 9. However, the median value was less than 4, since there were several very large values.

A complete theoretical explanation of this observation would be difficult, at present. But the following remarks are relevant. Theoretical speedups of $O(\log_2 T_1)$ for various classes of arithmetic expressions have been proved in Brent, et al[6], Maruyama[28], and Kogge and Stone[19]. Many DO loops yield an array of expressions to be evaluated simultaneously and this leads to speedups greater than $T_1/\log_2 T_1$. Other parts of programs use fewer processors than the maximum and yield lower speedups. However, we have typically observed speedups of two to eight in programs dominated by blocks of assignment statements and IF statements, assuming the IF tree logic of Davis[11].

In practice one is generally given a set of programs to be executed. If the problem is to design a machine—i.e., choose p—then the above approach is a reasonable one. Alternatively, the problem may be to compile them for a given number of processors. If the number available is less than that determined by the above analysis, the speedup will be decreased accordingly. If the number to be used is greater than that determined above, one must face reduced efficiency or multiprogramming the machine.

Several advantages are gained by the analysis of programs in high-level languages. First, more of a program can be scanned by a compiler than by lookahead logic in a control unit, so more global information is available. Second, in FORTRAN, an IF and a DO statement, for example, are easily distinguishable, but at run time the assembly language versions of these may be quite difficult to distinguish. Third, a program can be transformed in major ways at compile time so it may be run on a particular machine organization. All of these lead to simpler, faster control units at the expense of more complex compilation.

Finally, a number of realities of actual machines have been glossed over in this paper, as mentioned in the section on Goals, Assumptions, and Definitions. A more detailed discussion of the philosophy of our analysis work may be found elsewhere[21,23]. ∎

Reference Bibliography

1. Amdahl, G.M. "Validity of the Single Processor Approach to Achieving Large Scale Computing Capabilities." *AFIPS Conference Proceedings,* vol. 30, 1967. pp. 483-485.

2. Astill, K.N. and B.W. Arden. *Numerical algorithms: Origins and Applications.* Reading, Mass.: Addison-Wesley, 1970.

3. Baer, J.L. "A Survey of some Theoretical Aspects of Multiprocessing." *Computing Surveys,* vol. 5, no. 1 (March 1973) pp. 31-80.

4. Baer, J.L. and G. Estrin. "Bounds for Maximum Parallelism in a Bilogic Graph Model of Computations." *IEEE Transactions on Computers,* vol. C-18, no. 11 (Nov. 1969) pp. 1012-1014.

5. Bingham, H.W., E.W. Riegel, and D.A. Fisher. "Control Mechanisms for Parallelism in Programs." Burroughs Corp., Paoli, Pa., ECOM-02463-7, 1968.

6. Brent, R., D. Kuck, and K. Maruyama. "The Parallel Evaluation of Arithmetic Expressions Without Division." *IEEE Transactions on Computers,* vol. C-22, no. 5 (May 1973) pp. 532-534.

7. Budnik, P., and D.J. Kuck. "The Organization and Use of Parallel Memories." *IEEE Transactions on Computers,* vol. C-20, no. 12 (Dec. 1971) pp. 1566-1569.

8. Carnahan, B., H.A. Luther and J.O. Wilkes. *Applied Numerical Methods.* New York: John Wiley and Sons, 1969.

9. Chen, T.C., "Unconventional Superspeed Computer Systems," *AFIPS Conference Proceedings,* vol. 38, 1971. pp. 365-371.

10. Conte, S.D. *Elementary Numerical Analysis.* New York: McGraw-Hill, 1965.

11. Davis, E.W., Jr. "A Multiprocessor for Simulation Applications." Ph.D. thesis, Dept. of Computer Science, Univ. of Illinois, Urbana, Rep. 527, June 1972.

12. Davis, E.W., Jr. "Concurrent Processing of Conditional Jump Trees." Compcon 72, *IEEE Computer Society Conference Proceedings.* Sept. 1972, pp. 279-281.

13. De Lugish, B. "A Class of Algorithms for Automatic Evaluation of Certain Elementary Functions in a Binary Computer." Dept. of Computer Science, Univ. of Illinois, Urbana, Rep. 399, June 1970.

14. Flynn, M. "Some Computer Organizations and Their Effectiveness." *IEEE Transactions on Computers,* vol. C-21, no. 9 (Sept. 1972) pp. 948-960.

15. Foster, C.C. and E.M. Riseman. "Percolation of Code to Enhance Parallel Dispatching and Execution." *IEEE Transactions on Computers,* vol. C-21, no. 12 (Dec. 1972). pp. 1411-1415.

16. Han, J. "Tree Height Reduction for Parallel Processing of Blocks of FORTRAN Assignment Statements." M.S. thesis, Dept. of Computer Science, Univ. of Illinois, Urbana, Rep. 493 (Feb. 1972).

17. Hu, T.C. "Parallel Sequencing and Assembly Line Problems." *Operations Research.* vol. 9 (Nov.-Dec. 1961). pp. 841-848.

18. IBM, "System/360 Scientific Subroutine Package Version III." GH 20-0205-4, Aug. 1970.

19. Kogge, P. and H.S. Stone. "A Parallel Algorithm for the Efficient Solution of a General Class of Recurrence Equations." Rep. 25, Dig. Systems Lab., Stanford, Calif., Mar. 1972.

20. Kuck, D.J. "NASA Final Report." Contract NAS2-6724, Dec. 1972.

21. Kuck, D.J. "Multioperation Machine Computational Complexity." *Proceedings of Symposium on Complexity of Sequential and Parallel Numerical Algorithms.* invited paper, May 1973, to be published by Academic Press.

22. Kuck, D.J., D.H. Lawrie, and Y. Muraoka. "Interconnection Networks for Processors and Memories in Large Systems." Compcon 72, *IEEE Computer Society Conference Proceedings.* Sept. 1972. pp. 131-134.

23. Kuck, D.J., Y. Muraoka, and S-C Chen. "On the Num-ber of Operations Simultaneously Executable in FORTRAN-like Programs and Their Resulting Speed-Up." *IEEE Transactions on Computers,* vol. C-21, no. 12, Dec. 1972.

24. Künzi, H.P., H.G. Tzschach, and C.A. Zehnder. *Numerical Methods of Mathematical Optimization with ALGOL and FORTRAN.* (Werner C. Rheinboldt, tran.) New York: Academic Press, 1971.

25. Lawrie, D.H. "Memory-Processor Connection Networks." Ph.D. thesis, Dept. of Computer Science, Univ. of Illinois, Urbana, Rep. 557, Feb. 1973.

26. Lyness, J.N. "Algorithm 379 SQUANK (Simpson Quadrature Used Adaptively–Noise Killed)." *Communications of the ACM,* vol. 13, no. 4, April 1970.

27. Martin, D. and G. Estrin. "Experiments on Models of Computations and Systems." *IEEE Trans. Electron. Comput.* vol. EC-16, (Feb. 1967.) pp. 59-69.

28. Maruyama, K. "On the Parallel Evaluation of Polynomials." *IEEE Transactions on Computers,* vol. C-22, no. 1 (Jan. 1973) pp. 2-5.

29. Minsky, M. "Form and Content in Computer Science." 1970 ACM Touring Lecture, *Journal of the ACM,* vol. 17, no. 2, 1970. pp. 197-215.

30. Muraoka, Y. "Parallelism Exposure and Exploitation in Programs," Ph.D. thesis, Dept. of Computer Science, Univ. of Illinois, Urbana, Rep. 424, Feb. 1971.

31. Nakagawa, T. and H. Lai. "Reference Manual of FORTRAN Program ILLOD–(NOR-B) for Optimal NOR Networks." Dept. of Computer Science, Univ. of Illinois, Urbana, Rep. 488, Dec. 1971.

32. Ramamoorthy, C.V. and M. Gonzalez. "A Survey of Techniques for Recognizing Parallel Processable Streams in Computer Programs." in *1969 Fall Joint Computer Conference,* AFIPS Conf. Proc., vol. 35. Montvale, N.J.: AFIPS Press 1969. pp. 1-15.

33. Riseman, E.M. and C.C. Foster. "The Inhibition of Potential Parallelism by Conditional Jumps." *IEEE Transactions on Computers.* vol. C-21, no. 12. Dec. 1972, pp. 1405-1411.

34. Sakoda, J.M. "DYSTAL Manual," Dept. of Sociology and Anthropology. Brown Univ., Providence, R.I., 1965.

35. Senzig, D. "Observations on High-Performance Machines." *AFIPS Conference Proceedings,* vol. 31, 1967. pp. 791-799.

36. Simpson, S.M., Jr. *Time Series Computations in FORTRAN and FAP.* Reading, Mass.: Addison-Wesley, vol. 1, 1966.

37. Tjaden, G. and M. Flynn. "Detection and Parallel Execution of Independent Instructions." *IEEE Transactions on Computers.* vol. C-19, Oct. 1970, pp. 889-895.

38. Wilkinson, J.H. and C. Renish. *Linear Algebra.* F.L. Bauer, ed. New York: Springer Verlag, 1971.

Paul Budnik has been a graduate student in computer science at the University of Illinois since 1967. He is currently engaged in Ph.D. thesis research, and is employed by Systems Control, Inc., Palo Alto, California.

David J. Kuck joined the Department of Computer Science, University of Illinois, Urbana, in 1965 where he is now a Professor. He has been involved with several large research projects including Project MAC at MIT and the ILLIAC IV Project at the University of Illinois. Dr. Kuck was one of the system designers of ILLIAC IV and for several years directed the software development and applications activities. From 1963 to 1965 he was a Ford Postdoctoral Fellow and Assistant Professor of Electrical Engineering at the Massachusetts Institute of Technology, Cambridge, Massachusetts. Currently his research interests are in the coherent design of hardware and software systems.

His recent computer systems research has included theoretical studies of upper bounds on computation time, empirical analysis of real programs and the design of high performance processing, switching and memory systems for classes of computation ranging from numerical to nonnumerical.

He received the BSEE degree from the University of Michigan, Ann Arbor, in 1959, and the MS and Ph.D. degrees from Northwestern University, Evanston, Illinois, in 1960 and 1963, respectively.

Shyh-Ching Chen received his BSEE from the National Taiwan University, Taipei, Taiwan, in 1966 and his MSEE from Villanova University in 1972.

Since September 1970 he has been a Research Assistant in the Department of Computer Science at the University of Illinois, Urbana.

From August 1967 to August 1969 he was with the Electronic Computing Center, National Taiwan University.

Duncan H. Lawrie is a Visiting Research Assistant Professor of computer science at the University of Illinois. He received his BA from DePauw University in Greencastle, Indiana, and his BSEE from Purdue University, both in 1966, and his MS and Ph.D. degrees from the University of Illinois in 1969 and 1973.

While at the University of Illinois he held a NASA traineeship and research assistantship in the Department of Computer Science, and was Senior Research Programmer in the ILLIAC IV Project until 1972.

Dr. Lawrie is a member of Tau Beta Pi, Eta Kappa Nu, Sigma Xi, the ACM, and the IEEE.

Edward W. Davis, Jr., is a software specialist in the Digital Processor Engineering Department at Goodyear Aerospace Corporation, Akron, Ohio. He is coordinator of system software development for the STARAN parallel processor.

He received his BSEE from the University of Akron in 1964. He was a research assistant at the University of Illinois, where he received his Ph.D. in computer science in 1972.

Yoichi Muraoka is with the Electrical Communication Laboratory, Nippon Telephone and Telegram Company, in Tokyo. From 1966 to 1970, he was a Research Assistant with the ILLIAC IV Project of the Department of Computer Science, University of Illinois where his main responsibility was software development. Muraoka received his BE from Waseda University, Tokyo, in 1965 and his MS and Ph.D. in computer science from the University of Illinois, Urbana.

Joseph Han specializes in data processing. He received his BSEE in Taiwan in 1965. In 1971 he received his MS in computer science at the University of Illinois, Urbana.

Richard E. Strebendt is a Research Assistant in the Department of Computer Science at the University of Illinois. He is currently on leave of absence from Bell Telephone Laboratories, where he was previously responsible for the design and implementation of a descriptive language for digital machines.

Strebendt received his BSEE (1966) and MSEE (1968) from Wayne State University, Michigan.

Paul W. Kraska is with the Advanced Concept Research Laboratory at Control Data Corporation, specializing in the exploration of parallel processing using minicomputers. Earlier at Burroughs Corporation, he worked on the Atlas radio guidance system.

Dr. Kraska received his BS in mathematics from the University of Rochester in 1959, his MSEE from the University of Pennsylvania, and his Ph.D. from the University of Illinois in computer science. During his stay at the University of Illinois he worked on language development for ILLIAC IV.

Ross A. Towle received his BS and MS degrees in mathematics from the University of Illinois in 1972 and 1973, respectively, and is presently doing graduate work in the Computer Science Department at the same university.

Mr. Towle is a member of Phi Kappa Phi, Pi Mu Epsilon, and Delta Sigma Rho.

A LANGUAGE IMPLEMENTATION DESIGN
FOR A MULTIPROCESSOR COMPUTER SYSTEM

P. Hibbard, A. Hisgen, T. Rodeheffer

Department of Computer Science
Carnegie-Mellon University
Pittsburgh, Pennsylvania, 15213
U.S.A.

The work described here was supported in part by the Rome Air Development Center under contract F-30602-75-C-0218. The views expressed are those of the authors.

Theoretical and experimental results have indicated that automatic decompositions can discover modest amounts of parallelism. These investigations have tended to ignore the practical problems of language run-time organization, such as synchronization, communication, memory organization, resource management, and input/output. This paper describes a language implementation effort which combines the investigation of implicit and explicit parallel decomposition facilities with the practical considerations of system organization on a multiprocessor computer, Cm*.

1. Introduction

Difficulties in programming multiprocessor computer systems arise from many sources: the elusive nature of suitable algorithmic decompositions which provide reasonable amounts of parallelism, the intricate detail with which certain architectures require concurrency to be specified, the general lack of high-level programming tools for specifying parallelism, and the relative unfamiliarity of programmers with the standard techniques useful for parallel algorithms. For some special-purpose machines the problem of achieving concurrency is not as severe, because the choice of suitable algorithms has been made at the hardware design stage. However, a multiprocessor computer system which is intended for general purpose programming must provide assistance for solving these problems if the full potential of the system is to be realized.

In this paper we describe a language system implementation in which we attempt to overcome some of these difficulties.[†] As it happens, the hardware on which our system executes (Cm*, see section 2) belongs to the class of multiprocessor architectures which are built from discrete minicomputers, and this causes several additional problems. Such architectures provide only the most basic hardware facilities for controlling concurrency. The limited functional power of the processing components requires that a high degree of concurrency be maintained throughout a computation in order to obtain significant performance, though highly parallel decompositions of many algorithms are not available. On these architectures software must be tolerant to minor changes in configuration such as would be caused by malfunction or removal for maintainance. Finally, it is desirable that the language system give the appearance of a maxicomputer

language, even though it executes on a collection of minicomputers. Each of these factors has had an impact upon the implementation we present in this paper.

We first describe in outline the architecture upon which our experimental software system executes, then describe the principal properties of the system and results obtained from measurements of its performance, and finally comment upon its viability and the future work required.

2. Hardware organization

Cm* is a modular multi-miniprocessor computer developed at Carnegie-Mellon University.[20, 19, 12, 7] Its hierarchical design contains three levels of processor-to-memory interconnection, each with a different degree of control and a different access cost. At the lowest level, a processor is connected directly to its own local memory via a local switch, the Slocal; this combination of processor, associated memory, and local switch is called a <u>computer module</u>. At the next higher level, a <u>cluster</u> is built by connecting a number of computer modules via an inter-processor bus, the <u>map bus</u>, controlled by a microprogrammed controller, the Kmap. Finally, a number of clusters are connected via inter-cluster buses between Kmaps. This hierarchy is totally transparent to the processors, which only see a difference in memory access times.

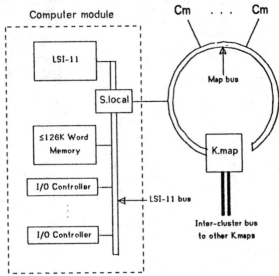

Figure 1. A Cm* Cluster

[†] We will not be concerned directly with the language which the implementation supports. It has been dealt with in other papers.[10, 14, 11] Section 3 gives a brief review of the language and details of relevant properties.

Reprinted from *Proceedings of the Fifth Annual Symposium on Computer Architecture*, 1978, pages 66-72. Copyright © 1978 by The Institute of Electrical and Electronics Engineers, Inc.

The system is reconfigurable — at milli-day bus re-plugging speeds — to allow the effect of different cluster sizes on the performance of critical hardware components and on the performance of the software to be measured. Currently the system includes ten LSI-11 processors, each with 24K or 28K words of memory, and three Kmaps (and therefore three clusters); expansion up to a 50 module/5 cluster system is in progress.

2.1. Hardware components

The LSI-11s are slightly modified to introduce the passive Slocal switch between the Pc and the memory. The Slocal intercepts memory accesses from the processor and either relocates them into local memory or puts them out onto the map bus for action by the Kmap. The Slocal also responds to requests from the map bus into local memory.

The Kmap, a powerful microprogrammed control, performs relocation for access requests originating from the Slocals in its own cluster, and either returns the request back onto the map bus for an intra-cluster reference, or transmits it onto an inter-cluster bus towards the desired cluster if the reference is in another cluster. The Kmap also services requests forwarded to it from other Kmaps for memory accesses and other functions on memory in its cluster. Additional functions may be performed during and in addition to address translation, for example the Kmap may perform capability checking actions and message switching actions on behalf of distributed operating systems.[12] The Kmap is equipped with a 4K writable control store and a 2K 80-bit data RAM and has a hardware multiprogramming feature to allow multiple requests to be serviced concurrently. The primitive Kmap address translation microcode (used by the present version of our software system) occupies less than 256 words of the writable control store.

2.2. Accessing costs

For references to the local memory of a processor, the Slocal introduces no delay in speed and imposes no load on the Kmap. References to remote memory in the same cluster (via the cluster Kmap) take about 3 times as long as references to local memory and references to out-of-cluster memory take about 9 times as long. A normal instruction mix on a PDP-11 has about 70% code references and 30% data references,[16, 15] thus a simple programming strategy for Cm* is to execute code locally, if necessary at the expense of accessing data remotely. Under the most unfavourable conditions, with the LSI-11 processors remotely executing code sequences maliciously contrived to generate the most traffic, a Kmap can handle up to six processors before saturating. With any reasonable balance of local to remote references, the Kmap easily handles all the address mapping traffic generated by a cluster.

3. Language implementation overview

The language which is supported by our implementation is a large subset of Algol 68[24, 9] (of about the power of PL/I), extended by the addition of facilities for explicitly specifying parallel subtasks. These facilities are eventual values,[†] which

---

[†] Eventual values are a form of "lazy evaluation" or "evaluation on demand", where the computation of a result need not be complete until the result is actually needed.[8, 6, 3] The programmer is able to specify this by using the symbol EVENT.

provide control primitives for data objects, and parallel clauses, which furnish fork and join primitives. For example:

par begin $u1, u2, u3, ..., un$ end

specifies that $u1, u2, u3, ..., un$ may be executed concurrently. Synchronization is achieved implicitly with eventual values and explicitly by the use of semaphores with parallel-clauses.

A compiler and a run-time system for this language have been designed and implemented on C.mmp[25] — another PDP-11 based multi-miniprocessor developed at Carnegie-Mellon University — and are in regular use on that system. The compiler runs both on C.mmp and as a cross-compiler on a PDP-10. The run-time system, which contains a special-purpose distributed operating system, utilizes only the basic hardware facilities of primitive memory sharing and a few indivisible operations in order to construct from an assemblage of PDP-11s the rich environment of the extended Algol 68 sublanguage. The undemanding and low-level nature of the requisites of the run-time system accounts in part for the speed with which it was brought up on Cm*, a machine whose architecture differs vastly from that of C.mmp.

Rather than the more usual stack organization, the run-time system uses a heap storage management regime, in order to allow blocks of storage to be deallocated in any order. All multi-word values, such as reals, arrays, and descriptors of various sorts, are stored in individual blocks of storage allocated in the heap, and are represented by pointers. Each block also contains a pointer count, whose value is the number of pointers to that block, which, when zero, indicates that the block cannot be referenced and should be garbage collected.

Each (explicitly specified) parallel subtask in a user program is known as an activity. The run-time system contains a distributed high-level scheduler which maps feasible activities onto available processors. An activity remains on its processor until it either blocks on a user-level semaphore or terminates.

4. Exploitation of low-level parallelism

Many programs, although written in a sequential fashion, actually contain significant amounts of potential parallelism when viewed on the operation-by-operation level. These operations, such as multiplication, assignment, array indexing, and storage allocation, may be executed concurrently in the absence of data dependencies. The Cm* system has been derived from the C.mmp system by adding a software mechanism for the automatic detection and exploitation of this low-level parallelism.

4.1. Master processors and slave processors

In charge of executing each activity is a master processor. A master sequences through the operations in an activity and resolves all control-flow decisions. In order that the potential parallelism of independent operations may be realized, some operations are not executed directly by the master but instead are parcelled up with their operands and placed in a queue for deferred operations. The choice of which operations a master executes directly and which operations are deferred has been made by consideration of the functional capability of the LSI-11 processing units; in general the master directly executes operations which produce single-word values such as integers and booleans and defers floating point operations (which produce two-word values).

The processors responsible for picking up deferred operations and executing them are known as slaves. Basically, any processor which is not a master functions as a slave. In conventional terms, our implementation scheme resembles that of a classical look-ahead processor,[1, 13, 23] with the master acting as the controller and the slave as a multiple functional unit.

Our system also resembles the data flow model of computation,[5] since the look-ahead window may be viewed as containing the active portion of the graph. The master is responsible for creating the graph by expanding a sequential instruction stream using control-flow information available at run-time. The slaves locate the active nodes, implement the distribution and arbitration networks, and act as functional units. A related scheme is described by Arvind and Gostelow.[2]

4.2. Multiple masters and multiple slaves

Whenever the program explicitly creates a new activity, the distributed high-level scheduler causes a slave to turn into a master to be in charge of that activity. (If no slaves are free, the activity will remain feasible until one becomes available.) Similarly, when a master completes its activity (or becomes blocked) it reverts to a slave provided that no other feasible activities exist. A master also reverts momentarily to a slave when its operation queue saturates or an incomplete result is needed for a control-flow decision. Since the number of masters depends upon the external characteristics of the program being executed, the ratio of masters to slaves may vary, and in particular may be greater than or less than one.

Because operations in different activities are by definition independent, each master can have its own queue. A distributed low-level scheduler causes each slave to service all of the master queues in turn by executing one operation from each in a round-robin fashion. In general this may result in two or more slaves trying simultaneously to execute operations on the same queue, especially in the case where there are few masters and many slaves. A number of slaves can execute operations from the same queue provided that each operation so executed is data independent both from (1) other operations which are currently being executed and from (2) operations which are data dependent on those being executed. Since there can be no data dependencies between queues, only operations on the same queue need be checked against.

Because of the distributed high- and low-level schedulers any program, irrespective of the number of activities it creates, may be executed by any number of processors. The ability to run on even one processor helps the debugging and testing of system and application software. Of course, in this limiting case, performance is considerably degraded since the single processor must perform both master and slave actions, incurring the additional overheads of placing operations in the queue only to end up removing and executing them itself at some later time.

4.3. Factors limiting concurrency

The number of slave operations which can take place concurrently depends both on the queue length, which is a function of the relative speeds of the master and slaves, and on

the data dependencies which exist between the operations in the queue. In our present software implementation a master is able to place sufficient operations in the queue to satisfy about 2-3 slaves in numerically oriented programs, and fewer in other programs; figure 2 gives the speedup of a single numerical task as a function of the number of slaves.

Figure 2. Speedup of a Typical Numerical Program

The low degree of concurrency is a result of the low speed of the master relative to the slaves. This arises from two factors: firstly, the master performs a relatively large proportion of the operations itself compared to the number which it places in the queue; secondly, the overheads that queue manipulations impose on the master limit the rate at which it can place operations. Since the average queue length with more than 3 processors is about 0.1 operations, data dependencies must be having a negligible effect on the observed concurrency.

We intend to refine the system to queue a wider variety of operations.[†] The queue overheads can be reduced by placing some of the queue manipulation in Kmap microcode. At this stage it is difficult to estimate the effects this change will have when combined with other modifications we make, however a ten-fold reduction in queue manipulation overheads seems to be a reasonable expectation. In order to predict the behaviour of the microcoded version a model system has been constructed in which the relative costs of queueing actions and other actions are adjustable. Figure 3 gives speedups obtained for various relative costs with numerically oriented programs.

If the average queue length is increased by these strategies, the observed concurrency will become limited, of course, by the data dependencies between the operations in the queue. In our implementation data dependencies are reduced by properties of the run-time system which are discussed elsewhere,[11] these cause the run-time system to act like that for a single-assignment language,[21, 4] except when performing certain operations upon arrays and structures.

---

† These additional operations will include array indexing and any copying of large values, as well as housekeeping actions such as those involved in storage maintainance and procedure calls, to allow us to obtain concurrency across a greater range of programs.

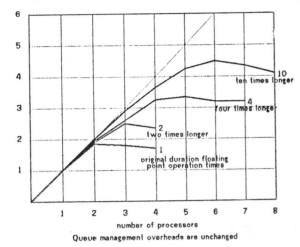

speedup

Queue management overheads are unchanged

Figure 3.   Effect of Relative Queue Overheads on Concurrency

For example, given the statement sequence:

$$a := (b + c) * (d + e);$$
$$x := a + f;$$
$$a := g + h;$$
$$y := (a * i) / j;$$

the statements are not executed as

[1] $t1 := b + c;$
[2] $t2 := d + e;$
[3] $a := t1 * t2;$
[4] $x := a + f;$
[5] $a := g + h;$
[6] $t3 := a * i;$
[7] $y := t3 / j;$

but instead as:

[1] $t1 := b + c;$
[2] $t2 := d + e;$
[3] $a := t1 * t2;$
[4] $x := a + f;$
[5] $a' := g + h;$
[6] $t3 := a' * i;$
[7] $y := t3 / j;$

where a' is a newly created variable. This allows, for example, concurrent execution of

([1],[2],[5]);   ([3],[6]);   ([4],[7]);

rather than

([1],[2]);   [3];   [4];   [5];   [6];   [7];

Table 1 indicates that data dependencies are not significant enough to be a problem. If they were, then adding more processors would not decrease the queue lengths, because many of the later operations in the queue could not be started until the earlier ones on which they would depend had completed.

Average number of incomplete operations on a master's queue

Floating Point Operation Times:	Number of Processors						
	1	2	3	4	5	6	7
Normal duration	33	5	0.2	0.1			
2 times longer	33	21	10	0.7	0.4	0.4	0.3
4 times longer	33	28	15	8.8	1.4	0.9	0.7
10 times longer	34	22	16	11	6.2	2.3	1.4

Table 1.

Any operation which produces a single-word result on the LSI-11 (for example rounding a real number to an integer or adding two integers) is performed directly by the master: a subset of the operations which produce values longer than one word (in particular floating point operations) are performed by the slave. Single-word operands to slave actions are thus always available, and their values are copied into the queue with the operation. Multi-word operands need not necessarily have been computed (depending on the state of the queue), and the address of the operand is placed in the queue with an associated tag-bit. This bit is cleared when the operation producing that result completes. If a slave finds the first operation in the queue is already being executed, it scans down the queue to find a non-executing operation with operands whose tag-bits are clear. In general the distance a slave has to scan in order to find an admissible operation is small.

Result of slave scanning when queue is non-empty
(floating point operations are twice normal duration)

	Number of Processors					
	1	2	3	4	5	6
% no independent operation found	0	0	1	6	46	57
% independent operation found	100	100	99	94	54	43
average number of operations examined in successful scan	1.0	1.7	2.2	1.6	1.7	1.5

Table 2.

4.4. Control-flow dependencies

A factor which limits the concurrency of a look-ahead processor is the presence of control-flow dependencies,[17, 13] which require the look-ahead controller to await the result of some operation in the window to determine the direction of a conditional branch. At these points concurrency falls to zero and then takes some time to build up again. A similar situation arises in our implementation; however, there are the following differences:

359

o Recall that the master performs all operations which compute a single-word result. If the operands to such an operation are multi-word values, as for example in the case of x < 0.5, they may be tagged. If so, the master must wait for the values to become available. Those cases in which a boolean single-word result is used immediately in a conditional correspond to control-flow dependencies, and the master will need the result to decide the branch. Instances in non-control contexts may cause the master to pause unnecessarily. However, measurements on a number of programs show that less than 5% of these operations occur outside the context of conditionals, so little degradation of performance will result.

o Those operations taking single-word operands and returning single-word results which would interrupt the flow of a look-ahead controller do not interrupt the master in our scheme. Thus, in our implementation, we do not need to unfold the vector inner product loop

```
sum := 0;
for i from 1 to n do
    sum := sum + a[i] * b[i]
od
```

since the master performs the increment of the counter and the implied conditional branch without reference to the queue. The number of loop control-flow dependencies involving multi-word values is small in most programs (less than 10% in programs measured), thus permitting the master to queue the operations from successive iterations of the loop without waiting for deferred values to be produced, and allowing the slaves to maintain high parallelism.

When the master requires some result which is tagged, it marks those operations in the queue which cover the operation it wishes to perform,[13] using a bit-marking scheme which encodes the data dependencies of the operations. Slaves perform marked actions in preference to other actions in the queue. The master temporarily dispatches itself as a slave during this period to assist the slaves, who also alter their scheduling policy by remaining on one queue until the result is produced. We call this mechanism operation preferencing, however, our measurements to date are inconclusive on whether this extra mechanism actually enables the value needed to be produced sooner.

4.5. Operation splitting

The operations executed by the slaves are generally not indivisible. A value is frequently produced before all the actions involved in performing the operation have been completed, since post-creation housekeeping actions may be required. These arise from two sources: those directly concerned with the operation, which would also be present if no queue were involved, and the additional housekeeping arising from queue manipulations. By changing the tag-bit immediately after the creation but before the housekeeping actions, the period during which subsequent operations in the queue are prevented from executing is reduced, and the concurrency increased.[18] In addition, several of the housekeeping operations

may be postponed if the slave is required for other tasks. During a period when a master is held up for a result, the slaves execute operations without performing deferrable housekeeping actions. In this way the execution time of an operation may be less than in the case of a sequential program, and some queue overheads can be removed from the critical path. The relative costs of the basic operations and the housekeeping actions are given in table 3.

Costs of basic operations and housekeeping actions
(relative to cost of floating point multiply)

Basic Operation cost of floating point multiply	1.00
Basic Operation cost of floating point add	0.80
Housekeeping costs associated with any floating point operation (can be postponed off of the critical path)	0.20
Queue housekeeping costs which can be postponed off the critical path	0.27

Table 3.

4.6. Sub-masters

Sometimes a whole sequence of operations in an activity is relatively independent of the operations which follow, because the operations which follow only use the final result computed by this sequence. This situation might arise from the execution of a user-defined function. Suppose that instead of having the master queue the component operations of the function, we turn a slave into a sub-master temporarily to mangage the execution of the function. This sub-master dispatches the component operations on its own queue. Once the result of the function is available, the sub-master reports back to the master and then reverts back to being a slave. This strategy has the following advantages:

o It reduces the overheads imposed on the master from those which would otherwise be imposed were the master to place each of the operations in its own queue separately;

o Any conditional flow dependencies which are present in the evaluation of the function can be removed from the master's computation path and placed on a sub-master's computation path.

Table 4 shows the difference in speed obtained by these strategies. As one might expect, the overheads of the extra queue manipulations and communication are reducing gains from increased parallelism; however, we expect that Kmap microcoded queue manipulation will improve these results.

Duration of a program execution (in seconds)
for different strategies of handling a user function
(full speed floating point)

	Number of Processors					
	1	2	3	4	5	6
Sub-master queues	39	20	13	11	10	9
Master queue only	30	18	13	11	12	13

Table 4.

5. Remarks

5.1. Implementation overheads

Comparisons with the C.mmp version of the system (which does not have the mechanisms for low-level parallelism), indicate that approximately 20-30% of a processor's time is involved in queue manipulations in a purely software implementation of our system.[†] We do not feel that these overheads are excessive, since Cm* is almost devoid of centralized control, and it is inevitable that a certain proportion of the available processing power should be used to supply it. Whether placing a small amount of the control in the centralized Kmaps, and then using software to supply a complex high-level control is a suitable use of the architecture still remains to be determined.

5.2. Multiple look-ahead windows

The deleterious effect that control-flow dependencies have on the parallelism obtainable by look-ahead processors has been commented upon frequently.[17] Multiple look-ahead windows, as a way of buffering functional units against periods of low utilization caused by dependencies, have been suggested previously,[22] and our implementation resembles those treatments in part. However our treatment of masters and slaves suggests that other advantages could be gained from multiple look-ahead windows. One could consider a machine which executes a single instruction stream using two windows, one for floating-point operations and one for integer and boolean operations. In the absence of transfer functions which compute an integer or boolean value from floating point numbers, or a floating point number from integers or booleans, no data dependencies can exists between the two windows, and the occurrence of a control-flow dependency in one window will not directly affect the action, or the parallelism, of the other window. Such a scheme could have two advantages. First of all, the complexity of the control for determining data dependencies, which increases as the square of the number of operations permitted in the window, is reduced by dividing the windows into two independent windows, and secondly, the degree of parallelism in the presence of control-flow dependencies is increased. Of course transfer functions do exist, and control is required to coordinate the two windows. Our implementation — which has a zero length integer/boolean window — is a compromise which takes advantage of the fact that most of the control-flow dependencies are imposed on the integer/boolean window, permitting the other window to run at maximum concurrency.

5.3. Compiling strategies

Our investigation of the treatment of user-functions is motivated by more than simply a desire to re-distribute overheads onto the slaves, since it explores how knowledge of the structure of a program, such as is inherent in its decomposition into routines, can be used to achieve increased parallelism by moving control-flow dependencies off the critical path of the master. These opportunities are lost in a conventional look-ahead processor, because no structural information is available to the controller, which consequently is only able to achieve concurrency at the grain size of the operations in the window.

We intend to explore compilation strategies which will allow us to feed additional explicit and derived control-flow information to the run-time system. This requires our low-level scheduler to be able to handle a hierarchy of concurrent operations, provisions for which have already been made. Our feeling, based on semi-automatic hierarchical decompositions on the C.mmp system (without the lowest level of concurrency),[11] is that the higher-grain concurrency which can be achieved using structural information is comparable to that which can be achieved by small-grain parallelism. If the effects are roughly multiplicative, there are possibilities of significant concurrency being achieved by this technique.

5.4. Memory use

A factor which is pertinent to the utility of programming systems on Cm*, but which is not easy to measure, is the effectiveness of their use of memory, since memory is scarce relative to processors. Also relevant, since it may have a large effect on performance, is the locality of reference to within the module and to within the cluster.

Our approach is to duplicate, in each processor, the code required for the master and slave functions and the code for the high- and low-level schedulers, and to distribute the user program, the user data area and the tables required by the schedulers across all the processors. Thus a processor may find a part of the program or a part of the work-space in its own local memory. It would be possible to reschedule processors onto subtasks as the locus of control moves from one local memory to another, though we have not yet implemented this part of the system; however, since most code memory accesses are generated inside the run-time system functions (rather than in the user program), we still achieve good locality — 80-85% of references are to local memory across a wide range of programs, compared to 85-97% achievable by careful hand-coding.[16] One reason this high figure is achieved is that the run-time system allows internal representations of values to be stored remotely from the pointers which are used by the masters (who formally possess the values). Thus a single internal representation can be stored close to a slave processor, whilst the abstract value it represents may be shared by several subtasks, and easily assigned between them by copying a pointer rather than the complete internal representation.

Our system does not yet recognize cluster boundaries, and hence makes no attempt to ameliorate inter-cluster memory accesses. Possibilities include collecting masters into "task forces" within clusters, based on the higher levels of the hierarchical decomposition of programs, and dispatching slaves preferentially onto operations with proximate operands.

[†] And we must admit that the C.mmp system, against which we are comparing, has properties which have proved convenient for our look-ahead scheme, and therefore has distributed overheads which ought to be added to those above. The cost of these overheads is difficult to assess, however.

5.5. Conclusion

The system we have described has been operational on Cm* since July 1977. Its intention is twofold — first, to provide a practical system for production programming on Cm*, an aim which has now been partly realized,[†] and second, to study the issues which are highlighted by implementations on such architectures.

[†] All the software components: low-level kernel, high- and low-level dispatcher, segment-swapper and overlayer, complete run-time system and cross-compiler have been completed and are operational; however, the user interface at present leaves much to be desired.

References

1. D.W. Anderson, F.J. Sparacio, and R.M. Tomasulo, The IBM System/360 Model 91: Machine Philosophy and Instruction-Handling, IBM Journal of Research and Development, Vol. 11, No. 1, January 1967, pp. 8-24.

2. Arvind and K.P. Gostelow, A Computer Capable of Exchanging Processing Elements for Time, Information Processing 77, B. Gilchrist (editor), North-Holland, New York, 1977, pp. 849-853.

3. H.G. Baker, Jr. and C. Hewitt, The Incremental Garbage Collection of Processes, Proceedings of the Symposium on Artificial Intelligence and Programming Languages, SigPLAN Notices, Vol. 12, No. 8, August 1977, pp. 55-59.

4. D.D. Chamberlin, The Single Assignment Approach to Parallel Processing, Proceedings AFIPS FJCC 71, pp. 263-269.

5. J.B. Dennis and D.P. Misunas, A preliminary Architecture for a Basic Data-Flow Processor, Second Annual Symposium on Computer Architecture, January 1977, IEEE, pp. 126-132.
   and
   J.B. Dennis, D.P. Misunas, and C.K. Leung, A Highly Parallel Processor Using a Data-Flow Machine Language, MIT, Computation Structures Group Memo 134, January 1977.

6. D.P. Friedman and D.S. Wise, The Impact of Applicative Programming on Multiprocessing, Proceedings of the 1976 International Conference on Parallel Processing, August 24-27, 1976, IEEE, pp. 263-272.

7. S.H. Fuller, A.K. Jones, and I. Durham (editors), Cm* Review June 1977, Computer Science Dept., Carnegie-Mellon University, June 1977.

8. P.G. Hibbard, Parallel Processing Facilities, New Directions in Algorithmic Languages, (editor) S.A. Schuman, IRIA, Rocquencourt, France, 1976, pp. 1-7.

9. P.G. Hibbard, A Sublanguage of Algol 68, SigPLAN Notices, Vol. 12, No. 5, May 1977, pp. 71-79.

10. P.G. Hibbard, P. Knueven, and B.W. Leverett, A Stackless Run-Time Implementation Scheme, Proceedings of the Fourth International Conference on the Design and Implementation of Algorithmic Languages, Courant Institute of Mathematical Sciences, New York, June 1976, pp. 176-192.

11. P.G. Hibbard, P. Knueven, and B.W. Leverett, Issues in the Efficient Implementation and Use of Multiprocessing in Algol 68, Proceedings of the Fifth International Conference on the Design and Implementation of Algorithmic Languages, IRIA, Rocquencourt, France, May 1977, pp. 202-221.

12. A.K. Jones, R.J. Chansler, Jr., I. Durham, P. Feiler, and K. Schwans, Software Management of Cm*-A Distributed Multiprocessor, Proceedings AFIPS NCC 77, pp. 657-663.

13. R.M. Keller, Look-Ahead Processors, Computing Surveys, Vol. 7, No. 4, December 1975, pp. 175-195.

14. P. Knueven, P.G. Hibbard, and B.W. Leverett, A Language System for a Multiprocessor Environment, Proceedings of the Fourth International Conference on the Design and Implementation of Algorithmic Languages, Courant Institute of Mathematical Sciences, New York, June 1976, pp. 262-274.

15. M. Marathe, Phd. Thesis, Computer Science Dept., Carnegie-Mellon University, 1977.

16. L. Raskin, Performance of a Stand Alone Cm* System, in 7.

17. E.M. Riseman and C.C. Foster, The Inhibition of Parallelism by Conditional Jumps, IEEE Trans on Computers, December 1972, pp. 1405-1411.

18. H.D. Shapiro, A Comparison of Various Methods for Detecting and Utilizing Parallelism in a Single Instruction Stream, Proceedings of the 1977 International Conference on Parallel Processing, August 23-26, 1977, IEEE, pp. 67-76.

19. R.J. Swan, A. Bechtolsheim, K. Lai, and J.K. Ousterhout, The Implementation of the Cm* Multi-Microprocessor, Proceedings AFIPS NCC 77, pp. 645-655.

20. R.J. Swan, S.H. Fuller, and D.P. Siewiorek, Cm*-A Modular, Multi-Microprocessor, Proceedings AFIPS NCC 77, pp. 637-644.

21. L.G. Tesler and H.J. Enea, A Language Design for Concurrent Processes, Proceedings AFIPS SJCC 1968, pp. 403-408.

22. G.S. Tjaden and M.J. Flynn, Detection and Parallel Execution of Independent Instructions, IEEE Trans on Computers, C-19, No. 10, October 1970, pp. 889-895.

23. J.E. Thornton, Design of a Computer System: the Control Data 6600, Scott, Foresman, and Company, 1970.

24. A. van Wijngaarden, et al., ed., Revised Report on the Algorithmic Language Algol 68, Acta Informatica 5, 1-3, 1976.

25. W.A. Wulf and C.G. Bell, C.mmp: A Multi-Mini-Processor, Proceedings AFIPS FJCC 1972, pp. 765-778.

SOME LINPACK TIMINGS ON THE CRAY-1*

by

J. J. Dongarra**
University of California
Los Alamos Scientific Laboratory
Los Alamos, New Mexico

ABSTRACT

This report compares the Los Alamos Scientific Laboratory (LASL) compilers and FORTRAN tools used in running programs on the CRAY-1 computer. A sample of linear equation routines from the LINPACK collection were tried using these compilers and tools to determine what aids give the fastest execution speed for FORTRAN codes run on the CRAY-1.

INTRODUCTION

This report gives timing data obtained from experiments performed on the CDC 7600 and CRAY-1 computers at the Los Alamos Scientific Laboratory (LASL). The timing studies were done using linear equation solvers from the LINPACK package.[1] The CDC 7600 does only scalar processing, whereas the CRAY-1 does both scalar and vector processing. Extremely high execution speeds can be achieved by utilizing the vector capabilities of the CRAY-1.[2] Algorithms for solving linear equations are amenable to a high degree of vectorization. This, together with their wide use at LASL and other Department of Energy (DOE) laboratories, motivated this study.

One of the ground rules for these experiments was that the algorithms would not be changed; no modifications were made to the structure of the algorithms. The LINPACK algorithms are designed to access matrix elements by column whenever possible. The results of other studies suggest that column orientation is beneficial for general computers.[3,4] This study finds that it is beneficial for vector computers as well.

---

*Also released as LA-7389-MS, August 1978.
**Current Address: Argonne National Laboratory, Argonne, IL 60439

Reprinted with permission from *Proceedings of the 1978 LASL Workshop on Vector and Parallel Processors*, 1978, pages 58-75. Copyright © 1978 by Los Alamos Scientific Laboratory.

All LINPACK routines used the Basic Linear Algebra Subprograms (BLAS)[5] in carrying out basic computations. Since the BLAS do most of the arithmetic work in the package, it is critical that they run efficiently. A decision to retain the BLAS in LINPACK has not been finalized at this point. If we decide the BLAS are a burden to the package, thereby making the execution time of the routines substandard, we are prepared to remove them automatically using a system designed by Boyle and Dritz called TAMPR.[6] TAMPR can remove calls to the BLAS and replace them with the corresponding inline code. This is done by describing the replacement transformations to TAMPR along with the code that is to be transformed. TAMPR detects the calls and replaces them with appropriate "optimum" inline FORTRAN code (see Appendix).

LASL currently has two FORTRAN compilers and a vectorization package available for the CRAY-1. First, there is the FORTRAN FTN cross-compiler (FTNX). This compiler is a modified Control Data Corporation (CDC) FTN compiler that is used on the CDC 7600 and generates CRAY Assembly Language (CAL) code. This CAL code can then be sent to the CRAY-1 and executed. The FTNX compiler performs some instruction scheduling and optimization of the generated CAL code. It has limitations in that it only generates scalar code.

LASL uses the Massachusetts Computer Associates' (MCA) Vectorizer[7] in conjunction with the FTNX compiler to utilize vector instructions on the CRAY-1. The vectorizer analyzes the FORTRAN source code for vectorization possibilities. If vectorization can be performed on a loop, the Vectorizer transforms the serial FORTRAN code into vector primitives, in the form of subroutine calls, which perform the same function as the serial code. When the code that has been passed through the Vectorizer is given to the FTNX compiler, the compiler replaces the calls to vector primitives with inline vector instructions.[7] This enables the user to access vector features of the CRAY-1 while keeping his source code in standard FORTRAN.

There is also a set of BLAS written in CAL code that takes advantage of the CRAY-1 vector hardware.[8] These routines have the same subroutine linkage conventions that were adopted in the FTNX compiler and therefore can be utilized by FORTRAN code that references the BLAS compiled by the FTNX compiler.

The second compiler, which runs on the CRAY-1, was developed by Cray Research, Inc. (CRI).[9] This compiler does no instruction scheduling, but does perform vectorization of the FORTRAN source code. The CRI compiler will examine FORTRAN loops for possible vectorization and, if it can, generate the appropriate CAL code to utilize vector hardware instructions. The user may also turn vectorization off, that is, the compiler generates only scalar instructions. At the present time the CRI compiler does very limited code optimization, such as common subscript elimination. Work is currently going on at CRI to include instruction scheduling and global optimization. Unfortunately, the subroutine linkage conventions of the FTNX compiler and the CRI compiler are not compatible. Therefore, the CAL BLAS used with the FTNX compiler cannot be utilized by the CRI compiler.

TIMING STUDIES

Timings were carried out on the CRAY-1 for four routines in LINPACK. The four routines deal with real general square matrices and perform the following operations: decompose a matrix into its LU factors and estimate the condition number (SGECO), decompose a matrix into its LU factors (SGEFA), solve a system given the factorized matrix (SGESL), and compute the determinate and inverse given the factorized matrix (SGEDI). The amount of work required for routines SGECO, SGEFA, and SGEDI is $O(N^3)$ and for SGESL is $O(N^2)$, where N is the order of the matrix.

Seven different implementations of these four routines were timed on the CRAY-1. Two different versions were used: one with calls to the BLAS and one with the BLAS replaced by inline code. These were compiled on both the FTNX and CRI compilers. In addition, on the FTNX compiler two versions of the BLAS code were used, one with a FORTRAN unrolled structure (see Appendix) and another with the BLAS coded in CAL. The inline version for the FTNX was also passed through MCA's Vectorizer. In the CRI compiler, runs were made with vectorization turned on and off. Table I summarizes the environments in which the codes were executed.

Figures 1 through 4 and Tables II and III summarize the results of the timings for routines SGECO, SGEFA, SGESL, and SGEDI. Timings were done on matrices of order 50 through 350 in steps of 50. The X-axis displays on a linear scale the order of the matrix timed, and the Y-axis displays on a log scale the time, T, divided by N^3 or N^2, depending on the work done by the routine.

TABLE I
CODE TIMING ENVIRONMENTS

Compiler	Graph Legend	Characteristics
FTNX	+	FORTRAN BLAS*
FTNX	∇	CAL BLAS
FTNX	□	inline code replaces calls to the BLAS
FTNX	X	inline code vectorized
CRI	Δ	FORTRAN BLAS*
CRI	O	inline code replaces calls to the BLAS, vectorization turned off
CRI	◇	inline code replaces calls to the BLAS, vectorization turned on

*FORTRAN BLAS have been unrolled.

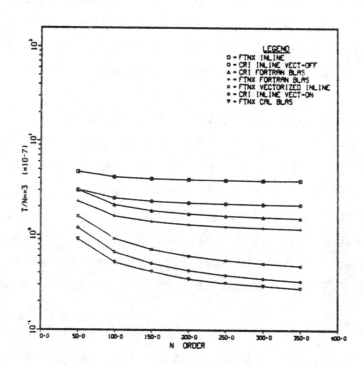

Fig. 1.   SGECO timing.

366

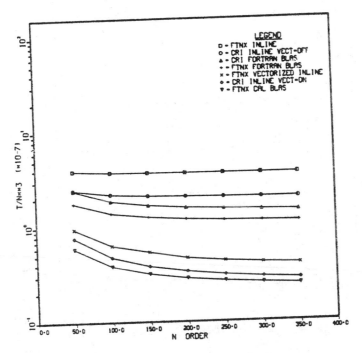

Fig. 2. SGEFA timing.

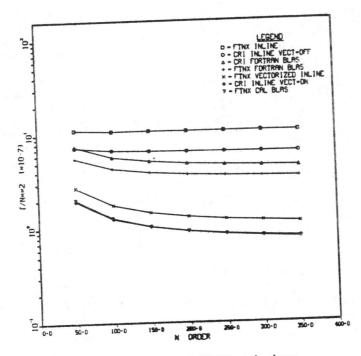

Fig. 3. SGESL timing.

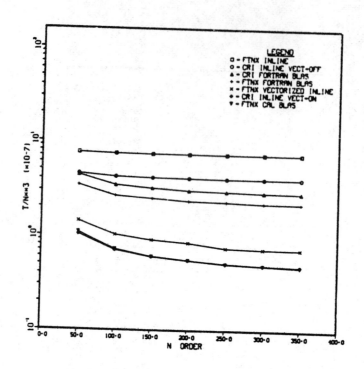

Fig. 4. SGED1 timing.

TABLE II

RATIOS OF EXECUTION TIME FOR SGEFA AT ORDER 350
RUN UNDER DIFFERENT CONDITIONS

	FTNX Inline	CRI Inline VECT=OFF	CRI FORTRAN BLAS	FTNX FORTRAN BLAS	FTNX Vectorized Inline	CRI Inline VECT=ON
CRI Inline VECT=OFF	1.2					
CRI FORTRAN BLAS	1.7	1.4				
FTNX FORTRAN BLAS	3.3	2.7	1.9			
FTNX Vectorized Inline	9.1	7.5	5.4	2.8		
CRI Inline VECT=ON	13.1	10.8	7.8	4.0	1.4	
FTNX CAL BLAS	15.1	12.4	8.9	4.6	1.7	1.2

(Row entries are so many times faster than column entries.)

TABLE III

MILLIONS OF FLOATING POINT OPERATIONS PER SECOND (MFLOPS) ACHIEVED IN DIFFERENT ENVIRONMENTS

	MFLOPS			
	SGECO	SGEFA	SGESL	SGEDI
FTNX Inline	1.8	1.8	1.9	2.0
CRI Inline VECT=OFF	3.2	3.3	3.1	3.7
CRI FORTRAN BLAS	4.4	4.5	4.5	5.2
FTNX FORTRAN BLAS	5.7	6.0	5.8	6.8
FTNX Vectorized Inline	14.0	16.6	17.7	20.6
CRI Inline VECT=ON	20.4	23.8	25.4	31.1
FTNX CAL BLAS	24.2	27.4	26.0	31.7

As can be seen from Figs. 1-4 and Tables II and III, there is a factor of 15 between the slowest and fastest execution speeds when run under different conditions. This wide range in execution rates is due to execution at scalar speeds compared to vector speeds. It should be pointed out that there is a version of Gaussian elimination, coded entirely in CAL, that executes around the 120-MFLOP range.[10] This version uses an algorithm designed to perform well with the CRAY-1's architecture.

We would expect the FTNX inline coding to be faster than the CRI inline VECT=OFF. They both deal exclusively with scalar code, but the FTNX compiler performs scheduling and optimization while the CRI compiler does not. The timings indicate the CRI inline VECT=OFF is faster by a factor of 1.2 than the FTNX inline. After studying the generated assembly language code for both compilers it became apparent why the timings were contrary to our expectations. The FTNX compiler does not keep the loop index in a register. Consequently, it must load and store the loop index each time the loop iterates. The CRI compiler, on the other hand, maintains the loop index in a register during the loop execution. The inline code in this comparison is typified by one-operation loops, which are executed $O(N^2)$ times. The FTNX compiler for the inline case is spending a large amount of time fetching and storing the loop index; this loop overhead can take as long to be performed as the operation itself. Because the CRI compiler keeps the index in a register, it can fetch and store in two cycles, thus giving it the advantage.

In the case where FORTRAN BLAS are used, the FTNX compiler is faster than the CRI compiler. The FORTRAN BLAS used are an unrolled version (see Appendix). The unrolled BLAS are perfect for concurrent operations and segmentation, since many results are defined per pass through the loop. Because the FTNX compiler does optimization and instruction scheduling and the CRI compiler does not, we would expect the FTNX execution to be faster even though the FTNX compiler forces a fetch and store of the loop index from memory each time through the loop. The loop-indexing operation in the unrolled case is a small part of the loop execution time. There is close to a factor of 2 in execution speeds between the FTNX and CRI compilers using the FORTRAN BLAS.

For the case of the vectorized FTNX inline compared with the inline CRI VECT=ON, the CRI code executes faster by a factor of 1.5. It appears that the vectorized FTNX inline code pays a substantial overhead for using FORTRAN code to manage vector segments (that is, vectors on the CRAY-1 must be partitioned into segments of length $\leq$ 64; see Appendix). The CRI compiler, of course, has the same structure but at an assembly level. The vectorized FTNX code appears to have another defect: because of the way calls to vector primitives are set up under FTNX, chain slots may be missed during execution. This is not the case in the CRI compiler. (The people at LASL have corrected the FTNX compiler, and it now catches chain slots.)

The CAL BLAS under the FTNX compiler provide the fastest execution speed. These BLAS are painstakingly and cleverly coded implementations. The CRI compiler VECT=ON comes very close to the execution speed of the CAL BLAS.

Timing of the routines was also carried out on a CDC 7600 using three different codings. The inline versions were compiled and run on the CDC 7600 as well as the versions involving calls to the BLAS. Two different implementations of the BLAS were used on the CDC 7600; one was the FORTRAN BLAS unrolled and the other was a COMPASS (CDC 7600 Assembly Language) version of the BLAS, which were tuned to run optimally on the CDC 7600. Table IV shows the ratios of execution time at order 100 for SGEFA, which was run in seven different environments on the CRAY-1 and three different environments on the CDC 7600.

The timings indicate that at order 100 the CDC 7600 FTN-compiled inline run is faster than the CRAY-1 FTNX-compiled inline run. Again, this is because the FTNX compiler stores and fetches the loop index every pass through the loop, while the CDC 7600 FTN compiler keeps the loop indexes in a register during loop execution.

TABLE IV

COMPARISON OF RELATIVE EXECUTION TIMES FOR SGEFA AT ORDER 100
ON THE CDC 7600 AND CRAY-1 USING THE FTN, FTNX, AND CRI COMPILERS

	FTNX Inline	7600 Inline	CRI Inline VECT=OFF	CDC 7600 FORTRAN BLAS	CRI FORTRAN BLAS	CDC 7600 COMPASS BLAS	FTNX FORTRAN BLAS	CRI Inline VECT=ON	FTNX Vectorized Inline
CDC 7600 Inline	1.4								
CRI Inline VECT=OFF	1.7	1.3							
CDC 7600 FORTRAN BLAS	1.9	1.4	1.1						
CRI FORTRAN BLAS	2.0	1.5	1.2	1.1					
CDC 7600 Compass BLAS	2.6	1.9	1.5	1.4	1.3				
FTNX FORTRAN BLAS	2.7	2.0	1.6	1.5	1.3	1.0			
CRI Inline VECT=ON	5.9	4.2	3.3	3.0	2.8	2.2	2.1		
FTNX Vectorized Inline	5.9	4.3	3.5	3.2	2.9	2.3	2.2	1.0	
FTNX CAL BLAS	7.2	5.3	4.3	3.9	3.6	2.8	2.7	1.3	1.2

(Row entries are so many times faster than column entries.)

The CRAY-1 FTNX run with FORTRAN BLAS was 1.5 times faster than the
CDC 7600 FTN run with FORTRAN BLAS. This is more typical of the results expected in comparing the CDC 7600 to the CRAY-1 run on scalar code.

The CDC 7600 COMPASS BLAS run about the same speed as the CRAY-1 FTNX
FORTRAN BLAS run. The COMPASS BLAS on the CDC 7600 have been carefully coded
so the loops are unrolled, and the instructions are scheduled so full overlap of
arithmetic operations can occur. The results here are not surprising; the
COMPASS BLAS can be thought of as running at "vector" speeds on the CDC 7600.

SUMMARY

This report describes what can be expected from the CRAY-1 for solving
linear systems in a FORTRAN environment at the present time. There are things
that can be done to the compilers to make the code generated more efficient.
For example, in the FTNX compiler the loop index should be held in a register,
and in the CRI compiler the performance could be improved by local and global
optimization and instruction scheduling. This report is not intended to
describe how the hardware performs. Readers who would like that information
are referred to a report by T. Keller.[11] This report shows that the way in
which an algorithm is implemented on the CRAY-1 affects the way it will perform.

After the timings were completed, an improvement was realized in the CAL
BLA SAXPY that made the four codes that used the CAL BLAS run between 15-20%
faster.

ACKNOWLEDGMENTS

I would like to thank Bill Buzbee, Thomas Jordan, and all the people at LASL who made my stay interesting and educational.

LINPACK ANECDOTE #1

One of the interesting things uncovered by the timing was a hardware problem in the LASL CRAY-1. During the timing runs, a check was made of the answers produced by the various routines. It was discovered that codes run in two different implementations produced the wrong answers. After some investigation by T. Jordan, the CRAY-1 engineers, and me, the problem was traced to a hardware board in the arithmetic unit that adjusts the exponents of operands before vector addition. The exponent adjustment was not being performed correctly in certain instances when operating in vector mode. Incorrect results were produced when the exponent to be adjusted had a certain bit pattern, making the errors in the answers appear somewhat mysterious. When it was finally tracked down and the defective board replaced, the correct results were obtained. The interesting thing is that the CRAY-1 had been in operation at LASL for a little over two months and no one seemed to notice any problems. The machine passed its diagnostic tests every morning and many hours of production work had been completed before the problem was uncovered.

REFERENCES

1. J. J. Dongarra, J. R. Bunch, C. B. Moler, and G. W. Stewart, "LINPACK Working Note #9, Preliminary LINPACK User's Guide," Argonne National Laboratory report ANL TM-313 (August 1977).

2. CRAY-1 Computer System Reference Manual, 2240004, Cray Research, Inc., (February 1977).

3. C. B. Moler, "Matrix Computation with Fortran and Paging," Comm. ACM 15 (April 1972), pp. 268-270.

4. J. J. Dongarra, "LINPACK Working Note #3, Fortran BLAS Timing," Argonne National Laboratory (December 1976).

5. C. L. Lawson, R. J. Hanson, D. R. Kincaid, and F. T. Krogh, "Basic Linear Algebra Subprogram for Use with Fortran," Submitted to Trans. Math. Software, July 1976.

6. J. M. Boyle and M. Matz, "Automating Multiple Program Relations," Proc. MRI Symposium XXIV; Computer Software Engineering, (Poly. Tech. Press, New York, 1977), pp. 421-457.

7. "LASL Guide to the CRAY-1 Computer, PIM-7, Los Alamos Scientific Laboratory report LA-5525-M, Vol. 7, (November 1977).

8. T. L. Jordan, private communications, Los Alamos Scientific Laboratory, (November 1977).

9. CRAY-1 Fortran Reference Manual, 2240009, Cray Research, Inc., (November 1977).

10. K. Fong and T. L. Jordan, "Some Linear Algebraic Algorithms and their Performance on CRAY-1," Los Alamos Scientific Laboratory report LA-6774 (June 1977).

11. T. W. Keller, "CRAY-1 Evaluation," Los Alamos Scientific Laboratory report LA-6456-MS (December 1976).

APPENDIX

SUBROUTINE SGEFA1 - EXAMPLE WITH CALLS TO THE BLAS

```
      SUBROUTINE SGEFA1(A,LDA,N,IPVT,INFO)
      INTEGER LDA,N,IPVT(1),INFO
      REAL A(LDA,1)
C
C     SGEFA1 FACTORS A REAL MATRIX BY GAUSSIAN ELIMINATION.
C
C     SGEFA1 IS USUALLY CALLED BY SGECO, BUT IT CAN BE CALLED
C     DIRECTLY WITH A SAVING IN TIME IF  RCOND  IS NOT NEEDED.
C     (TIME FOR SGECO) = (1 + 9/N)*(TIME FOR SGEFA1) .
C
C     ON ENTRY
C
C        A       REAL(LDA, N)
C                THE MATRIX TO BE FACTORED.
C
C        LDA     INTEGER
C                THE LEADING DIMENSION OF THE ARRAY  A .
C
C        N       INTEGER
C                THE ORDER OF THE MATRIX  A .
C
C     ON RETURN
C
C        A       AN UPPER TRIANGULAR MATRIX AND THE MULTIPLIERS
C                WHICH WERE USED TO OBTAIN IT.
C                THE FACTORIZATION CAN BE WRITTEN  A = L*U  WHERE
C                L  IS A PRODUCT OF PERMUTATION AND UNIT LOWER
C                TRIANGULAR MATRICES AND  U  IS UPPER TRIANGULAR.
C
C        IPVT    INTEGER(N)
C                AN INTEGER VECTOR OF PIVOT INDICES.
```

373

```
C        INFO     INTEGER
C                 = 0  NORMAL VALUE.
C                 = K  IF  U(K,K) .EQ. 0.0 .  THIS IS NOT AN ERROR
C                      CONDITION FOR THIS SUBROUTINE, BUT IT DOES
C                      INDICATE THAT SGESL1 OR SGEDI1 WILL DIVIDE BY ZERO
C
C                      IF CALLED.  USE  RCOND  IN SGECO FOR A RELIABLE
C                      INDICATION OF SINGULARITY.
C
C     LINPACK. THIS VERSION DATED 07/14/77 .
C     CLEVE MOLER, UNIVERSITY OF NEW MEXICO, ARGONNE NATIONAL LABS.
C
C     SUBROUTINES AND FUNCTIONS
C
C     BLAS SAXPY,SSCAL,ISAMAX
C
C     INTERNAL VARIABLES
C
      REAL T
      INTEGER ISAMAX,J,K,KP1,L,NM1
C
C
C     GAUSSIAN ELIMINATION WITH PARTIAL PIVOTING
C
      INFO = 0
      NM1 = N - 1
      IF (NM1 .LT. 1) GO TO 70
      DO 60 K = 1, NM1
         KP1 = K + 1
C
C        FIND L = PIVOT INDEX
C
         L = ISAMAX(N-K+1,A(K,K),1) + K - 1
         IPVT(K) = L
C
C        ZERO PIVOT IMPLIES THIS COLUMN ALREADY TRIANGULARIZED
C
         IF (A(L,K) .EQ. 0.0E0) GO TO 40
C
C           INTERCHANGE IF NECESSARY
C
            IF (L .EQ. K) GO TO 10
               T = A(L,K)
               A(L,K) = A(K,K)
               A(K,K) = T
   10       CONTINUE
C
C           COMPUTE MULTIPLIERS
C
            T = -1.0E0/A(K,K)
            CALL SSCAL(N-K,T,A(K+1,K),1)
C
C           ROW ELIMINATION WITH COLUMN INDEXING
C
            DO 30 J = KP1, N
               T = A(L,J)
               IF (L .EQ. K) GO TO 20
                  A(L,J) = A(K,J)
                  A(K,J) = T
   20          CONTINUE
               CALL SAXPY(N-K,T,A(K+1,K),1,A(K+1,J),1)
   30       CONTINUE
         GO TO 50
   40    CONTINUE
            INFO = K
```

```
   50    CONTINUE
   60 CONTINUE
   70 CONTINUE
      IPVT(N) = N
      IF (A(N,N) .EQ. 0.0E0) INFO = N
      RETURN
      END


    SUBROUTINE SGEFA2 - EXAMPLE WITH BLAS REPLACED WITH INLINE CODE
      SUBROUTINE SGEFA2(A,LDA,N,IPVT,INFO)
      INTEGER LDA,N,IPVT(1),INFO
      REAL A(LDA,1)
C
C     SGEFA2 FACTORS A REAL MATRIX BY GAUSSIAN ELIMINATION.
C
C     SGEFA2 IS USUALLY CALLED BY SGECO, BUT IT CAN BE CALLED
C     DIRECTLY WITH A SAVING IN TIME IF  RCOND  IS NOT NEEDED.
C     (TIME FOR SGECO) = (1 + 9/N)*(TIME FOR SGEFA2) .
C
C     ON ENTRY
C
C        A       REAL(LDA, N)
C                THE MATRIX TO BE FACTORED.
C
C        LDA     INTEGER
C                THE LEADING DIMENSION OF THE ARRAY  A .
C
C        N       INTEGER
C                THE ORDER OF THE MATRIX  A .
C
C     ON RETURN
C
C        A       AN UPPER TRIANGULAR MATRIX AND THE MULTIPLIERS
C                WHICH WERE USED TO OBTAIN IT.
C                THE FACTORIZATION CAN BE WRITTEN  A = L*U  WHERE
C                L  IS A PRODUCT OF PERMUTATION AND UNIT LOWER
C                TRIANGULAR MATRICES AND  U  IS UPPER TRIANGULAR.
C
C        IPVT    INTEGER(N)
C                AN INTEGER VECTOR OF PIVOT INDICES.
C
C        INFO    INTEGER
C                = 0  NORMAL VALUE.
C                = K  IF  U(K,K) .EQ. 0.0 .  THIS IS NOT AN ERROR
C                     CONDITION FOR THIS SUBROUTINE, BUT IT DOES
C                     INDICATE THAT SGESL2 OR SGEDI2 WILL DIVIDE BY ZERO
C
C                     IF CALLED.  USE  RCOND  IN SGECO FOR A RELIABLE
C                     INDICATION OF SINGULARITY.
C
C     LINPACK. THIS VERSION DATED 07/14/77 .
C     CLEVE MOLER, UNIVERSITY OF NEW MEXICO, ARGONNE NATIONAL LABS.
C
C     SUBROUTINES AND FUNCTIONS
C
C     BLAS SAXPY,SSCAL,ISAMAX
C
C     INTERNAL VARIABLES
C
      REAL T
```

```
      INTEGER ISAMAX,J,K,KP1,L,NM1
C
C
C     GAUSSIAN ELIMINATION WITH PARTIAL PIVOTING
C
      INFO = 0
      NM1 = N - 1
      IF (NM1 .LT. 1) GO TO 130
      DO 120 K = 1, NM1
         KP1 = K + 1
         ISAMAX = K
         IF (N .LT. K) GO TO 20
         DO 10 IAMAX = K, N
            IF (ABS(A(IAMAX,K)) .GT. ABS(A(ISAMAX,K))) ISAMAX = IAMAX
   10    CONTINUE
   20    CONTINUE
C
C
C        FIND L = PIVOT INDEX
C
         L = ISAMAX
         IPVT(K) = L
C
C
C        ZERO PIVOT IMPLIES THIS COLUMN ALREADY TRIANGULARIZED
C
         IF (A(L,K) .EQ. 0.0E0) GO TO 100
C
C
C           INTERCHANGE IF NECESSARY
C
            IF (L .EQ. K) GO TO 30
               T = A(L,K)
               A(L,K) = A(K,K)
               A(K,K) = T
   30       CONTINUE
C
C
C           COMPUTE MULTIPLIERS
C
            T = -1.0E0/A(K,K)
            KSCAL = K + 1
            IF (N .LT. KSCAL) GO TO 50
            DO 40 ISCAL = KSCAL, N
               A(ISCAL,K) = T*A(ISCAL,K)
   40       CONTINUE
   50       CONTINUE
C
C
C           ROW ELIMINATION WITH COLUMN INDEXING
C
            DO 90 J = KP1, N
               T = A(L,J)
               IF (L .EQ. K) GO TO 60
                  A(L,J) = A(K,J)
                  A(K,J) = T
   60          CONTINUE
               KAXPY = K + 1
               IF (N .LT. KAXPY) GO TO 80
               DO 70 IAXPY = KAXPY, N
                  A(IAXPY,J) = A(IAXPY,J) + T*A(IAXPY,K)
   70          CONTINUE
   80          CONTINUE
   90       CONTINUE
         GO TO 110
  100    CONTINUE
            INFO = K
  110    CONTINUE
```

```
    120 CONTINUE
    130 CONTINUE
        IPVT(N) = N
        IF (A(N,N) .EQ. 0.0E0) INFO = N
        RETURN
        END
```

SUBROUTINE SGEFA3 - EXAMPLE WITH INLINE CODE THAT HAS BEEN PASSED THROUGH THE VECTORIZER

```
        SUBROUTINE SGEFA3(A,LDA,N,IPVT,INFO)
        INTEGER LDA,N,IPVT(1),INFO,ISAMAX,J,K,KP1,L,NM1
        REAL A(LDA,1),T
        INTEGER NITER,OUTRXS,OUTRMX,OUTRWD,ISTRIP,OUTRNX
C
C
C       SGEFA3 FACTORS A REAL MATRIX BY GAUSSIAN ELIMINATION.
C
C       SGEFA3 IS USUALLY CALLED BY SGECO, BUT IT CAN BE CALLED
C       DIRECTLY WITH A SAVING IN TIME IF  RCOND  IS NOT NEEDED.
C       (TIME FOR SGECO) = (1 + 9/N)*(TIME FOR SGEFA3) .
C
C       ON ENTRY
C
C          A        REAL(LDA, N)
C                   THE MATRIX TO BE FACTORED.
C
C          LDA      INTEGER
C                   THE LEADING DIMENSION OF THE ARRAY  A .
C
C          N        INTEGER
C                   THE ORDER OF THE MATRIX  A .
C
C       ON RETURN
C
C          A        AN UPPER TRIANGULAR MATRIX AND THE MULTIPLIERS
C                   WHICH WERE USED TO OBTAIN IT.
C                   THE FACTORIZATION CAN BE WRITTEN  A = L*U  WHERE
C                   L  IS A PRODUCT OF PERMUTATION AND UNIT LOWER
C                   TRIANGULAR MATRICES AND  U  IS UPPER TRIANGULAR.
C
C          IPVT     INTEGER(N)
C                   AN INTEGER VECTOR OF PIVOT INDICES.
C
C          INFO     INTEGER
C                   = 0  NORMAL VALUE.
C                   = K  IF  U(K,K) .EQ. 0.0 .  THIS IS NOT AN ERROR
C                        CONDITION FOR THIS SUBROUTINE, BUT IT DOES
C                        INDICATE THAT SGESL3 OR SGEDI3 WILL DIVIDE BY ZERO
C
C                        IF CALLED.  USE  RCOND  IN SGECO FOR A RELIABLE
C                        INDICATION OF SINGULARITY.
C
C       LINPACK. THIS VERSION DATED 07/14/77 .
C       CLEVE MOLER, UNIVERSITY OF NEW MEXICO, ARGONNE NATIONAL LABS.
C
C       SUBROUTINES AND FUNCTIONS
C
C       BLAS SAXPY,SSCAL,ISAMAX
C
C       INTERNAL VARIABLES
C
C
```

```
C
C
C      GAUSSIAN ELIMINATION WITH PARTIAL PIVOTING
C
       INFO=0
       NM1=N-1
       IF(NM1.LT.1) GO TO 130
       DO 120 K=1,NM1
       KP1=K+1
       ISAMAX=K
       IF(N.LT.K) GO TO 20
       DO 10 IAMAX=K,N
       IF(ABS(A(IAMAX,K)).GT.ABS(A(ISAMAX,K))) ISAMAX=IAMAX
       CONTINUE
    10 CONTINUE
    20 CONTINUE
C
C          FIND L = PIVOT INDEX
C
       L=ISAMAX
       IPVT(K)=L
C
C       ZERO PIVOT IMPLIES THIS COLUMN ALREADY TRIANGULARIZED
C
       IF(A(L,K).EQ.0.0) GO TO 100
C
C             INTERCHANGE IF NECESSARY
C
       IF(L.EQ.K) GO TO 30
       T=A(L,K)
       A(L,K)=A(K,K)
       A(K,K)=T
    30 CONTINUE
C
C             COMPUTE MULTIPLIERS
C
       T=-1.0/A(K,K)
       KSCAL=K+1
       IF(N.LT.KSCAL) GO TO 50
       NITER=N+1-KSCAL
       CALL LOPCXXX(NITER,OUTRXS,OUTRMX)
       CALL SETLX(OUTRXS)
       OUTRWD=OUTRXS
       ISTRIP=KSCAL
       DO 90000 OUTRNX=1,OUTRMX
       CALL ILDVX0O(A(ISTRIP,K))
       CALL SRPVX01(T)
       CALL ISTV10X(0,0,A(ISTRIP,K))
       ISTRIP=OUTRWD+ISTRIP
       OUTRWD=64
       CALL SETLX(64)
90000 CONTINUE
    40 CONTINUE
    50 CONTINUE
C
C             ROW ELIMINATION WITH COLUMN INDEXING
C
       DO 90 J=KP1,N
       T=A(L,J)
       IF(L.EQ.K) GO TO 60
       A(L,J)=A(K,J)
       A(K,J)=T
    60 CONTINUE
```

```
      KAXPY=K+1
      IF(N.LT.KAXPY) GO TO 80
      NITER=N+1-KAXPY
      CALL LOPCXXX(NITER,OUTRXS,OUTRMX)
      CALL SETLX(OUTRXS)
      OUTRWD=OUTRXS
      ISTRIP=KAXPY
      DO 90001 OUTRNX=1,OUTRMX
      CALL ILDVX00(A(ISTRIP,K))
      CALL SRPVX01(T)
      CALL ILDVX02(A(ISTRIP,J))
      CALL VRAV213
      CALL ISTV30X(0,0,A(ISTRIP,J))
      ISTRIP=OUTRWD+ISTRIP
      OUTRWD=64
      CALL SETLX(64)
90001 CONTINUE
   70 CONTINUE
   80 CONTINUE
   90 CONTINUE
      GO TO 110
  100 CONTINUE
      INFO=K
  110 CONTINUE
  120 CONTINUE
  130 CONTINUE
      IPVT(N)=N
      IF(A(N,N).EQ.0.0) INFO=N
      RETURN
      END
```

SUBROUTINE SAXPY - EXAMPLE OF A BLA WITH UNROLLED LOOP

```
      SUBROUTINE SAXPY(N,SA,SX,INCX,SY,INCY)
C
C     CONSTANT TIMES A VECTOR PLUS A VECTOR.
C     USES UNROLLED LOOP FOR INCREMENTS EQUAL TO ONE.
C     JACK DONGARRA, LINPACK, 6/17/77.
C
      REAL SX(1),SY(1),SA
      INTEGER I,INCX,INCY,IX,IY,M,MP1,N
C
      IF(N.LE.0)RETURN
      IF (SA .EQ. 0.0) RETURN
      IF(INCX.EQ.1.AND.INCY.EQ.1)GOTO 20
C
C        CODE FOR UNEQUAL INCREMENTS OR EQUAL INCREMENTS
C          NOT EQUAL TO 1
C
      IX = 1
      IY = 1
      IF(INCX.LT.0)IX = (-N+1)*INCX + 1
      IF(INCY.LT.0)IY = (-N+1)*INCY + 1
      DO 10 I = 1,N
        SY(IY) = SY(IY) + SA*SX(IX)
        IX = IX + INCX
        IY = IY + INCY
   10 CONTINUE
      RETURN
```

```
C
C          CODE FOR BOTH INCREMENTS EQUAL TO 1
C
C          CLEAN-UP LOOP
C
   20 M = MOD(N,4)
      IF( M .EQ. 0 ) GO TO 40
      DO 30 I = 1,M
        SY(I) = SY(I) + SA*SX(I)
   30 CONTINUE
      IF( N .LT. 4 ) RETURN
   40 MP1 = M + 1
      DO 50 I = MP1,N,4
        SY(I) = SY(I) + SA*SX(I)
        SY(I + 1) = SY(I + 1) + SA*SX(I + 1)
        SY(I + 2) = SY(I + 2) + SA*SX(I + 2)
        SY(I + 3) = SY(I + 3) + SA*SX(I + 3)
   50 CONTINUE
      RETURN
      END
```

9. Operating Systems for Parallel Processors

Operating systems are, by their nature, parallel programs. Even in uniprocessors they control asynchronous parallel I/O activity. In this chapter, however, our attention is limited to an investigation of how parallel processors, the types of processors described in Chapters 2 through 6, influence operating system design and structure.

Operating systems for parallel processors can be roughly divided into three categories: operating systems for stand-alone single-instruction-stream parallel processors, operating systems for add-on single-instruction-stream parallel processors, and operating systems for stand-alone multi-instruction-stream processors (multiprocessors). In this chapter, there is one paper on each of these categories. The paper by Baskett, Howard, and Montague describes an operating system for the CRAY-1, a stand-alone parallel processor. The CRAY-1 does not have all of the architectural components that are useful for constructing robust operating systems. However, it does have the raw speed to move data around. This paper shows how this data movement facility is used to support a message-based operating system. We should emphasize that high-speed processors are often used in a production environment, an environment in which advanced software quality concepts, such as robustness, are sacrificed in favor of speed. The second paper, by Davis, discusses the interface that must be constructed between a host processor and an add-on parallel processor. In this example, there are actually two hosts involved for the STARAN array processor. A PDP-11 acts as control processor for the array processor. Its operating system is compatible with the standard DEC PDP-11 disk operating system, and the PDP-11 STARAN subsystem is then added on to a host time-sharing system, MULTICS. The third paper by Ousterhout *et al.* describes a distributed operating system for a multiprocessor. The design of distributed operating systems is a topic that is still in its infancy and deserves careful study in the future. This particular distributed operating system is noteworthy in our context, because it emphasizes performance in the closely-coupled environment which typifies multiprocessors as opposed to a loosely-coupled distributed processor environment. The reader may find other references to distributed and parallel operating systems in the *Proceedings of the Symposium on Operating Systems Principles* sponsored by ACM SIGOPS.

Task Communication in DEMOS[*]

Forest Baskett
John H. Howard
and
John T. Montague

Los Alamos Scientific Laboratory
Los Alamos, New Mexico 87545

ABSTRACT

This paper describes the fundamentals and some of the details of task communication in DEMOS, the operating system for the CRAY-1 computer being developed at the Los Alamos Scientific Laboratory. The communication mechanism is a message system with several novel features. Messages are sent from one task to another over links. Links are the primary protected objects in the system; they provide both message paths and optional data sharing between tasks. They can be used to represent other objects with capability-like access controls. Links point to the tasks that created them. A task that creates a link determines its contents and possibly restricts its use. A link may be passed from one task to another along with a message sent over some other link subject to the restrictions imposed by the creator of the link being passed. The link based message and data sharing system is an attractive alternative to the semaphore or monitor type of shared variable based operating system on machines with only very simple memory protection mechanisms or on machines connected together in a network.

1. Introduction

This paper describes the fundamentals and some of the details of task communication in DEMOS, the operating system for the CRAY-1 computer being developed at the Los Alamos Scientific Laboratory. The communication mechanism is a message system with several novel features. In this section we discuss the purpose of task communication and why a message system is an appropriate mechanism on the CRAY-1. In later sections we discuss the features of the message system.

A task consists of a program and its associated state information, including register contents, a memory area, and a link table. A task can be manipulated in certain ways; for example, it may be suspended, swapped out, swapped in, or resumed. We have chosen the term task instead of the term process because it seems less loaded with unrelated or contrary meanings. A task is what might be called a job or a program in simple cases. In less simple cases a job or a program will be a (time varying) collection of related tasks.

The first function of the task communication mechanism is to implement system calls. We think of the system as a collection of permanent tasks with which user tasks communicate. The system calls, i.e., the information that is communicated, we call messages. The mechanism of task communication provides an appropriate link or path between a user task and a particular system task that is to act on a given system call. For example, a user task will typically need links to the file system tasks if the user task is to perform I/O. Such standard links ordinarily will be provided to user tasks in an automatic and transparent way.

[*] Work performed under the auspices of the USERDA.

Reprinted with permission from *Proceedings of the Sixth Symposium on Operating Systems Principles*, 1977, pages 23-31. Copyright © 1977 by the Association for Computing Machinery, Inc.

The next function of the task communication mechanism is to provide a way for arbitrary and unrelated tasks to communicate with mutual consent. Since communication is via links, we must have a way of exchanging links between tasks. If tasks can exchange links dynamically, then we can have a flexible intercommunication facility. We have defined a standard way of passing links along with messges over existing links. One of the standard links that a task will usually receive when it is created is a link to a Switchboard task that can arrange to get two or more cooperating tasks together.

The last function of the task communication mechanism is to provide a method by which one task can encapsulate another task or group of tasks. An easy and transparent encapsulation facility is desirable for debugging, performance monitoring, and simulation of other operating system environments.

We classify operating system communication mechanisms in two basic types: shared variables and messages. The shared variables approach is typified by semaphores [Dijkstra 68] or monitors [Hoare 74]. Brinch Hansen [73] developed the best-known pure message system. Capability systems [Fabry 74] attempt to control memory sharing but do not imply either of these two types of communication mechanisms. The communication mechanism in DEMOS is mainly a message system.

The CRAY-1 has only one pair of base and limit memory protection registers for tasks; it does not have hardware segmentation or paging. Thus tasks cannot be physically segmented in memory. The message approach seems best if the hardware memory protection mechanism is to be used to isolate any given part of the operating system from other parts [Lampson 76]. Different modules of the operating system can be constructed as separate tasks that communicate with messages. Since each task is isolated by the base and limit hardware registers, tasks are protected from each other. This type of organization also naturally inherits the advantages obtained from minimizing global variables and using value type parameters and results. Furthermore, a message orientation is compatible with more types of distributed processing architectures than a shared variable orientation.

On the other hand, we do not see messages as sufficient for all forms of intertask communication just as value type parameters and results would not be sufficient in a programming language without global variables. We have provided a method of sharing data areas via the same links that are used to route messages. A link with such an associated data area is then like a pointer or reference parameter in a programming language. This data sharing can be used for the intertask communication needs for which messages are inappropriate or inadequate.

With this organization the only part of the operating system that needs hardware access to the memory of more than one task at a time is the kernel, that part of the system which is used to move both messages and data from one task to another. The two types of communication are unified in the link concept. We consider this to be a novel arrangement and we will now show how the two fit together in a harmonious way and give examples of link usage that illustrate the utility of the arrangement.

2. Links

A link permits a task to send messages to another task and possibly to read or write part of the memory of the task to which the message would be sent. For messages, it is a one-way (simplex) communication path. If two tasks wish to send messages to each other in full duplex communication, each must have a link to the other. A link is created by the task to which it points and then passed to the potential sender task.

Links are associated with but maintained outside of the address space of their sender tasks. They may be manipulated only by use of link ID's, which are indexes into a task's Link Table. Figure 1 illustrates this arrangement. Kernel calls which operate on links take link ID's as parameters. All operations on links are performed by the kernel of the operating system; requests to the kernel are made via the CRAY-1 supervisor call instruction.

A newly created task is given an initial set of links by its parent. These links define the environment in which the new task runs. In the case of tasks created by the job initiator the environment consists of standard links to system tasks such as the file system, the task manager, and the Switchboard.

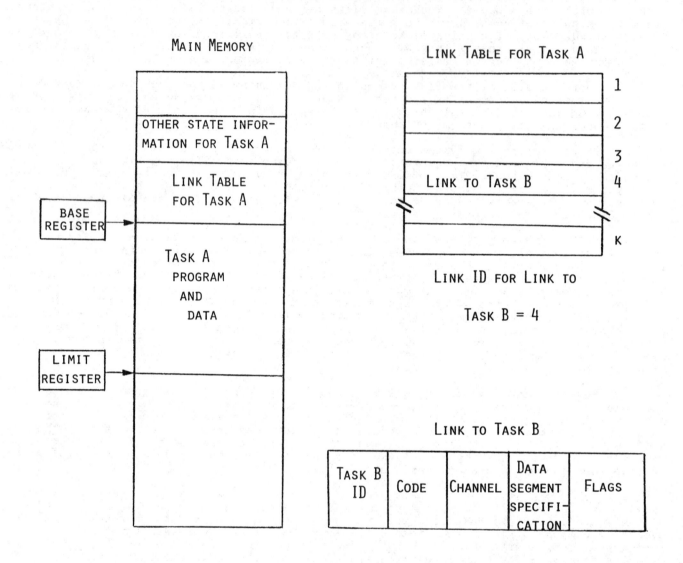

FIGURE 1

BASIC TASK AND LINK LAYOUT

A link may contain permission to move data to or from a specified area in the address space of the task which created the link. For example, when a task issues a Read request for a file, it sends a message to the file system containing the request and a link which permits the file system to move the requested data into the appropriate place in the requestor's address space. Figure 2 illustrates this example. This mechanism allows messages to be limited in size (since they are buffered by the kernel, this is desirable) while allowing the transmission of large blocks of data from one task to another efficiently in the absence of hardware supported memory sharing.

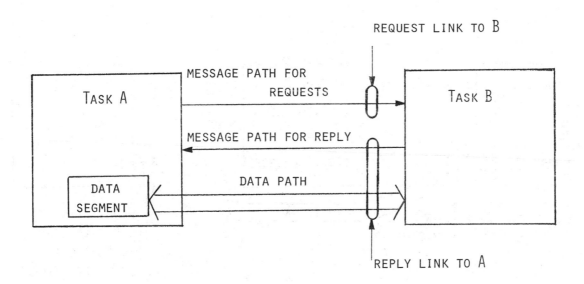

FIGURE 2

NORMAL MESSAGE & DATA SEGMENT LINK

A task may specify several attributes of each link it creates in order to identify incoming messages and to protect against unexpected or unauthorized messages. Messages are identified by means of a code which is simply a name specified by the task when it creates the link. The code from the link on which a message was sent is passed to a receiving task along with each message [Morris 73]. Permission flags in the link specify whether the task which holds the link may duplicate it, pass it to other tasks, or use it more than once.

The set of links held by a task defines its environment. A task may send messages using any link it holds, and in some cases can move data to or from the memory area of other tasks. Passing links between tasks allows programs to be divided into multiple tasks in a convenient manner which is transparent to the tasks which might receive messages from such programs. A link may be duplicated (with certain restrictions) so that a link may be passed to another task without loss of the original communication path. A message is sent to the task which created a link each time the link is duplicated or destroyed, so that an accurate count of outstanding links can be kept by the link creator. A variant of link passing allows duplicating the data area pointer of an existing link in a newly created link. This allows one task to monitor the messages of a subtask without having to move large amounts of data through intermediate buffers; the data connection but not the message connection bypasses the monitoring task. Figure 3 illustrates such a monitoring task.

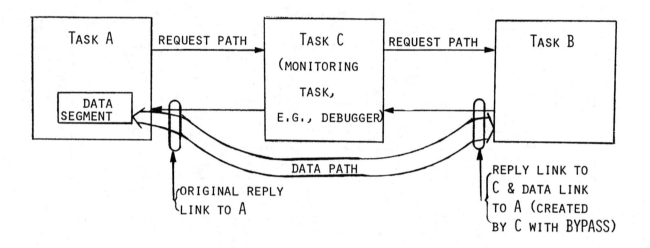

FIGURE 3

USE OF BYPASS LINKS

3. Object Descriptions

This section provides more detailed descriptions of tasks, links, messages, and channels, the primary objects defined by the DEMOS communication mechanism.

3.1. Tasks

A task consists of a program and its associated state information, including register contents, a memory area, and a link table. It has a parent task which created it, and is usually allowed to create child tasks. Task creation and termination are the responsibility of the Task Manager, discussed later. A task may be suspended, inspected, modified, and restarted by its parent. When a task terminates, it is suspended and its parent is notified if the parent has asked to be notified. Tasks which are not suspended and are not waiting for messages are given the CPU periodically.

3.2. Links

A link appearing in the link table of a task gives that task permission to send selected messages to another task. The recipient task originally created the link and specified its contents, namely, the type of operations that can be performed on the link, a code for use by the recipient, a channel, the type of links that can be passed over the link, and the address and size of a portion of the recipient's memory for direct data transfers. Links may be used to send messages and move data, may be passed along with messages, and may be created, duplicated, and destroyed.

In order to allow the kernel to check standard or common operations on links for consistancy and thus catch errors at their source, we have introduced the concept of a link type. There are four types of links: request, resource, reply, and general. Request and resource links are used for request messages, differing only in that a request link may be destroyed or duplicated by its possessor without notifying the task to which the link points. Resource links may be duplicated or destroyed by their possessor but such operations cause messages to be sent to the task to which such a link points. Resource links may not be passed to a task with a different user ID from the posessor of the link unless the posessor is also the creator. Reply links are used only for reply messages and are only used one, i.e., they are destroyed by their use. A link may be passed with a message across another link. A general link, request link, or a resource link may be passed across a reply link. Only a reply link may be passed across a request or resource link. Any type of link may be passed across a general link. No other possibilities are allowed.

3.3. Messages

Messages are small packets of information which can be transmitted across links. Messages are buffered by the kernel (up to some limit on the number of buffered messages for any one task). Messages are classified into requests, replies, and general messages depending on the type of link they are sent across.

A request message, sent across a request or resource link, is a request for some action by another task. Most request messages require replies, so a request message may be accompanied by a reply link back to the requesting task.

A reply message, sent across a reply link, is used only to reply to a previous request. The reply link is destroyed when the reply is sent. A reply may carry with it a general, request, or resource link, typically representing some abstract object being obtained in response to the original request.

General messages which use general links, give users an escape from the restrictions imposed on requests and replies. A general link can pass any kind of link, thus avoiding the asymmetry of requests and replies. With the exception of the Switchboard, no component of DEMOS uses general links.

3.4. Channels

Channels provide a way for a task to select classes of potential incoming messages. When a process creates a link, it specifies a channel on which messages associated with that link will be received. The RECEIVE operation specifies one or more channels. The oldest message whose link uses one of the specified channels will be returned to the task. If there is no such message, the task blocks until such a message arrives. Unlike link ID's which are determined by the kernel, channels are specified by the task and may be assigned in any manner desired (up to the maximum allowed number).

If a task wishes to operate in a completely synchronous manner, it should use a different channel for each outstanding link and specify only one channel in each RECEIVE. If a task wishes to operate in an asynchronous manner it can either perform conditional receive operations on channels and thus not block if no messages are available or it can ENABLE interrupts on a set of channels and be notified by the kernel when a message arrives on one of those channels.

4. Link Usage

The primary communication operations are CALL, REQUEST, REPLY, SEND, MOVE, and RECEIVE. SEND specified a message and an optional link to be passed with the message. It has two variants: DESTROY, which destroys the link used by the message, and DUPLICATE, which requests a second copy of that link. The recipient is notified if one of the variants was used unless the link is of type request. The DESTROY and DUPLICATE portions of the SEND operation are actually performed by the kernel. REQUEST sends a message and an implicitly created reply link on a request or resource link. REPLY sends a message and an optional link on a reply link held by a task. MOVE reads or writes data through a link. RECEIVE accepts the next incoming message. CALL is a composite of RE-QUEST and RECEIVE and is expected to be the operation most heavily used by user programs since it combines three kernel operations (CREATE, SEND, and RECEIVE) that would otherwise commonly be done in a tight sequence. Other operations on links are CREATE and BYPASS. CREATE creates a new link to the creating task, specifying a code, a channel, restrictions on how the link may be used, and (optionally) the address and size of a segment of the creating task's memory for direct data MOVEs. BYPASS also creates such a link, but uses the data pointer from a link possessed by the creator rather than a pointer into the creator's own memory.

The following example interaction with the file system is intended to provide an intuitive understanding of these basic operations. Suppose our example task, taskA, wishes to read file FILEX. It must open the file, do some read operations, then close the file. Each of these involves a message to the file system requesting an action and a reply saying that the action is done.

To open the file, taskA performs a CALL operation on its standard link to the file system, sending a message containing the file name and other required parameters. The kernel creates a reply link, specifying the standard reply channel, and sends the message and the reply link to the file system. When the file system receives the message, it interprets it, opens FILEX, and in turn CREATEs a resource link to itself. The code field of the resource link contains the internal index into the file system's open file table entry for FILEX. The file system then does a REPLY operation on the reply link sent by taskA, passing the resource link representing FILEX back along the reply link to taskA. The completion message and the link ID for the resource link representing FILEX are returned to taskA (which becomes ready because the implicit RECEIVE operation is satisfied). The reply link is destroyed by the kernel after it is used. TaskA now has two links to the file system, its standard request link and a resource link representing FILEX. The file system has no links to taskA.

Reading data from the file requires a similar series of steps. This time, however, taskA uses the resource link representing FILEX and specifies the address and size of its buffer on the CALL operation. The file system uses MOVE to transfer the data through the data segment descriptor of the reply link. When the data transfers are complete, the file system does a REPLY operation to return status information such as the number of bytes read or whether end of file was reached. This time the file system's reply specifies no new link. Having received the reply, taskA can safely process the data in the buffer.

When taskA is done with the file, it DESTROYs its link for FILEX. The resulting message to the file system tells it to close the file. TaskA is left with only its standard link to the file system.

5. Link Management

Links resemble capabilities, so their management must take into account many of the well known difficulties of managing capabilities. This section discusses a management scheme which addresses some of these difficulties.

One problem with capabilities is the possibility that they may continue to exist after the object they point to is destroyed. In the case of links, the objects are tasks. We use the standard technique of not reusing task identifiers to solve this problem.

Sometimes it is desirable to account for outstanding links to a task. For example, the file system will need to keep track of open file links in order to close files when their last link is destroyed. We allow this by notifying the creating task whenever a resource or general link is duplicated or destroyed. A task may restrict its links so that they may not be duplicated, in which case an explicit request for another link must be made to obtain a second copy.

Yet another problem with capabilities is the lack of control over their being given away to an unauthorized third party. Classifying links into types and restricting specific operations to specific types provides a partial solution to this problem. For example, resource links may only be passed to tasks with the same user ID. Reply links, which can be used only once, reduce the problem of uncontrolled passing of links.

Perhaps the thorniest problem is that of deadlocks. In DEMOS, a deadlock is a set of tasks each of which is waiting to RECEIVE messages from other tasks in the deadlock.

While such circular wait conditions can in principle be detected, we plan at present to use a hybrid approach to deadlock control, organizing the system-defined tasks hierarchically to prevent deadlocks [Howard 73] and timing out blocked user tasks.

6. Task Management

Tasks are created and destroyed by the Task Manager, which is itself a system task accessible by a standard link. When a task wishes to create a child task, it sends a message to the Task Manager specifying the initial size of the child's memory. The Task Manager allocates the memory and creates a suspended task with no links and zero registers and memory, then it returns a reply containing a link to itself. This child link has a bypass data segment pointer which allows the parent to read and write the child's memory. Using it, the parent can read and modify the child's registers, give it links and take them back, and suspend and resume the child.

When a task terminates, it is placed in a suspended state. The parent may ask to be notified when the child terminates; upon notification it can retrieve links and status information from the child. Destroying the child link destroys the child; the Task Manager suspends the child, destroys any links it has, and frees its memory. To give a child a lifetime independent of the parent's, the parent must pass the child link to some other task, for example the Job Initiator, which is willing to adopt such children, accept their termination messages, and produce a post-mortem if they terminate abnormally.

7. Other System Facilities

Several other system tasks will exist in DEMOS to complete the task communication structure. These include the Switchboard and the timer task.

The Switchboard task is provided to allow mutually consenting arbitrary tasks to communicate. A task willing to communicate with any arbitrary task (for example, a MAIL facility) creates a general or request link, and sends a message to the Switchboard, including this link and a name. A task wishing to communicate with another named task would send a message to the Switchboard requesting a link. The Switchboard task matches pairs of tasks based on the names specified and passes the link from the other task to the requesting task. Since reply links cannot be sent on reply links, and only reply links can be sent on request links, the standard link to the Switchboard task is a general link.

The timer task provides clocks for other tasks. It accepts requests from tasks which specify a time interval (either real time or task CPU time) and at the end of the requested interval the timer task sends a reply message to the requesting task. If the receiving task has enabled interrupts on the channel it specified in the link, it will be interrupted.

8. Remarks

This communication mechanism is not pure in several ways. The data segment that can be associated with a link allows an escape from communication via messages. The general link type allows an escape from the request-reply regime. The conditional receive operation and the interrupt mechanism allow an escape from the regime of synchronous tasks with all the asynchrony of the system captured in messages. While we believe these escapes should be avoided as much as possible, we believe they are necessary for a production operating system. If we were designing our own hardware we might be more tempted by purity.

We have attempted to provide a set of primitive operations in this communication mechanism that will support a wide variety of operating system structures. We think that the operations are general and flexible but sufficiently simple to be implemented efficiently. We have consciously attempted to avoid what John Cocke has called overpowerful operators. If a task is to perform read or write operations on a file, it must send messages to the file system task. If a task is to perform suspend or resume operations on another task, it must send messages to the task manager. While these requirements may seem obvious and natural, we have seen systems where such operations were made to appear as primitives. Proving that these operations can be done efficiently without being primitives is a challenge we have ahead of us.

We see the link concept as an especially nice vehicle for intertask communication in several environments. A network of processors with private primary memory is an appealing application for this communication mechanism. The CRAY-1 with its limited form of memory protection inspired this design and is our first application.

This communication mechanism does not imply a preferred organization for the rest of the operating system. A hierarchical or layered approach is as suitable as a more distributed and independent task approach as far as this communication mechanism is concerned. The link mechanism allows the construction of abstract objects, capabilities, domains, and other protection structures but it does not require any of these.

9. Acknowledgments

We gratefully acknowledge the many helpful suggestions and remarks from J. C. Browne, David Folger, Susan Owicki, Michael Powell, and R. W. Watson.

10. References

Brinch Hansen, P. Operating System Principles. Prentice-Hall, Englewood Cliffs, N.J., 1973.

Dijkstra, E. W. Cooperating sequential processes. in Programming Languages (F. Genuys, ed.). Academic Press (1968), 43-112.

Fabry, R. S. Capability-based addressing. Communications of the ACM 17, 7 (July 1974), 403-412.

Hoare, C. A. R. Monitors: an operating system structuring concept. Communications of the ACM 17, 10 (Oct. 1974), 549-557. Corrigendum, Communications of the ACM 18, 2 (Feb. 1975), 95.

Howard. J. H. Mixed Solutions to the Deadlock Problem. Communications of the ACM 16, 7 (July 1973), 427-430.

Lampson, B. W. and Sturgis, H. E. Reflection on an Operating System Design. Communications of the ACM 19, 5 (May 1976), 251-265.

Morris, J. H. Protection in programming languages Communications of the ACM 16, 1 (Jan. 1973), 15-21.

Reprinted with permission from *Proceedings of the National Computer Conference*, Volume 43, 1974, pages 17-22. Copyright © 1974 by AFIPS Press.

STARAN parallel processor system software

by EDWARD W. DAVIS

Goodyear Aerospace Corporation
Akron, Ohio

INTRODUCTION

This paper is concerned with the features and concepts of system software for a parallel associative array processor— STARAN.* Definitions of parallel processors have appeared often. Essentially they are machines with a large number of processing elements. They have the capability to operate on multiple data streams with a single instruction stream. STARAN is a line of parallel processors with a variable number of processing elements.

Along with the multiple processing elements, STARAN has a memory organization that allows access either by location or association. That is the address of a memory word can be used explicitly, or words can be selected by association based on their content. Processing elements can operate on data selected associatively, making the machine an associative processor.

An alignment, or permutation, network in the machine provides a flexible interconnection between processing elements. This network is used to align data in the memory with the processing elements requiring the data and to provide communication between processors. This results in an array organization, making the machine an array processor. STARAN is thus a true parallel, associative, array processor.

It is expected that one might be curious about the use of this machine: the operating system, language processing software, user program development, and execution control aids. This paper gives a brief description of software for all these purposes. Some parts will be recognizable as fundamental members of the software for other general purpose computing systems. Special development was required, however, to handle features unique to the parallel organization.

The programming language is new. It includes declarations for defining storage in the arrays and instructions for using the parallel and associative properties of the machine. Interactive execution control software has been written. It simplifies development and debugging of user programs. This software differs from conventional debugging tools by the extensions related to the array memory organization. Discussion of the language and control software, plus methods of interfacing STARAN to other machines, are the major points of the paper.

---

* TM, Goodyear Aerospace Corporation, Akron, Ohio.

STARAN SYSTEMS

STARAN is an operational computing system. The hardware architecture is described in a companion paper presented at this conference[1] and in other literature.[2,3] A particular installation and its potential use is described in a companion paper.[4] This paper is concerned with a description of the existing system software. There are two modes of operation. First, STARAN can be operated as a stand-alone parallel processing system. Peripherals for this mode typically include a card reader, line printer, paper tape reader and punch, and cartridge type disk unit. Second, STARAN and a cooperating, or host, machine can be operated in an integrated fashion. This means that: (1) commands to the STARAN disk operating system can originate in the other machine, (2) the storage system of the host is available to STARAN users for program or data storage, and (3) a single task can use both machines to satisfy its processing requirements. All peripherals belonging to a stand-alone STARAN and to the host are available when the machines are integrated.

This paper describes the software for the STARAN stand-alone mode of operation, then covers the additional software used with the integrated mode.

Since the STARAN processor architecture is detailed in a companion paper[1] only a basic diagram is given in Figure 1. The multi-dimensional access associative arrays and their controls are the main architectural features. The sequential control, a Digital Equipment Corporation (DEC) PDP-11 minicomputer, has a minor role in the architecture but is important for software considerations. Other architectural features are mentioned later in the paper.

SOFTWARE FOR STARAN STAND-ALONE MODE

Software for the STARAN stand-alone mode of operation can be discussed from the standpoints of the operating system, language processing, and execution control procedures.

Batch disk operation system

In this paper, an operating system means the collection of routines that give the user appropriate control of the com-

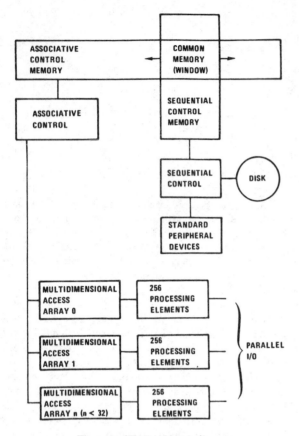

Figure 1—STARAN block diagram

puting system, inform him of system status, provide input/output (I/O) facilities, and provide access to system programs. STARAN features a disk operating system (DOS) and has a batch processing capability. The batch command stream can be assigned to any character input device, allowing control to originate at the control console or from a user's file on the batch device.

The disk is a file structured bulk storage medium. All system software is resident on the device for easy, rapid access by the user.

Listed below are the standard programs supplied with the DEC PDP-11 batch system:

Program Name	Function
MACRO	Macro-assembler
LINK	Linker
LIBR	Librarian
PIP	File utility package
EDIT	Text editor
ODT	On-line debugging package
FORTRAN	Fortran compiler

These programs are not discussed further since primary

emphasis in this paper is on the STARAN-related software that has been added to the above list to build the STARAN disk operating system.

One general rule used in software development was to avoid changes to the basic DEC batch system. This rule was intended to simplify any future change to a new DEC release.

Language processing

APPLE—Programs for STARAN are written in the APPLE* assembly language (**A**ssociative **P**rocessor **P**rogramming **L**anguag**E**).[5] This language has some mnemonics that generate one machine language instruction and others that generate a sequence of machine instructions. The one-to-many mnemonics generally implement a parallel algorithm for arithmetic or search operations using the arrays. Thus, APPLE is at a higher level than sequential machine assembly languages.

APPLE produces relocatable or absolute program sections and has a conditional assembly capability. Groups of instructions in the language are listed below:

1. Assembler directives
2. Branch instructions
3. Register load and store
4. Array instructions
   a. Loads
   b. Stores
   c. Associative searches
   d. Parallel moves
   e. Parallel arithmetic operations
5. Control and test instructions
6. Input/output (I/O) instructions

Most of these groups of instructions resemble those of other typical assemblers. The unique group—array instructions—deals with operations on the multi-dimensional access arrays and the registers in their processing elements (PE). Some general comments apply to all the array instructions listed above. Operations take place only on arrays enabled by the array select register.[2] Fields are of variable length within each array word and are defined for various instructions by field pointers and length counters. The common register, a part of associative control, can contain an operand, which is used in common by all selected array words.

More detail is presented below on the array instructions; i.e., loads, stores, associative searches, parallel moves, and parallel arithmetic operations.

The "load" array instructions load the processing element (PE) registers or the common register with data from arrays. Logical operations may be performed between the current PE register contents and the array data. The language has mnemonics for the common logical operations, while the machine supports all 16 functions of two logical variables.

* TM, Goodyear Aerospace Corporation, Akron, Ohio

A given load instruction can increment, decrement, or leave as is an array field pointer. Thus, a single one of these instructions can load registers, perform logic, and change pointer values. Operations to set, clear, or rotate the PE registers are included in this group.

The "store" array instructions are used to move PE or common register data into the arrays. A mask feature is provided that allows writing only in mask enabled array words. As with the load instructions, logical operations may be performed between the current PE registers contents and the array data. Also, the array field pointer can be incremented, or left unchanged.

The "associative search" array instructions allow the programmer to search for particular conditions in the arrays. Only those words enabled by the mask register take part in the searches. Searches can be performed that compare a value in the common register with a value in a field of all array words. Another variety of search compares one field of a word with a second field of the same word for all array words. Comparisons can be made for such conditions as equal, not equal, greater than, greater than or equal, etc. Maximum and minimum searches also can be performed. Combinations of searches yield such functions as between limits and next higher. Additional mnemonics in this group are provided to resolve multiple responders to the searches.

The "parallel move" instructions are provided to move an array memory field to another field within the same array word. As with searches, a word is active for this instruction only when enabled by the mask register. Types of moves are direct, complement the field, increment or decrement the field, and move the absolute value.

The "parallel arithmetic" array instructions allow the programmer to perform parallel operations in the arrays. These operations are subject to mask register word enabling. Arithmetic can use a value in the common register as one operand and a value in a field of all array words as the parallel operand. Alternatively, one field of a word can be arithmetically combined with a second field of the same word for all array words. Operations supplied by APPLE are add, subtract, multiply, divide, and square root.

Macro—A macro language is provided to increase the user's flexibility at assembly time.[6] The macro language has a large set of arithmetic, logical, relational, and string manipulation operators. Adding macro variable symbol handling, conditional expansion capability, and ability to nest macro calls make it possible to write powerful macro instructions. System and user macro libraries have been implemented.

Benefits to the user are the ability to define new mnemonics, redefine existing mnemonics, and conveniently generate standard instruction sequences.

Mnemonics have been added to the basic APPLE language by including macros in the system library. Primarily, the added mnemonics are floating point instructions. They are fixed field length operations in both single and double precision.

Building Load Modules—Software used to convert source language programs into executable load modules includes

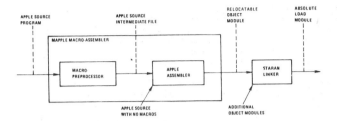

Figure 2—Language processing software

an APPLE assembler, macro-preprocessor, and relocating linker. Figure 2 shows this software and the flow of programs or modules through it.

Building load modules begins with the original program written in APPLE. This source program may contain macro instructions. Translation of the source into a machine language object module is by MAPPLE (APPLE assembler with Macro-preprocessor on the front end). If it is known that the source program does not contain macro instructions, it is possible to input the source directly to the APPLE assembler.

A relocatable object module is converted to an absolute load module by the STARAN linker. Multiple object modules may be input to the linker since it has the function of resolving symbols defined across object module boundaries (global symbols) as well as adjusting addresses for relocation.

Use of the language processing software is fully described in the STARAN User's Guide.[7]

Execution control

Execution control software is discussed below, covering loading, executing, and debugging programs on STARAN. Four modules are involved: the loader, STARAN program supervisor, debug module, and control module.

Loader—Output of the STARAN linker is shown in Figure 2 as an absolute load module. The loader has the straightforward task of moving a load module into STARAN control memory beginning at the address specified in a text block. Options on loading are to load and not execute or to load and begin execution either at an address given with the load module or at one given with the load command. The load module is accessible from a user program to enable calling for a load from an executing program. This means that overlay modules can be brought in dynamically.

STARAN Program Supervisor (SPS)—The SPS is the software interface between the associative and sequential portions of STARAN. This module has services for system users when programming in APPLE and when programming a PDP-11 routine to interact with an APPLE program.

For the APPLE program, SPS makes the I/O instructions of the disk operating system (DOS) available, provides a program overlay capability, and provides a programmable interrupt to a PDP-11 routine. The PDP-11 routine inter-

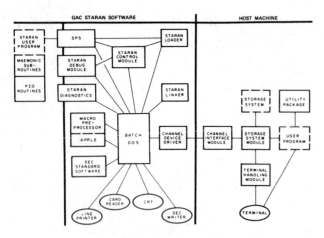

Figure 3—System software diagram

acts through a software link, which receives the APPLE interrupts, and through the issuing of control information to the associative control logic.

In addition, SPS supplies interface services. It transfers data between associative and sequential memory through the common memory window (Figure 1). SPS also fields associative processor error interrupts.

Concurrent execution of associative and sequential routines, with interaction, is made possible by SPS.

STARAN Debug Module (SDM)—The SDM helps the user debug APPLE programs by giving him control of the execution of the program being debugged, and access to memory and registers. Such features as single step, trace, and breakpoint provide good execution control. Dumps of all memory areas can be taken, with both word slice and bit slice available for the multi-dimensional access arrays. All memory locations also can be modified.

STARAN Control Module (SCM)—This final operational module is the interface between the user and execution of a STARAN program. By running SCM, the user enters a mode in which STARAN related commands are recognized. Such commands as start, halt, and continue execution are processed directly by SCM. When the load command is used, SCM passes control to the loader for that function. If debug aids are needed, a simple command adds all debug module features to SCM.

All the operational software modules are described more fully in the STARAN User's Guide.[7]

SOFTWARE FOR THE INTEGRATED MODE

General

The integrated use of the STARAN parallel processor and a host sequential computer makes additional software necessary. One major concern is the interface between the computers; this requires a software module in both machines. A second concern involves reasonable ease of use for the inte-

grated mode; procedure packages are added as needed to satisfy this concern.

Figure 3 is a block diagram of the software modules in STARAN and a typical host machine. Interface software can be seen as the channel device driver in STARAN and the channel interface module in the host. Routines that might be added to simplify operation in the integrated mode are the storage system module to provide access to the host's storage, a terminal handling module to provide smooth interaction with a terminal user, and a set of utilities.

The STARAN/HIS-645 software

Figure 4 shows the relationship between software modules in STARAN and the HIS-645, which runs under the Multics time-shared operating system.[8] This facility exists at Rome Air Development Center (RADC), N. Y. and is described in a companion paper presented at this conference.[4] As indicated, Multics contains three categories of software: command level, user process, and system related. Command level software is brought into execution by user-supplied commands, as from a Multics terminal. User process software consists essentially of subroutines called from a user program. System-related software is the collection of routines that support use of the system, such as handling input and output, and are usually called indirectly by the user program.

Additional details on the design and use of this software are described in the STARAN/HIS-645 User's Guide.[9]

Interface Modules—The two modules for the interface, shown in Figure 4, are the 645 device driver in the STARAN

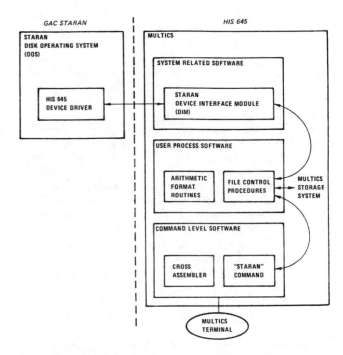

Figure 4—STARAN/645 system software relationship

batch disk operating system (DOS) and the STARAN device interface module (DIM).

The 645 device driver provides the interface between the DOS monitor and the 645 computer. It communicates with the monitor as do other device drivers for standard peripherals. If the device looks like an input for character information, then batch commands can come from it. The batch stream can be assigned to the device. This is the significance, for Multics, of the batch feature on the DOS.

In reality, the device treated by the 645 driver is used for much more than character input. The 645 appears as three logical devices.

One device looks like the disk, logically. The driver supports both ASCII and binary transfer modes, both formatted and unformatted. At any one time, up to 14 data-sets may be open on this device.

A second device looks like a card reader, logically. It is a read-only device with an ASCII transfer mode. This unit serves as the batch command stream input so a Multics user can control the system.

The third device looks like a paper tape punch, logically. It is a write-only device with ASCII and binary transfer modes. Job log output, in the integrated mode, is always assigned to this unit.

STARAN DIM—In Multics terminology, a device interface module (DIM) coordinates communications with a particular physical device. Data manipulation by the STARAN DIM assumes all Multics data is in character form. It converts characters into the form needed for output to STARAN and converts data received from STARAN into Multics character form. This means, for example, that Multics arithmetic data must be converted to a character form prior to output, and from characters following input. The conversion is done by a procedure superior to the DIM. The DIM also handles retransmission of bad data and reports a failure to its caller after a specific number of unsuccessful tries on the same data.

In the Multics software structure, the DIM is located in a position inferior to the file control procedures, shown in Figure 4 and described in the next part of this paper.

System Use Modules—The file control procedures (FCP) greatly simplify operation of STARAN from Multics. It enables a Multics user process (program) to interact with STARAN by initializing the interface, handling communication between the machines, and terminating the interface. The FCP also makes the necessary calls to the DIM to initialize and terminate the interface.

With FCP, a user process, executing in the 645, can call for STARAN, and it can pass commands, programs, and data to STARAN. The FCP raises the point at which the user becomes involved from sequences of calls to the DIM to a more symbolic call to FCP routines from the user process.

User involvement in the interface to STARAN is raised still higher from the user process to the Multics command level by a "STARAN" module. Essentially, this module is a supplied user process that passes parameters used in the terminal command to the FCP. The parameters identify the STARAN batch command stream input and output devices. The module calls appropriate FCP routines to establish interaction with STARAN.

In typical operation of STARAN from a terminal, this Multics command is used with STARAN commands also coming from the terminal. Initializing and terminating the interface are not a concern of the user. The Multics terminal becomes very similar to the STARAN control console when this module is used

STARAN and the 645 differ in the lengths of their data representations. STARAN has a 32-bit control memory, while the 645 has a 36-bit word length. Arithmetic format routines are provided to convert either integer or floating point data between the 645 format and the format used by the DIM for transmission to STARAN.

A cross assembler has been written in PL/1. This is a functionally equivalent version of the MAPPLE assembler to be run in Multics. It is available to terminal users on the time-shared basis. It accepts APPLE and macro statements and produces STARAN object code in the Multics character format required by the DIM for transmission to STARAN.

STARAN/Σ5 integrated mode

A second method of interfacing STARAN with a host machine has been implemented in the Evaluation and Test Facility at Goodyear Aerospace Corporation. This facility has an XDS Σ5 as the host. The direct memory access capability of STARAN has been used to allow an 8K area of Σ5 memory to be used as STARAN control memory. Either programs or data may be stored here with control provided by interrupts between the machines. Software for this system is a communications library package with subroutines callable from FORTRAN or machine language in the Σ5.

CONCLUSION

A brief description has been given of software packages that compose the system for the operational STARAN parallel associative array processor. Also described is the additional software that makes STARAN operational when integrated with HIS-645 or XDS Σ5 sequential computers. The goal of all the software is to provide tools to use STARAN in the stand-alone and integrated modes. The tools are intended to increase convenience for the user and improve total system throughput.

Many modules have been discussed. Some of these are essentially transparent to the user, some may not be needed by certain users, and some may be required by all users. For stand-alone STARAN operation, the programmer must know APPLE and the use of the assembler and linker. He must be able to run the control module and load programs.

He will probably be interested in the debug module. The STARAN program superivsor is transparent for most users. It is not necessary to know any of the sequential control programs or languages.

REFERENCES

1. Batcher, K. E., *STARAN Parallel Processor System Hardware*, GER-15996, Goodyear Aerospace Corporation, 19 November 1973.
2. Rudolph, J. A., "A Production Implementation of an Associative Array Processor—STARAN," *1972 Fall Joint Computer Conference Proceedings* December 1972, pp. 229–241.
3. *STARAN Reference Manual*, GER-15636A, Goodyear Aerospace Corporation, September 1973.
4. Feldman, J. D. and L. C. Fulmer, *RADCAP: An Operational Parallel Processing Facility*, GER-15946B, Goodyear Aerospace Corporation, 21 December 1973.
5. *STARAN APPLE Programming Manual*, GER-15637A, Goodyear Aerospace Corporation, September 1973.
6. *STARAN MACRO Programming Manual*, GER-15643, Goodyear Aerospace Corporation, September 1973.
7. *STARAN User's Guide*, GER-15644, Goodyear Aerospace Corporation, September 1973.
8. Organick, E. I., *The Multics System*, MIT Press, 1972.
9. *STARAN/HIS-645 User's Guide*, GER-15641, Goodyear Aerospace Corporation, September 1973.

Reprinted with permission from *Communications of the ACM*, Volume 23, Number 2, February 1980, pages 92-105. Copyright © 1980 by the Association for Computing Machinery, Inc.

Operating
Systems

R. Stockton Gaines
Editor

Medusa: An Experiment in Distributed Operating System Structure

John K. Ousterhout, Donald A. Scelza, and
Pradeep S. Sindhu
Carnegie-Mellon University

The design of Medusa, a distributed operating system for the Cm* multimicroprocessor, is discussed. The Cm* architecture combines distribution and sharing in a way that strongly impacts the organization of operating systems. Medusa is an attempt to capitalize on the architectural features to produce a system that is modular, robust, and efficient. To provide modularity and to make effective use of the distributed hardware, the operating system is partitioned into several disjoint *utilities* that communicate with each other via messages. To take advantage of the parallelism present in Cm* and to provide robustness, all programs, including the utilities, are *task forces* containing many concurrent, cooperating *activities*.

Key Words and Phrases: operating systems, distributed systems, message systems, task forces, deadlock, exception reporting
CR Categories: 4.32, 4.35

Permission to copy without fee all or part of this material is granted provided that the copies are not made or distributed for direct commercial advantage, the ACM copyright notice and the title of the publication and its date appear, and notice is given that copying is by permission of the Association for Computing Machinery. To copy otherwise, or to republish, requires a fee and/or specific permission.

This research was supported by the Department of Defense Advanced Research Projects Agency, ARPA Order 3597, monitored by the Air Force Avionics Laboratory under Contract F33615-78-C-1551. The views and conclusions contained in this document are those of the authors and should not be interpreted as representing the official policies, either expressed or implied, of the Defense Advanced Research Projects Agency or the U.S. Government.

Authors' present addresses: J.K. Ousterhout and P.S. Sindhu, Department of Computer Science, Carnegie-Mellon University, Pittsburgh, PA 15213; D.A. Scelza, PRIME Computer, Inc., Old Connecticut Path, Framingham, MA 01701.

1. Introduction

Medusa is a multi-user operating system under development for Cm*, a multimicroprocessor system recently completed at Carnegie-Mellon University [7, 24, 25, 26]. The project is an attempt to understand the effect on operating system structure of the distributed Cm* hardware and to produce a system that capitalizes on and reflects the underlying architecture. The resulting system combines several structural features that make it unique among existing operating systems.

Medusa is the second operating system for Cm*. The first system, StarOS [10, 11, 12], has been concerned with making Cm* programmable at a high level by users. Thus the StarOS system embodies a general object addressing mechanism and a set of tools for manipulating parallel programs. For Medusa we have chosen to emphasize problems of structure, rather than facilities. The goal of the project has been to gain an understanding of how to build distributed operating systems and to exploit the hardware to produce a system organization with three attributes:

Modularity. The system should consist of a large number of small, cooperating subcomponents that may be built, modified, and measured independently. Such a structure complements the Cm* hardware, which consists of a large number of small processors.

Robustness. The system should be able to respond in a reasonable way to changes in its environment. These changes include an increase or decrease in workload and the failures of hardware, firmware, or software components. The multiplicity of processors should aid in achieving this goal.

Performance. Both the structure of the operating system and the abstractions it provides to user programs should reflect the underlying hardware. Application programs should be able to run with approximately the same efficiency using Medusa as they could on the bare hardware.

The software organization required to achieve the above goals has been strongly influenced by the Cm* architecture. Two general attributes of Cm* have been especially important. First, the physical arrangement of the hardware components is a distributed one. For each processor there is a small set of local resources that is accessible immediately and efficiently: the other facilities of the system are also accessible, but with greater overhead. The second fundamental attribute of the hardware is the power of the interprocessor communication facilities, which permits an efficient implementation of a variety of communication mechanisms ranging from shared memory to message systems. Section 2 discusses the Cm* hardware in more detail.

The combination of distribution and sharing in the hardware gives rise to two corresponding software issues: partitioning and communication. How should

397

Communications
of
the ACM

February 1980
Volume 23
Number 2

© 1980 ACM 0001-0782/80/0200-0092 $00.75.

the operating system be partitioned in order to enhance its modularity and make use of the distributed hardware? How should the separate subunits communicate so as to function together in a robust way as a single logical entity? The remainder of this paper is a discussion of these issues and of the solutions embodied in Medusa.

Although the paper discusses the issues of partitioning and communication in a particular environment, that of Cm*, the issues have found relevance in many other areas of computer science. Research in structured programming has been concerned with reducing interactions within programs so that subportions of the programs can be designed and implemented separately [18]. Recent efforts in very large scale integrated (VLSI) circuit design are attempting to find ways to structure chip designs so as to reduce communication costs, since most of the area and complexity of the circuit stem from the interconnections [23]. Efforts to achieve fault tolerance must also be concerned with issues of partitioning and communication. For a system to be fault tolerant it must be subdivided into independent components with protected communication mechanisms so that (1) faults can be detected quickly, and (2) the occurrence of a fault in one portion of the system is not likely to destroy the other portions of the system [5].

The structure of Medusa resulted from the interaction of the three general goals (modularity, robustness, and performance) with the architecture of Cm*. The system has two significant characteristics:

(1) The control structure of the operating system is distributed. The functionality of Medusa is divided into disjoint *utilities*. Each utility executes in a private protected environment and implements a single abstraction for the rest of the system. Utilities communicate using messages.

(2) Parallelism is implicit and expected in Medusa. All programs are organized as *task forces*, each of which is a set of cooperating *activities*. By making the task force the central unit of control, Medusa makes it possible for very fine-grain interactions to occur within a task force. Each Medusa utility is a single task force.

Section 2 gives a brief discussion of the Cm* hardware and develops the distributed structure of Medusa. In Section 3 the task force notion is introduced. Section 4 gives an overview of the actual Medusa organization. Sections 5–7 discuss several topics in the implementation of the system: the use of pipes for utility communication (Section 5); the special privileges granted to utilities so that they can implement operating system functions (Section 6); deadlock in utility communication and the internal utility organization used to eliminate it (Section 7). Section 8 shows how the distribution and sharing in the system have impacted the exception reporting mechanism and discusses the benefits gained thereby. Section 9 concludes by comparing the Medusa structure with that of other systems.

2. The Distributed Structure

Figure 1 shows the organization of the Cm* hardware. It can be seen that the physical structure closely resembles that of a network. The system consists of a collection of 50 relatively autonomous processors called *computer modules* ("Cm"s in the PMS notation of Bell and Newell [2]), and five communication controllers (Kmaps). The Cm's are divided into *clusters*, with one Kmap presiding over each cluster. Each Kmap is responsible for the interprocessor communication to and from the Cm's in its cluster and must cooperate with the other Kmaps to handle intercluster transactions. All Kmaps are equal in stature; there is no central authority in the system.

Figure 2 gives a closer view of an individual computer module. Each Cm contains an LSI-11 processor, 64 or 128 kbytes of memory, and perhaps one or more I/O devices. A local switch, or Slocal, connects the computer module with the interprocessor communication structure. It is the presence of the Slocal as a switch in the computer module's addressing path (rather than as an I/O device on the Cm's bus) that distinguishes Cm* from networks. Tables in the Slocal allow it to decide on a reference-by-reference basis whether processor memory references are to proceed to local memory or be passed out to the Kmap of the cluster. Since Kmaps are general purpose processors with writable control stores, system designers have substantial freedom to choose their own methods of interprocessor communication. The Kmap microcode used by Medusa, which implements both shared memory and messages, is the third addressing structure to be implemented on Cm* (see [6] for a discussion of the others).

The ability to provide a variety of communication mechanisms efficiently, in spite of the distributed nature of the hardware, makes Cm* unique in the space of multicomputer systems and is fundamental to the development of Medusa.

Table I, taken from [19], shows the effect on program speed of making references to memory other than that of the processor executing the program. Although any processor may potentially access any memory location in the system, the cost of so doing varies by an order of magnitude, depending on the relative locations of processor and memory. The efficiency of a program running on Cm* is critically dependent on the "local hit ratio," or fraction of memory references that proceed from a processor directly to its local memory without involving a Kmap. A rule of thumb is that local hit ratios should generally be 90 percent or better in order to avoid serious performance degradation due to contention and/or the nonlocal access times.

Relatively high hit ratios can be achieved in a straightforward way by physically localizing information that need not be shared. Table II, also taken from [19], shows the dynamic distribution of memory references

Fig. 1. The 50-Processor Cm* System.

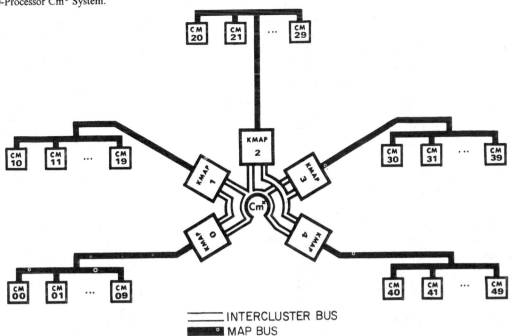

INTERCLUSTER BUS
MAP BUS

made by three multiprocess programs running on Cm*. Code references alone account for three-fourths of all memory references. Global information, that is, the information that must be accessible to all processes in a concurrent program, rarely accounts for more than a few percent of the references. Table II suggests that it makes relatively little difference where in the system global data is placed. On the other hand, code cannot be shared efficiently between concurrent processes; the primary problem facing system designers for Cm* is how to distribute the control structure.[1]

Fig. 2. Organization of a Cm.

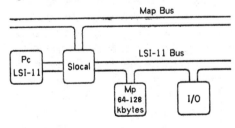

Table I. Average time per memory reference for a typical program making all code and data references to a single memory unit in a lightly loaded system

Memory position relative to Pc	Average reference time (microseconds)
Local	3.5
Nonlocal but within cluster	9.3
Cross-cluster	24

Fig. 3. One possible OS organization for Cm*: A single copy of the operating system code is shared by all processors.

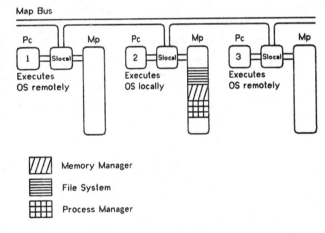

Memory Manager
File System
Process Manager

Table II. Dynamic distribution of memory references between four program components for three multiprocess programs

Program	Code (%)	Stack (%)	Owns (%)	Globals (%)
Partial differential equations	82	11.5	4	2.5
Quicksort	71	12.5	6	9.5
Set partitioning	71.5	23.5	4	1

2.1 Traditional Operating System Approaches

Using performance as a basis for judgment, this section shows why certain basic assumptions made by existing operating systems are inappropriate for Cm*.

Consider the application of a traditional operating system structure to Cm*. It is an assumption of virtually

---

[1] This is in contrast to most of the past work in distributed systems, which has been concerned with distributed data structures.

all existing operating systems that all of the functionality of the OS is immediately available at every point within the system. Typically, a user program invokes the OS using a "trap" or "supervisor call" instruction. The processor switches execution environment to that of the kernel or supervisor, executes the function, then returns to the user program.

Figure 3 shows one possible operating system organization for Cm*. For purposes of this discussion it is assumed that the operating system must provide three functions: memory management, a file system, and process management. These functions must be accessible to all programs running anywhere on the system. The approach of Figure 3 is much like that of a traditional uniprocessor or multiprocessor operating system. A single copy of the operating system resides in one of the memories of the system. One processor is capable of executing the code directly, and the other processors have their memory mapping tables set up so that they can execute the code remotely. Unfortunately, the processors executing the operating system remotely will run at only about one-third speed because of the nonlocal access times. Processors executing the code from other clusters will suffer even more than this. In systems of any size, contention for the shared communication facilities will also degrade performance. In addition to the performance problems, the reliability of this system is limited by the reliability of the computer module containing the shared operating system code.

An alternative approach is to replicate the operating system code in each processor of the Cm* system. This is similar to the approach taken by networks, where each processor contains a copy of basic operating system functions; sharing occurs at a higher level, for example, via a shared file structure. Unfortunately, the size of local memories in Cm* is only 64 or 128 kbytes. A moderate sized operating system of 40–60 kbytes would consume most of the primary memory of the system. The utilization of this memory would be very low, especially when compared with the utilization of the shared memory in Figure 3. (Of course, even in the replicated system some global data still has to be shared between processors; Table II indicates that references to this memory do not substantially affect system performance.)

A static form of caching could be used to combine the approaches of the preceding paragraphs. Frequently executed portions of the operating system code could be replicated in each processor, while infrequently used code could be centralized in a shared memory. This scheme was used by the first version of the StarOS system. Unfortunately, the determination of which portions of the operating system are frequently executed is relatively difficult to make and likely to be application dependent. We decided not to attempt to make such decisions statically. The availability of hardware caches would make this scheme rather more attractive; given that there are no caches on Cm* we have not pursued it any further.

Fig. 4. The organization of Medusa: The operating system is divided into utilities that are distributed around the system. A processor executes a particular utility only if it can do so locally.

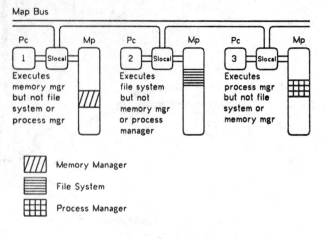

Memory Manager

File System

Process Manager

2.2 A Distributed Approach

The solution adopted for Medusa was to discard the assumption that all operating system code may be executed from any point in the system. A simplified example of this is depicted in Figure 4. The operating system is divided into disjoint *utilities*. Utilities are distributed among the available processors, with no guarantee that any particular processor contains a copy of the code for any particular utility. Furthermore, to avoid contention or memory access delays, a given processor is permitted to execute code for a particular utility only if it can do so locally.

Since no processor is guaranteed to be capable of executing any particular piece of utility code, it may be necessary for a program's flow of control to switch processors when it invokes utility functions. Trap or subroutine call instructions cannot be used for invocation because they are incapable of crossing processor boundaries. In Medusa, messages provide a simple mechanism for cross-processor function invocation. If one program wishes to invoke a function of another, it does so by sending a message to a particular *pipe* (see Section 5 for details of the pipe implementation). The invocation message contains parameters for the function invocation, as well as an indication of a *return pipe*; the return pipe is analogous to a return address for a subroutine call. The destination program receives the message, performs the requested operation, and sends a return message (containing result values) to the return pipe indicated in the invocation message. This message transaction is equivalent in power and effect to a call-by-value-result procedure invocation, with two major differences. First, the message crosses protection boundaries as well as processor boundaries, so that the invoker and server may exist in disjoint execution environments. Second, the invoker need not immediately suspend execution to await the requested service; if it has other functions to perform it may execute them concurrently with the execution of the server. Lauer and Needham discuss the duality

Communications of the ACM

February 1980
Volume 23
Number 2

between messages and procedure calls in more detail in [15].

There is an important difference of view between the Medusa system organization and the organizations presented in the previous sections. In the previous examples, a locus of control existed on a single processor. At the level of memory references, control and data information were transmitted to and from that processor by the Cm* hardware. In the Medusa paradigm, the control information (code) is fixed and is used by a single processor. As various loci of control (user programs and other utilities) need to access the control information, they must move to the processor containing the code. The message transaction is logically equivalent to a transfer of control from one processor to another.

2.3 Distribution for Modularity and Robustness

In the above development of Medusa's distributed structure, performance was used as the main motivation. However, the resulting structure is also desirable for other reasons; these may be even more compelling than the performance considerations. Given that the system must be partitioned into relatively autonomous subunits, the module scheme of Parnas [18] seems the most attractive. Each of the utilities encapsulates a single abstraction for the rest of the system. The use of messages for communication with utilities permits each utility to exist in its own protected execution environment. The boundaries between utilities are rigidly enforced and are crossed only by messages. Message communication is without side effects; that is, a message is received only when requested and the only effects it has on the receiver are those caused by the receiver. This is not true with shared writable memory, where either party may arbitrarily modify the memory without the other's knowledge. Although the utilities still depend on each other to perform certain services, Medusa has attempted to eliminate all interactions between utilities except those absolutely necessary for them to function. The strong separation between system components should simplify the tasks of building and maintaining the system.[2]

The distributed utility structure is also a first step toward robustness. Boundaries between utilities are firm enough that it is difficult for mishaps in one utility to contaminate the others. At the same time, message pipes do not restrict either the location or internal organization of the senders and receivers. Once the format of messages has been agreed upon and particular pipes have been selected for communication, utilities may migrate around the system without affecting their ability to communicate. A different pipe may be substituted for an existing one to change the handler for a particular class of requests. The use of pipes both limits damage and permits transparent system reconfiguration.

System designers have traditionally resigned themselves to the "fact" that a performance penalty must be paid if a system is to have a manageable structure. Although the performance of Medusa has not yet been measured, it is encouraging to note that the same structure appears to be both efficient and modular. We speculate that the compatibility of good performance and good system structure is not just a statistical fluctuation in Medusa but a trend in large systems, where much of a system's cost stems from communication. For example, Sutherland and Mead suggest in [23] that the trend will hold for design in the domain of VLSI.

3. The Task Force Structure

LSI-11's are a relatively plentiful resource in Cm* but individually are not very powerful (16-bit virtual address space, 170,000 instructions per second). We have assumed in the design of Medusa that all interesting Cm* programs will be concurrent ones combining the computational power of several processors. This has led to the definition at the system's lowest level of a simple structure to support concurrency, called the *task force* after a similar structure of the same name used in the StarOS system [12, 13]. A task force is defined to be a collection of concurrent *activities* that cooperate closely in the execution of a single logical task. Activities are the entities that actually get scheduled for execution on processors. They are roughly analogous to processes or programs in other systems except that they exist only as part of a task force. A purely serial program is a degenerate task force with only one activity. All programs, including the operating system utilities, are task forces.

When a task force is created, its activities are allocated statically to individual processors (because of the importance of accessing code locally it makes little sense to execute an activity from any processor but the one containing its code). In general each of the activities of a task force will be allocated to a different processor. Individual processors may be multiplexed between several activities belonging to different task forces.

In addition to its activities a task force contains a collection of objects that may be manipulated by those activities. There are several types of objects in Medusa, each with its own set of type-specific operations. Access to objects is obtained through *descriptors* that are kept in protected objects called *descriptor lists*. The various types of objects may be divided into three general classes according to where the operations upon the objects are implemented. The simplest class consists of *page objects*; these may be associated with any of 16 portions of an activity's 64-kbyte virtual address space and may then be read or written using LSI-11 memory references. The second class of objects consists of *pipes* and *semaphores*, whose implementations are managed by Kmap microcode. Pipes and semaphores are protected so that LSI-11 programs cannot directly access their internal represen-

_____
[2] The Family of Operating Systems project [9] has had favorable experiences with a system structure consisting of several isolated modules communicating only via a call-by-value-result mechanism.

Fig. 5. The organization of the Medusa file system utility. All activities are identical; they serve different requests in parallel.

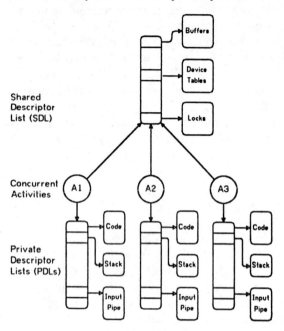

tations; requests must be made to a Kmap to manipulate them. The third class of objects, containing file control blocks, task forces, descriptor lists, and others, is implemented by the operating system utilities. User programs make requests to the utilities in order to perform operations upon these objects. Plans exist for a fourth class of objects, whose implementation would be managed by other user-level programs; the initial system will not provide for objects of this class.

The descriptors used by a task force to access objects are held in two kinds of descriptor lists. Each activity has exclusive access to a *private descriptor list* (PDL). A *shared descriptor list* (SDL) contains descriptors that may be used by all of the activities of the task force. The activities of a task force generally share a common abstract function; the SDL is the encapsulation of that shared task. In general, descriptors may be moved and/ or copied, subject to the restriction that the total number of descriptors that may simultaneously exist for each object may not exceed a limit specified when the object was created. Page objects are special in that only a single descriptor may exist. Although a page may be shared within a task force by placing the descriptor in the SDL of the task force, it cannot be shared between task forces.[3]

As an example of a task force, the Medusa file system utility is shown in Figure 5. The several activities are identical. Each contains in its private descriptor list (PDL) a copy of the file system code and a stack page; both are allocated in the memory of the Cm executing

the activity, so that access may be made locally. In addition, each PDL contains descriptors for one or more pipes over which service requests are made to that activity. The shared descriptor list contains information that must be accessed by all of the file server activities in order to use I/O devices in a consistent way. This includes the physical device registers, buffer space, device descriptors, and locks used to synchronize file access. The size of the file system task force varies dynamically to provide load-balancing and fault tolerance. If the existing activities become overloaded, they create new activities to assume some of the workload. When activities become underloaded, they give their work back to other activities and delete themselves. For reliability purposes, there will always be at least two activities in each utility task force. In this simple example, global data is centralized in the SDL while control information, particularly that associated with error handling, is replicated.

An alternative task force organization is shown in Figure 6. In this example we have speculated about the structure an optimizing compiler might take. The organization proposed here is a pipelined one. The program being compiled passes through every activity of the compiler, undergoing a transformation at each step. For example, the lexical scan activity reads the source code, generates symbol table entries, and outputs lexemes to the parser. The parser activity generates intermediate code from the lexemes and so on. The symbol table is the only piece of information needed by all of the activities; it is referenced through descriptors in the SDL and could probably be stored in any processor in the system without degrading the performance of the compiler (see Table II). The task force structure is used in different ways in these two examples. For the file system, the activities are used to serve multiple independent requests; the multiplicity of activities provides robustness and increased throughput. In the compiler the many activities serve to encapsulate subtasks of the compilation process and to speed up the processing of a single request.

The SDL/PDL task force organization has levels of locality that reflect the Cm* hardware organization. The PDLs are roughly analogous to individual computer modules, and the SDLs are roughly analogous to clusters. Of course, Medusa does not force all information in a PDL/SDL to be in the same Cm/cluster, but we hope that this structure will encourage programmers to organize their programs in ways that map cleanly onto Cm*. Each PDL is always allocated in the processor that will execute the corresponding activity, as is the *activity control block* that contains saved registers and other execution state of the activity. If an activity allocates its critical information in its own processor and keeps descriptors for that information in its PDL, then the activity is not likely to be destroyed by hardware failures in other processors in the system.

The Medusa structures are organized so as not to associate unrelated information arbitrarily. The strong

---

[3] We felt that activities that are not closely related in their abstract functions should not interact in uncontrolled ways. Since the task force is the unit of abstraction, we decided to restrict read/write memory sharing to within a single task force.

Fig. 6. A Concurrent Compiler. Each activity of the task force implements one stage of the compilation process.

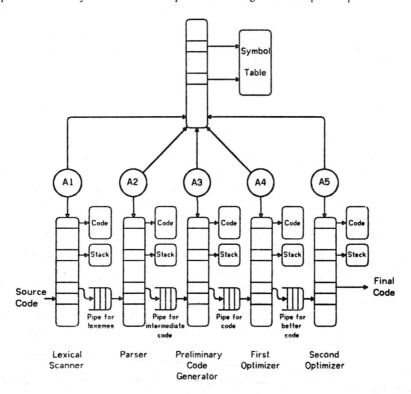

separation between the utilities is one example of this design goal. The descriptor organization is another. In many operating systems all of the descriptor information for all user programs is kept in one large array; a small failure in the array, or in a program that manipulates the array, may affect many otherwise unrelated portions of the system. In contrast, Medusa places descriptor information for each activity in a separate structure and places that structure in the processor that will execute the activity. The distribution and reliability of the system are roughly those of the user programs; the operating system imposes no hidden centralities.

There are two reasons for implementing the task force notion as a low-level system structure. First, most of the operating system functions are provided by task forces, hence the structure must exist at the operating system level. Second, for activities within a task force to interact on a fine grain, certain guarantees must be made to the task force. Foremost among these is the notion of *coscheduling* which, if not provided by the operating system, cannot be implemented using higher level protocols. A task force is said to be coscheduled if all of its runnable activities are simultaneously scheduled for execution on their respective processors. In large task forces whose activities interact frequently, it is often the case that the descheduling of a single activity can cause the whole task force to block on locks held by that activity. If the task force is not coscheduled, a form of thrashing occurs that is very similar to the thrashing in early demand paging systems. The set of activities that must execute together for a task force to make progress on its task is analogous to a process' working set in a paging system. If the operating system does not provide for coscheduling of this "activity working set," there is no way to simulate it at user level short of disabling time sharing. Simple algorithms have been developed for task force allocation and scheduling in Medusa to maximize coscheduling.

4. Overview of the Current System

The complete Medusa operating system consists of three parts:

The several Kmaps, each using about 4,000 80-bit words of microcode, cooperate to provide the basic interprocessor communication mechanisms. These include references to page objects, simple operations on descriptors that help to guarantee the consistency of descriptor space, block transfers, and operations upon message pipes and semaphore objects. A relatively powerful event system has been implemented, partially in Kmap microcode and partially by the utilities: it provides for events to be associated with many different kinds of objects in a similar way so that programs may signal and await events in a type-independent fashion.

A small *kernel* is replicated in each processor to respond to interrupts generated by that Cm. The kernels supply simple multiplexing and device handling code, currently amounting to about 400 words of basic kernel code and 250 additional words for each device type present on the processor's LSI-11 bus (most of the Cm's have no devices at all). The multiplexing code makes no policy decisions about which of the activities allocated to a processor should be executed; it merely provides a mechanism for switching execution contexts. Device routines translate interrupts into messages to the various utilities. In addition the device routines chain device commands to maximize throughput of the devices.

Almost all of the operating system functions are provided by a collection of five utilities. Each utility is a task force that implements one or a few abstractions for the rest of the system. The *memory manager* is responsible for the allocation of primary memory and also aids the Kmap microcode in descriptor list manipulation. The *file system* task force acts as a controller for all the input and output devices of the system and implements a hierarchical file system nearly identical to that of Unix [20]. The *task force manager* creates and deletes task forces and activities and provides some simple debugging functions. Two often overlooked portions of operating systems have been formalized in Medusa by making them utilities: the *exception reporter* and a *debugger/tracer*. When an exception occurs on a processor, the kernel of that processor reports the exceptional condition to the exception reporter. It is the responsibility of the exception reporter to communicate information about the exception to relevant parties. The debugger/tracer holds symbol tables and performance measurement information for all of the utilities. It provides facilities for on-line debugging of the system and for gathering performance data.

The activities of the utility task forces are spread among the available processors, typically with no more than one utility activity per processor. Although no memory is shared between utilities, central tables and synchronization locks for a given utility are shared between all the activities of that utility. The Kmaps route messages from user activities to utilities when the user activities request services from the utilities (see below); the same scheme is also used for service requests made by one utility of another.

5. Pipes and Utility Communication

5.1 The Implementation of Pipes

Pipes in Medusa are similar to those of Unix [20] in that they hold uninterpreted strings of bytes. The operation of Medusa pipes differs from that of Unix pipes in two important ways: (1) the integrity of messages in Medusa is insured by maintaining byte counts for each message and by permitting only whole messages to be read from pipes; (2) the identity of the sender of each message is made available to the receiver of the message. Descriptors may not be passed using the pipe mechanism; instead, descriptors are moved by the memory manager utility in response to requests issued via pipes.

In a system that uses message transactions as a procedure invocation mechanism, the overhead involved in such transactions is of fundamental importance. The degree to which the system can be partitioned is limited from an efficiency standpoint by the cost of an interaction between components. The time required for a 5–10 word message interaction in Medusa is approximately the same as the time used in executing 30 LSI-11 instructions; that is, assume that a server has attempted to receive a message from an empty pipe and hence has been suspended; the time between the initiation of a "send" operation by an invoker (executing on a different processor) and the fetch of the first instruction by the server after receiving the message is roughly 250 microseconds, or about 30 average LSI-11 instruction times. This is about the same time overhead as a high-level language procedure call in which registers must be saved and a display updated.

A primary reason for the efficiency of the message mechanism is the treatment of the "pipe empty" and "pipe full" conditions. In a producer–consumer relationship between activities, it is unlikely that the producer and consumer will operate at exactly the same speed. The communication pipe will almost always be either empty or full and one of the activities will usually have to wait for the other. Virtually all existing operating systems reschedule a processor as soon as the current activity blocks on an empty or full pipe; this means that when the pipe becomes nonempty or nonfull a second context swap must be executed to reactivate the now-runnable activity. Thus almost every interaction between activities results in processor context swaps. In uniprocessor systems the context swaps are necessary since only a single activity can execute at a time; however, in a multiprocessor system the context swaps may become the efficiency bottleneck in the interprocess communication mechanism.

For Medusa, we wished to provide a mechanism that would permit interactions to occur on a substantially finer grain than that of a context swap. When an activity attempts to send to a full pipe or receive from an empty pipe, its execution is suspended until the operation can proceed. However, the activity does not relinquish its processor immediately. For a small interval of time, called the *pause time* and specifiable by the activity, the activity's processor remains idle with the activity loaded. If the activity becomes runnable within the pause time it is reactivated without incurring any context swaps. If the pause time is exceeded, then the processor reschedules itself to another activity. Note that if the time for which the activity is blocked is less than two context swap times, then the lost processor time due to the pause is less than the time that would otherwise have been wasted in context swaps.

5.2 Utility Descriptor Lists

Communication between user activities and utilities, and also between utilities and other utilities, is accomplished via a set of message pipes using the message-passing mechanism described above. The collection of pipes used for utility communication is a critical system

404

Communications
of
the ACM

February 1980
Volume 23
Number 2

resource whose organization affects both the reliability and modularity of the system.

Every processor contains a special descriptor list, called a *utility descriptor list* (UDL), that is used by the activities of that processor to communicate with utilities. To invoke a utility operation a user activity specifies to its Kmap the index of a pipe descriptor in its processor's UDL and a message to be placed into the selected pipe. Each descriptor in a UDL corresponds to a set of operating system functions. The assignment of particular slots of utility descriptor lists was made at system design time, and is analogous to the assignment of trap numbers to particular functions in other operating systems. The descriptors in the UDLs are divided into two groups: the first group may be used by either user or utility activities; the second group is visible only to utility activities and is used to invoke functions that are privileged to utilities.

If there were only a single utility descriptor list, then both the reliability and performance of Medusa would be jeopardized. The assignment of UDL slots to functions is the same for all UDLs; however, having several UDLs makes it easier to share the implementation of a function between several activities. For example, consider the pipes used to invoke the OPEN operation provided by the file system. Normally, the file system task force contains two activities. Half of the UDLs in the system will contain descriptors for a pipe serviced by the first activity, and the other half will contain descriptors for a pipe serviced by the second. If one of the file system activities becomes overloaded, it will spawn a new activity in the file system task force and replace several of the OPEN descriptors in UDLs with descriptors for a new pipe served by the new activity. If at some later time the new activity becomes underloaded, it may overwrite its UDL descriptors with descriptors for the pipes serviced by the other file system activities and kill itself. Similarly, one activity may take over for another activity that has failed. Having one UDL per processor makes it relatively easy for workload to be exchanged between utility activities in a way that is transparent to the rest of the system. Note that it is also important that utility communication pipes are kept exclusively in the UDLs; if user activities were given private copies of these descriptors and allowed to move them around it would be extremely difficult for the utilities to find all the relevant descriptors during reconfiguration.

6. Utility Privileges

In order to guarantee the integrity of protected types such as descriptor lists, there must exist mechanisms to insure that the utility that implements each type may access its internal representation while other, less-trusted, programs may not. Thus, each utility activity executes with a status bit set to grant it several privileges not given to user activities. The privileges allow utilities to (1) share address space with other activities, and (2) perform certain special operations denied to user programs.

The sharing of address space is accomplished through an *external descriptor list* (XDL) accessible to each utility activity in addition to its PDL, the SDL of its task force, and the UDL of its processor. The XDL is not a distinct descriptor list, but just a mechanism to give a utility shared access to the PDL or SDL of another activity in the system. By presenting the absolute system name of a descriptor list to its Kmap, a utility activity maps its XDL onto that descriptor list such that references to the activity's XDL refer to the named descriptor list.

A simple form of *amplification* is provided to the utilities so that they can manipulate the representations of protected types of objects.[4] This is accomplished by allowing utilities to make special requests to the Kmaps, wherein an object is made readable and writable by the activity as if it were a page object, even though it is really of a protected type. The amplification affects only the utility activity that requested it: if other activities attempt to make read or write references to the object, then type violations will occur.

The combination of XDL usage and amplification provides a simple *seal* on objects. Thus objects can be stored with their owners yet be manipulated only by the utilities that implement them. Without this seal, each object would have to be stored with the utility that manipulated it and would consequently be more vulnerable to failures in the utility. Having some sort of seal mechanism is critical to our ability to distribute and reconfigure the system. Medusa's protection mechanism is a relatively simple one; readers are referred to [21] and the protection literature for a more detailed discussion of these issues.

The XDL and amplification privileges are used extensively by the utilities. For example, when a user activity requests that information be written into a file, the file system utility amplifies a *file control block* (accessible through the user's SDL or PDL) to determine where on disk to write the information. Upon completion of the write, the information in the file control block is updated. The file system uses its XDL to read information from the user activity's pages into the actual disk buffers. Task force creation also illustrates how the XDL and amplification privileges are used: the memory manager uses its utility privileges to access allocation tables and thereby create the descriptor lists for the new task force; the task force manager then amplifies the kernel areas of relevant processors to enter the new activities into scheduling tables.

During the design of Medusa a tradeoff was made between the number of special utility privileges and the degree of distribution of the system. The replicated por-

---

[4] Amplification is a mechanism that permits users to hold tokens for objects without being able to access their representations. When the token is passed to the subsystem responsible for the object's implementation, the subsystem *amplifies* the token to obtain access to the information that represents the object. Thus tokens for objects may be passed around the system at will, yet operations upon the object may be performed only by the subsystem with the ability to amplify the tokens [14].

tion of the system consists of 400 words of kernel code in each processor and 4,000 microinstructions in each Kmap. The kernel and Kmap code provide what we perceive to be the minimum functionality needed to tie together a distributed system in an efficient and protected way. The largest portion of the operating system (thirty to forty thousand words) is distributed among the utilities. It would have been desirable to provide a general enough object addressing mechanism that utilities could get all the privileges they needed via the object mechanism. For example, a mechanism like that of Hydra [4] would have provided a substantially finer grain of protection than we have with the single utility status bit, would have enabled a closer enforcement of the "need-to-know" principle, and would have eliminated the need for any special utility privileges. Unfortunately, the implementation of such a general mechanism would have enormously increased the complexity of the replicated kernel and Kmap code. This is not to say that such general mechanisms are undesirable. Rather, we contend that for a system to be distributed it must be *layered*; if all mechanisms are implemented at the system's lowest level, then they must be replicated everywhere. Since one of the principal design goals of Medusa was to distribute its functionality, we decided that the proper place to implement a general object mechanism would be *in* the utilities rather than underneath them.

7. The Internal Structure of Utilities

7.1 Deadlock

The potential for deadlock arises as a direct consequence of the low-level distribution of operating system functions among disjoint utilities. This section introduces the deadlock problem and the restrictions placed on utility interactions in order to eliminate it.

Consider the OPEN operation implemented by the file system utility. In order to open a file, storage must be allocated for the file control block that will be used during transfers to and from the file. Thus a file system activity executing the OPEN operation must invoke the memory manager utility to allocate the storage. It might turn out that the memory manager was unable to meet the allocation request without swapping information between primary and secondary memory, so it would have to request one or more I/O transfers from the file system. This circularity of requests between the file system and the memory manager could result in a deadlock situation with all the file system activities awaiting results from the memory manager and all of the memory manager activities awaiting I/O transfers from the file system; there would be no file system activities to service the I/O requests.

Another example of an operating system containing circular dependencies between system modules is described by Schroeder at al. in [22]. Habermann et al. [9] have argued that in general there is no correspondence between the notions of *module* and *invocation level*; even though the invocation dependencies of a system are hierarchical, the dependencies between modules may still be circular. Figure 7 depicts the example of the previous paragraph. There are three invocation levels, consisting of the OPEN, ALLOC, and I/O operations. There are two modules, the file system and memory manager, and two invocation dependencies, represented by arrows. Deadlock could occur if all of the service resources of the file system become allocated to OPEN requests, leaving none to service I/O requests.

The standard implementation used in operating systems has been to allocate service resources dynamically from a large central pool to each invocation level of an operation. For example, many uniprocessor systems allocate an independent kernel stack for each user process. When a kernel operation is invoked, frames on the user's kernel stack are allocated for each invocation of a procedure within the kernel. As long as the total depth of the stack is not exceeded, circularities may exist in the interactions between kernel modules.

The distribution of the Medusa utilities makes it impossible to share service resources between invocation levels. An invocation of one utility by another crosses execution environments such that a common call stack is infeasible. An alternative solution would be to pass all of the execution state of a transaction from each utility to the next one that it calls, thus freeing up the resources of the caller. Unfortunately this would be intolerably inefficient, and would make the execution state of each utility vulnerable to the whims of other utilities that it invokes. Another approach would be to allocate new resources at the time of each call, for example by creating a new utility activity to serve each request. In addition to being rather inefficient, the creation of a new activity, or even the allocation of memory, would itself require a utility call and hence could not be done as part of the calling sequence. The potential for deadlock is a result of the fact that even the low-level system functions are distributed among several disjoint environments.

Two conditions must be met for a distributed system like Medusa to be deadlock free. First, all of the functions provided by utilities must be divided up into *service classes* such that (1) a single utility provides all of the services in each class and (2) there are no circularities in the dependencies between service classes. A single utility may implement more than one service class. In the terminology of [9] each service class is the collection of functions provided by a single module at a single invocation level. In the example of Figure 7 the OPEN and CLOSE functions, as well as several others, are included in one service class while I/O functions are contained in another and memory allocation functions in a third. The second condition for deadlock avoidance is that each utility must contain separate (statically allocated) pools of resources so that it can provide independent service to each of its service classes. In the current Medusa system the utilities provide about five service classes apiece, and

406

Communications
of
the ACM

February 1980
Volume 23
Number 2

Fig. 7. A hierarchical set of calls that leads to circular utility interactions.

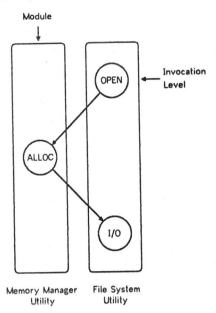

Fig. 8. The internal structure of a utility activity.

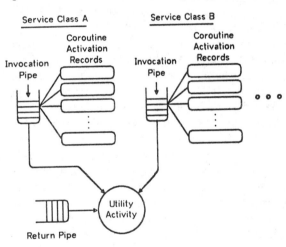

the invocation hierarchy of the system as a whole contains eight levels.

7.2 Coroutines and Multi-Eventing

One way to satisfy the requirement that independent facilities be provided for each class of utility service is to dedicate particular activities of a utility to provide each of the classes of service supported by the utility. This eliminates the possibility of deadlock, but makes relatively poor use of the utility activities since some service classes are rarely invoked. It also precludes load-sharing between utility activities that are responsible for different service classes.

The solution used in Medusa is to structure utility activities as collections of coroutines or processes, as shown in Figure 8. Every activity in a utility task force is capable of providing any and all of the classes of

service implemented by the utility. For each class of service provided by the utility there is a separate invocation pipe and a pool of coroutines that serve requests received via the pipe. Descriptors with receive privilege for the invocation pipes are held in the PDL of the activity, and descriptors with send privilege are present in one or more UDLs around the system. Each coroutine has its own activation record containing a stack and other local information. The coroutines are allocated statically to the service of particular invocation pipes, so that the overloading of any one pipe cannot affect the activity's ability to service the others.

When a message arrives from an invocation pipe, one of that pipe's coroutines is allocated to serve the message. The coroutine remains allocated to the request until it completes, at which time the coroutine's activation record is returned to the free pool associated with the pipe. If the coroutine needs to request a service from another utility, then the activity executes other runnable coroutines while the remote service is being provided. When a reply is received for the coroutine it is reactivated and continues service. To the coroutine the remote service request appears like a procedure call. In addition to eliminating the deadlock problem, the use of coroutines increases the throughput of each utility activity by allowing it to process one transaction while another waits for remote service.

A single return pipe is shared by all of the coroutines of the activity to receive acknowledgments from other utilities. When an invocation message is sent from one utility to another, as in the case of the ALLOC request of Figure 7, a *transaction identifier* is sent in the message. The invoked utility must return the transaction identifier in the acknowledging message. The identifier indicates which coroutine is to be reactivated and provides a simple validity check on the acknowledging message.

At any given time a utility activity could potentially receive messages over any of several pipes. The Kmap microcode used by Medusa implements a *multi-event* system whereby an activity may wait for the first message to arrive from any of a set of pipes. For a utility this normally includes all of its invocation pipes and its return pipe. When the current coroutine of the activity cannot continue execution, either because it completed its current operation or because it invoked another utility, the *MultiEventWait* Kmap operation is invoked. This causes the activity to suspend until a message is received on one of the pipes in the set. When a message is received, the activity is reactivated with an indication of the pipe from which the message was received. If the pipe is an invocation pipe, then a coroutine is allocated to service the message and the activity begins executing the coroutine at a standard startup address. If the pipe is the return pipe, then the transaction identifier in the return message is verified and a return is made to the coroutine that invoked the transaction. If all the activation records for a particular invocation pipe become allocated, the pipe is removed from the activity's multi-event set so that requests via the pipe will be stored in the pipe until coroutines become available to service them.

The coroutine structure of the utilities is visible only to a few routines that are used to invoke other utilities and recycle coroutines after they have completed requests. The vast majority of utility code is completely unaffected by the internal multiplexing of each activity. Since the utilities already contain multiple concurrent activities, there are no additional synchronization constraints imposed by the internal multiplexing except that busy-waiting on locks cannot be permitted (busy-waiting prevents another coroutine of the same activity from executing code to release the lock).

8. Exception Reporting

The combination in Medusa of distribution and cooperation has had interesting effects on several portions of the system. Section 7 discussed some of the difficulties encountered in the design of the utilities because of their distribution. This section briefly describes two ways in which the distribution and sharing have impacted the exception reporting mechanism. The sharing of objects has led to two different views of exceptions, *internal* and *external*. The sharing of a control function within a task force, combined with the distribution of the activities of the task force, has resulted in the notion of a *buddy* that can handle exceptions remotely.

For a discussion of what constitutes an exception, readers are referred to [16]; our informal definition is that an exception is just an unusual occurrence, which may *or may not* be an error. Several exception classes are defined in Medusa, ranging from parity errors to the execution of unimplemented instructions. Each activity is allowed to specify for each class a *handler* to be invoked when an exception from that class is generated by the activity.

When an object is shared, it is reasonable for all the co-owners of that object to participate in the handling of exceptions that occur for the object. However, the exception may manifest itself in two ways to the different co-owners. For each detection of an exceptional condition there is exactly one activity whose explicit action uncovered the exception. To this activity the exception is manifested as an *internal condition*; the execution state of the activity is directly involved with the exception, and the handler may have to unwind operations in progress. The other co-owners, although interested in being notified of the exception, were not directly involved in its detection. The exception is seen by them as an *external condition* whose occurrence is not necessarily related to the current actions of the co-owners. The handler for an external condition is generally concerned with the state of the shared abstraction but not with the execution state of its activity. An exception may be reported internally without being reported externally if no shared abstraction is involved; however, all external conditions also

have corresponding internal conditions.[5] The double view of exceptions arises only because it is possible to share objects between independent activities.

While the distinction between internal and external conditions arose because of data sharing, the notion of a buddy has arisen because of control sharing in a distributed environment. It is often easier to handle an exceptional condition at a point that is physically and logically distinct from the site of the exception's discovery (see the next paragraph for examples). Medusa allows an activity to present the name of a *buddy* activity within the same task force as handler for any exception class. When the exception occurs the buddy activity is notified. While handling the exception the buddy receives access to all the private information of the exception-generating activity, which is suspended. Buddies are only useful if the buddy is relatively distinct from the exception-generating activity, yet has enough knowledge of the other activity's function to take reasonable actions on its behalf; fortunately, this is almost exactly the relationship between the activities of a task force.

We believe the notion of a buddy to be an especially useful one: two examples follow. A failure in a code page is conceptually a simple one to recover, since virtually all modern-day code is pure. However, it may be extremely difficult for the activity whose code page is lost to recover itself, since recovery code may have been contained in the page. A solution is for the activity to specify a buddy handler for hard errors in the page. The buddy need merely locate a duplicate copy of the code and replace the bad page with a fresh copy (in the case of Medusa utilities, each activity contains an identical copy of the code, making this task especially simple). The activity that generated the exception then repeats the instruction that failed and goes on its way with no explicit knowledge that an error occurred. Another potential use of the buddy mechanism is in emulation. Programs written for an operating system that use TRAP instructions for invocation can be run as one activity of a task force, with TRAP instruction exceptions being handled by a buddy. The buddy activity uses Medusa calls to emulate the desired effects of the TRAP instruction and then allows the trapping activity to proceed. In this way programs written for other operating systems may be run on Medusa with no changes to their code.

9. Comparisons and Conclusions

Many similarities exist between Medusa and the StarOS system. Both systems are object oriented and both provide for task forces of cooperating activities. However, tradeoffs in StarOS generally were made in favor of providing an extremely flexible set of facilities to high-level users; tradeoffs in Medusa generally were made in favor of producing a highly distributed operating system structure that closely matched the hardware.

---

[5] This is just another way of saying that exceptional conditions do not arise spontaneously, but must be explicitly checked for.

For example, StarOS task forces are much more general than Medusa task forces. The precisely defined structure of Medusa task forces may occasionally constrain users, but allows us to support the structure with coscheduling and with buddy exception handling; these facilities would be much more difficult to support in the more general StarOS task force framework. The StarOS object mechanism provides a finer grain of protection than Medusa's mechanism, but has resulted in a more centralized structure.

Message communication in Medusa is similar to the usage of links in DEMOS to communicate with the operating system [1], while task forces are somewhat similar to teams of processes in Thoth [3]. A substantial difference between the systems is the presence of concurrency in Medusa. Thus issues not present in DEMOS arise concerning the sharing of work between the activities of a utility task force and the dynamic reconfiguration of the system. Memory sharing in Thoth is restricted to processes in the same team, just as it is restricted to activities of the same task force in Medusa. However, Thoth guarantees that only a single process of a team executes at any one time and that it is not interrupted by any other processes of the team; Medusa attempts to insure that ALL activities of a task force execute simultaneously.

Several designs for exception reporting mechanisms have been proposed in the literature, among them [8], [16], and [17]. All of these are based in programming languages; the reporting mechanism for Medusa is not intended to replace them. Rather it provides an entry mechanism into the reporting schemes of individual languages, leaving the languages to propagate exception information among the abstract levels of a program. Medusa's scheme also provides facilities for passing exception information between programs.

The design of Medusa was begun in the late fall of 1977, and coding started in the summer of 1978. The status of Medusa at the time of this writing (November 1979) is as follows: all of the Kmap microcode and utility code has been written and microcode testing is nearly complete. The Medusa system has been successfully loaded onto the machine and the debugger utility is operational. Testing of the remaining utilities has just begun, with roughly two-thirds of all the utility code yet to be tested. We expect preliminary utility testing to be complete by early 1980, with a Unix emulator running shortly thereafter.

In summary, Medusa has attempted to achieve modularity, robustness, and performance in a Cm* operating system using a structure that embodies at its lowest level both distribution and concurrency. No processor of the system is self-sufficient, yet no processor should be critical to the operation of the system. We intend to evaluate our success by measuring how well the system can deal with changes in its environment, including changes in user load as well as failures in hardware, firmware, and software.

Acknowledgments. The authors wish to thank Prof. Nico Habermann, whose comments concerning both the operating system and this paper have been extremely helpful.

Received June 1979; accepted September 1979; revised November 1979

References
1. Baskett, F., Howard, J.H., and Montague, J.T. Task communication in DEMOS. Proc. 6th Symp. Operating Systems Principles, SIGOPS, 1977, pp. 23–32.
2. Bell, G.C., and Newell A. *Computer Structures: Readings and Examples.* McGraw-Hill, New York, 1971.
3. Cheriton, D.R., Malcolm, M.A., Melen, L.S., and Sager, G.R. Thoth, a portable real-time operating system. *Comm. ACM 22,* 2 (Feb. 1979), 105–114.
4. Cohen, E., and Jefferson, D. Protection in the Hydra operating system. Proc. 5th Symp. Operating Systems Principles, SIGOPS, 1975, pp. 141–160.
5. Denning, P.J. Fault tolerant operating systems. *Comput. Surv. 8,* 4 (Dec. 1976), 359–389.
6. Fuller, S.H., Jones, A.K., Durham, I., Eds. Cm* Review, June 1977. Carnegie-Mellon Univ., June 1977.
7. Fuller, S.H., Ousterhout, J.K., Raskin, L., Rubinfeld, P., Sindhu, P.S., and Swan, R.J. Multi-microprocessors: An overview and working example. *Proc. IEEE 66,* 2 (1978), 216–228.
8. Goodenough, J.B. Exception handling: Issues and a proposed notation. *Comm. ACM 18,* 12 (Dec. 1975), 683–696.
9. Habermann, A.N., Flon, L., and Cooprider, L. Modularization and hierarchy in a family of operating systems. *Comm. ACM 19,* 5 (May 1976), 266–272.
10. Jones, A.K., Chansler, R.J. Jr., Durham, I., Feiler, P., and Schwans, K. Software management of Cm*—A distributed multiprocessor. Proc. AFIPS 1977 NCC, Vol. 46, AFIPS Press, Arlington, Va., 1977, pp. 657–663.
11. Jones, A.K., Chansler, R.J. Jr., Durham, I., Feiler, P., Scelza, D.A., Schwans, K., and Vegdahl, S.R. Programming issues raised by a multiprocessor. *Proc. IEEE 66,* 2 (1978), 229–237.
12. Jones, A.K., et al. StarOS, a multiprocessor operating system for the support of task forces. Proc. 7th Symp. Operating Systems Principles, SIGOPS, 1979, pp. 117–127.
13. Jones, A.K., and Schwans, K. TASK forces: Distributed software for solving problems of substantial size. 4th Int. Conf. Software Eng., SIGSOFT, 1979, pp. 315–330.
14. Jones, A.K. Protection in programmed systems. Ph.D. Th., Carnegie-Mellon Univ., Pittsburgh, Pa., 1973.
15. Lauer, H.C., and Needham, R.M. On the duality of operating system structures. Proc. 2nd Int. Symp. Operating Systems, IRIA, 1978; Reprinted in *Operating Syst. Rev. 13,* 2 (April 1979), 3–19.
16. Levin, R. Program structures for exceptional condition handling. Ph.D Th., Carnegie-Mellon Univ., Pittsburgh, Pa., June 1977.
17. Liskov, B., and Snyder, A. Structured exception handling. Lab. for Computer Science, M.I.T., Cambridge, Mass., March 1979.
18. Parnas, D.L. On the criteria to be used in decomposing systems into modules. *Comm. ACM 15,* 12 (Dec. 1972), 1053–1058.
19. Raskin, L. Performance evaluation of multiple processor systems. Ph.D. Th., Carnegie-Mellon Univ., Pittsburgh, Pa., Aug. 1978.
20. Ritchie, D.M., and Thompson, K. The UNIX time-sharing system. *Comm. ACM 17,* 7 (July 1974), 365–375.
21. Saltzer, J.H., and Schroeder, M.D. The protection of information in computer systems. *Proc. IEEE 63,* 9 (1975), 1278–1308.
22. Schroeder, M.D., Clark, D.D., and Saltzer, J.H. The Multics kernel design project. Proc. 6th Symp. Operating Systems Principles, SIGOPS, 1977, pp. 43–56.
23. Sutherland, I.E., and Mead, C.A. Microelectronics and computer science. *Sci. Amer. 237,* 3 (Sept. 1977), 210–229.
24. Swan, R.J. The switching structure and addressing architecture of an extensible multiprocessor: Cm*. Ph.D. Th., Carnegie-Mellon Univ., Pittsburgh, Pa., Aug. 1978.
25. Swan, R.J., Bechtolsheim, A., Lai, K., and Ousterhout, J.K. The implementation of the Cm* multi-microprocessor. Proc. AFIPS 1977 NCC, Vol. 46, AFIPS Press, Arlington, Va. 1977, pp. 645–655.
26. Swan, R.J., Fuller, S.H., and Siewiorek, D.P. Cm*—A modular, multi-microprocessor. Proc. AFIPS 1977 NCC, Vol. 46, AFIPS Press, Arlington Va., 1977, pp. 637–644.

10. Algorithms for Parallel Computers

In this chapter the first paper by Sameh is a survey of parallel numerical algorithms, most of which are suitable for pipelined and array processors. A discussion on parallel algorithms for multiprocessors is presented in the second paper by Kung. Although parallel numeric algorithms are more prevalent than parallel nonnumeric algorithms, the majority of the world's computing budget is spent on nonnumeric processing. Particular parallel nonnumeric algorithms are described in the last two papers. Stone's paper describes sorting in a pipelined processor, and Bayer and Schkolnick's paper studies operations on B-trees.

Additional information and many references on parallel numeric algorithms can be found in the surveys by Heller (1977) and Ortega and Voight (1977). In Kung's (1980) paper, the reader can find, among other things, information on the parallel processing of database operations; and on parallel algiorithms suitable for implementation in VLSI technology. Some parallel algorithms for graph theoretical problems are studies in Wisniewski and Sameh (1979) and Reghbati and Corneil (1978). Sorting algorithms for parallel architectures other than a pipelined processor are studied by Thompson and Kung (1977), Robinson (1977), and Stone (1971).

EHO182-6/81/0000/0411 © 1981 IEEE

NUMERICAL PARALLEL ALGORITHMS -- A SURVEY[*]

Ahmed H. Sameh

University of Illinois at Urbana-Champaign

Reprinted with permission from *High Speed Computer and Algorithm Organization*, 1977, pages 207-228. Copyright © 1977 by Academic Press.

I. INTRODUCTION

Many of the available sequential numerical algorithms make poor use of parallel and vector computers that have appeared recently. Efforts have been going on for some time for developing parallel algorithms for various applications. Some success has been realized judging by the papers published on the subject. Several excellent surveys have also appeared. Miranker [71] summarized the situation as it existed in the late 1960s, recently Heller [77] has given an up-to-date account of parallel algorithms in numerical linear algebra, and Ortega and Voigt [77] gave a detailed account of available algorithms for solving partial differential equations on vector computers. Much work remains to be done. For example, we are still far from obtaining a collection of such high quality algorithms as those available for sequential computers as in Wilkinson and Reinsch [71], the EISPACK package (Smith, et al [74]), or LINPACK package which is still under development. Great efforts have been expended in developing and analyzing such reliable sequential algorithms, and we do not expect the job of developing corresponding parallel algorithms to be any easier.

In this brief survey we present an account of numerical algorithms suitable for parallel computers. We do not include the various algorithms developed for vector computers such as the CDC-STAR and the CRAY-1. To facilitate the analysis and presentation of these algorithms, we adopt the following model of a parallel computer:

(i) an unlimited number of processors are available,

(ii) each processor can evaluate any of the four arithmetic operations and the maximum (or minimum) of two numbers in one time step, and

(iii) no memory or data alignment time penalties are incurred.

While assumptions (i) and (iii) may be unrealistic, the algorithms presented here can be easily modified if only a limited number of processors are available. As for assumption (iii), it is not difficult to add to the arithmetic time required by any algorithm the additional time due to memory conflicts and data alignment on a certain realizable computer. Admittedly, such extra time ("overhead") may overshadow the time required by arithmetic, and comparing the speedup of two algorithms cannot be complete without taking overhead into account. In some recent computers such as the BSP, see Stokes [77], pipelining does mask much of this time.

[*]This work was supported in part by the National Science Foundation under Grant No. MCS75-21758.

In section II, we briefly review algorithms for evaluating arithmetic expressions. With the exception of this section, all the algorithms presented here have been originally developed for single-instruction, multiple-data (SIMD) computers (adopting Flynn's notation, Flynn [72]), rather than multiple-instruction, multiple-data (MIMD) computers. In section III, we present a comprehensive summary of direct linear system solvers, and in section IV we discuss the few algorithms available for solving the algebraic standard eigenvalue problem. We do not consider iterative linear system solvers, or algorithms for the numerical handling of differential equations. Such subjects are adequately covered by Heller [77] and Ortega and Voigt [77].

Throughout this paper, we define the speedup of a parallel algorithm as the ratio of the corresponding sequential and parallel times. For example, if τ is the time required by an algorithm using π processors, and σ is the minimum time required by the same algorithm using one processor, then the speedup is given by $\sigma/\tau \geq 1$. We also define the efficiency of the calculation by $\sigma/(\pi \tau) \leq 1$. Another important parameter is the redundancy of a parallel algorithm. If the parallel algorithm requires ω arithmetic operations, then its redundancy is defined by $\rho = \omega/\sigma \geq 1$; ($\omega$ is the number of distinct nodes in the computational graph of the parallel algorithm). The larger the redundancy of a parallel algorithm, the larger the probability that the parallel algorithm is not as numerically stable as its sequential counterpart. Several people are investigating the numerical stability of parallel algorithms and we report such available results here.

We use Householder's notation (Householder [64]), so unless otherwise indicated, lower case Greek letters represent scalars; lower case Latin letters, column vectors; capital letters, Greek or Latin, matrices. In what follows, A is a real matrix of order n. We also denote the bandwidth of a matrix by (m + 1). Without loss of generality, we assume that both m and n are powers of 2, and log x denotes $\lceil \log_2 x \rceil$.

II. EVALUATION OF ARITHMETIC EXPRESSIONS

By an arithmetic expression E(n) we mean any well-formed string composed of the four arithmetic operations (+, -, x, /), left and right parentheses, and n distinct atoms which are constants or variables. By distinct, we mean that each atom appears just once in the expression. On a sequential machine such an expression can be evaluated in 0(n) time steps. If we have a parallel computer with an unlimited number of processors, then by a simple fan-in argument the lower bound on the evaluation time of E(n) is log n steps. One important arithmetic expression that can be evaluated in a time close to this lower bound is the inner product of two n-vectors. Let x, y be such vectors, then the inner product $x^t y = \sum_{i=1}^{n} \xi_i \eta_i$ can be computed sequentially in (2n - 1) steps, (n multiplications and n - 1 additions). On a parallel computer with n processors, this inner product can be computed in (1 + log n) steps, (one multiplication and log n additions). This results in an approximate speedup and efficiency of (2n/log2n) and (2/log2n),

respectively. Note that the number of operations is the same as the sequential algorithm, i.e., no redundancy.

A comparison of the rounding errors in the sequential and parallel algorithms is of interest. Let * denote any of the four arithmetic operations, then a floating-point operation satisfies $f\ell(\xi_1 * \xi_2) = (\xi_1 * \xi_2)(1 + \delta)$ where $|\delta| \le \varepsilon$ in which ε is the unit roundoff. If β is the radix of the machine and d is the length of the fraction, then $\varepsilon = (1/2)\beta^{1-d}$ for rounded operations, and β^{1-d} for chopping. An error analysis of the sequential algorithm, e.g., see Wilkinson [63] or Stewart [73], shows that if σ_s is the computed inner product, then

$$\sigma_s = \sum_{i=1}^{n} \xi_i \eta_i (1 + \gamma_i) \tag{2.1}$$

where $|\gamma_1| < 1.06\, n\, \varepsilon$ and $|\gamma_j| < 1.06\,(n - j + 2)\, \varepsilon$ for $j \ge 2$. Here we assume that $n\, \varepsilon < 0.1$ which is not restrictive for computers with reasonable word length. An error analysis of the parallel algorithm has been given by Linz [70], if σ_p is the computed value, then

$$\sigma_p = \sum_{i=1}^{n} \xi_i \eta_i (1 + \rho_i) \tag{2.2}$$

where $|\rho_i| < 1.06\, \varepsilon\, \log 2n$ for $i \ge 1$. For values $|\xi_i \eta_i|$ that do not vary greatly, the parallel algorithm certainly has a lower absolute error bound than that of the sequential algorithm, and generally yields more accurate results.

A direct application of inner products is in computing matrix-vector and matrix-matrix products. Let A, B be two matrices of order n and x be an n-vector. Then the products $f = Ax$ and $C = AB$ can be obtained in $(1 + \log n)$ steps provided we have n^2 and n^3 processors, respectively. The respective speedups are $0(n^2/\log n)$ and $0(n^3/\log n)$ with the same efficiency as an inner product. Note also that the number of operations is identical to the sequential process in each case, i.e., no redundancy.

Various parallel algorithms have been developed for evaluating more general arithmetic expressions E(n). All these algorithms show that, given enough processors, E(n) can be evaluated in $0(\log n)$ steps resulting in $0(n/\log n)$ speedup over the sequential algorithm. In what follows, we present a brief survey of the fundamental results. Brent [74] has shown that, given $3(n - 1)$ processors, E(n) may be evaluated in time no more than $4\log n$ steps with $0(n)$ operations, i.e., redundancy $\rho = 0(1)$. It was also indicated, via Miller's software package for automatic roundoff error analysis, e.g., see Miller [75], that the algorithm is not stable in the presence of division. Muller and Preparata [76] reduced the time to $2.88 \log n + 1$ steps at the cost of increasing the processors and operations to $0(n^{1.44})$ yielding a redundancy $\rho = 0(n^{0.44})$. For expressions E(n) that do not contain division, some savings can be realized. Brent [73] showed that given only $(n - 1)$ processors, an algorithm requiring no more than $4\log n$ steps and $0(n)$ operations is numerically stable. Muller and Preparata [76] reduced the time to $2.08 \log n$ for such expression but again at the cost of increasing the processors and operations to $0(n^{1.817})$

resulting in an even higher redundancy of $O(n^{0.817})$. This leads us to believe that their algorithm is likely to be less stable than Brent's. An error analysis of the algorithms in Muller and Preparata [76] is not yet available.

Brent [74] also showed that if any computation can be completed in τ time steps with ω operations and sufficiently many processors π, then for $\hat{\pi} < \pi$ processors it can be completed in time $\hat{\tau} \leq \tau + (\omega - \tau)/\hat{\pi}$. Thus, using $\hat{\pi}$ processors $E(n)$ can be evaluated in time $4\log n + 10(n - 1)/\hat{\pi}$. If $E(n)$ does not contain division the time reduces to only $4\log n + 2(n - 1)/\hat{\pi}$. For small number of processors $\hat{\pi}$, Winograd [75] has improved on Brent's results: $(3n/2\hat{\pi})$ $+ O(\log^2 n)$ for expressions without division, and $(5n/2\hat{\pi})$ $+ O(\log^2 n)$ for general expressions.

Finally, we consider matrix expressions. Muraoka and Kuck [73] solved the problem of minimizing the time to evaluate the product of a sequence of conformable arrays on a parallel computer. Kuck and Maruyama [75] showed that, given enough processors, any matrix expression including addition, multiplication, and matrix inversion requires $\alpha \log n + O(1)$ steps where $\alpha = 3 \tau_m + 2 \tau_a + \tau_i$ in which τ_m, τ_a and τ_i denote time for matrix multiplication, addition, and inversion, respectively.

III. DIRECT LINEAR SYSTEM SOLVERS

In this section we discuss direct parallel algorithms for solving linear systems $Ax = f$ where A is a nonsingular matrix of order n. Usually, the first step in solving such systems is to factor the matrix A. The two familiar factorizations are: (i) $PA = LU$, and (ii) $QA = R$. Here P is a permutation matrix, L is lower triangular, U and R are upper triangular, and Q is an orthogonal matrix. Once such factorizations are realized, solving the system $Ax = f$ reduces to solving triangular systems of equations. Therefore, we start this section by reviewing the various parallel algorithms for solving triangular systems, followed by algorithms for dense and tridiagonal matrices.

A. Triangular Systems

The problem of solving triangular systems of equations arises in many situations. One important case is the evaluation of linear recurrences of order $m \leq n - 1$

$$\xi_1 = \phi_1$$

$$\xi_i = \phi_i - \sum_{j=k}^{i-1} \lambda_{ij} \xi_j \qquad \begin{matrix} i = 2, 3, \ldots, n \\ k = \max\{1, i - m\} \end{matrix} \qquad (3.1)$$

In matrix notation, (3.1) may be written as $x = f - \tilde{L}x$, where $x^t = (\xi_1, \xi_2, \ldots, \xi_n)$, $f^t = (\phi_1, \phi_2, \ldots, \phi_n)$, and $\tilde{L}$ $= [\lambda_{ij}]$ is strictly lower triangular. Denoting $(I + \tilde{L})$ by L we obtain the unit lower triangular system of equations

$$Lx = f \tag{3.2}$$

where L is of bandwidth $m + 1$, i.e., $\lambda_{ij} = 0$ for $i - j > m$.

The sequential algorithm (3.1) requires $0(mn)$ steps. If we have m processors, a parallel scheme (column sweep algorithm, Kuck [76]) can be easily developed requiring $2(n - 1)$ steps. It also has the same stability properties as the sequential algorithm. If $\tilde{x}$ is the computed solution then $(L + \delta L) \tilde{x} = f$ where $||\delta L|| \leq m ||L|| \varepsilon$, Wilkinson [63], where $||\cdot||$ denotes the ∞-norm and ε is the unit roundoff error. The column sweep algorithm has a speedup of approximately m with efficiency $0(1)$ and no redundancy ($\rho = 1$). Heller [74], Orcutt [74], Borodin and Munro [75], and Chen and Kuck [75] presented three different algorithms for solving (3.2) for $m = n - 1$ in $0(\log^2 n)$ time steps using $0(n^3)$ processors. The resulting speedup over the sequential algorithm is $0(n^2/\log^2 n)$ with efficiency proportional to $1/(n \log^2 n)$. Among the above algorithms, the one given by Chen and Kuck [75] requires the lowest number of processors, $(n^3/68) + 0(n^2)$ and $(1/2) \log^2 n + (3/2) \log n$ time steps. We sketch briefly this algorithm as described in Sameh and Brent [77]. The inverse of L can be written as $L^{-1} = M_{n-1} M_{n-2} \cdots M_2 M_1$, where each M_i is an elementary lower triangular matrix given by $M_i = [e_1, e_2, \ldots, e_{i-1}, \ell, e_{i+1}, \ldots, e_n]$ with $\ell = (0, \ldots, 0, 1, -\lambda_{i+1,i}, -\lambda_{i+2,i}, \ldots, -\lambda_{n,i})^t$. Thus the solution can be expressed as

$$x = M_{n-1} M_{n-2} \cdots M_2 M_1 f \tag{3.3}$$

This product can be evaluated in parallel in $\log n$ stages, obtaining the above time and processor bounds. An error analysis of this algorithm, Sameh and Brent [77], shows that if $\tilde{x}$ is the computed solution then $(L + \delta L) \tilde{x} = f$ where $||\delta L|| \leq \varepsilon \alpha(n) \kappa^2(L) ||L||$, in which $\kappa(L)$ is the condition number of L and $\alpha(n) = 0(n^2 \log n)$. This bound on δL can be large compared to the sequential algorithm. Many experiments show that both the sequential and this parallel algorithm yield identical results. Certain ill-conditioned problems, however, show that the sequential algorithm indeed yields more accurate results. Consider problem (3.2) with,

$$L = \begin{bmatrix} 1 & & & \\ 1.07 & 1 & & \\ 1.02 & 1.10 & 1 & \\ \alpha & \beta & \gamma & 1 \end{bmatrix}, \text{ and } f = \begin{bmatrix} 1 \\ 2.07 \\ 3.12 \\ -4.00017 \end{bmatrix}$$

where $\alpha = 0.993 \times 10^{14}$, $\beta = -(\alpha + 4.0)$, $\gamma = -0.34 \times 10^{-3}$. The sequential algorithm (forward substitution) yielded the exact solution, $\xi_1 = \xi_2 = \xi_3 = 1.0$ and $\xi_4 = 0.00017$, on an IBM 360 with long precision (machine epsilon $\simeq 2.22 \times 10^{-16}$). The parallel algorithm also obtained the correct result for the first three components of the solution, but gave the value -0.0039 for ξ_4 (not even the correct sign). Using a software package developed by Miller [75] for automatic roundoff analysis, M. Heller [76] and Larson [76] independently observed such instability of the parallel algorithm. Finally, we note that the parallel algorithm has a redundancy $\rho = O(n)$.

Orcutt [74], and Chen and Kuck [75] also showed that if $m \leq (n/2) - 1$, then system (3.2) may be solved in $O(\log m \log n)$ steps using $O(m^2 n)$ processors. The algorithm in Chen and Kuck [75] is described in matrix notation in Sameh and Brent [77] as follows. Let L be partitioned as a block bidiagonal matrix with diagonal submatrices L_i, $i = 1, 2, \ldots, n/m$, and subdiagonal matrices

R_j, $j = 1, 2, \ldots, (n/m) - 1$, where L_i and R_j are lower and upper triangular, respectively. Premultiplying both sides of (3.2) by $D = \text{diag} (L_i^{-1})$ we obtain the system $L^{(0)} x = f^{(0)}$ where $L^{(0)}$ is block bidiagonal with identities of order m on the diagonal and matrices $G_j^{(0)} = L_{j+1}^{-1} R_j$ on the subdiagonal, and $f^{(0)} = Df$. Note that we do not invert the L_j's, but obtain $f^{(0)}$ and $G_i^{(0)}$ by solving triangular systems using the previous parallel algorithm. We repeat the process by multiplying both sides of $L^{(0)} x = f^{(0)}$ by $D^{(0)} = \text{diag} (L_i^{(0)})^{-1}$ where,

$$L_i^{(0)^{-1}} = \begin{bmatrix} I_m & 0 \\ -G_{2i-1}^{(0)} & I_m \end{bmatrix}.$$

Now $L^{(1)} = D^{(0)} L^{(0)}$ and $f^{(1)} = D^{(0)} f^{(0)}$ are obtained by simple multiplication. Eventually, $L^{(\log(n/m))} = I_n$ and $f^{(\log(n/m))} = x$. For $m \ll n$, such an algorithm yields approximate speedup and efficiency of $(2mn/\log 4m \log n)$ and $(4/m \log 4m \log n)$, respectively. The required number of operations is $O(m^2 n \log(n/2m))$ resulting in a redundancy $\rho = O(m \log(n/2m))$. Furthermore, for a given m the upper bound on the absolute error $||\tilde{x} - x||$ grows exponentially with n, Chen, Kuck, and Sameh [76]. Numerical experiments again indicate that except for few ill-conditioned cases the results obtained by this algorithm are identical to those of the sequential algorithm.

Chen [75], Chen and Sameh [75], and Hyafil and Kung [75] have discussed parallel algorithms for solving (3.2), with $m = n - 1$, when only a limited number of processors are used. Chen [75], and Chen, Kuck, and Sameh [76] have also described parallel algorithms for the banded case with a limited number of processors $2m \leq \hat{\pi} \leq n$, showing that the time reduces to $O(m^2 n/\hat{\pi})$. For $m, \hat{\pi} \ll n$, the speedup is approximately $(\hat{\pi}/m)$ with efficiency $(1/m)$. The required number of operations is $O(m^2 n)$ yielding a redundancy $\rho = O(m)$. Moreover, it was shown that if $\hat{\pi} \leq m \log n$ the bound on the absolute error is proportional to a low degree polynomial in n.

If these triangular systems are Toeplitz, i.e., λ_{ij} = α_{i-j}, then savings in the number of processors are realized. Chen [75] has shown that the time remains the same for the dense and banded cases, but the numbers of processors reduce to $O(n^2)$ and $O(mn)$, respectively, instead of $O(n^3)$ and $O(m^2n)$. For the banded case with limited number of processors $2m \leq \hat{\pi} \leq n$, the time reduces to $O(mn/\hat{\pi})$ instead of $O(m^2n/\hat{\pi})$.

We present our own interpretation of the algorithm for the dense Toeplitz case. First, we observe that if L is Toeplitz, then L^{-1} is Toeplitz, Lafon [75]. Hence, if we determine the first column of L^{-1}, the whole inverse is also determined. Now the algorithm presented in Borodin and Munro [75] can be applied efficiently. Consider a leading principal submatrix

$$\begin{bmatrix} L_1 & 0 \\ G_1 & L_1 \end{bmatrix}$$

of L, where L_1, G_1 are of order q and $L_1^{-1} e_1$ is known. The inverse of this principal submatrix is given by

$$\begin{bmatrix} L_1^{-1} & 0 \\ -L_1^{-1} G_1 L_1^{-1} & L_1^{-1} \end{bmatrix} ,$$

and can be computed in $2(1 + \log q)$ steps using q^2 processors. Starting with a leading principal submatrix of order 4, where

$$L_1^{-1} = \begin{bmatrix} 1 & 0 \\ -\alpha_1 & 1 \end{bmatrix} ,$$

and doubling the size every stage, we obtain the inverse of the leading principal submatrix M of order n/2 in

$$\sum_{q=2}^{n/4} 2(1 + \log q) = (\log^2 n - \log n - 2) \text{ steps with } n^2/16$$

processors. Thus the solution of (3.2), or

$$\begin{bmatrix} M & 0 \\ N & M \end{bmatrix} \begin{bmatrix} x_1 \\ x_2 \end{bmatrix} = \begin{bmatrix} f_1 \\ f_2 \end{bmatrix} ,$$

is given by $x_1 = M^{-1} f_1$, $x_2 = M^{-1} f_2 - M^{-1} NM^{-1} f_1$. Both x_1 and x_2 can be computed in $(1 + 3\log n)$ using no more than $n^2/4$ processors. This yields a total of $(\log^2 n + 2\log n - 1)$ steps with only $n^2/4$ processors. A scheme for the banded case can be similarly developed. It is of interest to note that evaluating a polynomial $p_{n-1}(x)$, of degree $(n - 1)$, at a given point $x = \xi$ reduces to obtaining the last element of the solution vector of a Toeplitz banded unit lower triangular with m = 1. In this case the time is only $1 + 2\log n$ steps with (n/2) processors.

418

B. Dense Systems

We consider first the most popular factorization, i.e., LU-factorization via Gaussian elimination, e.g., see Stewart [73]. Without pivoting, such an algorithm requires $3(n - 1)$ steps with $(n - 1)^2$ processors. The method fails, however, if any leading principal minor is zero. A pivoting strategy is necessary for the completion of the factorization. Observing that, for many models of parallel computers the maximum of n elements can be determined in log n steps using n/2 processors, then the factors L and U in Gaussian-elimination with partial pivoting, can be obtained in $O(n \log n)$ steps with $(n - 1)^2$ processors. This results in a speedup of $O(n^2/\log n)$ and efficiency proportional to $1/\log n$. Note also that the sequential and parallel algorithms have the same operation count, and stability properties.

Several methods are available for orthogonal factorization of A, e.g., see Stewart [73] or Wilkinson [65]. It is not difficult to show that using $O(n^2)$ processors, direct implementation of Householder's reduction and the Gram-Schmidt algorithm require $O(n \log n)$ steps. Givens' reduction, however, can be modified to produce a parallel algorithm of $O(n)$ steps with $O(n^2)$ processors, see Sameh and Kuck [76]. This yields a speedup of $O(n^2)$ with efficiency $O(1)$. Again we have no redundancy, $\rho = 1$, and the algorithm is as numerically stable as its sequential counterpart. Hence, Givens' reduction is the cheaper algorithm to use unless Gaussian elimination without pivoting does not fail. We describe the algorithm briefly. In the sequential algorithm the orthogonal matrix Q, in QA = R, is formed as the product of plane rotations each annihilating an element below the diagonal of A. In the parallel scheme, Q is the product of orthogonal matrices Q_j each being the direct sum of independent rotations. Thus, each Q_j can annihilate more than one element below the diagonal. There are several annihilation schemes. One such scheme achieves the reduction in $(2n - 3)$ transformations, i.e., $Q = Q_{2n-3} \cdots Q_2 Q_1$. Each Q_j is a block diagonal matrix with 2×2 matrices (rotations) on the diagonal. These rotations are chosen such that Q_j does not destroy any zeros in $(Q_{j-1} \cdots Q_2 Q_1 A)$. In the figure below, we illustrate the pattern of element annihilation for n = 10. By an integer k we denote all the elements annihilated by Q_k.

*	*	*	*	*	*	*	*	*	*
9	*	*	*	*	*	*	*	*	*
8	10	*	*	*	*	*	*	*	*
7	9	11	*	*	*	*	*	*	*
6	8	10	12	*	*	*	*	*	*
5	7	9	11	13	*	*	*	*	*
4	6	8	10	12	14	*	*	*	*
3	5	7	9	11	13	15	*	*	*
2	4	6	8	10	12	14	16	*	*
1	3	5	7	9	11	13	15	17	*

Csanky [76] observed that the method of Leverrier (see Faddeev and Faddeeva [63] or Wilkinson [65]), for computing the characteristic polynomial of a matrix may be used to solve the system Ax = f. By the Cayley-Hamilton theorem we have

$$(-1)^n [A^n - \gamma_1 A^{n-1} - \gamma_2 A^{n-2} \ldots - \gamma_{n-1} A - \gamma_n I] = 0,$$

hence, $A^{-1} = (1/\gamma_n)[A^{n-1} - \gamma_1 A^{n-2} - \gamma_2 A^{n-2} - \ldots - \gamma_{n-2} A - \gamma_{n-1} I]$. The coefficients γ_i are given by the lower triangular system $\sigma_1 = \gamma_1$, and $\sigma_k = k \gamma_k + \sum_{i=1}^{k-1} \gamma_i \sigma_{k-i}$ ($k = 2, 3, \ldots, n$) where $\sigma_k = tr(A^k)$. Simultaneously, computing the various powers of A, and hence the σ_k's, and solving the lower triangular system (Newton's identities), we obtain the coefficients γ_i in $O(\log^2 n)$ steps. Csanky [76] required $n^4/2$ processors. Preparata and Sarwate [77] reduced the processors required to less than $2n^{3.31}/\log^2 n$ by observing all the powers of A need not be computed, since only the diagonal elements of A^k are required, $k < n$, and by using Strassen's method for matrix multiplication. Needless to say, the method is numerically unstable (see Wilkinson [65]).

C. Tridiagonal Systems

Stone [73] was the first to develop a parallel tridiagonal linear system solver that requires $O(\log n)$ steps using $O(n)$ processors. The algorithm is a parallel version of the sequential LDU-factorization of a tridiagonal matrix without pivoting, e.g., see Forsythe and Moler [67]. The parallel algorithm is usually referred to as "recursive doubling". An interpretation of Stone's algorithm follows. Let $A = [\gamma_i, \alpha_i, \beta_i]$ be a nonsingular tridiagonal matrix where α_i, $i = 1, 2, \ldots, n$, are the diagonal elements, and β_j, γ_{j+1}, $j = 1, 2, \ldots, n - 1$, are the off-diagonal elements. Let D be a diagonal matrix with elements δ_i, L and U be unit lower and upper bidiagonal matrices with off-diagonal elements λ_{j+1} and μ_j, $j = 1, 2, \ldots, n - 1$, respectively. From the relation A = LDU we obtain the nonlinear recurrence relation $\delta_i + (\beta_{i-1} \gamma_i / \delta_{i-1}) = \alpha_i$, $i = 2, 3, \ldots, n$, with $\delta_1 = \alpha_1$. Multiplying both sides by $\tau_{i-1} = \delta_1 \delta_2 \ldots \delta_{i-1}$, we obtain the linear recurrence $\tau_i - \alpha_i \tau_{i-1} + \beta_{i-1} \gamma_i \tau_{i-2} = 0$, $i = 2, 3, \ldots, n$, with $\tau_0 = 1$ and $\tau_1 = \alpha_1$. Using the algorithm described in section A for solving banded triangular systems with m = 2, τ_i ($i = 2, 3, \ldots, n$) can be evaluated in $2 \log n + O(1)$ steps using $(2n - 4)$ processors. Note here that we have taken advantage of the fact that the right-hand side is the first column of the identity of order $(n + 1)$, see Sameh and Kuck [77]. Thus, $\delta_i = \tau_i / \tau_{i-1}$ ($i = 2, 3, \ldots, n$), $\mu_j = \beta_j / \delta_j$, $\lambda_{j+1} = \gamma_{j+1} / \delta_j$ ($j = 1, 2, \ldots, n - 1$), and the decomposition is completely determined. Now we solve the systems, Ly = f, Dz = y, and Ux = z using the appropriate algorithm in section A, in $4 \log n + O(1)$ steps using no more than n processors. Hence, the total time for solving Ax = f is $6 \log n + O(1)$ steps using 2n - 4 processors. Since the sequential algorithm is $O(n)$, we have a speedup of $O(n/\log n)$ with efficiency proportional to $(1/\log n)$. The number of operations required by this parallel algorithm is $O(n \log n)$, yielding a redundancy of $O(\log n)$. Clearly, the algorithm fails if any leading principal submatrix of A is singular. Observe that if pivoting is necessary for completing the factorization, the parallel algorithm reduces to its sequential counterpart, requiring time $O(n)$. Even if pivoting is not necessary, this parallel algorithm suffers from the possibility of over- or underflow; for example, if $\delta_j = j$ then $\tau_n = n!$. Furthermore, the bound on the absolute error in evaluating the second-order linear recurrence in τ_j grows exponentially with n, see Sameh and Kuck [77]. The stability of Stone's algorithm is also discussed by Dubois and Rodrigue [77].

The method of cyclic odd-even reduction, originally developed by Gene Golub, e.g., see Buzbee, Golub, and Nielson [70], proved to be a viable parallel scheme for solving tri-diagonal systems of equations. Jordan [74], Stone [75], Lambiotte and Voigt [75], and Heller [76] (the scalar version), have all discussed such an algorithm. This parallel algorithm requires $O(\log n)$ steps with operation count of only $O(n)$, i.e., with redundancy $\rho = O(1)$. Stone [75] gave a comprehensive evaluation of the arithmetic complexity of cyclic odd-even reduction compared to "recursive doubling" (Stone [73]) and Buneman's algorithm (Buneman [69]) for solving tridiagonal systems. Jordan [74], Stone [75], and Heller [76] have also showed that if A is diagonally dominant, the cyclic reduction algorithm can be used as an iterative algorithm. For in this case the magnitudes of the off-diagonal elements relative to those of the main diagonal decrease quadratically, allowing the process to terminate early with an approximation to the solution. However, since cyclic reduction is equivalent to an LU-factorization without pivoting of PAP^t where P is a permutation matrix, the algorithm fails if any leading principal minor of PAP^t is zero.

Sameh and Kuck [76] proposed a parallel algorithm to circumvent the shortcomings of LDU-factorization without pivoting and cyclic odd-even reduction for general tridiagonal systems. The algorithm is based on the orthogonal factorization, $QA = R$, of a tridiagonal matrix, e.g., see Reinsch [71]. Here Q is an orthogonal matrix and R is upper tri-angular with bandwidth 3. The nonlinear recurrence resulting from the orthogonal decomposition is reduced to two linear recurrences, of order 2 and 1, the solution of which determines the elements of Q and R. Once Q and R are determined, the solution x is obtained by solving $Rx = Qf$. The algorithm requires $9\log n + O(1)$ steps using less than $3n$ processors. While the time is larger than LDU-factorization without pivoting, it does not fail for any nonsingular matrix. It shares, however, the remaining two disadvantages of Stone's algorithm, namely, the possibility of over- and underflow and the exponential growth of the error bound. To overcome these difficulties the problem is decomposed, under the restriction that $\beta_i \gamma_{i+1} > 0$, so that the QR-factorization may be applied to submatrices of order no larger than $\log n$. This reduces the chance of over- or underflow and the error bound of the solution of second-order linear recurrences no longer grows exponentially, but only proportional to a low degree poly-nomial in n. This is achieved, however, at an additional cost in time and processors. The time becomes $O[(\log \log n)$

(log n)] instead of only O(log n), and the number of processors is 5n instead of 3n. The number of operations remains O(n log n), i.e., a redundancy of O(log n).

Bukhberger and Emelyaneko [73] presented a sequential algorithm based on Cramer's rule for obtaining the inverse of a general nonsingular tridiagonal matrix. The algorithm can be readily adapted for parallel computing. It solves unit lower triangular systems of bandwidth no more than 3 to obtain three vectors: $u = (\mu_1, \mu_2, \ldots, \mu_n)^t$, $v = (\nu_0, \nu_1, \ldots, \nu_n)^t$, and $w = (\omega_1, \omega_2, \ldots, \omega_n)^t$ such that the elements θ_{ij} of A^{-1} can be computed by $\theta_{ij} = \mu_i \nu_j \omega_i$. The vectors u, v, and w can be obtained in $3\log n + O(1)$ steps using no more than 4n processors. This algorithm is quite fast if only selected components of the solution vectors corresponding to several right-hand sides are desired. Swarztrauber [76] also presented an algorithm for solving tridiagonal systems based on Cramer's rule that requires only O(n) operations. The numerical stability of the above two algorithms remains to be investigated.

All the algorithms in this section can be modified when the tridiagonal matrix is Toeplitz. An efficient and numerically stable algorithm, not discussed above, that does not fail for any nonsingular symmetric-Toeplitz tridiagonal system is the following. Let $A = [\beta, \alpha, \beta]$, then we can write it as $A = \alpha I + \beta(J + J^t)$, where $J = [e_2, e_3, \ldots, e_n, 0]$. The spectral decomposition $(J + J^t) = Q \Lambda Q^t$ is known, $\Lambda = \text{diag}(\lambda_k)$ with $\lambda_k = 2 \cos [k\pi/(n + 1)]$, $(k = 1, 2, \ldots, n)$, and $Q = [q_1 q_2, \ldots, q_n]$ is orthogonal with $q_k^t = [2/(n + 1)]^{1/2}$ $[\sin (k\pi/n + 1), \sin (2k\pi/n + 1), \ldots, \sin (nk\, \pi/n + 1)]$. Hence $A = Q \Omega Q^t$ where $\Omega = \alpha I + \beta \Lambda$. Since A is nonsingular Ω^{-1} exists, and the solution of $Ax = f$ is given by $x = Q \Omega^{-1} Q^t f$. Using a parallel algorithm for the fast Fourier transform, e.g., see Pease [68], $Q^t f$ may be obtained in $3\log n + O(1)$ steps with n processors (Sameh, Chen, and Kuck [76]). Also, with n processors $\Omega^{-1} (Q^t f)$ requires one step, and $Q^t (\Omega^{-1} Q^t f)$ requires another $3\log n + O(1)$ steps. Thus, the total time is $6\log n + O(1)$ using only n processors, the same time as LDU-factorization (without pivoting) using only half the number of processors.

IV. ALGORITHMS FOR THE EIGENVALUE PROBLEM $Ax = \lambda x$

Fewer parallel algorithms have been developed for handling this problem than for solving systems of linear equations. Those available are parallel versions of Jacobi and Jacobi-like algorithms (Sameh [71]), a multisectioning method (Kuck and Sameh [71]) and the QR-algorithm (Sameh and Kuck [77]) for obtaining selected or all eigenvalues of a symmetric tridiagonal matrix.

We discuss first Jacobi's algorithm for finding all the eigenvalues and eigenvectors of a real symmetric matrix. The sequential algorithm is described in detail in Wilkinson [65] and by Rutishauser, Contribution II/1 in Wilkinson and Reinsch [71]. A real symmetric matrix, A, can be reduced to the diagonal form by a sequence of plane rotations. Theoretically, we need an infinite number of plane rotations; in practice, however, the process is terminated when the off-diagonal elements become "negligible" compared to the main diagonal. In the classical Jacobi algorithm, each rotation $R_k = R(p, q, \alpha_{pq}^{(k)})$ eliminates the off-diagonal element in the position (p, q) and its symmetric counterpart. It is possible though to eliminate more than one element simultaneously. For example, for a matrix of order 4, an orthogonal transformation Q may contain two independent rotations

$$Q = \begin{bmatrix} c_1 & 0 & s_1 & 0 \\ 0 & c_2 & 0 & s_2 \\ -s_1 & 0 & c_1 & 0 \\ 0 & -s_2 & 0 & c_2 \end{bmatrix}$$

where $c_i \equiv \cos \alpha_i$ and $s_i \equiv \sin \alpha_i$, and α_1, α_2 are determined simultaneously such that the elements in positions (1, 3), (2, 4), and (3, 1), (4, 2) of Q^t AQ are annihilated. For a matrix of order n, the maximum number of elements that can be annihilated simultaneously is (n/2). The task of choosing the sequence of transformations Q_k is simpler than that in Givens' reduction, discussed in section B, since we need not be concerned about destroying zeros that we previously introduced. However, for the sake of avoiding redundancy of the parallel computation, we annihilate each of the $(n^2 - n)/2$ pairs of off-diagonal elements only once during one sweep. Here, a sweep consists of (2w - 1) transformations, with $w = \lfloor (n + 1)/2 \rfloor$. Several annihilation regimes are possible. In the figure below we illustrate one such pattern of annihilation for a matrix of order 8, in one sweep.

```
*   3   6   2   5   1   4   7
    *   2   5   1   4   7   6
        *   1   4   7   3   5
            *   7   3   6   4
                *   6   2   3
                    *   5   2
                        *   1
                            *
```

By an integer j we denote all the elements annihilated by the j-th transformation, j = 1, 2, ..., 2w - 1. If after ℓ sweeps (say) the matrix becomes practically diagonal, then the diagonal elements are taken as the eigenvalues and the product of the individual transformations Q_k is taken as the eigenvectors of A. Given $O(n^2)$ processors, one sweep requires $O(n)$ steps yielding a speedup over the sequential algorithm of $O(n^2)$ with efficiency $O(1)$, and no redundancy.

A related algorithm, norm reducing Jacobi-type method, has been developed by Eberlein [62] for handling any matrix, complex in general. As before, let A be a real matrix of order n, then there exists a matrix $U = \Pi_\ell U_\ell(j, k)$ generated from a sequence of two-dimensional transformations $U_\ell(j, k)$, where (j, k) is the pivot pair, such that $A_L = U^{-1} AU$ is arbitrarily close to being normal, i.e., $(A_L A_L^t - A_L^t A_L)$ is arbitrarily small. At each stage of the iteration, based on the elements of the j-th and k-th rows and columns, the parameters of U_ℓ are chosen such that $||A_\ell||_F^2 - ||U_\ell^{-1} A_\ell U_\ell||_F^2$ $\geq [\frac{1}{3n(n-1)}] ||A_\ell A_\ell^t - A_\ell^t A_\ell||_F^2$ where $||A||_F$ denotes the Frobenius norm of A. The above norm-reducing procedure has been modified for parallel computation, Sameh [71]. The transformations U_ℓ are changed to n-dimensional with their parameters based on all the elements of the matrix A_ℓ. This results in a larger decrement in the Frobenius norm of A_ℓ,

$$||A_\ell||_F^2 - ||U_\ell^{-1} A_\ell U_\ell||_F^2 \geq (\frac{1}{4n}) ||A_\ell A_\ell^t - A_\ell^t A_\ell||_F^2$$

Since A is real, its eigenvalues are either real or complex conjugate. Consequently, we obtain a practically normal matrix A_L with pivotal elements $\alpha_{pq}^{(L)}$ such that either $\alpha_{pq}^{(L)} = \alpha_{qp}^{(L)}$; or $\alpha_{pq}^{(L)} = -\alpha_{qp}^{(L)}$ and $\alpha_{pp}^{(L)} = \alpha_{qq}^{(L)}$ to within a given tolerance. The matrix A_L can then be reduced to the diagonal form using the parallel Jacobi scheme described earlier, except for the case when $\alpha_{pq}^{(L)} = -\alpha_{qp}^{(L)}$ where the Jacobi rotation is replaced by $\frac{1}{\sqrt{2}} \begin{bmatrix} 1 & i \\ i & 1 \end{bmatrix}$, in which $i = \sqrt{-1}$.

Other "transformation" methods reduce the matrix under consideration to a condensed form via similarity transformations. The reduced matrix is either tridiagonal or upper Hessenberg (say) depending on whether the matrix is symmetric or not, see Wilkinson [65] for more details. Given $O(n^2)$ processors, it is not difficult to show that such methods require $O(n \log n)$ steps to achieve such reduction. Since the sequential algorithms require $O(n^3)$ steps, we obtain speedups of $O(n^2/\log n)$ with efficiencies proportional to $1/\log n$ and no redundancies. A result due to Kung [76], regarding nonlinear recurrence relations, indicates that we cannot achieve speedups higher than $O(n^2/\log n)$. Recent results by Parker [77], however, may show that the situation is not without hope.

If the reduced matrix is symmetric tridiagonal and we wish to obtain all the eigenvalues, then we may use the QR-algorithm, e.g., see Wilkinson and Reinsch [71], Contributions II/3, 4. A parallel version of the algorithm in Contribution II/3, TQL1, has essentially been given by Sameh and Kuck [77] and practically described in section C. In this algorithm we explicitly subtract the origin shift from the diagonal elements of the tridiagonal matrix. If the elements vary greatly in their orders of magnitudes, the algorithm yields poor approximations to the eigenvalues of smaller magnitudes. This is remedied in Contribution II/4,

IMTQL1. In attempting to produce a parallel version of it, however, one is faced with nonlinear recurrences and the time for one iteration remains $O(n)$, rather than $O(\log n)$ as in the parallel version of TQL1. If only a few eigenvalues are desired, then a generalization of the bisection method, using the Sturm sequence properties, can be most effective on a parallel computer, e.g., see Kuck and Sameh [71], and Huang [74].

V. ACKNOWLEDGMENT

I wish to thank David J. Kuck for various discussions and comments regarding this paper. Special thanks go also to Mrs. Vivian Alsip for a good job in typing this manuscript.

VI. REFERENCES

Borodin, A., and Munro, I. (1975), Computational Complexity of Algebraic and Numeric Problems, American Elsevier.

Brent, R. (1973), "The Parallel Evaluation of Arithmetic Expressions in Logarithmic Time," pp. 83-102 in Complexity of Sequential and Parallel Numerical Algorithms, J. F. Traub, ed., Academic Press.

Brent, R. (1974), "The Parallel Evaluation of General Arithmetic Expressions," J. of the ACM, Vol. 21, pp. 201-206.

Bukhberger, B., and Emelyneko, G. (1973), "Methods of Inverting Tridiagonal Matrices," USSR Computational Math. & Math. Physics, Vol. 13, pp. 10-20.

Buzbee, B., Golub, G., and Nielson, C. (1970), "On Direct Methods for Solving Poisson's Equations," SIAM J. on Numer. Anal., Vol. 7, pp. 627-656.

Chen, S. (1975), "Speedups of Iterative Programs in Multiprocessing Systems," Ph.D. thesis, Dept. of Computer Science, University of Illinois at Urbana-Champaign.

Chen, S., and Kuck, D. (1975), "Time and Parallel Processor Bounds for Linear Recurrence Systems," IEEE Trans. Comput., Vol. C-24, pp. 701-717.

Chen, S., and Sameh, A. (1975), "On Parallel Triangular System Solvers," Proc. of the Sagamore Comput. Conf., T. Feng, ed., pp. 237-238.

Chen, S., Kuck, D., and Sameh, A. (1976), "Practical Parallel Triangular System Solvers," submitted for publication.

Csanky, L. (1976), "Fast Parallel Matrix Inversion Algorithms," SIAM J. on Computing, Vol. 5, pp. 618-623.

Dubois, P., and Rodrigue, G. (1977), "An Analysis of the Recursive Doubling Algorithm," this proceedings.

Eberlein, P. (1962), "A Jacobi-like Method for the Automatic Computation of Eigenvalues and Eigenvectors of an Arbitrary Matrix," J. of SIAM, Vol. 10, pp. 74-88.

Faddeev, D., and Faddeeva, V. (1963), Computational Methods of Linear Algebra, Freeman.

Flynn, M. (1972), "Some Computer Organizations and Their Effectiveness," IEEE Trans. Comput., Vol. C-21, pp. 948-960.

Forsythe, G., and Moler, C. (1967), Computer Solution of Linear Algebraic Systems, Prentice-Hall.

Heller, D. (1974), "On the Efficient Computation of Recurrence Relations," ICASE technical report.

Heller, D. (1976), "Some Aspects of the Cyclic Reduction Algorithm for Block Tridiagonal Linear Systems," SIAM J. on Numer. Anal., Vol. 13, pp. 484-496.

Heller, D. (1977), "A Survey of Parallel Algorithms in Numerical Linear Algebra," to appear in SIAM Review.

Heller, M. (1976), "Experiments on the Stability of Parallel Matrix Methods," Computer Science Dept., Technical Rpt. No. 212, The Pennsylvania State University.

Householder, A. (1964), The Theory of Matrices in Numerical Analysis, Blaisdell Publ. Co.

Huang, H. (1974), "A Parallel Algorithm for Symmetric Tridiagonal Eigenvalue Problems," Center for Advanced Computation, Doc. No. 109, University of Illinois at Urbana-Champaign.

Hyafil, L., and Kung, H. (1975), "Parallel Algorithms for Solving Triangular Linear Systems with Small Parallelism," Dept. of Computer Science, Carnegie-Mellon University.

Jordan, T. (1974), "A New Parallel Algorithm for Diagonally Dominant Tridiagonal Matrices," Los Alamos Scientific Lab., Los Alamos, NM.

Kuck, D., and Sameh, A. (1971), "Parallel Computation of Eigenvalues of Real Matrices," IFIP Congress 1971, North-Holland, Vol. 2, 1972, pp. 1266-1272.

Kuck, D., and Maruyama, K. (1975), "Time Bounds on the Parallel Evaluation of Arithmetic Expressions," SIAM J. on Computing, Vol. 4, pp. 147-162.

Kuck, D. J. (1976), "Parallel Processing of Ordinary Programs," Advances in Computers, Vol. 15, pp. 119-179.

Kung, H. (1976), "New Algorithms and Lower Bounds for the Parallel Evaluation of Certain Rational Expressions and Recurrences," J. of the ACM, Vol. 23, pp. 252-261.

Lambiotte, J., and Voigt, R. (1977), "The Solution of Tridiagonal Linear Systems on the CDC STAR-100 Computer," ACM Trans. on Math. Software, Vol. 1, pp. 308-329.

Lafon, J. (1975), "Base tensorielle des matrices de Hankel (on de Toeplitz) applications," Numer. Math., Vol. 23, pp. 349-361.

Larson, J. (1976), Private communication.

Linz, P. (1970), "Accurate Floating-Point Summation," Comm. of the ACM, Vol. 13, pp. 361-362.

Miller, W. (1975), "Software for the Roundoff Analysis," ACM Trans. on Math. Software, Vol. 1, pp. 108-128.

Miranker, W. (1971), "A Survey of Parallelism in Numerical Analysis," SIAM Review, Vol. 13, pp. 524-547.

Muller, D., and Preparata, F. (1976), "Restructuring of Arithmetic Expressions for Parallel Evaluation," J. of the ACM, Vol. 23, pp. 534-543.

Muraoka, Y., and Kuck, D. (1973), "On the Time Required for a Sequence of Matrix Products," Comm. of the ACM, Vol. 16, pp. 22-26.

Orcutt, S. (1974), "Parallel Solution Methods for Triangular Linear Systems of Equations," Technical report No. 77, Stanford Electronics Labs., Stanford, CA.

Ortega, J., and Voigt, R. (1977), "Solution of Partial Differential Equations on Vector Computers," to appear in the Proc. of the 1977 Army Numerical Analysis and Computer Conf.

Parker, D. (1977), "Nonlinear Recurrences and Parallel Computation," this proceedings.

Pease, M. (1968), "An Adaptation of the Fast Fourier Transform for Parallel Processing," J. of the ACM, Vol. 15, pp. 252-264.

Preparata, F., and Sarwate, D. (1977), "An Improved Parallel Processor Bound in Fast Matrix Inversion," submitted for publication.

Reinsch, C. (1971), "A Stable Rational QR-Algorithm for the Computation of the Eigenvalues of an Hermitian Tridiagonal Matrix," Math. Comp., Vol. 25, pp. 591-597.

Sameh, A. (1971), "On Jacobi and Jacobi-like Algorithms for a Parallel Computer," Math. Comp., Vol. 25, pp. 579-590.

Sameh, A., Chen, S., and Kuck, D. (1976), "Parallel Poisson and Biharmonic Solvers," Computing, Vol. 17, pp. 219-230.

Sameh, A., and Kuck, D. (1976), "On Stable Parallel Linear System Solvers," submitted for publication.

Sameh, A., and Brent, R. (1977), "Solving Triangular Systems on a Parallel Computer," to appear in SIAM J. on Numer. Anal.

Sameh, A., and Kuck, D. (1977), "A Parallel QR-Algorithm for Symmetric Tridiagonal Matrices," IEEE Trans. Comput., Vol. C-26, pp. 147-153.

Smith, B., et al (1974), Matrix Eigensystem Routines--Eispack Guide, Spring-Verlag.

Stewart, G. W. (1973), Introduction to Matrix Computations, Academic Press.

Stokes, R. (1977), "BSP: The Burroughs Scientific Processors," this proceedings.

Stone, H. (1973), "An Efficient Parallel Algorithm for the Solution of a Tridiagonal Linear System of Equations," J. of the ACM, Vol. 20, pp. 27-38.

Stone, H. (1975), "Parallel Tridiagonal Equation Solvers," ACM Trans. on Math. Software, Vol. 1, pp. 289-307.

Swarztrauber, P. (1976), "A Parallel Algorithm for Solving General Tridiagonal Equations," National Center for Atmospheric Research, Boulder, CO.

Wilkinson, J. H. (1963), Rounding Errors in Algebraic Processes, Prentice-Hall.

Wilkinson, J. H. (1965), The Algebraic Eigenvalue Problem, Oxford.

Wilkinson, J. H., and Reinsch, C. (1971), Handbook for Automatic Computation, Vol. 2, Linear Algebra, Springer-Verlag.

Winograd, S. (1975), "On the Parallel Evaluation of Certain Arithmetic Expressions," J. of the ACM, Vol. 22, pp. 477-492.

SYNCHRONIZED AND ASYNCHRONOUS PARALLEL ALGORITHMS
FOR MULTIPROCESSORS

H. T. Kung
Department of Computer Science
Carnegie-Mellon University
Pittsburgh, Pa.

Reprinted with permission from *Algorithms and Complexity*,
1976, pages 153-200. Copyright © 1976 by Academic Press.

Abstract

Parallel algorithms for multiprocessors are classified
into synchronized and asynchronous algorithms. Important
characteristics with respect to the design and analysis of
the two types of algorithms are identified and discussed.
Several examples of the two types of algorithms are considered in depth.

Table of Contents

This research was supported in part by the National Science
Foundation under Grant MCS75-222-55 and the Office of Naval
Research under Contract N00014-76-C-0370, NR 044-422.

1. Introduction

The multiprocessor user is currently confronted with a large and increasing number of processors. For efficient system utilization and fast response to the user, it is necessary to use parallel algorithms for solving a single problem. This paper studies parallel algorithms for multiprocessors.

Following Flynn's [66] classification scheme, parallel computers are classified into SIMD (single-instruction stream-multiple-data stream) machines and MIMD (multiple-instruction stream-multiple-data stream) machines. With SIMD machines, one stream of instructions controls a number of synchronized processors, each operating upon its own memory. An example of SIMD machines is the array processor such as ILLIAC IV (Barnes, et al. [68]). With MIMD machines, the processors have independent instruction counters, and operate in a speed independent manner on shared memories. In this paper, by multiprocessors we mean MIMD machines. An example of multiprocessors is C.mmp (Wulf and Bell [72]) at Carnegie-Mellon University. Considerations in designing algorithms for SIMD machines and those for multiprocessors are quite different. Algorithms for SIMD machines are not dealt with in this paper. The reader is referred to the recent survey by Heller [76] for numerical SIMD algorithms, and the paper by Thompson and Kung [76] for an example of nonnumerical SIMD algorithms. For a survey of parallel computation in a broad sense, the reader is referred to Kuck [75]. Although quite a lot of research has been done on SIMD algorithms, there are few results available concerning the design and analysis of multiprocessor algorithms. As multiprocessors with increasing numbers of processors are becoming available, research on multiprocessor algorithms seems to be of utmost importance at this time. This is the motivation behind this paper.

This paper intends to identify some of the important and unique issues concerning multiprocessor algorithms. They are illustrated by three specific examples, which are given in Sections 3, 4, and 5. In Section 2, multiprocessor algorithms are classified into synchronized and asynchronous algorithms, and basic concepts are introduced. Section 6 considers asynchronous algorithms where processes can be interrupted, and Section 7 contains considerations on the optimal number of processes one should create for a multiprocessor algorithm. Summary and conclusions are given in the last section.

Parts of this paper are summaries of results from other papers, in particular, results of Section 3, belong to Hyafil and Kung [76], and results of Section 4.2 belong to Baudet, Brent and Kung [76].

2. Basic Concepts and Definitions

2.1 Parallel Algorithm as a Collection of Concurrent Processes

We define a parallel algorithm for multiprocessors as a collection of concurrent processes that may operate simultaneously for solving a given problem. We do not attempt to define formally the term "process" here. The reader could read, for example, Habermann[76] for a good discussion on the concept of processes. For our purpose we view a process as the execution of a procedure in a multiprocessor operating system. Thus, a process is controlled by a program and at most one processor, which is assigned by the operating system, carries out this program at any given time. During the lifetime of a process, different processors may be assigned to it on various time intervals. It turns out that it is convenient and more useful to think that a program for solving a given problem is carried out by processes rather than processors. For instance, with this concept one can often regard a piece of the program to be carried out by _one_ process, although it may actually be done by many processors. This is part of the motivation for our definition of a parallel algorithm. As the section proceeds, the reader will find that it is useful to have such a definition for describing many other concepts. If a parallel algorithm is a collection of k processes, we shall often say it is a parallel algorithm with k processes. If $k = 1$, it is called a sequential algorithm.

To ensure that a parallel algorithm works correctly and uses parallelism effectively for solving a given problem, it is usually necessary to have interactions among the processes. Hence in the program which controls a process there may be

430

some points where the process can communicate with other processes. We call such points <u>interaction points</u>. The interaction points divide a process into <u>stages</u>. Thus, at the end of each stage a process may communicate with other processes before starting the next stage.

2.2 Fluctuations in Process Speed

The time taken by a fixed stage of a process is usually not a constant. The fluctuations may be due to both the multiprocessor system and the input to the stage.

System

(i)   The multiprocessor may consist of processors with different speeds. For example, the current configuration of C.mmp includes both PDP-11/20 and PDP-11/40 processors. The latter processors are considerably faster than the former ones. A process may be run in a fast or slow manner, depending upon which processors are assigned to it during the stage.

(ii) The individual processors may be asynchronous.

(iii) A process may be delayed due to memory conflicts.

(iv) From time to time the operating system on the multiprocessor may assign certain processors to perform I/O, allocate processors to processes, switch a processor from one process to another, and so on. Hence during the period when a processor is carrying out a stage of a process, it could be interrupted by the operating system and start doing something else. In this case, a time consuming context swap is performed, and the stage is either taken over by another processor or suspended for an indefinite amount of time.

(v)   In a multiple user environment, the amount of resources allocated to a particular process at a given time is a variable, depending upon the number of processes the users have created and their priorities. Thus, the speed of a process may be influenced by the whole user community.

431

Input

The work taken by an algorithm may depend on the instances of its input. For example, the number of comparisons needed to sort n elements by Quicksort ranges from $O(n \log n)$ to $O(n^2)$, depending upon the ordering of the input elements. As another example, consider the problem of evaluating a function. Suppose that we want to evaluate the normal distribution function

$$f(x) = \frac{1}{\sqrt{2\pi}} \int_x^\infty e^{-\frac{1}{2}t^2} dt$$

at a point. To achieve good accuracy, the evaluation at a point in the "central area" is done by a Taylor series approximation, while that at a point in one of the "tail areas" is done by a continued fraction approximation. Hence the work needed to evaluate a function at a point may depend upon the position of the point. Since in general the property of the input to a stage of a process is unpredictable (or regarded as unpredictable), so is the work performed by the stage. This implies that the time taken by a stage can very in an unpredictable way.

Motivated by the preceding discussion, we assume in this paper that in running a parallel algorithm the time taken by a stage of any of its processes is a random variable satisfying some distribution function. In a fixed computing environment the distribution function can (hopefully) be estimated.

2.3 Synchronized Parallel Algorithms

A synchronized parallel algorithm is a parallel algorithm consisting of processes with the following property: There exists a process such that some stage of the process is not activated until another process has finished a certain portion of its program. The needed timing can be achieved by using various synchronization primitives. For example, suppose that we want to compute $(A \times B) + (C \times D \times E)$ by two processes. We may construct a parallel algorithm by creating process P_1 consisting of only one stage, $X \leftarrow A \times B$, and process P_2 consisting of two stages, $Y \leftarrow C \times D \times E$ and $S \leftarrow X+Y$. Clearly, the activation of the second stage of process P_2 is subject to the condition that process P_1 is complete. Thus, this is a synchronized parallel algorithm. More examples will be presented later in the paper. If we use notation in Habermann [76], then a parallel algorithm consisting of "cooperating pro-

cesses" is a synchronized parallel algorithm. For convenience, we shall often say synchronized algorithms instead of
synchronized parallel algorithms.

Since the time taken by a stage of a process is a random
variable, synchronized algorithms have the drawback that some
processes may be blocked at a given time, so the performance
of the algorithm is degraded. To be more precise, consider a
synchronized algorithm with k processes. Assume that
this algorithm is run on a multiprocessor system which consists of k identical processors and the algorithm takes time
U. During the time U let u_i denote the total time that i
processes are active, i.e., k-i processes are blocked. Note
that $U = u_0 + u_1 + \ldots + u_k$ and that the algorithm can be run
on a single processor of the system in time at most $\sum_{i=1}^{k} i u_i$.
Thus, by using k processors, the algorithm is sped up at most
by a factor of

$$\bar{S}_k = \sum_{i=1}^{k} i u_i \Big/ \sum_{i=1}^{k} u_i,$$

which is $\leq k$ as one might expect. $\bar{S}_k$ may be computed if the
u_i are known. For example, if we know that at most k/2 processes are active 50 percent of the time,
i.e., $\sum_{i=1}^{k/2} u_i \geq \sum_{i=(k/2)+1}^{k} u_i$, then

$$\bar{S}_k \leq \frac{k}{2}\left[1 + \left(\sum_{i=(k/2)+1}^{k} u_i \Big/ \sum_{i=1}^{k} u_i\right)\right] \leq \frac{3k}{4}.$$

Hence in this case the speed up is at most 3/4 of what one
would hope.

The degradation of performance can be made even clearer
by considering the class of synchronized parallel algorithms, where only identical stages of processes are synchronized. In general, the synchronized parallel algorithms
adapted from algorithms for SIMD machines are of this type.
Suppose that we want to synchronize k identical stages and
that the time taken by the ith stage is a random variable t_i.
Since the stages are all identical, $t_1, \ldots, t_k$ are identically

433

distributed random variables with mean, say, $\bar{t}$. Synchronizing the stages means that until all stages are complete a new stage of any process can not be activated. Therefore the expected time taken by the synchronized stage of any process is the mean $\bar{T}$ of the random variable $T = \max(t_1, \ldots, t_k)$ rather than $\bar{t}$. In general, $\bar{T}$ is larger than $\bar{t}$. We define the ratio $\lambda_k = \bar{T}/\bar{t}$ to be the penalty factor of synchronizing the k identical stages. Clearly if the penalty factor is large, then the performance of the synchronized algorithm is largely degraded. G. Baudet has made an interesting observation that if the t_i are identical and independent exponentially distributed random variables, then the penalty factor λ_k is the kth harmonic number H_k. Note that H_k grows like ln k as k increases.

Both the speed up bound $\bar{S}_k$ and the penalty factor discussed above give us some indications of the average performance of synchronized algorithms. But in the worst cases, synchronized algorithms may take an unacceptably long time, since it is possible that a process is blocked while waiting for a signal which is supposed to be issued by some "dead" process. Finally, we note that the execution time of the needed synchronization primitives in synchronized algorithms is often non-negligible in practice (see Section 7).

2.4 Asynchronous Parallel Algorithms

An asynchronous parallel algorithm is a parallel algorithm with the following properties:

(i) There is a set of global variables accessible to all processes.

(ii) When a stage of a process is complete, the process first reads some global variables. Then based on the values of the variables togetner with the results just obtained from the last stage, the process modifies some global variables, and then activates the next stage or terminates itself. In many cases, to ensure logic correctness, the operations on global variables are programmed as critical sections (cf. Dijkstra [68]).

Thus in an asynchronous parallel algorithm, the communications between processes are achieved through the global variables, or shared data. There is no explicit dependency between processes, as found in synchronized parallel algo-

434

rithms. The main characteristic of an asynchronous parallel algorithm is that its processes never wait for inputs at any time but continue or terminate according to whatever information is currently contained in the global variables. It is called an "asynchronous" parallel algorithm because synchronizations are not needed for ensuring that specific inputs are available for processes at various times. However, one should note that processes may be blocked from entering critical sections, which are needed in many algorithms. We shall often say asynchronous algorithms for short, instead of asynchronous parallel algorithms.

2.5 The Time Taken by a Parallel Algorithm

The time taken by a parallel algorithm is defined to be the elapsed time of the process in the algorithm which finishes last. The elapsed time of a process is the sum of the following three quantities:

(i) Basic Processing Time

Recall that a process consists of consecutive stages and that the time taken by a stage is a random variable. The basic processing time of a process is the sum of the times taken by its stages. In this paper, it is always assumed that the random variable associated with each stage is known.

(ii) Blocked Time

A process may be blocked at the end of a stage because it waits for inputs in a synchronized algorithm, or for the entering of a critical section in an asynchronous algorithm. The blocking time of a process is the total time that the process is blocked.

(iii) Execution Time of Synchronization Primitives

Synchronization primitives are needed for synchronizing processes and implementing critical sections. The execution time of these primitives is often non-negligible in practice.

We assume that the random variable associated with a stage of a process is invariant under the addition of another process to the multiprocessor system, as long as the total number of processes having been created is no more than the number of processors in the system. In other words, we assume that the basic processing time of a process is not affected by the presence of other processes in the system when the system is not "over-saturated". This assumption seems to hold for most plausible multiprocessor systems. Throughout the paper, when we compare the times taken by parallel algorithms consisting of different numbers of processes, it is always assumed that the system is not over-saturated as any of the algorithms is running. Thus, in the analysis, the time taken by a stage of a process in a parallel algorithm is a random variable, which is defined independently of how many processes the algorithm consists of. However, when we compare two parallel algorithms with the same number of processes, we can allow the situation where the system is over-saturated. In this case, we just imagine that each process is run by a virtual processor which has only a fraction of the processing power of a real processor.

3. The First Example: Search for Zeros

In this section we consider the classical problem of locating a zero of a function, which is defined as follows: Given a continuous function f having opposite signs at the endpoints of an interval of length L, locate a zero of f within a unit interval. One should note that the algorithms presented in this section can be easily modified to deal with discrete f, so they can, for example, be used for searching an ordered list for a desired item in the list. Furthermore, our asynchronous zero-searching parallel algorithms can also be modified to locate the maximum of a unimodal function (see the end of Section 3.4).

In the following definitions we assume that a single process is used. Let the time needed to evaluate f at a point in the interval be a random variable t with mean $\bar{t}$, and, following each function evaluation, the time needed to calculate the position of the next evaluation point and to check the stopping criteria be another random variable c with mean $\bar{c}$. In this section we assume that $\bar{t}$ is much larger than $\bar{c}$ so that c can be ignored in the analysis. We also assume that execution time of synchronization primitives can be ignored. These assumptions will be dropped in Section 7.

436

Binary search is probably the best known search method. It takes at most $\lceil \log_2 L \rceil$ function evaluations and is optimal in the minimax sense. The expected running time is $\lceil \log_2 L \rceil \cdot \bar{t}$. The method is inherently sequential, since only one function evaluation can be done at any given time. In the following we consider some parallel algorithms.

3.1 Synchronized Zero-Searching Algorithms

The obvious parallel zero-searching algorithm consisting of k processes is defined as follows. At each "iteration" each process evaluates f at one of the k points which divide the current interval of uncertainty into k+1 subintervals of equal length. The evaluation is considered as a stage of the process. The k identical stages are synchronized in the sense that when all of them are complete, one of the processes computes a new interval of uncertainty. Clearly, every iteration reduces the length of the interval of uncertainty by a factor of k+1. Hence the algorithm uses $\lceil \log_{k+1} L \rceil$ iterations. As far as the number of iterations is concerned, the algorithm is clearly optimal in the minimax sense, among all synchronized parallel algorithms with k processes. However, the expected time for each iteration is $\lambda_k \bar{t}$ rather than $\bar{t}$, where λ_k is the penalty factor of synchronizing k function evaluations. Thus the expected running time of the algorithm is $\lceil \log_{k+1} L \rceil \cdot \lambda_k \bar{t}$. The synchronized parallel algorithm can be inefficient when λ_k is large, which usually happens when k is large.

3.2 An Asynchronous Zero-Searching Algorithm with Two Processes - Algorithm AZ_2

We shall introduce a natural asynchronous zero-searching algorithm with two processes, which is based on a Fibonacci law. The algorithm, called Algorithm AZ_2, will be defined by its transitions between various states. There are two types of states, $A_1(\ell)$ and $A_2(\ell)$, which are defined by the following graphs:

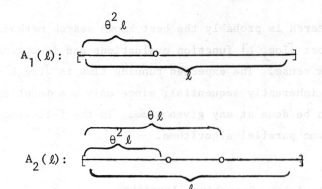

where $\theta^2 + \theta = 1$, i.e., $\theta = .618 \ldots$ is the reciprocal of the golden ratio ϕ. The first graph indicates that state $A_1(\ell)$ is the state for which the interval of uncertainty is of length ℓ and f is evaluated simultaneously at the point "o" inside the interval and another point outside the interval, which is not shown in the graph. Similarly, the second graph indicates that state $A_2(\ell)$ is the state for which the interval of uncertainty is of length ℓ and f is evaluated simultaneously at two points, denoted by "o", both inside the interval. Suppose that we are at state $A_2(\ell)$ and that without loss of generality the evaluation at the left point will finish first. Then after the evaluation at the left point is complete, the new interval of uncertainty is either

$\longmapsto$ o or o $\longmapsto$ o $\longmapsto$, depending upon the sign of

the outcome. (Here we assume that the outcome is nonzero, for otherwise a zero is found and we are done.) If the first case occurs, then the process which just finished the evaluation at the left point activates a new evaluation at the point "Δ", which is defined by the following graph:

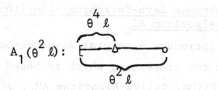

Hence state $A_1(\theta^2 \ell)$ is obtained. Similarly, state $A_2(\theta \ell)$ can arise from the second case, as depicted by the graph:

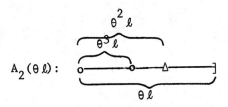

Hence state $A_2(\ell)$ is transited to either state $A_1(\theta^2 \ell)$ or $A_2(\theta \ell)$. This transition is denoted by

438

(3.1) $A_2(\ell) \rightarrow A_1(\theta^2 \ell) \vee A_2(\theta \ell)$.

It is not difficult to see that the corresponding rule for state $A_1(\ell)$ is:

(3.2) $A_1(\ell) \rightarrow A_1(\theta^2 \ell) \vee A_1(\theta \ell) \vee A_2(\ell)$.

In fact, transition rules (3.1) and (3.2) completely define Algorithm AZ_2. Suppose that the algorithm starts from state $A_1(L)$. Then it associates with the following transition tree (assume that f does not vanish at any of the evaluation points):

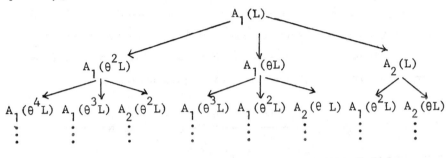

Figure 3.1

The algorithm passes through all the states on one of the paths in the tree. The particular path taken by the algorithm depends upon the input function f and the relative speeds of the two processes.

Formally we can define Algorithm AZ_2 as an asynchronous algorithm consisting of two identical concurrent processes P_i, $i = 1,2$, which are controlled by the following program:

<u>process</u> P_i
<u>begin</u>

    <u>while</u> the length of the interval of uncertainty > 1 <u>do</u>
        <u>begin</u>

(3.3) compute the position of the next evaluation point "Δ";

(3.4) evaluate f at the point "Δ";

(3.5) read and update the global variables
        <u>end</u>;

<u>end</u>

The global variables in the program consist of the type of the current state and the positions of the endpoints of the current interval of uncertainty. By examining the global

439

variables, the position of the next evaluation point "Δ" can
be computed at step (3.3). After the function evaluation at
step (3.4) is complete, the global variables are updated at
step (3.5). To guarantee that transition rules (3.1) and
(3.2) are satisfied it is necessary that steps (3.3) and (3.5)
be programmed within a critical section.

An important property of Algorithm AZ_2 is that it associates with a very simple transition tree (Figure 3.1), so it
can be analyzed. Let N be the number of function evaluations
completed by the algorithm. Since the evaluations are done
by two concurrent processes, the expected time taken by the
algorithm is $\sim N\bar{t}/2$ as $N \to \infty$. (A rigorous proof of this, in
fact, will be given later in Section 5 in a rather different
context.) Thus, the speed-up ratio between the expected time
taken by binary search and that by Algorithm AZ_2 is

$$S_2 \sim \frac{(\log_2 L)\bar{t}}{\frac{N}{2}\bar{t}} = \frac{2 \log_2 L}{N}, \qquad \text{as } N \to \infty.$$

Therefore we are interested in determining the value of N.
Note that the value of N in the worst case is given by the
length of a longest path in the transition tree, in the best
case by the length of a shortest path, and in the average
case by the average path length.

Let p be the probability that two consecutive evaluations
are executed by the same process. Some of the results in
Hyafil and Kung [76] are summarized in the following:

(i)   In the worst case:
$$N \sim \log_\phi L, \quad S_2 \sim 1.388.$$
Algorithm AZ_2 is optimal in the minimax sense, as
far as the number of required function evaluations
is concerned. Algorithm AZ_2 beats the synchronized
algorithm with two processes, when the penalty factor $\lambda_2 > 1.142$.

(ii) In the best case:
$$N \sim (\log_\phi L)/2 , \quad S_2 \sim 2.777.$$

(iii) In the average case:
$$N \sim a(p) \cdot \log_\phi L, \quad S_2 \sim 1.388\frac{1}{a(p)},$$
Algorithm AZ_2 beats the synchronized algorithm with
two processes, when $\lambda_2 > 1.142 \cdot a(p)$, where $a(p)$ is a
function of p defined as follows:

Case 1: If the zero is uniformly distributed in the original interval of uncertainty, then

$$a(p) = \frac{2.236 - 1.618p}{2.236 - 1.382p} \ .$$

Case 2: If the sign of the function value at any point inside the original interval of uncertainty is equally likely to be positive or negative, then

$$a(p) = \frac{6 - 4p}{6 - 3p} \ .$$

Note that in both cases, a(p) decreases as p increases. This means that the algorithm is better when the variances in the evaluation time are large. The value of p can be derived from a formula in Baudet, Brent and Kung [76], as long as, for example, the probability density function of the random variable t is known.

3.3 Asynchronous Zero-Searching Algorithms with Three or More Processes

The basic pattern for defining the states in Algorithm AZ_2 is

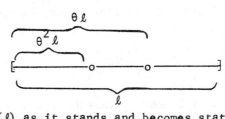

which is state $A_2(\ell)$ as it stands and becomes state $A_1(\ell)$ if the right middle point is deleted. An asynchronous algorithm with three processes can be similarly defined by using the following two patterns:

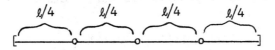

and

Figure 3.2

In general, $\lfloor k/2 \rfloor +1$ patterns are sufficient for defining an asynchronous algorithm with k processes. If k is odd, the algorithm is optimal in the minimax sense. No similar result is known if k is even. In particular, we do not know whether or not an asynchronous algorithm with four processes can be constructed by using two patterns. This is an interesting open problem.

An asynchronous zero-searching algorithm with k processes corresponds, in a natural way, to an asynchronous algorithm with k-1 processes for locating the maximum of a unimodal function. For example, if k = 2, the pattern used for Algorithm AZ_2 is exactly that used in the well-known Fibonacci search for the maximum (Kiefer [53]). The patterns in Figure 3.2 give us an asynchronous algorithm with two processes for locating the maximum of a unimodal function, which turns out to be always faster than the optimal synchronized algorithm with two processes (Avriel and Wilde [66] and Karp and Miranker [68]) as long as the penalty factor is greater than one. The details of the results mentioned above can be found in Hyafil and Kung [76].

4. The Second Example: Iterative Algorithms

Many problems in practice are solved by iterative methods. For example, zeros of functions f may be computed by the Newton iteration:

$$(4.1) \quad x_{i+1} = x_i - f'(x_i)^{-1} f(x_i),$$

and solutions of linear systems by iterations of the form

$$(4.2) \quad \bar{x}_{i+1} = A\bar{x}_i + \bar{b},$$

where the $\bar{x}_i$, $\bar{b}$ are n-vectors and A is an n×n matrix. Assume that we are given a general iterative method,

$$(4.3) \quad x_{i+1} = \varphi(x_i, x_{i-1}, \ldots, x_{i-d+1}),$$

and are interested in designing algorithms for which multiprocessors can be employed to speed up the computation of the iterative process (4.3). Several types of algorithms will be presented in this section. All of them are based on the following two strategies or a combination:

(i) The first strategy is to exploit parallelism within

442

the iteration function φ. For example, one may observe that in the iteration (4.1) the evaluations of f and f' at x_i can be done in parallel, and in the matrix iteration (4.2) all the components of the vector $\bar{x}_{i+1}$ can be computed simultaneously.

(ii) The second strategy is to exploit the fluctuations in process speed (cf. Section 2.2). The idea is to use more than one process to compute the same function in parallel, and expect that the process which obtains the result first takes less than the average time.

Iterations (4.1) and (4.2) will often be used for illustrating the algorithms.

4.1 Synchronized Iterative Algorithms

In a synchronized iterative algorithm, the iteration function is decomposed so that each iteration step is done by more than one process, and the processes are synchronized at the end of each iteration. Essentially, the algorithm generates the iterates by (4.3) just as the sequential algorithm does, except that within each iteration parallel computation is used. Thus, the algorithm differs from the sequential algorithm in the time taken by each iteration.

There is a natural synchronized iterative algorithm with two processes for performing the Newton iteration (4.1). At each iteration of the algorithm, $f(x_i)$ and $f'(x_i)$ are computed in parallel, and only after both evaluations are complete the computation for x_{i+1} is allowed to start (this is the place where synchronization is needed). Since f and f' are not the same function in general, the times needed for evaluating f and f' are probably different. In fact, when f is a vector function consisting of n components, a good approximation to $f'(x_i)$ will need n+1 evaluations of f. Hence, if n is large, then the process which evaluates f probably wastes much of its time in waiting at each iteration for the other process to finish the evaluation of f'. This certainly degrades the performance of the algorithm. This example illustrates the fact that synchronized iterative algorithms are not suitable for those iteration functions which cannot be decomposed into mutually independent tasks of the same complexity.

Synchronized iterative methods which do not suffer from

443

the drawback mentioned in the preceding remark can be easily
constructed for the matrix iteration (4.2). For simplicity,
let us assume that we are interested in constructing a parallel algorithm consisting of two concurrent processes. Perhaps the most natural approach (especially for SIMD machines)
is to decompose each vector $\bar{x}_i$ into two segments $\bar{x}_i^{(1)}$ and $\bar{x}_i^{(2)}$
each of size $n/2$, and update them by two parallel processes
as follows:

$$(4.4) \qquad \begin{bmatrix} \bar{x}_{i+1}^{(1)} \\ \bar{x}_{i+1}^{(2)} \end{bmatrix} = \begin{bmatrix} A_{11} & A_{12} \\ A_{21} & A_{22} \end{bmatrix} \begin{bmatrix} \bar{x}_i^{(1)} \\ \bar{x}_i^{(2)} \end{bmatrix} + \begin{bmatrix} \bar{b}^{(1)} \\ \bar{b}^{(2)} \end{bmatrix} ,$$

where $\bar{x}_{i+1}^{(1)} = A_{11}\bar{x}_i^{(1)} + A_{12}\bar{x}_i^{(2)} + \bar{b}^{(1)}$ and $\bar{x}_{i+1}^{(2)} = A_{21}\bar{x}_i^{(1)} + A_{22}\bar{x}_i^{(2)} + \bar{b}^{(2)}$. That is, at an iteration step, each process
updates half of the components and starts the next iteration
only after both processes have finished the updating. Since
the computations for $\bar{x}_{i+1}^{(1)}$ and $\bar{x}_{i+1}^{(2)}$ involve the same amount of
work (here we do not assume any sparsity structure on the
matrix A), one might be tempted to conclude that this is the
best scheme using two processors. This is not necessarily
true! Note that, though the amounts of work for computing
$\bar{x}_{i+1}^{(1)}$ and for $\bar{x}_{i+1}^{(2)}$ are the same, the actual times for
computing them could still differ significantly due to vari-
ous reasons as discussed in Section 2.2. Thus, it is possible
that the penalty factor of synchronizing two processes at the
end of each iteration is very large, which is certainly undesirable. One general solution to this kind of problem will
be introduced in Section 5.

4.2 Asynchronous Iterative Algorithms

Asynchronous iterative algorithms are parallel iterative
algorithms consisting of parallel processes which are not
synchronized at any time. In particular, by removing all
the synchronization restrictions from a synchronized iterative algorithm an asynchronous iterative algorithm will be
obtained. For illustration, we first show an asynchronous
iterative algorithm corresponding to the Newton iteration
(4.1). It is convenient to suppose that each iteration step
updates the three variables $f(x)$, $f'(x)$, x, rather than x
alone. For example, after the iteration step (4.1), $f(x_{i-1})$,
$f'(x_{i-1})$, x_i are updated as $f(x_i)$, $f'(x_i)$, x_{i+1}. Suppose
that the evaluation of f' is more expensive than that of f.

444

Then a reasonable asynchronous iterative algorithm consisting of two processes P_1 and P_2 can be defined as follows. Let v_1, v_2, v_3 be global variables which are accessible to both processes and contain the current values of $f(x)$, $f'(x)$, x, respectively. In the algorithm, v_1, v_3 are updated by P_1 and v_2 by P_2 in parallel. More precisely, processes P_1 and P_2 are controlled by the following programs:

process P_1
begin
    while condition S is not satisfied do
        begin

$$(4.5) \qquad \begin{aligned} v_1 &\leftarrow f(v_3); \\ v_3 &\leftarrow v_3 - v_2^{-1} v_1 \end{aligned}$$

        end;
end

process P_2
begin
    while condition S is not satisfied do

$$v_2 \leftarrow f'(v_3)$$

end

(In this paper, Condition S always stands for some global criterion for stopping a process.) Thus, as soon as a process finishes updating a global variable, it starts the next updating by using the current values of the relevant variables, without any delay. Suppose that the iterates are labeled in the order they are computed by step (4.5) of process P_1. Then in general they do not satisfy the recurrence (4.1). For example, suppose that $v_1 = f(x_0)$, $v_2 = f'(x_0)$, $v_3 = x_1$ are given initially and that the time lines of the processes are as follows:

where the subdivisions on each line give the sequence of tasks executed by the corresponding process. Then

445

$$x_2 = x_1 - f'(x_0)^{-1} f(x_1);$$
$$x_3 = x_2 - f'(x_1)^{-1} f(x_2),$$
$$x_4 = x_3 - f'(x_2)^{-1} f(x_3).$$

In general, we have

$$(4.6) \quad x_{i+1} = x_i - f'(x_j)^{-1} f(x_i) \quad \text{where } j \leq i.$$

Hence the iterates generated by the asynchronous iterative algorithm are different from those generated by the sequential algorithm or synchronized iterative algorithms. It seems difficult to derive any general theory of the properties of the sequence $\{x_i\}$.

To design an asynchronous iterative algorithm for a general iterative process (4.3), we first identify some variables $v_1, \ldots, v_m$ such that each iterative step can be regarded as computing the new values of the v_i's from their old values. Generally speaking, it is desirable to choose the v_i's such that the updating of each v_i constitutes a significant portion of the work involved in one iteration. For the Newton iteration (4.1), $\{v_1, v_2, v_3\} = \{f(x), f'(x), x\}$ seems to be a good choice for the v_i's. For the matrix iteration (4.2), v_i's may be chosen as segments of equal size of the components in a vector iterate. After the v_i's have been chosen, concurrent processes which update the v_i's asynchronously can be defined as follows. Note that a process can be specified by a permutation on some subset of $\{v_1, \ldots, v_m\}$ in the following sense: the process updates the v_i's in the subset sequentially according to the sequence which defines the permutation. Suppose that a permutation on a set of size s is represented by an s-tuple. Then, for example, the previous asynchronous iterative algorithm corresponding to the Newton iteration is defined by the processes specified by the permutations (v_1, v_3) and (v_2). Hence in general we define a process as an s-tuple over the set $\{v_1, \ldots, v_m\}$ for some s, and an asynchronous iterative algorithm is a collection of such processes which work asynchronously and have the property that each v_i appears in at least one of the tuples associated with the processes. The latter restriction guarantees that every v_i is taken care of by at least one process.

One can easily see that an unlimited number of asynchronous iterative algorithms can be constructed, even based on a

simple iteration such as the Newton iteration. The problem
is how to choose an algorithm. Since the iterates generated
by an asynchronous iterative algorithm in general do not satisfy any recurrence such as (4.3), it is difficult to obtain a
general theory concerning conditions for convergence or the
speed of convergence. Perhaps a more fruitful approach
here is to run experiments on multiprocessors, or on simulated multiprocessors as done in Rosenfeld and Driscoll [68].
Gerard Baudet of Carnegie-Mellon University has done experiments on C.mmp for solving the Dirichlet problem. It is
found that the formulas developed from the observed results
can help us to predict with reasonable accuracy the performance of certain asynchronous algorithms. The experiments
also show the superiority in speed of some asynchronous iterative algorithms over the synchronized counterparts. The advantage of asynchronous iterative algorithms is that processes are never blocked and the overheads due to the execution
of synchronization primitives are avoided. It seems that in
practice those asynchronous iterative algorithms which are
carefully chosen can be very competitive to the best synchronized iterative algorithms. Research on the performance of
asynchronous iterative algorithms is of most interest.

4.3 Simple Asynchronous Iterative Algorithms

In this section we give parallel algorithms for speeding
up the iterative process (4.3), which do not use any parallelism inside the iteration function φ. The algorithms are derived purely from the second strategy mentioned in the beginning of the section. We shall examine how much we can gain
in speed by making use of fluctuations in the evaluation
time.

Consider the asynchronous parallel algorithm which consists of k identical processes $P_1, \ldots, P_k$ each of which
evaluates the iteration function φ by using the most
recent iterates available at the time when the evaluation
starts. To be more precise, P_ℓ is controlled by the following
program, where the i and x_i are global variables and the variable j is local to the process.

447

process P_ℓ

begin

       while condition S is not satisfied **do**

           begin

               $j \leftarrow i+1;$

               $x_j \leftarrow \varphi(x_{j-1}, x_{j-2}, \ldots, x_{j-d});$

(4.7)   **if** $i < j$ **then** $i \leftarrow j$

          end;

end

It is our intention that at any time the value of variable i will be the index of the iterate which was most recently computed. To achieve this, statement (4.7) is assumed to be programmed as a critical section. The remarkable thing about the algorithm just described is that it always generates the same sequence of iterates as the sequential algorithm does, no matter what φ is. Such an algorithm is called a simple asynchronous iterative algorithm. In the following, we illustrate some properties of the algorithm. For simplicity, we shall only take into account the time needed for evaluating the iteration function φ and assume that the algorithm consists of only two processes. The time lines of the processes in Figure 4.1 illustrate a possible outcome by executing the algorithm for the iteration, say, $x_{i+1} = \varphi(x_i, x_{i-1})$ starting from x_0, x_{-1}:

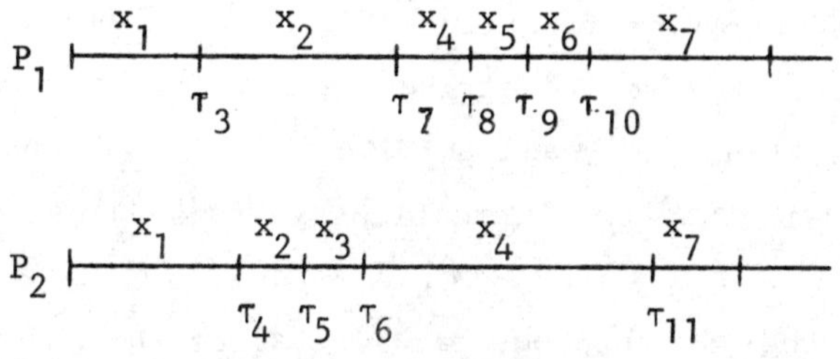

Figure 4.1

In the figure, τ_i denotes the time when the ith evaluation starts, and the iterate computed by a process at any time inside a time interval is shown above the interval. One should note that by the time P_1 completes its computation for x_2, x_3 is already computed by P_2. Thus, when P_1 completes x_2, it starts to compute x_4 by using x_2 and x_3. This means that the computation for x_3 is skipped by P_1. Similarly, the computations for x_5 and x_6 are skipped by P_2. After both processes have each completed five evaluations, iterate x_7

rather than x_5 is computed. A speed up has been achieved!
Note that at any time at most one process is doing useful computation. Thus the speed up is not achieved by sharing work
in two processes, but is achieved by taking advantage of the
fluctuations in the evaluation time.

Let u_i be the index of the iterate computed by the ith
evaluation. Then the iterate computed by the evaluation
starting at time τ_i is x_{u_i}. For example, in Figure 4.1, we
have $u_3 = 2$, $u_4 = 2$, $u_5 = 3$, $u_6 = 4$, $u_7 = 4$, $u_8 = 5$, $u_9 = 6$,
$u_{10} = 7$ and $u_{11} = 7$. We observe that

$$u_i = \begin{cases} u_{i-1} + 1 & \text{for } i = 5, 6, 8, 9, 10, \\ u_{i-2} + 1 & \text{for } i = 7, 11. \end{cases}$$

It turns out that $u_i = u_{i-1} + 1$ should be used whenever the
evaluations starting at times τ_{i-1} and τ_i are executed by the
same process; otherwise, $u_i = u_{i-2} + 1$ should be used. Let
p be the probability that two consecutive evaluations are
executed by one process. (Note that the same p was used in
Section 3.2.) Then we have

$$(4.8) \qquad u_i = \begin{cases} u_{i-1} + 1 & \text{with probability p,} \\ u_{i-2} + 1 & \text{with probability 1-p.} \end{cases}$$

It follows that the expected value of u_i is

$$\bar{u}_i = \frac{i}{2-p} + O(1).$$

For computing x_n, we expect to evaluate ω j times such that
$\bar{u}_j = n$. This implies that $j \sim (2-p)n$. For large n, $(2-p)n/2$
evaluations are expected to be executed by each process.
Hence the speed-up ratio between the expected time taken by
the sequential algorithm and that by the simple asynchronous
iterative algorithm with two processes is

$$S_2 = \frac{n}{\frac{(2-p)n}{2}} = \frac{2}{2-p},$$

as $n \to \infty$ (here the blocked time and the execution time of
synchronization primitives due to critical sections are ignored). Note that S_2 increases as p increases. When $p = 0$,
i.e., when the τ_i's on the time lines of the two processes are
interleaved, the algorithm has its worst performance. Suppose
that we are given the probability density function of the ran-

dom variable t, which is the time needed for one evaluation of the iteration φ by one process. In Baudet, Brent and Kung [76] a closed form for computing p is derived. Some of the results reported there concerning the speed-up factor are summarized in the following:

(i) If t may be approximated by a random variable normally distributed with mean $\bar{t}$ and standard deviation σ, then $S_2 = \dfrac{2}{2-(1/\sqrt{\pi})\,(\sigma/\bar{t})}$.

(ii) If t is exponentially distributed, then $S_2 = 4/3$,

(iii) If t is Erlang-2 distributed, then $S_2 = 16/13$.

(iv) If t is uniformly distributed in the interval (a,b), then

$$S_2 = \frac{6(b+a)}{5b+7a}$$

which approaches its maximum 1.2 as $\dfrac{b-a}{a} \to \infty$.

(v) If a simple asynchronous iterative algorithm with k processes is used and if t is exponentially distributed, then the speed-up factor is $\sqrt{2/\pi} \cdot \sqrt{k} \doteq .798\sqrt{k}$.

The main advantage of simple asynchronous iterative algorithms is their general applicability. The algorithms are not restricted to numerical iterative processes only. They can be employed to speed up any sequence of tasks. The algorithms become particularly attractive when the decomposition of the tasks is difficult. There are, however, some disadvantages. First, we note that critical sections are needed in the algorithms. Second, it seems that unless fluctuations in computation time due to the system are large and $\sigma/\bar{t}$ is large, the speed up of the algorithms is quite limited. See Baudet, Brent and Kung [76] for further results on this.

4.4 Semi-Synchronized (or Semi-Asynchronous) Iterative Algorithms

Synchronized iterative algorithms (cf. Section 4.1) have the drawback that processes may be blocked, and general asynchronous iterative algorithms (cf. Section 4.2) have the drawback that the analysis of the algorithms seems to be extremely difficult. Here we are interested in iterative algorithms which are compromises between the two types of algorithms. In general such algorithms can be constructed by making use of the special features of individual iterations. In the following, we illustrate an idea along this line by considering iterations (4.1) and (4.2).

Consider first the asynchronous iterative algorithm corresponding to the Newton iteration (4.1). We may impose a condition that i-j < b on (4.6) for all i,j. This condition implies that no update uses a value of f' at an iterate which was produced by an update more than b steps previously. Using this fact and the standard techniques of iteration theory, it is possible to deduce properties of the sequence of the iterates such as its order of convergence. However, to enforce the condition i-j < b, it is necessary to synchronize processes P_1 and P_2, which are defined in Section 4.2. Note that the "strictly" synchronized iterative algorithm considered in Section 4.1 corresponds to this scheme with b = 1. Thus, if b > 1. then the chance that some process is blocked in this scheme is not as big as if b = 1. Furthermore, it is well-known that in a Newton-like iterative process, there is no need to update the value of f' very often. Therefore, the scheme produces iterates which are guaranteed to have favorable rates of convergence without paying the excessive synchronization penalty which might be found in the strictly synchronized iterative algorithm. The optimal choice of b depends on the relative speeds of P_1 and P_2. Its analysis will be reported in a future paper. Clearly, this idea is also applicable to the matrix iteration (4.2). The resulting scheme is called "chaotic iterative scheme" by Chazan and Miranker [60]. In their paper, conditions guaranteeing convergence of the scheme are given.

In the following, we consider another semi-synchronized iterative algorithm, based on a different idea. In practice, band linear systems Bx = b are often solved by Gauss-Seidel's method. Unlike Jacobi's method, Gauss-Seidel's method seems inherently sequential. The components of its iterates cannot be computed in parallel, since they are logically dependent upon each other. Note, however, that if d is the band width of the matrix B, then components whose indices differ by more than d-1 are in fact independent. Thus, for solving Bx = b by Gauss-Seidel's method we may use a parallel algorithm, in which each process performs the sequential Gauss-Seidel iteration, but the processes are synchronized so that components whose indices differ by less than d are not allowed to be updated simultaneously. In other words, the synchronization

451

ensures that one process will not follow "closely" on the heels of another. In case the size of the linear system is much larger than d and than the number of processes, we may expect that the processes will not be blocked very often. Note that the iterates generated by this scheme are exactly the ones generated by the sequential Gauss-Seidel's method.

The main characteristics of a semi-synchronized iterative algorithm can be summarized as follows.

(i) The algorithm is "loosely" synchronized so that processes are not expected to be blocked very often.

(ii) The synchronization, however, guarantees that the iterates generated by the algorithm satisfy some desirable properties.

A semi-synchronized iterative algorithm is attractive because it reduces the drawback of synchronized iterative algorithms by its first characteristic and also the drawback of asynchronous iterative algorithms by its second characteristic.

5. The Third Example: Adaptive Asynchronous Algorithms

We consider the problem of executing n independent tasks $J_1, \ldots, J_n$ by parallel algorithms. Let the execution time of the task J_i by one process be a random variable t_i. We assume that all the tasks are of the same complexity, i.e., $t_1, \ldots, t_n$ are identically distributed random variables, say, with mean $\bar{t}$ and standard deviation σ. For example, J_i may be the task of updating the ith component of an iterate in the synchronized iterative algorithm for performing the matrix iteration (4.2) (cf. Section 4.1). For simplicity, we mainly consider parallel algorithms with two processes.

The first algorithm is the obvious one which performs the first n/2 tasks by one process and the second n/2 by the other process. Thus the time taken by the algorithm is the random variable $T_1 = \max(t_1 + \ldots + t_{n/2}, t_{(n/2)+1} + \ldots + t_n)$. We wish to compute the mean $\bar{T}_1$ of T_1. By the central limit theorem, as $n \to \infty$ the distribution of $t_1 + \ldots + t_{n/2}$ or $t_{(n/2)+1} + \ldots + t_n$ approaches to the normal distribution with mean $(n/2)\bar{t}$ and standard deviation $(\sqrt{n/2})\sigma$. Using a result from order statistics for normally distributed random variables (see, e.g., Gibbons [71, p.34]), we obtain that

452

(5.1) $\bar{T}_1 \sim \dfrac{\bar{t}}{2} \cdot n + \dfrac{\sigma}{\sqrt{2\pi}} \cdot \sqrt{n}$

as $n \to \infty$.

In the second algorithm, the list of tasks is made into a global deque ("double-ended queue", Knuth [69]), which is accessible to both processes of the algorithm. One process is allowed to remove tasks from only one end of the deque. In the algorithm, each process repeats the following until the deque becomes empty: remove a task from one end of the deque and execute it. Observe that the finishing times of the two processes can differ at most by the execution time of the task which finishes last. Thus, the algorithm is expected to be efficient, since the time that only one process is active is small. Indeed, the following analysis supports this argument. Consider the time line of the n tasks:

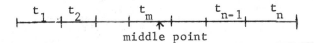

middle point

Note that the execution time of the task which finishes last is the length t_m of subinterval containing the middle point, since the algorithm works from both ends toward the middle. By a result from renewal theory (see, for example, Kleinrock [75]), we know that the expected value of t_m is $\bar{t} + \dfrac{\sigma^2}{\bar{t}}$ as $n \to \infty$. Hence if the time taken by the algorithm is a random variable T_2, then its mean $\bar{T}_2$ satisfies

(5.2) $\bar{T}_2 \leq \dfrac{\bar{t}}{2} \cdot n + \dfrac{\bar{t}}{2} + \dfrac{\sigma^2}{2\bar{t}}$.

Comparing (5.1) and (5.2) we conclude that the mean time of the second algorithm is less than that of the first one when n is large.

The implementation of the second algorithm, which uses a deque, is of interest. For example, we can use the following programs to control the two processes P_1 and P_2, where i,j are global variables and initially i = 1 and j = n.

```
process P₁
begin
    while i < j do
        begin
            execute task J_i;
            i ← i+1
        end;
    execute task J_i
end

process P₂
begin
    while i < j do
        begin
            execute task J_j;
            j ← j-1
        end;
end
```

It is not difficult to check that all the tasks $J_1, \ldots, J_n$, except the one which finishes last, will be executed exactly once. (There is a chance that the task which finishes last is executed by both processes. We do not regard this as a serious drawback.) The point we want to make here is that the second algorithm can be implemented without using critical sections. The reason that we can achieve this is mainly due to the fact that only one process is allowed to operate at each end of the deque. (A critical section is needed if more than one process operates at one end of a list.) Hence the second algorithm essentially does not involve more overheads than the first one. If tasks were removed from only one end of the list as in the case where a queue or a stack is used, then the extra overheads due to critical sections would be involved.

The use of a deque could be advantageous even in parallel algorithms with more than two processes. We can let, say, half of the processes obtain their tasks from one end of the deque, and the other half from the other end. This is better than the scheme where all the processes obtain their tasks from only one end of the list. The reason is that the less processes operating at an end of a list, the less chance there is that processes are blocked from entering critical sections. However, if the tasks are of various complexities, it is often desirable to perform the tasks in the order of

454
```
```

decreasing complexities, in order to reduce the difference
in the finishing times of the processes. Then in this case
a priority queue is more appropriate than a deque. Moreover,
we note that the number of times that critical sections are
executed can be reduced by letting processes take more than
one task from the list at a time. However, in this case, the
difference in the finishing times of processes will increase.
Careful analysis on various techniques mentioned above will be
reported elsewhere.

The tasks performed by a particular process in the
second algorithm are not specified a priori but depend upon
the relative speeds of the two processes. Thus, it is an
adaptive algorithm. The first algorithm is not adaptive
because it assigns tasks to processes statically. The efficiency of an adaptive algorithm is obtained from the fact that
the processes are able to adjust themselves during the computation so that they can all finish in about the same time.
The concept of adaptive algorithms seems to be fundamental
to the design of many efficient asynchronous algorithms. For
example, two ordered files can be merged by two asynchronous
processes in the following way: One process merges from left
to right and the other one from right to left, until one of
the files is exhausted. The two subfiles merged by a particular process are unpredictable; they depend on the relative
speeds of the processes and the orderings in the original
files. Note that in this example, two deques are needed; one
for each file.

6. Asynchronous Algorithms Where Processes can be Interrupted

The speed of an asynchronous algorithm may be improved if
those processes which are not doing useful computations can
be interrupted promptly and if the extra cost due to interruption is not excessive. Note that whether or not a process
is doing useful computation at a given time may be determined
by examining the current contents of some of the global variables. Hence interruptions may be implemented by letting the
process check the new status of those variables as soon as it
realizes that the value of some variable has been modified by

some process. The ability of a process to be interrupted certainly causes overheads in the time taken by the process. However, for a given asynchronous algorithm and a given interruption scheme, the overheads usually can be estimated. Hence in this case it is possible to decide whether we should allow processes to be interrupted in the algorithm. In the following we briefly study two examples.

First consider Algorithm AZ_2 in Section 3.2. It is clear that at state $A_1(\ell)$ the process which is evaluating the point outside the interval of uncertainty will not lead to any useful information. Thus, the process could be interrupted and start a new evaluation at an appropriate point in the interval, resulting in state $A_2(\ell)$. Suppose that we do so. Then, only states of type $A_2(\ell)$ will ever occur. They satisfy the transition rule:

$$A_2(\ell) \rightarrow A_2(\theta \ell) \vee A_2(\theta^2 \ell).$$

At any state, two evaluations are performed simultaneously. The time that the algorithm is at the state is bounded above by the time taken by the evaluation which finishes first. Because the interruption facility introduces extra overheads, the evaluation time by one process is a random variable t', which is greater than t. Hence the expected time that the algorithm is at a state is bounded above by the mean $\bar{T}'$ of the random variable $T' = \min(t'_1, t'_2)$, where t'_1 and t'_2 are independent and identically distributed random variables satisfying the same distribution function as t'. Let $M(\ell)$ be the number of state transitions the algorithm encounters, if it starts from state $A_2(\ell)$. Then the expected time of the algorithm is at most $M(L) \cdot \bar{T}'$. Since, if t' is given $\bar{T}'$ can always be computed at least numerically, we assume $\bar{T}'$ is known. It remains to compute $M(L)$. Assume that $L \rightarrow \infty$. It is easily seen that $M(L) \sim \log_\phi L$ in the worst case and $M(L) \sim (\log_\phi L)/2$ in the best case. On the average, we have the following (notation in Section 3.2 is assumed).

Case 1:
$$M(L) = \theta M(\theta L) + \theta^2 M(\theta^2 L) + 1. \quad \text{Thus}$$

$$M(L) \sim \frac{1}{1+\theta^2} \log_\phi L \doteq .276 \log_\phi L.$$

Interruptions should be used when $.276(\log_\phi L)\bar{T}' < \frac{a(p)}{2} \cdot$ $(\log_\phi L)\bar{t}$, i.e., $\bar{T}' < 1.81\, a(p) \cdot \bar{t}$.

<u>Case 2</u>:

$$M(L) = \frac{1}{2} M(\theta L) + \frac{1}{2} M(\theta^2 L) + 1. \quad \text{Thus}$$

$$M(L) \sim \frac{2}{3} \log_\phi L.$$

Interruptions should be used when $\frac{2}{3}(\log_\phi L)\bar{T}' < \frac{a(p)}{2}(\log_\phi L)\bar{t}$, i.e., $\bar{T}' < \frac{3}{4} a(p)\bar{t}$.

As our second example, we consider a simple asynchronous iterative algorithm with two processes which is defined in Section 4.3. We observed that at any time at most one process is doing useful computation. Thus, it is natural to consider interruptions here. Assume that interruptions are allowed. Let the evaluation time of the iteration function by one process be a random variable t', which is presumably larger than t. Then the expected time of computing a new iteration by the algorithm is the mean $\bar{T}'$ of the random variable $T' = \min(t_1', t_2')$, where the t_i' are independent and identically distributed random variables satisfying the same distribution function as t. For computing x_n, the expected time is $n\bar{T}'$. Hence, interruption should be used when $\bar{T}' < \frac{2-p}{2}\bar{t}$.

We observe that the minimum of a number of random variables is concerned in the case where processes can be intertupted. This is contrary to the case for synchronized algorithms where the maximum of a number of random variables should be considered. Hence large fluctuations in process speed in fact will often reduce the time taken by an asynchronous algorithm if processes can be interrupted.

7. <u>On the Optimal Number of Processes One Should Create</u>

To perform a given task on a multiprocessor, one has to decide how many processes should be created. Some considerations on choosing the optimal number of processes are given in this section.

Consider synchronized parallel algorithms first. Note that the execution of synchronization primitives is usually time consuming and that the penalty factor tends to increase as the number of synchronized processes increases. Hence those synchronized parallel algorithms which are based on the maximal decomposition of a given problem may not be desirable. For example, suppose that we have three tasks J_1, J_2, J_3, where J_1, J_2 have to be completed before J_3 is allowed to start. Assume that the time needed for J_1 or J_2 is approximated by a normally distributed random variable with mean $\bar{t}$ and standard deviation σ and that for J_3 is another random variable with mean $\bar{t}$. Suppose that the time of executing the synchronization primitives needed for synchronizing two tasks is s. Consider the following two methods of performing the three tasks.

The first method is based on the maximal decomposition principle. J_1 and J_2 are done in parallel, and when both have finished, J_3 starts. Hence, the expected time needed by the method is

$$\bar{t} + \frac{\sigma}{\sqrt{\pi}} + s + \bar{t}'.$$

(See Section 5.)

The second method is the obvious method which performs J_1, J_2, J_3 sequentially. The expected time needed by the method is $2\bar{t} + \bar{t}'$. Hence when $s > \bar{t} - \frac{\sigma}{\sqrt{\pi}}$ the sequential algorithm should be used even if more than one processor is available. This example shows that the maximal decomposition of a problem may not necessarily lead to the optimal number of processes that should be created for solving the problem.

Now consider asynchronous parallel algorithms. As noted in the preceding sections, critical sections are needed in many asynchronous algorithms. In these algorithms, processes may be blocked from entering critical sections, so the performance of the algorithms is degraded. The amount of degradation can be estimated as follows. Consider an asynchronous algorithm with k processes, $P_1, \ldots, P_k$. Let T_i be the total time taken by process P_i and C_i the time spent in the critical sections of the process, under the assumption that the process is never blocked. Define $\alpha_i = C_i/T_i$ and let α be a lower bound on the $\alpha_1, \ldots, \alpha_k$. In general, an estimate on α can be obtained by examining the programs of the processes. α may or may not be a function of k. For example, in the asynchronous zero-searching algorithms considered in Section 3, each process has to update the global variables within critical sections. As the number k of concurrent processes increases, so does the number of possible states. This implies that the complexity of updating the global variables grows as k increases. Thus, α is an increasing function of

k. As another example, we consider simple asynchronous iterative algorithms defined in Section 4.3. In this case, we may
take $\alpha = s/\bar{t}$ where s is the execution time of the synchronization primitives needed in implementing critical sections
and $\bar{t}$ is the evaluation time of the iteration function. Here
α is independent of k. At any rate, we shall write $\alpha(k)$
for α.   Note that the executions of critical sections in
the parallel algorithm cannot be overlapped. Hence the speedup **factor** of the algorithm is at most

$$\frac{T_1 + \ldots + T_k}{C_1 + \ldots + C_k} \leq \max\left(\frac{1}{\alpha_1}, \ldots, \frac{1}{\alpha_k}\right) = \frac{1}{\alpha(k)}$$

It is trivial that the speed-up factor is also bounded by k.
Therefore, an optimal choice of k exists, which is, in fact,
bounded above by the smallest positive solution of the equation $k = 1/\alpha(k)$. The above arguments indicate that a large
number of processes in an asynchronous algorithm cannot help
unless α can be kept small. In practice, it is important to
design algorithms which use small critical sections and to
select the synchronization tool which takes as little time as
possible.

How to find out the optimal number of processes in a
synchronized or asynchronous parallel algorithm for performing a given task is a real problem in multiprocessor programming. The problem, however, does not have easy solutions, as
we have seen in this section. The good choice generally would
require a rather involved analysis.

8. Summary and Conclusions

A parallel algorithm is viewed as a collection of concurrent processes. To ensure that the algorithm works correctly and uses the parallelism effectively, processes must
communicate with each other. However, due to various reasons
as stated in Section 2.2, the speed of a process is unpredictable. Thus, one can never be sure that an input needed by one
process will be produced in time by another process. There
are two approaches for solving the problem. The first one is
to synchronize processes so that they wait for inputs whenever necessary. This results in a synchronized parallel algorithm. The second approach is to let processes continue or
terminate according to the information currently contained in
some global variables, so processes never wait for inputs.
This results in an asynchronous parallel algorithm. Several

459

examples of the two types of parallel algorithm are considered in the paper. It is hoped that through these examples important features of each type of parallel algorithms can be identified. Some of them are summarized and discussed in the following.

In a synchronized algorithm, a task is decomposed into subtasks, which, hopefully, are of the same size, so that each subtask is solved by one process of the algorithm. **Processes** are synchronized at interaction points. At those points processes may be blocked while waiting for inputs. The loss due to waiting may be captured by the penalty factor defined in Section 2.3. The penalty factor increases as the number of synchronized processes increases. Hence synchronized algorithms should be used when the fluctuations in process speed are small and when there are only few processes to be synchronized. Furthermore, the execution time of the needed synchronization primitives is usually non-negligible. Thus, it is not always advantageous to create as many processes as possible according to the maximal decomposition of a task (cf. Section 7). In general, the analysis of a synchronized algorithm is not too much different from that of its sequential counterpart, except that techniques of order statistics may be needed in analyzing the time taken by the synchronized algorithm.

Asynchronous parallel algorithms arise naturally in the use of multiprocessors, where the processors are not synchronized and communication between cooperating processors is by means of shared data. When the fluctuations in computation time are large, asynchronous algorithms are in general more efficient than synchronized ones for the following three reasons. First, the processes never waste time in waiting for inputs. Second, the algorithms can take advantage of processes which are run fast. Results produced by those processes can be immediately used. In particular, by making use of these results those "slow" processes which are doing useless computations may be discovered and aborted at early times (cf. Section 7). Third, the algorithms are "adaptive", so the processes can finish at about the same time (cf. Section 6). This guarantees that the maximal parallelism is used during most computation times. Furthermore, we note that in general, asynchronous algorithms are more reliable than synchronized algorithms in the following sense. Even if some processes are blocked forever, an asynchronous algorithm may

460

still continue computing the solution of its problem, as
long as no blocking occurs in critical sections, which are
presumably small, and there remains at least one active process. (One may easily verify that, for example, Algorithm AZ_2
and simple asynchronous iterative algorithms indeed have
this nice reliability property.) For solving a given problem,
it is almost always possible to construct a large number of
asynchronous algorithms (cf. Section 4.2.). However, the
analysis of an asynchronous algorithm seems to be always non-
trivial. But if an asynchronous algorithm is defined by few
simple state transition rules such as (3.1), (3.2) and (4.8),
then it can be analyzed. How to construct asynchronous algorithms which involve simple state transitions is an interesting and challenging task for many problems.

A promising direction is to design semi-synchronized (or
semi-asynchronous) algorithms which are compromises between
synchronized and asynchronous algorithms, and which may take
advantage of the special features of individual problems (cf.
Section 4.4).

One of the motivations for analyzing multiprocessor algorithms is to determine how many processes should be created
for solving a problem. In the analysis it is crucial to include overheads due to the execution of synchronization primitives and critical sections (cf. Section 7.3). In practice,
programming techniques, such as the use of deques as described
in Section 5 and the selection of synchronization tools which
take as little time as possible, are often important to the
performance of algorithms. However, if the existence of
some indivisible operations such as "add to store" $\{x \leftarrow x +1\}$
and "swap (x,local)" is assumed, then many problems due to
critical sections can be eliminated (see Dijkstra [72]).

In view of the parallel algorithms considered in this
paper, it is found that there are tradeoffs among the basic
processing time, blocking time and synchronization time of a
process (cf. Section 2.5) in the following sense. In order
to reduce one quantity, it is often necessary to increase one

or two other quantities. For example, processes in a synchronized algorithm generally have smaller basic processing
times but larger blocked times than those in its asynchronous
counterpart. It is of interest to build abstract models
for studying these tradeoffs.

Acknowledgments

The author wishes to thank G. Baudet for many discussions.
Helpful comments on a draft of paper were made by G. Baudet,
J. Robinson, J. Traub, B. Weide and G. Yuval at Carnegie-
Mellon University, H. Chang at the Institute for Advanced Com-
putation, and R. Brent at the Australian National University.

References

Avriel and Wilde [66] Avriel, M. and D. J. Wilde, "Optimal
            Search for a Maximum with Sequences of Simultaneous
            Function Evaluations," Management Sci., 12, 1966,
            722-731.

Baudet, Brent and Kung [76] Baudet, G., R. P. Brent and H.
            T. Kung, "Simple Asynchronous Iterative Algorithms
            for Multiprocessors," to appear.

Barnes, et al. [68] Barnes, G. H., R. M. Brown, M. Kato,
            D. J. Kuck, D. L. Slotnik, R. A. Stoker, "The
            ILLIAC IV Computer," IEEE Trans. on Comp. 17, 1968,
            746-757.

Chazan and Miranker [69] Chazan, D. and W. L. Miranker,
            "Chaotic Relaxation," Linear Algebra and Appl, 2,
            1969, 207-217.

Dijkstra [68] Dijkstra, E. W., "Cooperating Sequential
            Processes," in Programming Languages (F. Genuys,
            ed.), Academic Press, New York, 1968, 43-112.

Dijkstra [72] Dijkstra, E. W., "Hierarchical Ordering of
            Sequential Processes," in Operating Systems
            Techniques (C. A. R. Hoare and R. H. Perrott, ed.),
            Academic Press, London, 1972, 72-93.

Flynn [66] Flynn, M. J., "Very High-Speed Computing Systems,"
            Proc. IEEE 54, 1966, 1901-1909.

Gibbons [71] Gibbons, J. D., Nonparametric Statistical In-
            ference, McGraw-Hill Book Co., New York, 1971.

Habermann [76] Habermann, A. N., Introduction to Operating
            System Design, Science Research Associates, Inc.,
            Chicago, 1976.

Heller [76] Heller, D., A Survey of Parallel Algorithms in
            Numerical Linear Algebra, Carnegie-Mellon Department
            of Computer Science Report, 1976.

Hyafil and Kung [76] Hyafil, L. and H. T. Kung, "Search for
          Zeros and Maxima by Asynchronous Multiprocessors,"
          to appear.

Karp and Miranker [68] Karp, R. M. and W. L. Miranker, "Par-
          allel Minimax Search for a Maximum," J. Comb. Theory
          4, 1968, 19-35.

Kiefer [53] Kiefer, J., "Sequential Minimax Search for a
          Maximum," Proc. Amer. Math. Soc. 4, 1953, 502-506.

Kleinrock [75] Kleinrock, L., Queueing Systems, Vol. 1:
          Theory, John Wiley and Sons. New York, 1975.

Knuth [69] Knuth, D. E., The Art of Computer Programming,
          Vol. 1: Fundamental Algorithms, Addison-Wesley,
          Reading, Massachusetts, 1969.

Kuck, David J., "Parallel Processor Architecture--A Survey,"
          1975 Sagamore Computer Conference on Parallel Pro-
          cessing, 1975, 15-39.

Rosenfeld and Driscoll [69] Rosenfeld, J. L. and G. C.
          Driscoll, "Solution of the Dirichlet Problem on a
          Simulated Parallel Processing System," Information
          Processing 68, North-Holland Publishing Co.,
          Amsterdam, 1969, 499-507.

Thompson and Kung [76] Thompson, C. D. and H. T. Kung, "Sort-
          ing on a Mesh-Connected Parallel Computer," Proc.
          8th Annual ACM Symposium on Theory of Computing,
          1976, 58-64. Also to appear in Communications
          of the ACM.

Wulf and Bell [72] Wulf, W. A. and C. G. Bell, "C.mmp - A
          Multi-Mini-Processor," Proc. AFIPS 1972 FJCC, Vol.
          41, Part II, AFIPS Press, Montvale, N. J., 1972,
          765-777.

Sorting on STAR

HAROLD S. STONE, MEMBER, IEEE

Abstract—This paper gives timing comparisons for three sorting algorithms written for the CDC STAR computer. One algorithm is Hoare's Quicksort, which is the fastest or nearly the fastest sorting algorithm for most computers. A second algorithm is a vector version of Quicksort that takes advantage of the STAR's vector operations. The third algorithm is an adaptation of Batcher's sorting algorithm, which makes especially good use of vector operations but has a complexity of $N(\log N)^2$ as compared to a complexity of $N \log N$ for the Quicksort algorithms. In spite of its worse complexity, Batcher's sorting algorithm is competitive with the serial version of Quicksort for vectors up to the largest that can be treated by STAR. Vector Quicksort outperforms the other two algorithms and is generally preferred. These results indicate that unusual instruction sets can introduce biases in program execution time that counter results predicted by worst-case asymptotic complexity analysis.

Index Terms—Batcher sort, CDC STAR, parallel computation, pipeline computers, Quicksort, sorting.

I. INTRODUCTION

SORTING is perhaps one of the best understood problem areas of computer science. Theory indicates that the computation time required to sort N items must grow as $N \log_2 N$, provided that each of the $N!$ initial configurations of the items is equally likely. Algorithms are known that attain these bounds either on the average [5], or in the worst case [3]. The bound is attained to within a small constant factor for sufficiently large N in both cases. Knuth's book [6] contains complete analyses for these algorithms in a definitive work on the subjects of sorting and searching. Loeser [8] did extensive comparisons of several sorting algorithms on randomly selected data, and presents strong empirical evidence to substantiate Knuth's analyses. One conclusion that we may draw from Knuth and Loeser is that Hoare's Quicksort or a variant of it [4], [11] is likely to have the fastest average sorting time on any conventional computer operating on random input data.

Vector computers are sufficiently different from conventional serial computers to reopen the question of what is the fastest way to sort. Computers such as the CDC STAR and the Illiac IV operate on vectors much the way conventional

computers operate on scalars. They operate most efficiently on algorithms that lend themselves to vector parallelism, and they operate least efficiently on algorithms that deal with scalars exclusively in a manner that cannot be adapted to vector computation. For these computers, computation time is no longer measured accurately by counting the number of elementary comparisons, fetches, stores, and exchanges. The hardware techniques that speed up such computers bias certain specific elementary operations to run relatively many times faster than other elementary operations in comparison to the speed of corresponding operations for a conventional machine. Timing studies are very much dependent upon how much time is spent in performing the very fast operations in relation to the time spent in performing slower operations, and this ratio in turn depends on the size of the problem. For sorting, timing depends very much on the size of N, and we cannot ignore the size of N by such statements as "for sufficiently large N" if we wish to reach conclusions about relative running times for problems of realistic sizes.

In this paper we look into the problem of sorting on the CDC STAR. We compare Quicksort and its variants to Batcher's sorting algorithm [1] as adapted to a vector processor with a perfect shuffle connection [10]. The most surprising aspect of this study is that Batcher's sort comes close to a vector adaptation of Quicksort, and is competitive with a serial version of Quicksort, yet it does not have minimum computational complexity $O(N \log_2 N)$, but has computational complexity $O[N (\log_2 N)^2]$ on STAR. We show in the timing analysis that the timing dependency on $N (\log_2 N)^2$ has a very small constant coefficient because this term is charged to operations for which the STAR is very efficient. Consequently, asymptotic estimates of relative timings are invalid for sizes of N of most practical interest.

In Section II of this paper we briefly review the aspects of the STAR architecture that determine its timing characteristics. In Section III we review the Quicksort algorithm and determine its approximate running time, both in a serial version executing on STAR and in a highly vectorized version running on the same machine. Section IV contains the Batcher algorithm as adapted to STAR. In Section V we compare and comment on the results of the analyses.

We mention here that timings are inherently approximate for several reasons. STAR timing is not merely a function of what instructions are executed, but depends on the storage addresses of the operands, the sequence in which instructions are issued, data dependent conditions, and a host of subsidiary conditions that are too difficult to include in an analysis, and too small to perturb the analysis a great deal. The timings in

Manuscript received June 10, 1975; revised July 8, 1977. This work was supported by the Institute for Computation Applied to Science and Engineering, NASA Langley Research Center, and by the National Science Foundation under Grant NSF DCR 74-20025.

The author is with the Department of Electrical and Computer Engineering, University of Massachusetts, Amherst, MA, on leave at the Department of Electrical Engineering and Computer Science, University of California, Berkeley, CA 94720.

EHO182-6/81/0000/0464 © 1978 IEEE

Reprinted from *IEEE Transactions on Software Engineering*, Volume SE-4, Number 2, March 1978, pages 138-146. Copyright © 1978 by The Institute of Electrical and Electronics Engineers, Inc.

this paper are based on implementations of the algorithms done by the author, and run and tested on a STAR. They are deemed to be good implementations, but we do not rule out the possibility that someone can improve the implementations by altering them slightly. All timings are based on data furnished by CDC that have been used in other research to obtain estimates of execution time (cf. [7]), and the actual runs were timed to verify the timing estimates.

II. THE TIMING MODEL OF THE CDC STAR

The CDC STAR computer is a computer with a vector instruction set in addition to a conventional multiregister instruction set [2]. The machine is so designed to make vector operations particularly efficient. Memory is organized into 32 independent banks, each of which can support a memory access while accesses are made concurrently to other memory banks. The vector instruction set has been designed so that successive elements of a vector are derived from successive memory banks. Fetches are initiated to these successive elements at uniform delay intervals, so that all 32 banks can be active in different phases of operation.

A typical vector instruction forms a result vector C whose elements are the results of combining two operand vectors, A and B, element-by-element. The time to execute a vector operation as measured in minor cycles is roughly approximated by the equation

$$\text{vector time} = s + k \cdot L$$

where L is the length of the vector operation (the number of elements in an operand or result vector), s is a constant associated with vector startup, and k is a small integer or fraction that depends on the operation. While the constant s depends on the operation, it is slightly less than 100 for the vector operations used in this paper. For specific examples of vector operations on full-word floating-point operands, the timing for a vector add or subtract is $94 + L/2$, for a vector multiply is $154 + L$, for a vector divide is $154 + 2L$, and for a vector element-by-element compare is $112 + L/2$. The important aspect of this timing is that after paying a penalty for vector startup, results are produced at the rate $\frac{1}{2}$, 1, 2, or more per minor cycle.

The cost of executing a load or store in a conventional type of instruction for this machine is relatively high. An item fetched is available in a machine register no sooner than 31 minor cycles after the instruction is initially executed. However, the machine is designed to support simultaneous scalar operations in up to three different banks, with the results from a succession of fetches available at the maximum rate of one operand every 19 minor cycles after an initial delay of 31 minor cycles for the first one. Items can be stored at the rate of one item every 16 minor cycles, provided the stores are made to different memory banks. Thus, the very fastest that two items can be retrieved from memory in scalar mode, added, and stored in a third location is one result every $19 + 19 + 16 = 54$ minor cycles, as compared to one result every $\frac{1}{2}$ minor cycle in vector mode. For this type of operation, vector mode is potentially 100 times faster than scalar mode for sufficiently long vectors. For short vectors, the overhead

due to vector startup becomes dominant, and in many situations scalar mode is preferred.

The actual execution time for scalar instructions is somewhat longer than indicated here. Memory performance is degraded when successive fetches are made to the same memory bank because a full memory operation requires 30 minor cycles, and fetches to the same bank cannot be made at shorter intervals. (Each memory fetch, however, retrieves eight 64-bit operands in a contiguous block, so that successive fetches to the same 8-word block can be honored without paying 30 minor cycles for each one.)

Scalar instructions that involve no memory operations require 9 to 15 minor cycles to complete, but design considerations permit these instructions to be overlapped in many cases to reduce their effective execution time to 5 to 10 minor cycles. There is no penalty for instruction fetches in straight-line code because the instructions are buffered well ahead. Conditional branches require from 13 to 43 minor cycles depending on whether the branch target is in the instruction buffer or in memory.

The data given here are sufficient for good estimates of relative sorting times. In all cases in the analyses that follow we have used the exact timing information supplied by the manufacturer on debugged versions of the algorithm tested on a STAR at NASA Langley Research Center. In treating the uncertainties in execution time that exist we have simply ignored them because they are small and do not alter the relative execution times materially.

III. QUICKSORT—SCALAR AND VECTOR VERSIONS

Quicksort has been the subject of extensive analyses, particularly by Hoare [5] and Knuth [6]. We refer the reader to these sources for full details concerning the algorithm and its running time. We describe the algorithm briefly in this section, then obtain timing estimates for it in scalar and vector versions.

The algorithm requires a procedure PARTITION (X, FIRST, LAST) that operates on the elements of an array X to be sorted starting at X[FIRST] and ending at X[LAST]. Given the array in its initial condition, the procedure reorders the elements of this subarray so that

1) X[FIRST] is moved to a new position J, FIRST ⩽ J ⩽ LAST,
2) the elements finally residing in the region beginning at FIRST and ending at J – 1 are all less than X[J], and
3) the elements in the region from J + 1 to LAST are all not less than X[J]. PARTITION returns the value of J.

Given the procedure PARTITION, the following algorithm sorts an array X whose indices run from FIRST to LAST.

```
procedure SORT(X,FIRST,LAST);
array X; integer FIRST, LAST; value FIRST, LAST;
begin integer J;
        J := PARTITION(X,FIRST,LAST);
        if J-FIRST>1 then SORT(X,FIRST,J-1);
        if LAST-J>1 then SORT(X,J+1,LAST);
end SORT;
```

This is not intended to be the best implementation of Quicksort, but illustrative of the idea behind the algorithm. After partitioning X, element X[J] is in place and the subarrays below and above X[J] have to be sorted in place as subarrays.

TABLE I
INSTRUCTION TIMINGS FOR STAR

Instruction type	Min time	Max time	Est time	Instruction Frequency							Const
				A	B	C	D	E	S	N	
Register operation	6	11	8	6	0	2	1	2	7	4	5
Load	19	32	23	3	3	1	0	3	1	3	-1
Store	16	29	20	2	2	0	1	1	1	0	0
Branch (branch taken)	19	37	25	3.5	1	.5	-2	1	-.5	2	-4.5
Branch (branch not taken)	13	13	13	2.5	0	.5	2	0	-.5	0	1.5

This sorting is done through the recursive calls on SORT in the given implementation. It is actually more efficient to avoid the overhead of the recursive procedure call. The index pairs that define a sorting operation need to be stacked and unstacked, but recursion is unnecessary. The depth of the stack can be limited to grow no more than logarithmically in the size of the initial array if the longer of the two subarrays is stacked and the shorter is sorted immediately.

A direct translation of the algorithm given by Knuth [6, pp. 118-119] due to Sedgewick [9] into code for the CDC STAR scalar instruction set is quite straightforward because almost every MIX instruction in that algorithm has an exact counterpart in the CDC STAR instruction set. The only difference of consequence is the MIX instruction CMPA which compares the accumulator to memory and sets a condition code. For the STAR, it is necessary to first load the item into a machine register, then compare two registers with a conditional branch on the relative value of the registers. Thus where Knuth sets a condition code and tests it with a sequence of the form CMPA, JGE, the corresponding code for the STAR is LOAD, BGE. (The MIX instruction CMPX should be treated similarly.) The resulting code for the STAR is not necessarily the absolute fastest version of Quicksort, but it is fast and error free, so we can make accurate timing estimates without the availability of an operational machine or timing simulator.

In converting the MIX program to the STAR, we make use of five types of STAR instructions, as shown in Table I. Table I gives the minimum and maximum execution times for these instructions and gives the time estimate used for this study. We used near minimum times on nonbranch instructions under the assumption that instructions can be overlapped maximally with negligible degradation due to memory conflicts. The branches were estimated to require near minimal execution time under the assumption that most branches are in tight loops in which case the target is resident in the instruction buffer, and in relatively few instances is the target outside the instruction buffer. These estimates tend to be slightly optimistic about the speed of computation.

Also given in Table I are the number of times each instruction type is executed during a sort of N 64-bit floating point numbers. The columns labeled A, B, C, D, E, and S are the functions derived by Knuth [6] given in Table II. The parameter M in these functions is the maximum size of a subarray that is sorted by an insertion sort. All larger subarrays are partitioned into smaller subarrays until the subarrays reach size M

TABLE II
FREQUENCY OF EXECUTION FUNCTIONS (AVERAGE FREQUENCIES)

$$A \simeq 2(N+1)/(M+2)$$

$$B \simeq (1/3)(N+1) \ln[(N+1)/(M+2)]$$

$$C \simeq 2(N+1) \ln[(N+1)/(M+1)]$$

$$D \simeq (N+1)(1 - 2H_{M+1}/(M+2))$$

$$E \simeq (1/6)(N+1)M(M-1)/(M+2)$$

$$S \simeq (N+1)/(2M+3) - 1 \quad \text{for } N > 2M+1$$

when $H_N \simeq \ln N + .57721\ 56649 \ldots$ for large N.

or smaller. For the data given in Tables I and II, the fastest time occurs for M = 9, in which case the time required to sort $N \geqslant 32$ items is given by:

serial quicksort time = $153(N+1)\ln(N+1) + 132(N+1) - 532.9$

To derive the time for a vector quicksort, we note that the procedure PARTITION can be done in four vector operations with a few scalar overhead operations. The partition algorithm in vector form is as follows.

1) With a vector comparison operation, compare the scalar operand X[FIRST] to X[I], FIRST < I < LAST, to create a 0,1-vector whose elements indicate whether or not X[FIRST] < X[I].

2) With a vector compress operation and the 0, 1-vector produced in Step 1, copy to a temporary vector all elements identified to be not less than X[FIRST]. The elements retain their relative order in the temporary vector.

3) With a vector compress, compress in place the elements identified to be less than X[FIRST]. This moves all elements less than X[FIRST] to the beginning of the subarray, while retaining their relative position in the array.

4) With a vector count ones, count the 1's in the 0,1-vector to find the number of elements moved to the temporary array.

5) With a vector copy operation, recopy the elements not less than X[FIRST] from the temporary vector back to the original array starting with the first element beyond the subarray formed in Step 3. The number of elements moved is determined from Step 4.

The timing estimates for the vector compare, compress, count ones, and copy operations appear in Table III. The average number of times that each of the vector steps above is executed is given by parameter A in Table II. This accounts for

TABLE III
INSTRUCTION TIMINGS FOR VECTOR QUICKSORT

Instruction	STAR timing	Time charged to PARTITION execution
Compare	112 + length/2	102A + C/2
Compress	92 + length + (number moved)/8	184A + 17C/8
Count ones	90 + length/16	90A + C/16
Copy vector	91 + length/2	91A + C/4
Other overhead	33	33A

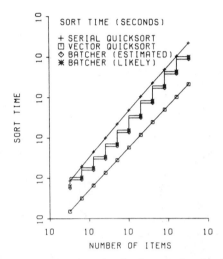

Fig. 1. Execution times for the three sorting algorithms.

the vector startup times. But the vector execution time depends on the length of the vectors as well as the number of startups. The sum of the lengths of the vectors executed in each step is given by parameter C in Table II. When the vector PARTITION algorithm is inserted in place of a scalar algorithm for the same process, then the contributions due to scalar instructions in columns B and C of Table I vanish. To this we add the contribution of 510A and 2.9375C from Table III to obtain a timing function that we can use for comparison purposes. Again we find an M that minimizes this function, namely M = 8, from which we obtain the timing function as:

$$\text{vector quicksort time} = 5.875(N + 1)\ln(N + 1)$$
$$+ 101.875(N + 1) - 294.2.$$

Plots of this function and scalar execution time appear in Fig. 1. Data shown are absolute times computed with one minor cycle equal to 40 ns. We assume that there is sufficient memory available to sort the arrays in core, and note that the STAR is configured with one megaword of memory to make this assumption valid.

IV. THE STAR IMPLEMENTATION OF BATCHER'S ALGORITHM

The algorithm described in this section was first presented by Batcher in the context of sorting networks constructed from elementary cells that do only comparison and exchange operations. The sequence of comparisons and exchanges is not data dependent, which is not the case for Quicksort, or, in fact, for any known sorting algorithm whose average sorting time is $O(N \log_2 N)$. Because the full sequence of comparisons is fixed ahead of time, and because the sequence lends itself to vector implementation, the STAR implementation of this algorithm is faster than the STAR implementation of Quicksort for N in the thousands and tens of thousands.

The algorithm implemented on STAR described in this section is a modification of Batcher's algorithm due to Stone [10]. It makes use of a permutation known as the *perfect shuffle* to reorder the elements of a vector between comparison phases. A perfect shuffle of a vector shuffles the elements of that vector in the same way that the cards in a deck of cards are shuffled when the deck is cut exactly in half and the two halves are perfectly interlaced. In addition to undergoing a perfect shuffle permutation, the elements of the vector are compared and exchanged according to a fixed strategy as follows. Consider any element X[I] in the first half of the vector. This is compared to X[I + N/2] to compute a comparison-result bit that indicates whether or not X[I] is less than X[I + N/2]. Then a 0, 1 mask vector is EXCLUSIVE OR'ed to the result bit vector. Finally, if the result bit for a comparison after alteration by the mask bit is a 1, the elements X[I] and X[I + N/2] are exchanged, otherwise they are left in place. This operation in the algorithm is indicated as COMPARE-EXCHANGE (X, MASK[K]), where MASK[K] is the mask vector that conditions the exchange.

In Stone's version of the algorithm the mask vectors are recomputed at various stages of the algorithm. Knuth [6, pp. 237-239] shows a simpler set of mask vectors that are more easily calculated when needed. In any event it is unnecessary to calculate the mask vectors more than once. It is most reasonable to calculate them ahead of time and store them during the execution of the sorting algorithm. We do not include the overhead to calculate the mask vectors in our timing analysis because it is relatively insignificant compared to the time to sort N items.

Before stating the algorithm implemented in STAR code, we should mention that the algorithm is effective only when N is a power of 2. If N is not a power of 2, then dummy records with maximal keys should be added to the end of the file to make the total number of records a power of 2.

The following algorithm statement is the perfect shuffle version of the algorithm due to Stone [10] with the simplified mask calculations due to Knuth [6]. It appears to have one extra shuffle at the end in this version, but the shuffle is required for the STAR because of a modification in the comparison-exchange operation.

4, 0), which is the desired shuffle operation. A merge with th mask 00111010 produces the result vector $(1, 2, 5, 6, 7, 3$ 0, 4).

```
procedure SORT (X,N);
array X; integer N; comment X is declared X[0:N-1], and N is a power of 2;
begin integer I, J, LOGN;
    COMPARE-EXCHANGE (X,MASK[1]);
    SHUFFLE(X);
    LOGN := log₂ N;
    for I := 1 step 1 until LOGN - 2 do
        begin
            for J := 1 step 1 until LOGN - 1 - I do
                SHUFFLE(X);
            for J := LOGN - I step 1 until LOGN do
                begin
                    COMPARE-EXCHANGE(X,MASK[J + I + 1 - LOGN]);
                    SHUFFLE(X);
                end J loop;
        end I loop;
    comment the last loop does a compare and exchange at every step,
        and no mask is used to change the effect of the exchange;
    for J := 1 step 1 until LOGN do
        begin
            COMPARE-EXCHANGE(X,NULL MASK);
            SHUFFLE(X);
        end;
end SORT
```

The mask vector MASK[1] is the vector $01010101 \cdots$, MASK[2] is the vector $00110011 \cdots$, and mask vector MASK[I] has 2^{I-1} 0s followed by 2^{I-1} 1s with the pattern repeating 2^{N-I-1} times. The NULL mask is the all 0s vector. The result bit that controls an exchange operation is the EXCLUSIVE OR of the corresponding comparison result bit and mask bit. Note that the algorithm has $O(\log_2 N)^2$ shuffle operations and comparison-exchange operations, with each such operation involving $O(N)$ items to give the algorithm a total complexity of $O[N (\log_2 N)^2]$, which is greater than the complexity of Quicksort.

The STAR implementation of this algorithm is quite straightforward, and requires only four vector operations to do a compare-exchange-shuffle sequence.

The shuffle itself is done in a single vector operation by using the STAR *merge* instruction with a mask vector $010101 \cdots 01$. The merge operation produces a result vector from two operand vectors under the control of a mask vector. As its name implies, the operation merges the two operand vectors using two pointers to scan the two operand vectors sequentially. A 0-bit in a mask vector selects an element from the first operand vector for the result vector, and the selection updates the pointer to the first operand vector to point to the next element in the vector. A 1-bit in the mask has a similar effect, except the second operand vector supplies the next element of the result vector, and the pointer to it is updated. Given the two operand vectors (1, 2, 3, 4) and (5, 6, 7, 0), a merge with the mask 01010101 produces the result vector (1, 5, 2, 6, 3, 7,

The compare-exchange operation in the Stone and Knuth versions of the sort operates on pairs of elements of a vector whose indices are of the form $2i$ and $2i + 1$. The STAR has no instructions that can do this type of comparison efficiently in vector mode. However, two vectors can be compared, element-by-element, in a single vector operation. Consequently, we choose to partition a vector of length N into two equal contiguous subvectors, one whose elements are indexed by i in the interval $0 \leqslant i \leqslant N/2 - 1$, and the other whose elements are indexed by i in the interval $N/2 \leqslant i \leqslant N - 1$. A vector compare matches $x[i]$ in the first vector to $x[i + N/2]$ in the second vector. This produces $N/2$ bits whose values indicate the outcomes of the comparisons.

To implement the compare-exchange operation in the spirit required for the sorting, note that the compare-exchange is always followed by a shuffle. We implement the sequence of compare-exchange shuffle by doing the comparison to obtain the result vector, and from the result vector we build a mask vector for a merge. The merge operation then not only shuffles the vector but exchanges pairs as well as required by the exchange portion of the algorithm. Specifically, we do the following:

1) using the first and last halves of the x vector as operands, perform a vector comparison to produce a result vector whose bits indicate "greater than or equal" for each pair of elements $x[i]$ and $x[i + N/2]$;

2) append the complement of the result vector to the result vector;

TABLE IV
DATA FOR TIMING OF BATCHER ALGORITHM

Operation	Time	Number of Executions	Phase of Algorithm
Vector merge	123 + 3N	(LOGN - 2)(LOGN - 1)/2	Shuffle
Overhead	65	"	"
Vector compare	143 + N/4	(LOGN - 2)(LOGN + 1)/2	Comparison-exchange-shuffle with mask
Complement bit vector	110 + (4.5)N/128	"	"
EXCLUSIVE OR bit vector	110 + (4.5)N/128	"	"
Merge bits	92 + 5N/64	"	"
Vector merge	123 + 3N	"	"
Overhead	118	"	"
Vector compare	143 + N/4	LOGN	Comparison-exchange-shuffle with NULL mask
Complement bit vector	110 + (4.5)N/128	"	"
Merge bits	92 + 5N/64	"	"
Vector merge	123 + 3N	"	"
Overhead	81	"	"

3) produce the EXCLUSIVE OR of this vector with the mask vector for this compare-exchange;

4) merge the bits of the 0,1-vector of Step 3 using the vector $0101 \cdots 01$ as the control vector for the merge (the *bit merge* instruction is the same as the merge instruction, except that it operates on vectors of bits instead of vectors of words);

5) merge the two halves of the x array using the vector produced in Step 4 as a control vector.

To show that this algorithm implements the compare-exchange shuffle correctly, we first show an example of the algorithm, then indicate through the example how the algorithm operates. Suppose the x vector is the vector (1, 3, 7, 6, 0, 4, 2, 5). After the comparison the result vector is 1011, whose 1s indicate that $1 \geqslant 0$, $7 \geqslant 2$, and $6 \geqslant 5$, respectively, and whose 0 indicates that $3 < 4$. We append 0100 to the result vector 1011 to obtain 10110100. This is shuffled via a bit merge to obtain 10011010, and then it is used as a control vector for a merge of the vector x to obtain the resulting vector (0, 1, 3, 4, 2, 7, 5, 6). This is the same vector obtained by first exchanging elements in positions indicated by 1's in the comparison result vector to produce (0, 3, 2, 5, 1, 4, 7, 6) followed by a shuffle as described above. Thus steps 1, 2, 4, and 5 implement a compare-exchange with the NULL mask, followed by a shuffle. Step 3 is included to obtain the effect of the mask vector required in the algorithm.

It is very easy to see from this example why the process simulates the compare-exchange shuffle correctly. The comparison vector 1011 indicates the high values in the first subvector; its complement 0100 indicates the low values in the first subvector. The effect of appending 0100 to 1011 and then shuffling is to create a vector with four 0,1-pairs 10, 01, 10, 10. Each pair specifies the outcome of a specific comparison. A pair 10 forces the merge to select an element from the second half, then from the first half; a pair 01 reverses this order. Thus items are shuffled with or without pairwise exchanges.

The sorting algorithm terminates with a final shuffle operation whereas Stone and Knuth show algorithms that do not contain the final shuffle. The real difference lies in the initial arrangement of data for their algorithms. There the first comparison compares elements whose indices are of the form 2i and 2i + 1, whereas in the algorithm for the STAR, the vector comparison compares elements whose indices are of the form i and i + N/2. Thus instead of presenting the x vector with indices ordered (0, 1, 2, 3, 4, 5, 6, 7) to the algorithm, we can simulate the other versions of the algorithm exactly by reordering the indices into the order (0, 2, 4, 6, 1, 3, 5, 7), but the algorithm will terminate with indices ordered as (0, 2, 4, 6, 1, 3, 5, 7) by key size instead of in the order (0, 1, 2, 3, 4, 5, 6, 7) by key size. We do not actually reorder the initial indices, because the sorting algorithm will place them in the order (0, 2, 4, 6, 1, 3, 5, 7) by key size regardless of the initial index ordering. To obtain the ordering (0, 1, 2, 3, 4, 5, 6, 7) we have to append a final shuffle to the Stone and Knuth versions of the algorithm as we have done here.

The timing of this algorithm is determined from Table IV. The shuffle by itself requires a merge operation charged at 123 + 3N cycles plus overhead to compute descriptors for the vector operands, and to perform indexing. The overhead can be done by five register instructions and one conditional branch. The compare-exchange shuffle operation is charged as shown for the vector operations plus overhead of 88 cycles to account for a shift and six register operations to create descriptors and one conditional branch. With other overhead properly accounted, the total time to execute Batcher's sort is then given by

$$\text{Batcher sort time} = 3.492 N (\log_2 N)^2 - 2.859 N \log_2 N - 3 N$$
$$+ 424.5 (\log_2 N)^2 - 2.5 \log_2 N + 1183$$
$$= (\ln N)^2 (7.268 N + 883.5)$$
$$- N(4.125 \ln N + 4.328)$$
$$- 63.607 \ln N + 1706.708$$

469

The timing is clearly $O[N(\log_2 N)]^2$ as expected, but the term $883.5 (\ln N)^2$ dominates the expression until $N = 122$, at which point the term $7.268 N (\ln N)^2$ becomes dominant. The former term accounts for the number of vector startups, and the latter term accounts for the number of fetches, stores, and comparisons. Terms of other orders are negligible with respect to these terms for most values of N.

The timing equation for Batcher sort does not reflect additional overhead necessary to pad an array of records to the next higher power of 2, and it does not account for the time to compute the mask vectors during initialization if the masks are computed once instead of stored in the program. Both of these overhead functions contribute negligibly to the algorithm. The timing equation is plotted in Fig. 1. Note the "staircase" form of the plot to acknowledge the fact that the sorting time for i elements is identical for all i in an interval $2^m + 1 \leqslant i \leqslant 2^{m+1}$.

V. COMPARISON OF TIMINGS

The timings given for Quicksort and vector Quicksort are deemed to be accurate for the present generation of STAR computers. The timing formula for the Batcher sort appears to be roughly 15 percent below observed timings for reasons that are currently inexplicable. The plot in Fig. 1 shows both the computed timing of Batcher's algorithm and a run time of 15 percent above this time to reflect the times one would actually observe. The timings were observed and validated in the following manner.

1) Each algorithm was encoded by hand in STAR assembly language, and recoded into equivalent STAR Fortran. STAR Fortran has an embedded assembly language facility so that the generated code can be carefully controlled up to a point. The algorithms used simple Fortran assignment statements, GO TO's and DO's where the assembly language had one-for-one equivalents. Tight loops made use of the assembly language facility to generate the vector instructions and instructions to create vector descriptors. The resulting Fortran object code had some resulting inefficiencies in it that would not be present in a tightly coded hand optimized version.

2) The algorithms were run, debugged, and timed using facilities in Fortran. Some subroutine entry and exit overhead were recorded in these times; such overhead may be absent in a hand assembled version.

3) Timing formulas for the Fortran algorithms were generated according to timing estimates for each instruction and the actual number of times each instruction was executed. These estimates were used to calibrate the timing model and are not the timing estimates given here.

4) The result of the calibration showed that the vector Quicksort timing estimates and actual run times agree to within 2 percent for files of size 256 to 32768, and are within 20 percent for shorter file sizes down to length 32. Subroutine entry and exit overhead not included in the timing estimates accounts for the discrepancy for short file sizes. Vector Batcher sort, unfortunately, did not yield as well to the calibration. Timing estimates consistently ran 15 percent or lower below observed run times, and the discrepancy has not yet been explained satisfactorily. Some possible reasons for the discrepancy are mentioned later.

The timing estimates were made in a multiprogrammed environment, but they are supposedly repeatable since the timings are specified to be the actual elapsed CPU times in user state. Each algorithm was run a minimum of five times over a period of six months so as to determine the variability of the timing. Timing variations of ± 5 percent were observed. These variations could be due to any one of a number of sources including the fact that the vector instructions have an execution time that depends on the exact physical addresses of the operand and result vectors. This variability was not included in the timing model. Timing is also dependent on the concurrent input/output traffic, and this is uncontrollable by the program.

5) The Fortran compiled algorithms were then hand optimized to eliminate unnecessary instructions inserted by Fortran. The timing estimates in this paper are the estimates for the optimized algorithms. In the case of Batcher's algorithm, we also graph a time 15 percent above the estimated time to show what the observed time will probably actually be. These generally fall slightly below the observed timing for unoptimized Fortran versions.

It is rather unfortunate that the timing estimate of the Batcher algorithm does not agree with the observed time as closely as it should. The source of error is most likely to be in the timing of the vector instructions used by Batcher sort that are not also used by vector Quicksort since the timings for the other instructions in the Batcher algorithm have been calibrated by their use in vector Quicksort. The vector merge and bit merge instructions are particularly likely to be the source (or sources) of the error since the internal structure of STAR makes these instructions difficult to implement. The timings for both instructions have changed since the original announcement, and it is quite likely that the timing formulas given for these instructions today are not accurate.

We attempted to compute the timing for the vector merge and bit merge instructions from the observed data using a least squares estimate technique. Unfortunately, the timings obtained by this process were very sensitive to the exact observations, which proved to be noisy measurements in themselves. The coefficients in the instruction timings varied greatly for small perturbations in the input data, so that no significance could be attached to the computed instruction timings.

With respect to the quality of the coding of the algorithms, there are probably some additional tricks that can be performed to bring the timing down by a little bit, but we suspect the improvement for these particular algorithms will not be dramatic. One can, for example, make use of the 256 word register file in serial Quicksort by fetching small vectors of data into the file where they can be compared sequentially. This tends to reduce the charge of approximately 23 cycles for an operand fetch to one cycle for the operand fetch in vector mode plus approximately 8 cycles for the register access to the operand when it is needed. Unfortunately, the additional overhead to keep track of the subset of items in high-speed memory and for the vector startup to move a subset to high-speed memory reduce the gain in having the items in registers. For the algorithms coded, all operands that could be allocated to registers were so allocated. The only items resident in main memory were the input and temporary data files, and the pushdown stack.

In choosing to implement the vector Quicksort as we did, the reader should observe that the insertion sort of the partially sorted file after partitioning is done using serial code. This could be recoded from serial code into a vector form. However, the Sedgewick algorithm attains its high efficiency because the items are very nearly in their final position before the insertion sort is performed. Thus, items are compared only to items that are physically nearby. In vector mode this type of comparison can be done with a vector mode comparison that terminates when it finds the insertion point. Unfortunately, the high startup overhead for vector instructions makes them inefficient for short vectors so that a vector version of the insertion sort does not increase the speed of the insertion sort for the type of files produced by the partition phase of the algorithm. If the partition phase were altered to give more work to do in the insertion sort phase, then the relative inefficiency of insertion sort as compared to the partition process would tend to slow the sorting algorithm instead of improve it. We believe that the vector Quicksort studied is a reasonably efficient vector version of Quicksort based on the consideration of other alternatives.

In considering the numerical results reported above, the vector version of Quicksort runs faster than the scalar version of the same algorithm because fetches, comparisons, and stores are done roughly 100 times faster in vector mode than in scalar mode. The net speed increase is not a factor 100, however, because the number of vector startups is high for the vector Quicksort, and the cost of these startups is considerable. Note that the timing formula for vector Quicksort has a small constant for the $N \ln N$ term and a very large constant for the linear term to reflect the relatively expensive vector startup cost. The linear term dominates the term of $O(N \ln N)$ in this expression for N less than $\exp(101.875/5.875) \simeq 3.4.10^7$. Hence for all reasonable values of N, Quicksort sorts in *linear* time on STAR in spite of its asymptotic complexity of $N \ln N$.

The vector version of Batcher's algorithm is clearly faster than serial Quicksort for most file sizes up to 32768, the maximum vector size on a STAR. The interesting observation here is that the complexity of Batcher's algorithm is strictly worse than the complexity of serial Quicksort since the former is $O[N (\log_2 N)^2]$ and the latter is $O[N \log_2 N]$. Because the STAR is organized to do some operations extremely efficiently, it reduces the constant coefficient on terms that dominate complexity arguments. Consequently, complexity arguments that hold for large enough N are invalid for values of N of most interest to the programmer. In this particular example the STAR's idiosyncracies can be put to good use in improving serial Quicksort to cast it into a vector form, and thus vector Quicksort generally outperforms the vector Batcher sort.

Even this latter conclusion is subject to review as improvements to STAR are made and relative timings change. Earlier releases of the timing manual indicated that the vector merge instruction used in the perfect shuffle ran in a time equal to a constant plus N, where N is equal to the number of items shuf-

fled. The timing formula used in this report reflects the timing of the delivered machine, for which the time is a constant plus $3N$. The change from N to $3N$ altered the Batcher timing significantly. An earlier version of this paper based on the faster vector merge timing concluded that the vector Batcher sort outperformed vector Quicksort for a reasonably large range of file sizes. Thus the comparison between vector Quicksort and vector Batcher sort rests strongly on the timing of the merge instruction. If the machine were to meet its original specifications, our conclusions would change.

We acknowledge that the algorithms studied are not necessarily the ultimate sorting algorithms for STAR. The specific ones studied might be improved in unpredictable ways, and yet other algorithms might prove to be ideally suited to STAR's unusual instruction set. Quite apart from determining the definitive way to sort on STAR, the study has produced numerical results that show that the instruction set and internal design of a computer can have a very significant influence on the type of algorithm to use for that computer. In this case, we cannot even limit attention to the class of algorithms known to have minimum complexity for this problem because there may be an algorithm of poorer complexity that actually runs faster for all runable problems. This has been demonstrated here in a sense since Batcher's algorithm is a strong competitor to serial Quicksort.

We mention in passing that the graphs in Fig. 1 have been derived on the assumption that records are one word (64 bits) long. In actual practice, the length of records moved is likely to be short because the records will consist of key plus a pointer. If both the key and pointer are packed into a 64-bit computer word, then Fig. 1 tells the whole story of comparative timings except for the permutation of the records at the end of the sort, which requires the same time for all three algorithms. If records are actually longer than one word, we have to account for the additional time to move the extra words. Analysis of longer records quickly reveals that it is better to pay a cost proportional to N to permute a file according to a list of sorted pointers than to pay a cost of $N \ln N$ to permute the file itself during the sort. Since the cost in Batcher's algorithm is proportional to $N (\ln N)^2$ to move records during a sort and proportional only to N to move the records according to a sorted list of pointers, it is more advantageous to keep records short during a Batcher sort. The effect of lengthening records for sorting is to raise the Batcher timing estimates relative to the Quicksort estimates, so as to enhance the attractiveness of vector Quicksort. Nevertheless, records sorted are likely to be of size 1 or 2 in practice to achieve maximum performance so that the curves in Fig. 1 are representative of what one might reasonably expect to hold.

ACKNOWLEDGMENT

The author gratefully acknowledges the suggestions of D. Knuth, R. Sedgewick, and the referees that have been incorporated into the paper. R. Voigt and J. Knight have been extremely helpful in running STAR programs at the NASA Langley Research Center. S. Bokhari prepared the graphical data, which under the conditions at that time was in itself an accomplishment.

REFERENCES

[1] K. E. Batcher, "Sorting networks and their applications," in *1968 Spring Joint Comput. Conf., AFIPS Conf. Proc.*, vol. 32. Washington, DC: Thompson, 1968, pp. 307–314.

[2] Control Data, *CDC STAR-100 Instruction Execution Times* and *Control Data STAR-100 Computer System Hardware Reference Manual*, Control Data Corp., Arden Hills, MN, revision 6, Oct. 3, 1973.

[3] R. W. Floyd "Algorithm 245," *Commun. Ass. Comput. Mach.*, vol. 7, p. 701, Dec. 1964.

[4] W. D. Frazer and A. C. McKellar, "Samplesort: A sampling approach to minimal storage tree sorting," *J. Ass. Comput. Mach.*, vol. 17, pp. 496–507, July 1970.

[5] C. A. R. Hoare, "Quicksort," *Computer J.*, vol. 5, no. 1, pp. 10–15, 1962.

[6] D. E. Knuth, *The Art of Computer Programming, Vol. 3, Sorting and Searching*. Reading, MA: Addison-Wesley, 1973.

[7] J. J. Lambiotte, Jr. and R. G. Voigt, "The solution of tridiagonal linear systems on the CDC STAR-100 computer," *Trans. Math. Software*, vol. 1, no. 4, pp. 308–329, Dec. 1975.

[8] R. Loeser, "Some performance tests of 'quicksort' and descendants," *Commun. Ass. Comput. Mach.*, vol. 17, no. 3, pp. 143–152, Mar. 1974.

[9] R. Sedgewick, "Quicksort," Ph.D. dissertation, Stanford Univ., Stanford, CA, 1974.

[10] H. S. Stone, "Parallel processing with the perfect shuffle," *IEEE Trans. Comput.*, vol. C-20, no. 2, pp. 153–161, Feb. 1971.

[11] M. H. van Emden, "Increasing the efficiency of Quicksort," *Commun. Ass. Comput. Mach.*, vol. 13, no. 9, pp. 563–567, Sept. 1970.

Harold S. Stone (S'61–M'63) received the B.S.E. degree from Princeton University, Princeton, NJ, in 1960, and the M.S. and Ph.D. degrees from the University of California, Berkeley, in 1961 and 1963, respectively.

From 1963 until 1968 he was with Stanford Research Institute, and from 1968 until 1974 he was Associate Professor of Electrical Engineering and Computer Science at Stanford University. He is currently Professor of Electrical and Computer Engineering at the University of Massachusetts, Amherst. His recent research activities have been in the areas of distributed computing, parallel computation, computer architecture, and advanced memory system organization. Past activities include work in design automation, operating systems, and combinatorial algorithms. He has authored over thirty technical publications, and is the author, coauthor, or editor of five textbooks in computer science. Among the institutions at which he has been affiliated as a visitor are the University of Chile, the University of Sao Paulo, the Technical University of Berlin, NASA Ames Research Center, and IRIA.

Dr. Stone is a member of the Association for Computing Machinery. He has served as a Technical Editor of *Computer Magazine* and as a member of the Governing Board of the IEEE Computer Society.

Acta Informatica 9, 1 – 21 (1977)

© by Springer-Verlag 1977

Concurrency of Operations on *B*-Trees

R. Bayer* and M. Schkolnick

IBM Research Laboratory, San José, CA 95193, USA

Summary. Concurrent operations on *B*-trees pose the problem of insuring that each operation can be carried out without interfering with other operations being performed simultaneously by other users. This problem can become critical if these structures are being used to support access paths, like indexes, to data base systems. In this case, serializing access to one of these indexes can create an unacceptable bottleneck for the entire system. Thus, there is a need for locking protocols that can assure integrity for each access while at the same time providing a maximum possible degree of concurrency. Another feature required from these protocols is that they be deadlock free, since the cost to resolve a deadlock may be high.

Recently, there has been some questioning on whether *B*-tree structures can support concurrent operations. In this paper, we examine the problem of concurrent access to *B*-trees. We present a deadlock free solution which can be tuned to specific requirements. An analysis is presented which allows the selection of parameters so as to satisfy these requirements.

The solution presented here uses simple locking protocols. Thus, we conclude that B-trees can be used advantageously in a multi-user environment.

1. Introduction

In this paper, we examine the problem of concurrent access to indexes which are maintained as *B*-trees. This type of organization was introduced by Bayer and McCreight [2] and some variants of it appear in Knuth [10] and Wedekind [13]. Performance studies of it were restricted to the single user environment. Recently, these structures have been examined for possible use in a multi-user (concurrent) environment. Some initial studies have been made about the feasibility of their use in this type of situation [1, 6], and [11].

An accessing schema which achieves a high degree of concurrency in using the index will be presented. The schema allows dynamic tuning to adapt its performance to the profile of the current set of users. Another property of the

---

* *Permanent address:* Institut für Informatik der Technischen Universität München, Arcisstr. 21, D-8000 München 2, Germany (Fed. Rep.)

Reprinted with permission from *Acta Informatica*, Volume 9, Number Fasc. 1, 1977, pages 1-21. Copyright © 1977 by Springer/Verlag.

schema is that it is deadlock free. This is achieved by providing a set of strict locking protocols which must be followed by each process accessing an index. The properties of the locks and the protocols together guarantee that deadlocks cannot arise. Furthermore, the schema is shown to be a generalization of several methods used in earlier attempts to achieve concurrent operations in B-trees.

In Section 2, we define terms which will be used in the paper. Then in Section 3, we introduce the problem and some basic solutions to it. In Section 4, we present the general schema to be studied. In Section 5, the schema is shown to be deadlock free. Section 6 contains a quantitative analysis of the schema. Using the results of this analysis, tuning parameters can be selected to optimize the performance of the schema. Finally, Section 7 briefly discusses some extensions to the schema.

2. Definitions

We assume the reader is familiar with B-trees ([2, 10]). In the sequel we will be using the variant known as B^*-tree [13]. A B^*-tree with parameter k is a tree structure for storing entries. An *entry* is a pair (entry key, associated information). The keys are linearly ordered, the associated information is of no interest in this paper. B^*-trees have the following properties:

1) All entries are stored on leaf nodes. Each leaf node contains a number μ of entries.

2) All paths from the root to a leaf node have the same length.

3) All nonleaf nodes contain a number of elements: $p_0, r_1, p_1, r_2, p_2, \ldots, r_\mu, p_\mu$, where the p_i's are pointers to immediate descendants of this node and the r_i's are elements which can be compared with the keys in the entries. They are called *reference keys*. All keys in the subtree pointed to by p_{i-1} are less than the reference key r_i and all keys in the subtree pointed to by p_i are greater than or equal to the reference key r_i.

4) The number μ referred to in 1 and 3, may vary from node to node but satisfies $k \leq \mu \leq 2k$ for all nodes except for the root, where $1 \leq \mu \leq 2k$.

We will say that a node in a B^*-tree is at a *level i* if the path from that node to a leaf contains i nodes. Because of property 2, this number is well defined for all nodes. The level of the root is said to be the height of the tree. We will use $\ell(n)$ to denote the level of node n and h to denote the height of the tree.

An example of a B^*-tree with $h=3$ and $k=2$ is shown in Figure 1. Entries on the leaf nodes are shown as parenthesized objects. The value in parentheses is the entry key. Nodes have been given labels in order to refer to them.

The operations to be performed on these structures will be of three kinds: A *search* for a given key, an *insertion* of a given entry, and a *deletion* of an entry with a given key. A process executing the first operation is said to be a *reader*. A process executing the second or third operation is said to be an *updater*. Note that a search does not result in a modification of the tree. If an insertion (respectively a deletion) is attempted and the key to be inserted (deleted) is (is not) found

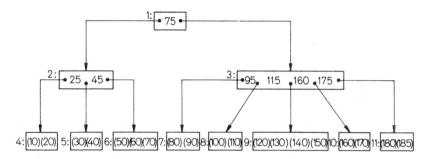

Fig. 1. A *B**-tree with $h = 3$, $k = 2$

in a leaf node then the insertion (deletion) is said to be *unsuccessful*. A successful operation done by an updater results in a modification of the tree. We assume the reader is familiar with the way these modifications affect the tree structure. We will use the following important fact: When an updater attempts an insertion (deletion) and scans node n, it can easily check a sufficient condition on n that any ancestors will not be affected by the insertion (deletion). If the condition is satisfied, n will be known as *safe*; otherwise, n is said to be *unsafe*.

In a *B**-tree, the criterion for determining safeness of a node is very simple: on insertions, a node is safe if the number μ is less than $2\,k$. On deletions, a node is safe if the number μ is greater than k. For example, a process trying to insert the key (186) in the tree shown in Figure 1 would first scan the root (node 1) and it would determine it is safe. It would then branch to node 3. Since for this node $\mu = 2\,k$, it would determine this node is unsafe, i.e., it cannot tell whether its ancestors, in this case node 1, would be affected by the insertion. Finally, it would move on to node 11 which it would determine to be safe, i.e., neither node 3 nor node 1 will be affected by the insertion. (In what follows, we will not worry about changing the unsafeness status of node 3 to being safe.)

The fact that we can determine safeness of a node is the feature of a *B**-tree that is used in all solutions described in this paper. In fact, any other tree structure for which the same property can be established can be accessed concurrently using the protocols described here. Examples of these are prefix *B*-trees [4] and enciphered *B*-trees [3].

3. Basic Solutions

In a multiuser environment, concurrent access of processes to an index structure must be supported. The problem of concurrent access is that of allowing a maximum number of processes to operate on the tree without impairing the correctness of their operations.

A simple-minded solution for the problem of concurrent access would be to strictly serialize all updaters, by requiring each updater to gain exclusive control

Fig. 2. Compatibility graph for locks: Solutions 1 and 2

of the tree — e.g., by placing an exclusive lock on the whole tree — before it begins accessing it, thus, preventing all other updaters and readers from altering or reading the index while the specific update takes place. Readers, on the other hand, could access the structure concurrently with other readers. Clearly this simple mechanism can only be used if the level of activity is rather low.

We will now present three solutions to the problem of concurrent access in a B^*-tree. For each solution we will give a protocol for both readers and updaters. All solutions use locks on the nodes of the tree. These locks are granted by a scheduler upon request by a process. We will assume that, except as noted in Solution 3, the scheduler services these requests in a FIFO order. This order is maintained by having one service queue for every node in the tree. A process requesting a lock on a node will be placed at the end of the queue for that node and the scheduler will service processes that are at the beginning of the queues.

Solution 1. This solution is essentially the one presented by Metzger [11]. It is derived from the simple-minded solution when the fact that safeness of a node can be established is used. The solution uses two types of locks: a *read* lock, or ρ-lock, and an *exclusive* lock, or ξ-lock. A node cannot simultaneously be locked with a ρ-lock and a ξ-lock. In fact, these locks satisfy the compatibility relation shown in Figure 2.

An edge between any two nodes in a compatibility graph means that two *different* processes may simultaneously hold these locks on the same node. The absence of an edge indicates that two different processes cannot hold these locks simultaneously on a node. These constraints are enforced by the lock scheduler.

The protocol for readers is as follows:

          0) Place ρ-lock on root;

          1) Get root and make it the current node;

main loop: 2) **While** current node is not a leaf node **do**
          {Exactly one ρ-lock is held by process}
          begin
            3) Place ρ-lock on appropriate son of current node;
            4) Release ρ-lock on current node;
            5) Get son of current node and make it current;
          end mainloop

By executing this protocol, a reader would scan the B^*-tree, starting at the root and moving down towards a leaf node.

The protocol for an updater is as follows:

          0) Place ξ-lock on root;

          1) Get root and make it the current node;

main loop: 2) **While** current node is not a leaf node **do**
          {number of ξ-locks held ≥ 1}

begin

    3) Place ξ-lock on appropriate son of current node;

    4) Get son and make it the current node;

    5) **If** current node is safe

        then release all locks held on ancestors of current node

end

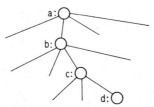

Fig. 3. Skeletal *B**-tree

As an example of how this last protocol would work, consider an update on the node *d* of the (skeletal) *B**-tree shown in Figure 3. Assume that, for this update, nodes *a*, *b*, and *d* are safe and *c* is not. Before execution of the mainloop, a ξ-lock would be placed on node *a* and this node would be scanned.

Then the following sequence of events would take place.

    i) [Step 3] A ξ-lock is requested on node *b*.

    ii) [Step 4] After ξ-lock is granted, node *b* is retrieved.

    iii) [Step 5] Since node *b* is safe, the ξ-lock on node *a* is released, thereby, allowing other updaters or readers to access node *a*.

    iv) [Step 3] A ξ-lock is requested on node *c*.

    v) [Step 4] After ξ-lock is granted, node *c* is retrieved.

    vi) [Step 5] Since node *c* is unsafe, the ξ-lock on node *b* is kept.

    vii) [Step 3] A ξ-lock is requested on node *d*.

    viii) [Step 4] After ξ-lock is granted, node *d* is retrieved.

    ix) [Step 5] Since node *d* is safe, the ξ-locks on nodes *b* and *c* can be released.

This solution has the advantage of requiring only a simple protocol to achieve a reasonable gain in concurrency over the simple minded solution described at the beginning of this section. However, it suffers from the fact that updaters first ξ-lock the root of a subtree when updating this subtree (and thus preventing all other accesses to this subtree) even when, as it happens most of the time, the update will have no effect on this root. In the above example, the entire tree remained ξ-locked while node *b* was being retrieved and examined (a slow process). In turn, the subtree rooted at *b* had a ξ-lock on its root while both nodes *c* and *d* were retrieved and examined to find that node *b* would not be modified as a result of the update.

To achieve higher concurrency one may let updaters behave like readers in the upper part of the tree. This leads to the next solution.

Solution 2. This solution is a variant of one used by one of the authors in the design of an interactive data base system [12]. It uses the same locks as in Solution 1. The protocol for a reader is also as in Solution 1. Updaters however, have a different protocol, as follows:

          0) Place ρ-lock on root;
          1) Get root and make it the current node;

main loop: 2) **While** current node is not a leaf node **do**
            begin
               3) **If** son is not a leaf node
                  then place ρ-lock on appropriate son
                  else place ξ-lock on appropriate son;
               4) Release lock on current node;
               5) Get son and make it the current node
            end mainloop;
          6) {A leaf node has been reached}
            If current node is unsafe
            then release all locks and repeat access to the tree, this time
               using the protocol for an updater as in Solution 1;

By following this protocol, updaters will proceed down the tree as if they were readers until they are about to go to a leaf node. At this point, they ξ-lock the leaf node in order to make the update. However, if it is found that the update would affect nodes higher in the tree, all the analysis done so far would be lost and the update must be retried (note that this only involves the release of one lock and the time lost in scanning the tree). There is no actual modification done to any node which would have to be restored.

The protocol shown works for trees of height greater than one but it is a simple matter to accommodate for this case, so from now one we assume all of our trees have heights greater than one.

Solution 2 achieves high concurrency by allowing both readers and updaters to share all higher levels of the tree. It is only when the update is to be performed on an unsafe leaf that the updater adopts the protocol of the previous solution and thus prevents concurrency as occurred in that solution. Since this only happens roughly once every k updates done to the tree it is a very infrequent action, for typical uses of B*-trees is with a large k [2].

If the time spent in the unsuccessful analysis or the interference with readers becomes critical, as would be for example, on a very deep tree, then Solution 3 is more attractive.

Solution 3. This solution uses three types of locks, a ρ-lock, an α-lock, and a ξ-lock. The compatibility graph is shown in Figure 4. In this diagram, a new type of edge is shown by a directed broken line from the α node to the ξ node. This means that the α-lock can be converted into a ξ-lock.

Conversion from one type of lock to another type is taken to be a basic (or atomic) operation which happens in one step. To request a conversion from one type of lock to another, a process has to hold a lock of the first type on a node. When making a request for a conversion, a process will be placed *at the beginning* of the queue for the node in question (thus, these conversion requests are serviced before any other requests). If the conversion is granted the process now holds a lock of the second type on this node. If the conversion requests a lock incompatible with a lock placed by another process then the conversion is not granted

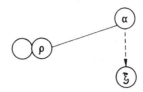

Fig. 4. Compatibility and convertibility graph for locks: Solution 3

and the requesting process is placed on a wait status at the beginning of the queue for that node.

For the three types of locks as defined for Solution 3, the only time a conversion (from α-lock to ξ-lock) fails is when another process holds a ρ lock on the resource on which a conversion is being attempted. (Note that a ρ-lock is the only type of lock which is compatible with an α-lock.) An attempt to convert this α-lock into a ξ-lock will be delayed until the ρ-lock on the resource is released since the ξ-lock is incompatible with the ρ-lock.

Readers use the same protocol as in Solution 1. Updaters now use the following protocol:

0) Place an α-lock on the root;
1) Get the root and make it the current node;

main loop: 2) **While** current node is not a leaf node **do**
{number of α-locks held $\geqq 1$}
begin
3) Place an α-lock on appropriate son of current node;
4) Get son and make it the current node;
5) **If** current node is safe
then release all locks held on ancestors of current node
end mainloop;
6) {A leaf node has been reached. At this time we can determine if update can be successfully completed.}
If the update will be successful
then convert, top-down, all α-locks into ξ-locks;

Using this protocol, an updater descends the tree as in Solution 1 but using α-locks instead of ξ-locks. This has the advantage of allowing readers to share the nodes on which an updater has placed its α-locks, thus increasing concurrency. On the other hand, all nodes that need to be modified as a result of the update, are locked exclusively after Step 6. Thus, the analysis phase need not be repeated, as occurred in Solution 2. Moreover, ξ-locks are placed only on those nodes that will be modified, thus readers are prevented from examining only the minimal possible set of nodes.

The main disadvantage of this solution is that, as in Solution 1, one updater may temporarily block other updaters from scanning a node, even if this node will not be affected by the update. Also, there is overhead time spent in doing lock conversions.

Although the α-lock on the leaf node needs to be converted to a ξ-lock everytime the update can be successfully completed, conversion of locks in higher

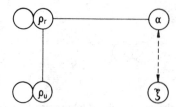

Fig. 5. Compatibility and convertibility graph for locks: Generalized solution

nodes occurs as infrequently as the repetition of analysis in Solution 2, a very small proportion of time. Note that the required α to ξ conversion on the leaf node could be eliminated by changing the protocol to set up a ξ-lock directly on a leaf node, instead of an α-lock. If the update affects higher nodes still held with α-locks, then as will be seen in the generalized solution, the ξ-lock on the leaf must first be converted to an α-lock and then the α- to ξ-lock conversion can be made. Thus, the very frequent operation of converting the α-lock on the leaf to a ξ-lock can be replaced by a slightly more complicated protocol and the infrequent conversion of a ξ-lock on a leaf to an α-lock. A new conversion property among locks is needed, namely ξ-locks must be convertible into α-locks.

4. A Generalized Solution

In the **previous** section, we presented three solutions to the problem of deadlock free concurrent operations on B-trees. We observed that these solutions were complimentary in the sense that each had advantages over the other in certain situations. Thus, none of them was a best solution in all possible cases. This suggests that a combined solution may be more suitable. In this section, we present such a generalized solution.

There are 4 locks needed in this approach. A ρ_r-lock, a ρ_u-lock, an α-lock, and a ξ-lock. Their compatibility-convertibility diagram is shown in Figure 5. Note that, as mentioned already in the remarks following Solution 3, there is a need for conversion from α to ξ and from ξ to α.

The protocol for a reader is as in Solution 1, with ρ_r replacing ρ. The protocol for an updater is given below. As can be observed, there are two parameters P and $\varXi$. Intuitively, these stand for the maximum number of levels in the tree on which an updater may place ρ_u-locks and ξ-locks respectively. A variable H is introduced which has as its value, the current value of the height h of the tree. In an implementation of a B^*-tree the value h can be stored in a directory entry together with a pointer to the root of the tree. The variable H then refers to this entry and the root of the tree is considered a descendant of H.

Protocol for an updater:
begin
{Let variable H always contain the height h of the tree, $h \geq 0$}
   procedure process son of current;

```
begin      get son of current;
           current := son of current;
           if current is safe
           then remove locks on all ancestors of current;
end;
0) If P ≠ 0 then place ρ_u-lock on H else place α-lock on H;
   current := H; {root = son of H};
1) Ē := min {ℎ, Ξ};
   P̄ := min {P, ℎ − Ē};
   ᾱ := ℎ − Ē − P̄;
2) for L := 1 step 1 until P̄ do
      begin  place a ρ_u-lock on son of current;
             release ρ_u-lock on current;
             get son of current;
             current := son of current
      end;
3) for L := 1 step 1 until ᾱ do
      begin  place an α-lock on son of current;
             process son of current;
      end;
4) for L := 1 step 1 until Ē do
      begin  place a ξ-lock on son of current;
             process son of current;
      end;
5) if ρ_u-lock still held
   then begin  release all locks;
               P = 0; Ξ = 0;
               repeat protocol and exit.
        end;
6) if α-locks still held
   then begin  6a): convert top-down all ξ to α;
               6b): convert top-down all α to ξ;
        end;
7) MODIFY: modify all nodes with ξ-locks, requesting additional ξ-locks
           for overflows, underflows, splits and merges as necessary;
8) release all locks;
end;
```

After Step 6 of this protocol is executed, the updater can proceed with the actual change. This is done in Step 7. All nodes in the locked subpath are locked with ξ-locks. The rules for insertion and deletion on B^*-trees determines whether additional ξ-locks will be acquired. This happens when attempting an overflow (or underflow) into a brother. This situation is shown in Figure 6. Assume that, at the end of Step 6, nodes b and c are held with ξ-locks and an update operation is to be performed on node c. Nodes d and e are immediate brothers of c. Since b has a ξ-lock we know that the update on c will propagate up to b. An overflow (or underflow) operation is then attempted into one of d or e. To do this, a ξ-lock is requested on d and when granted, an attempt is made to combine c and d

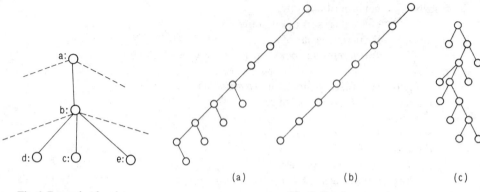

Fig. 6. Example of update

Fig. 7. Combs

together. (If this is not possible, an attempt to combine c and e is made.) After the required modifications at this level have been completed, node b is updated. Note that node b is safe (since there is no lock on node a) so after it is modified, the update terminates.

The following observations follow directly from the protocols:

Observation 1. All nodes which are locked by a process form a comb. (A comb of a tree is a subtree with the following restriction: if a node has more than one subtree as descendants, only one of them can have more than one node.) Examples of combs are shown if Figure 7.

Observation 2. If a process holds a ρ_r, ρ_u, or α-locks, then its comb is reduced to a path (as in Fig. 7b). Let this path be $(p_1, p_2, \ldots, p_n)$. Then

a) The process has not been granted any α to ξ conversions. In this case, there are integers j, k, with $0 \leq j \leq k \leq n$ such that all nodes $p_1, p_2, \ldots, p_j$ have ρ_r-locks (if a reader, in this case $j = k = n$) or ρ_u-locks (if an updater), all nodes $p_{j+1}, \ldots, p_k$ have α-locks and all nodes $p_{k+1}, \ldots, p_n$ have ξ-locks.

b) The process has been granted α to ξ lock conversions. Then it no longer holds ρ_u-locks, p_n is a leaf node and there is an integer k such that $1 \leq k \leq n$, $p_1, \ldots, p_k$ have ξ-locks and $p_{k+1}, \ldots, p_n$ have α-locks.

In the following sections we will examine these protocols more closely. We will show that they are deadlock free and will analyze the amount of concurrency they provide.

5. Deadlock Freeness of the Generalized Solution

In this section we will show that the generalized solution is deadlock free. As can be observed, the protocols for this solution are combinations of protocols for Solutions 1, 2, and 3. In fact, the main loop of each of these solutions can be obtained from the generalized solution by appropriate choices of the parameters P and $\varXi$ (this will be done in Section 6) and by identifying both ρ_r and ρ_u locks with

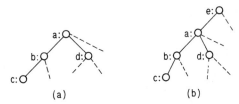

Fig. 8. Example of deadlock

the ρ lock. Since each one of Solutions 1, 2, and 3 can be shown to be deadlock free, it would appear that a solution as presented in Section 4 but with just 3 locks, a ρ-lock (instead of a ρ_r and a ρ_u-lock), an α-lock and a ξ-lock could be also shown to be deadlock free (the ρ-lock would be compatible with itself and an α-lock but not with a ξ-lock). Thus a simpler generalized solution would be obtained. This turns out not to be the case as shown by the following example:

Example. Consider a tree as in Figure 8a, where node c is unsafe and all other nodes shown are safe.

Assume $P = 2$, $\Xi = 1$. An updater, U_1 on node c would: set up a ρ-lock on a and get node a;
set up a ρ-lock on b; release ρ-lock on a; get b;

Now, other updaters can enter the tree through node a and go down towards node d. As a result of successive updates along this path, node a may split and a new root e be created as in Figure 8b.

A second updater U_2 may now want to update node c.

He would then: set up a ρ-lock on node e; get node e;
set up a ρ-lock on node a; release ρ-lock on e; get a;
set up an α-lock on b (this would be granted since the only other lock on b, which is held by U_1, is a ρ-lock, compatible with α); get b;
since b is safe, release ρ-lock on a;
get ξ-lock on node c; get node c since node c is unsafe, no locks are released;

At this point, U_2 would begin converting its ξ-locks into α-locks:
Convert ξ-locks in node c into an α-lock.

Then, the α-locks would be converted into ξ-locks:
Convert α-lock in node b into a ξ-lock;

This last conversion would be blocked since there is another process, U_1, holding a ρ-lock on b which is incompatible with a ξ-lock. Thus U_2 could not proceed. But U_1 is now also blocked since it would try to set up a ξ-lock on node c next. This request cannot be granted since another process, U_2, holds an α-lock which is incompatible with a ξ-lock. Thus, U_1 and U_2 are in a deadlock situation.

Forcing a read lock requested by an updater to be incompatible with an α-lock, as is done in the generalized solution by distinguishing between the ρ_r and ρ_u locks, resolves the above problem. In fact, as we now proceed to show, it makes this solution deadlock free. We first introduce some definitions:

Definition 1. A lock request on a node is said to be *pending* until granted by the scheduler.

Definition 2. Given two processes U and V, we say that U *waits on* V, denoted $U \vdash V$, if U has a pending request to lock a node on which V has a lock incompatible with the one U is requesting.

Definition 3. A process is called a c-process if it has a pending request for a lock conversion.

Definition 4. If a process U has a pending lock request on a node n then n is said to be the *critical node* of U. If U is not requesting a lock or the request was granted then U does not have a critical node.

Definition 5. The *critical level* of a process U, denoted by $\lambda(U)$ is the level of its critical node, if U has one, or 0 otherwise.

Our intent is to show that the given locking protocol is deadlock free. Intuitively, this means that any given process using these protocols to request locks will not be forever prevented from completing its task because of the existence of other locks placed by other processes. We must, however, be careful not to include the lock scheduler as an interfering process. In fact, a lock scheduler can arbitrarily produce deadlock situations by consistently failing to service a given process request, thus preventing it from completing its task. We then request that the scheduler have the following properties:

a) It shouldn't grant incompatible lock requests (or conversions) since this would create a situation inconsistent with the attributes of the locks.

b) It should grant lock conversion requests on a node before any other requests on that node. Note that since both α and ξ locks are incompatible among themselves, there can be at most one lock conversion request on any given node. Granting the unique lock conversion possible on a node before other requests eliminates the possibilities of trivial deadlock situations.

c) It should be fair in servicing requests, i.e., there should be a finite number of requests granted by the scheduler before a given request is finally granted. Servicing a request which doesn't result in an incompatible lock to be placed in a node should result in granting the requested lock.

There are many lock schedulers satisfying these restrictions and we have chosen one using a FIFO model to illustrate our protocols. Any other scheduler satisfying a), b), and c) will also result in a deadlock free operation.

Now we present a series of lemmas, all of which follow from the observations on the protocols made at the end of the previous section.

Lemma 1. If a process V holds a ρ_r or ρ_u-lock on a node m then

$$\lambda(V) < \ell(m).$$

(Recall that $\ell(m)$ is the level of node m.)

Proof. Follows directly from observation 2a. $\quad\square$

Lemma 2. If a process V holds a ξ-lock on a node m then either
   2a) $\lambda(V) < \ell(m)$ or
   2b) $\lambda(V) \geq \ell(m)$ and V also holds a ξ-lock on the father of m.

Proof. We use observation 2. If V has not requested α to ξ conversions then Case 2a applies (Steps 0 through 5 of the protocol). In Step 6a) since a ξ to α conversion is always granted then $\lambda(V) = 0$. In Step 6b), α to ξ conversion is top down, and $\lambda(V) <$ level of any node on which V holds a ξ-lock. Thus, $\lambda(V) < \ell(m)$. If, on the other hand, V has been granted all α to ξ conversions then V holds a comb made up of nodes all of which are ξ-locked and V is performing the actual update on some node in Step 7. If $\lambda(V) \geq \ell(m)$ it means that V is acquiring a ξ-lock on a node q to perform an overflow (or underflow) or split (or merge) operation. But in this case, V holds a ξ-lock on the father r of q. Since all nodes held with ξ-locks by V form a comb, if $\lambda(V) \geq \ell(m)$ it means that m is a descendant of r, and V holds a ξ-lock on the father of m. This completes the proof of Lemma 2. $\square$

Lemma 3. If a process V holds an α-lock on a node m then either

    3a) $\lambda(V) < \ell(m)$ or

    3b) $\lambda(V) = \ell(m)$ and V is attempting an α to ξ conversion on node m or

    3c) $\lambda(V) > \ell(m)$ and V is attempting an α to ξ conversion and has an α-lock on the father of m.

Proof. Assume $\lambda(V) \geq \ell(m)$. Since V holds an α-lock, observation 2 applies. Thus, if $\lambda(V) = \ell(m)$, V must be attempting an α to ξ conversion on m while if $\lambda(V) > \ell(m)$, V must be attempting an α to ξ conversion on an ancestor of m, and since all nodes locked by V form a path, holds an α-lock on a father of m.

    This proves the lemma. $\square$

Lemmas 1, 2, and 3 are now used to prove Lemma 4. This is the key lemma in proving deadlock freeness of the generalized solution.

Lemma 4. If U, V are processes and $U \vdash V$ then either

    4a) $\lambda(U) > \lambda(V)$ or

    4b) $\lambda(U) = \lambda(V)$, V is a c-process and U is not a c-process.

Proof. Let $U \vdash V$ and let m be the critical node for U. Thus $\lambda(U) = \ell(m)$. We consider 3 cases.

Case 1. If V holds a ρ_u or ρ_r lock on m, then by Lemma 1,

$$\lambda(U) = \ell(m) > \lambda(V)$$

and Case 4a) of Lemma 4 holds.

Case 2. If V holds a ξ-lock on m, Lemma 2 applies. Thus, either $\lambda(V) < \ell(m)$ and the lemma holds or $\lambda(V) \geq \ell(m)$. But this last case is not possible for then V would hold a ξ-lock on the father of m also, which means that U could not have any locks set up on the father of m and so it could not be attempting to acquire a lock on m. Clearly, U could not be attempting a conversion either since V has a ξ-lock on m.

Case 3. If V holds an α-lock on m, Lemma 3 applies. Thus, either $\lambda(V) < \ell(m)$ (and we are done) or $\lambda(V) \geq \ell(m)$. If $\lambda(V) = \ell(m)$, we know V is attempting an α- to ξ-conversion on node m. But since no two processes can be attempting a conversion simultaneously on the same node (they would both have to hold α-locks on the node which is not possible) we get that U cannot be a c-process.

Finally, if $\lambda(V) > \ell(m)$ then V holds α-locks on both m and its parent. We already saw that U cannot be attempting a conversion on node m since V has an α-lock on it. Thus, U must be attempting to acquire a new lock on m. But to do this it must have a lock on a parent of m. If U were a reader then U would not be waiting to get a ρ_r-lock on m. Thus U has to be an updater. But this cannot happen since any lock U holds on a parent of m is incompatible with α. This concludes the proof of the lemma. $\quad\square$

Lemma 4 allows us to show:

Theorem. The generalized solution is deadlock free.

Proof. Assume to the contrary that a deadlock exists. Then, there exist processes $U_1, U_2, \ldots, U_k$ such that

$$U_1 \vdash U_2 \vdash U_3 \vdash \cdots \vdash U_{k-1} \vdash U_k \vdash U_1 \qquad (*)$$

and there is no way to grant any pending locks in the chain. Note that since $U_1 \vdash U_1$ cannot happen, $k \geq 2$ and so, there are at least three processes U_1, U_2, U_3 with $U_1 \vdash U_2 \vdash U_3$ and $U_2 \neq U_1$, $U_2 \neq U_3$.

By Lemma 4, $\lambda(U_1) \geq \lambda(U_2)$ with $\lambda(U_1) = \lambda(U_2)$ if U_2 is a c-process. On the other hand, $\lambda(U_2) \geq \lambda(U_3)$ with $\lambda(U_2) = \lambda(U_3)$ only if U_2 is not a c-process. Thus $\lambda(U_1) > \lambda(U_3)$.

The above result implies that in $(*)$ we have $\lambda(U_1) > \lambda(U_1)$ a contradiction. Thus, the theorem holds. $\quad\square$

6. Selection of P and Ξ

As presented in Section 4 the generalized solution depends on the parameters P and Ξ.

By varying these parameters, many different concurrency patterns can be obtained.

For example, if $P = 0$, $\Xi = \hbar$ Steps 2 and 3 of the protocol would not be executed and Step 4 essentially reduces this solution to Solution 1. Note that setting up Ξ to $\hbar$ is not possible since one does not know in advance how high the tree is. But it is easy to define a way of simulating the protocol for the generalized solution to work as if one knew what $\hbar$ was before accessing the tree. Also, in order to get Solution 1, one has to change ρ_r to ρ, but clearly this is no problem either since α-locks are not present so that the locks ρ_r and ξ in the generalized solution can be mapped to the ρ and ξ-lock respectively of Solution 1. In the sequel, when saying that the generalized solution reduces to one of Solution 1, 2, or 3 we mean it modulo these types of changes.

If we let $P = \hbar - 1$ and $\Xi = 1$ then we get Solution 2 (in this case, the retry would have to have $P = 0$, $\Xi = \hbar$). Finally, setting $P = 0$, $\Xi = 0$ one gets Solution 3. As was mentioned in Section 3 each one of these solutions has advantages and disadvantages over the other. A proper choice of P and Ξ will *tune* the generalized solution to yield the best performance for a given application. In what follows we show a model of access with an analysis of the relevant components of the cost of a solution. Expressions for these components will be obtained from which

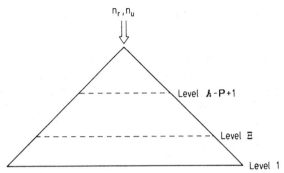

Fig. 9. Model for concurrency and overhead analysis

suitable values of P and Ξ can be chosen. We will assume that all readers and updaters access the structure using the same P and Ξ (as will be explained below, this may not be the case, but helps to evaluate a strategy).

There are two main components in the cost of a given solution. One is the time spent by processes waiting for locks to be removed before they can proceed. The second one is the time overhead due to placing locks on the nodes, converting locks, or repeating part of an analysis.

Assume a tree as in Figure 9, and a given number n_r of readers and n_u of updaters. The updaters will place ρ_u-locks from level h down to level $h-P+1$. From level $h-P$ down to $\Xi+1$ they will place α-locks and finally, for the last Ξ levels, they will place ξ-locks.

Now, in the upper P levels there are no conflicts, since updaters and readers use compatible ρ_u and ρ_r locks. But in level $h-P$, the updaters set up α-locks which are incompatible among themselves. Thus, at this level, some updaters will have to wait for other updaters.

Let v_i denote the number of nodes of the tree at level i. We will assume that each updater has equal probability $\dfrac{1}{v_i}$ of scanning each node at level i when traversing the tree from the root to a leaf node. Then, since there are n_u updaters, the expected number of nodes which are visited by the n_u updaters at level $h-P$ is given by

$$\Phi(h-P, n_u) = v_{h-P}\left(1 - \left(1 - \frac{1}{v_{h-P}}\right)^{n_u}\right).$$

To obtain this expression, note that $\left(1 - \dfrac{1}{v_{h-P}}\right)^{n_u}$ is the probability that a given node will not be scanned by any of the n_u updaters. Thus, $1 - \left(1 - \dfrac{1}{v_{h-P}}\right)^{n_u}$ gives the probability that a given node will be scanned by at least one updater. The expected number of nodes which will be scanned by at least one updater is then $\Phi(h-P, n_u)$.

This expression also gives the expected number of updaters that will proceed down the tree (from level $h-P$) without waiting for an α-lock to be granted.

Thus, the expected number of updaters that will wait is given by:

$$W_u = n_u - \Phi(v_{\hbar-P}, n_u).$$

The $\Phi(\hbar-P, n_u)$ updaters that can proceed downwards from level $\hbar-P$ will do so without interfering with each other. When they get to level Ξ they may interact with readers. Assuming the updaters acquire the ξ-locks before the readers request ρ_r-locks (this will give a worst case value for the quantity being computed), the expected number of readers that wait is:

$$W_r = \begin{cases} n_r \dfrac{\Phi(\hbar-P, n_u)}{v_\Xi} & (\text{if } \Xi \neq 0) \\ 0 & (\text{if } \Xi = 0). \end{cases}$$

W_u and W_r together give a measure of the number of processes that will have to wait when accessing the tree. Besides this component of the cost of a (P, Ξ) solution there is the overhead cost involved. This cost has three subcomponents. One is given by the fact that, after scanning the tree from the root to the leaf, a process may find that all his processing has to be repeated (this happens if in Step 5 of the protocol an updater finds that it still holds a ρ_u-lock). We will measure this component by computing Q, the expected number of nodes per updater that are scanned again to repeat an analysis. The second subcomponent is C_ξ, the expected number of ξ-locks that an updater will convert into α-locks. Finally, the third subcomponent is C_α, the expected number of α-locks that an updater will convert into ξ-locks.

To compute Q, we will assume that all updaters are performing insertions. In this case, one out of k updaters will, on the average, cause a split of a node at the leaf level which propagates up the tree; one out of k^2 updaters will, on the average, cause a split of a node at level 2 which will propagate up the tree, and so on. Thus, we consider the probability that an updater will *modify* a node at level i or above to be $\left(\dfrac{1}{k}\right)^{i-1}$.

An updater will repeat his analysis if it causes a node at level $\hbar-P+1$ or above to be modified. Since when this happens, $\hbar$ nodes will be scanned again, we have that

$$Q = \begin{cases} \hbar \cdot \left(\dfrac{1}{k}\right)^{\hbar-P} & \text{if } P \neq 0 \\ 0 & \text{if } P = 0. \end{cases}$$

(Note that if $P=0$, there is no retry involved.)

To compute C_ξ we note that an updater will convert ξ-locks into α-locks whenever it reaches Step 5 of the protocol and discovers it holds an α-lock, but not a ρ_u-lock. This, in turn happens only if the update will modify nodes at a level $\Xi+1$ or higher, but lower than level $\hbar-P+1$. The number of locks to be modified in this case is always Ξ. Thus,

$$C_\xi = \begin{cases} \Xi \cdot \left[\left(\dfrac{1}{k}\right)^\Xi - \left(\dfrac{1}{k}\right)^{\hbar-P} \right] & \text{if } \hbar > P+\Xi \\ 0 & \text{otherwise}. \end{cases}$$

Finally, to compute C_α, we note that if the update will modify nodes exactly up to a level i, $\Xi + 1 \leq i \leq h - P$ then i α-locks are converted into ξ-locks. Thus, if $h > P + \Xi$

$$C_\alpha = \sum_{i=\Xi+1}^{h-P} i \cdot \left[\left(\frac{1}{k} \right)^{i-1} - \left(\frac{1}{k} \right)^{i} \right]$$

$$= \frac{k-1}{k} \sum_{i=\Xi+1}^{h-P} i \left(\frac{1}{k} \right)^{i-1}.$$

Clearly, if $h \leq P + \Xi$ no α-locks are placed in the first place so $C_\alpha = 0$.

In Table 1, we give values for these 5 components for various choices of h, k, n_r, and n_u. Notice that W_u and W_r are shown in two columns, a high and a low. This is because the actual number of nodes at level i, v_i can fluctuate according to:

$$v_h = 1$$

$$2 \leq v_{h-1} \leq 2k+1$$

$$2(k+1)^{h-i-1} \leq v_i \leq (2k+1)^{h-i} \qquad i \leq h-2.$$

The high value is obtained when using the upper bound for v_i and the low value is obtained when using the lower bound for v_i.

From Table 1, we can choose values of P and Ξ which will guarantee an average performance prescribed in advance. For example, a concurrency of more than 50% of the updaters and more than 99% of the readers would be possible, in the case $h = 5$, $k = 10$, $n_u = 30$, $n_r = 70$ by choosing $\Xi = 1$, P = 2. The average number of nodes that are scanned again after a retry by an updater is 0.005 and the number of lock conversions per updater is on the average, 0.099 for ξ to α conversion and 0.207 for α to ζ conversion.

For $h = 3$, $k = 100$ good concurrency levels are achieved with $\Xi = 1$ and P = 1 or 2. In the latter case, there is an increase in the number of nodes that are accessed before a retry which is compensated by reducing to 0 the number of lock conversions.

We have shown how to select the parameters P and Ξ to obtain a given level of concurrency. This assumes that all updaters use the update protocol with the same values of P and Ξ. But there is nothing that prevents an updater from using its own P and Ξ. By doing this, an updater may use information he has gathered on previous accesses to further contribute to an increase in concurrency. For example, an updater that accesses an index to perform an insertion on a leaf node he has visited recently and found to be very far from full could choose $P = h - 1$ and $\Xi = 1$ and be almost guaranteed not to perform a retry while at the same time allowing for maximum concurrency with other processes. (If the updater had found the node almost full on a previous access, it may use $P = h - 2$, $\Xi = 1$ to insure that even a split to level 2 would not cause a retry and still allow for high concurrency!)

The fact that each updater may use its own parameters P and Ξ gives the generalized solution an added flexibility while at the same time preserving deadlock freeness of the schema. In fact, in proving deadlock freeness in Section 5, no assumptions where made as to the values for P and Ξ each updater might choose.

Table 1

Ξ	P	W_u low	W_u high	W_r low	W_r high	Q	C_ξ	C_α
			$n_u=5$	$n_r=95$	$h=5$	$k=10$		
0	0	4.00	4.00	0.00	0.00	0.0000	0.0000	1.1110
0	1	3.06	0.45	0.00	0.00	0.0005	0.0000	1.1106
0	2	0.43	0.02	0.00	0.00	0.0050	0.0000	1.1070
0	3	0.04	0.00	0.00	0.00	0.0500	0.0000	1.0800
0	4	0.00	0.00	0.00	0.00	0.5000	0.0000	0.9000
1	0	4.00	4.00	0.04	0.00	0.0000	0.1000	0.2110
1	1	3.06	0.45	0.07	0.00	0.0005	0.0999	0.2106
1	2	0.43	0.02	0.16	0.00	0.0050	0.0990	0.2070
1	3	0.04	0.00	0.18	0.00	0.0500	0.0900	0.1800
1	4	0.00	0.00	0.18	0.00	0.5000	0.0000	0.0000
2	0	4.00	4.00	0.39	0.01	0.0000	0.0200	0.0310
2	1	3.06	0.45	0.76	0.05	0.0005	0.0198	0.0306
2	2	0.43	0.02	1.79	0.05	0.0050	0.0180	0.0270
2	3	0.04	0.00	1.95	0.05	0.0500	0.0000	0.0000
3	0	4.00	4.00	4.32	0.22	0.0000	0.0030	0.0040
3	1	3.06	0.45	8.37	0.98	0.0005	0.0027	0.0036
3	2	0.43	0.02	19.72	1.07	0.0050	0.0000	0.0000
4	0	4.00	4.00	47.50	4.52	0.0000	0.0004	0.0004
4	1	3.06	0.45	92.03	20.57	0.0005	0.0000	0.0000
5	0	4.00	4.00	95.00	95.00	0.0000	0.0000	0.0000
			$n_u=5$	$n_r=95$	$h=3$	$k=100$		
0	0	4.00	4.00	0.00	0.00	0.0000	0.0000	1.0101
0	1	3.06	0.05	0.00	0.00	0.0003	0.0000	1.0098
0	2	0.05	0.00	0.00	0.00	0.0300	0.0000	0.9900
1	0	4.00	4.00	0.47	0.00	0.0000	0.0100	0.0201
1	1	3.06	0.05	0.91	0.01	0.0003	0.0099	0.0198
1	2	0.05	0.00	2.33	0.01	0.0300	0.0000	0.0000
2	0	4.00	4.00	47.50	0.47	0.0000	0.0002	0.0003
2	1	3.06	0.05	92.03	2.34	0.0003	0.0000	0.0000
3	0	4.00	4.00	95.00	95.00	0.0000	0.0000	0.0000
			$n_u=5$	$n_r=95$	$h=2$	$k=1000$		
0	0	4.00	4.00	0.00	0.00	0.0000	0.0000	1.0010
0	1	3.06	0.00	0.00	0.00	0.0020	0.0000	0.9990
1	0	4.00	4.00	47.50	0.05	0.0000	0.0010	0.0020
1	1	3.06	0.00	92.03	0.24	0.0020	0.0000	0.0000
2	0	4.00	4.00	95.00	95.00	0.0000	0.0000	0.0000

7. Extensions to Sequential Readers

In some uses of B^*-trees to support indexes, the nodes of the tree can also belong to sequential data structures. A common situation would be that of readers performing sequential scans through a sequence of nodes at the same level in

Table 1 (continued)

Ξ	P	W_u low	$n_u=30$ W_u high	$n_r=70$ W_r low	$h=5$ W_r high	$k=10$ Q	C_ξ	C_α
0	0	29.00	29.00	0.00	0.00	0.0000	0.0000	1.1110
0	1	28.00	13.86	0.00	0.00	0.0005	0.0000	1.1106
0	2	13.45	0.97	0.00	0.00	0.0050	0.0000	1.1070
0	3	1.73	0.05	0.00	0.00	0.0500	0.0000	1.0800
0	4	0.16	0.00	0.00	0.00	0.5000	0.0000	0.9000
1	0	29.00	29.00	0.03	0.00	0.0000	0.1000	0.2110
1	1	28.00	13.86	0.05	0.01	0.0005	0.0999	0.2106
1	2	13.45	0.97	0.44	0.01	0.0050	0.0990	0.2070
1	3	1.73	0.05	0.74	0.01	0.0500	0.0900	0.1800
1	4	0.16	0.00	0.78	0.01	0.5000	0.0000	0.0000
2	0	29.00	29.00	0.29	0.01	0.0000	0.0200	0.0310
2	1	28.00	13.86	0.58	0.12	0.0005	0.0198	0.0306
2	2	13.45	0.97	4.79	0.22	0.0050	0.0180	0.0270
2	3	1.73	0.05	8.18	0.23	0.0500	0.0000	0.0000
3	0	29.00	29.00	3.18	0.16	0.0000	0.0030	0.0040
3	1	28.00	13.86	6.36	2.56	0.0005	0.0027	0.0036
3	2	13.45	0.97	52.66	4.61	0.0050	0.0000	0.0000
4	0	29.00	29.00	35.00	3.33	0.0000	0.0004	0.0004
4	1	28.00	13.86	70.00	53.80	0.0005	0.0000	0.0000
5	0	29.00	29.00	70.00	70.00	0.0000	0.0000	0.0000

Ξ	P	W_u low	$n_u=30$ W_u high	$n_r=70$ W_r low	$h=3$ W_r high	$k=100$ Q	C_ξ	C_α
0	0	29.00	29.00	0.00	0.00	0.0000	0.0000	1.0101
0	1	28.00	2.07	0.00	0.00	0.0003	0.0000	1.0098
0	2	2.06	0.01	0.00	0.00	0.0300	0.0000	0.9900
1	0	29.00	29.00	0.35	0.00	0.0000	0.0100	0.0201
1	1	28.00	2.07	0.69	0.05	0.0003	0.0099	0.0198
1	2	2.06	0.01	9.68	0.05	0.0300	0.0000	0.0000
2	0	29.00	29.00	35.00	0.35	0.0000	0.0002	0.0003
2	1	28.00	2.07	70.00	9.73	0.0003	0.0000	0.0000
3	0	29.00	29.00	70.00	70.00	0.0000	0.0000	0.0000

Ξ	P	W_u low	$n_u=30$ W_u high	$n_r=70$ W_r low	$h=2$ W_r high	$k=1000$ Q	C_ξ	C_α
0	0	29.00	29.00	0.00	0.00	0.0000	0.0000	1.0010
0	1	28.00	0.22	0.00	0.00	0.0020	0.0000	0.9990
1	0	29.00	29.00	35.00	0.03	0.0000	0.0010	0.0020
1	1	28.00	0.22	70.00	1.04	0.0020	0.0000	0.0000
2	0	29.00	29.00	70.00	70.00	0.0000	0.0000	0.0000

the tree. The ideas developed in the protocols presented in Section 4 can also be adapted to allow sequential read accesses concurrently with random read and update accesses. We will briefly discuss how this can be done for one case. The reader will then quickly see how these concepts could be used in other situations.

Consider the very frequent case of readers accessing the nodes of the tree following a path from the root down, with the additional freedom of allowing a left to right scan of some adjacent nodes to be made at the same level of the tree. Thus, a reader could, for example, start at the root, follow a downward path to a node, move right on adjacent nodes at the same level to another node then continue down the tree.

A similar analysis to that done in Lemmas 1, 2, and 3 would show that no deadlocks could occur by allowing such traversals, except for one case. This occurs when an updater, having locked with ξ-locks all nodes that will be modified, begins to perform the actual modifications and discovers that an overflow or underflow exists and wishes to scan the left brother q of a node p (on which it holds a ξ-lock) to see if there is room to accommodate for this overflow or underflow. Instead of acquiring a ξ-lock on q, as indicated in Step 7 of the protocol for the generalized solution, the updating process would then have to:

1) convert the ξ-lock on p to an α-lock;

2) place a ξ-lock on q;

3) Examine node q. If it can be used to accommodate the overflow or underflow, convert the α-lock on p to a ξ-lock and perform the operation; otherwise, release the ξ-lock on q and convert the α-lock on p to a ξ-lock; {Examination of the right brother would not require any changes to our original protocol}.

It can be shown that with this modification, the new protocols are still deadlock free.

Other modes of traversals by readers can also be accommodated using the ideas presented here.

8. Conclusions and Implementation Considerations

In this paper we have examined several solutions to the problem of concurrency in indexes implemented as B^*-trees. A generalized solution has been presented which allows tuning the access to these structures to optimize concurrency of operations. Furthermore, this solution has been shown to be deadlock free. This shows that with proper locking techniques, B^*-trees support easy and highly concurrent access to indexes.

When implementing B^*-trees with the provision for parallel operations some structuring concept should be chosen, which allows to consider a B^*-tree together with the operations and their lockprotocols as one conceptual unit. Several such concepts, most of them related to the Simula classes, have been offered in the literature, but they usually ignore the problem of parallel operations, assuming that these units will be used by one sequential process only. This automatically results in a serial application of operations.

To deal with parallel (from an external point of view) operations the concept of a Monitor has been introduced [5, 7]. Monitors, however, deal with external parallelism essentially by enforcing internally a serialization of operations. Unfortunately this means that a Monitor would cancel exactly the effect we are trying to achieve.

In the Operating Systems Project BSM at the Technical University in Munich a structuring concept called *Manager* was developed [8, 9]. *Managers* deal with parallel external operations but allow in a carefully controlled way also internal parallelism of operations. It seems that Managers would be a suitable structuring concept for implementing the solutions presented in this paper.

Acknowledgements. Mike Blasgen participated in the initial discussions that lead to the generalized solution presented here. His ideas about locking in *B**-trees as implemented in System R [1] and his cooperation with the authors are sincerely appreciated.

References

1. Astrahan, M.M., et al.: System R: Relational approach to database management. ACM Transactions on Database Systems 1, 97–137 (1976)
2. Bayer, R., McCreight, E.: Organization and maintenance of large ordered indexes. Acta Informat. 1, 173–189 (1972)
3. Bayer, R., Metzger, J.: On the Encypherment of Search Trees and Random Access Files. ACM Transactions on Database Systems 1, 37–52 (1976)
4. Bayer, R., Unterauer, K.: Prefix *B*-trees. IBM Research Report RJ 1796, San Jose, Calif., 1976. ACM Transactions on Database Systems 2, 11–26 (1977)
5. Brinch Hansen, P.: A programming methodology for operating system design. IFIP Congress 1974, Stockholm, pp. 394–397. Amsterdam: North Holland 1974
6. Held, G., Stonebraker, M.: *B*-trees reexamined. ERL, College of Engineering, Univ. of California, Berkeley, Calif., Memo. ♯ERL-M 528, July 2, 1975
7. Hoare, C.A.R.: Monitors: An operating system structuring concept. Comm. ACM 17, 549–557 (1974)
8. Jammel, A., Stiegler, H.: Verwalter, eine Methode der rekursiven Prozeßzerlegung. Leibniz-Rechenzentrum der Bayerischen Akademie der Wissenschaften, LRZ Internschrift 7604/1, München, 1976
9. Jammel, A., Stiegler, H.: Managers versus Monitors. Submitted to: IFIP Congress (1977)
10. Knuth, D.E.: The art of computer programming, Vol. 3. Sorting and searching. Reading, Mass.: Addison-Wesley 1972
11. Metzger, J.K.: Managing simultaneous operations in large ordered indexes. Technische Universität München, Institut für Informatik, TUM-Math. Report, 1975
12. Schkolnick, M.: Initial specifications for DFMAS. Unpublished document, May 1975
13. Wedekind, H.: On the selection of access paths in a data base system (J.W. Klimbie, K.L. Koffeman, eds.), Data base management, pp. 385–397. Amsterdam: North-Holland 1974

Received June 10, 1976

Acknowledgments

We wish to thank Professor T-y. Feng for suggesting the need for a tutorial on parallel processing, and Professor D. J. Kuck for his many valuable suggestions. We also want to thank the two referees for their many useful recommendations. We are indebted to Mrs. Vivian Alsip for the careful typing of the introductory paragraphs.

References

Amdahl, G. M. Validity of the Single-Processor Approach to Achieving Large Scale Computing Capabilities. *AFIPS Conference Proceedings*, 1967, *30*, 483–485.

Anderson, D. W., Sparacio, F. J., & Tomasulo, R. M. The Model 91: Machine Philosophy and Instruction Handling. *IBM Journal of Research and Development*, 1967, *11*, 8–24.

Anderson, G. A., & Jensen, E. D. Computer Interconnection Structures: Taxonomy, Characteristics, and Examples. *ACM Computing Surveys*, 1975, *7*, 197–213.

Anderson, J. P., Hoffman, J. A., Shifman, J. & Williams, R. J. D825—A Multiple-Computer System for Command and Control. *AFIPS Conference Proceedings*, 1962, *22*, 86–96.

Baer, J. L. Survey of Some Theoretical Aspects of Multiprocessing. *ACM Computing Surveys*, 1973, *5*, 31–80.

Banerjee, U. Speedup of Ordinary Programs (Ph.D. Thesis, 1979). *University of Illinois at Urbana-Champaign, Department of Computer Science, Report No. 79–989*.

Barnes, G. H., Brown, R. M., Kato, M., Kuck, D. J., Slotnick, D. L., & Stokes, R. A. The ILLIAC IV Computer. *IEEE Transactions on Computers*, 1968, *C-17*, 746–757.

Batcher, K. E. The Multi-Dimensional Access Memory in STARAN. *IEEE Transactions on Computers*, 1977, *C-26*, 174–177.

Burroughs Corporation. *Numerical Aerodynamic Simulation Facility Feasibility Study*, March 1979.

Calahan, D. A. *High Speed Computation: Vector Processing.* (An Engineering Short Course held August 1979 and August 1980 at the University of Michigan, Ann Arbor, unpublished.)

Campbell, R. H., & Habermann, A. N. The Specification of Process Synchronization by Path Expressions. In G. Goos & J. Hartmanis (Eds.), *Lecture Notes in Computer Science* (Vol. 16). New York: Springer-Verlag, 1974.

Control Data Corporation. *Feasibility Study for a Numerical Aerodynamic Simulation Facility.* May 1979.

Chen, T. C. Overlap and Pipeline Processing. In H. S. Stone (Ed.), *Introduction to Computer Architecture.* Chicago: SRA, 1975.

Dijktra, E. W. Cooperating Sequential Processes. In F. Genuys (Ed.), *Programming Languages.* New York: Academic Press, 1968.

Enslow, P. H., Jr. Multiprocessor Organization—A Survey. *ACM Computing Surveys*, 1977, *9*, 103–129.

Falk, H. What Went Wrong V-Reaching for a Gigaflop. *IEEE Spectrum*, 1976, *13*(10), 65–69.

Flynn, M. J. Very High-Speed Computing Systems. *Proceedings of the IEEE*, 1966, *54*, 1901–1909.

Flynn, M. J. Some Computer Organizations and Their Effectiveness. *IEEE Transactions on Computers*, 1972, *C-21*, 948–960.

Foster, C. C., & Riseman, E. M. Percolation of Code to Enhance Parallel Dispatching and Execution. *IEEE Transactions on Computers*, 1972, *C-21*, 1411–1415.

Gilbert, B. K., & Harris, L. D. Advances in Processor Architecture, Display, and Device Technology for Biomedical Image Processing. *IEEE Transactions on Nuclear Science*, 1980, *NS-27*, 1197–1206.

Händler, W. On Classification Schemes for Computer Systems in the Post Von Neumann Era. In G. Goos & J. Hartmanis (Eds.), *Lecture Notes in Computer Science* (Vol. 26). New York: Springer-Verlag, 1975.

Heller, D. A Survey of Parallel Algorithms in Numerical Linear Algebra. *SIAM Review*, 1977, *20*, 740–777.

Hoare, C. A. R. Monitors: An Operating System Structuring Concept. *Communications of ACM*, 1974, *17*, 549–557.

Ichbiah, J. D., Heliard, J. C., Roubine, O., Barnes, J. G. P., Kneg-Brueckner, B., & Widemann, B. A. Rationale for the Design of the ADA Programming Language. *Sigplan Notices*, 1979, *14* (6, Pt. B).

Jones, A. K., Chansler, R. J., Jr., Durham, I., Schwans, K., & Vegdahl, S. R., StarOS: A Multiprocessor Operating System for the Support of Task Force. *Proceedings of the Seventh ACM Symposium on Operating Systems Principles*, 1979, 117–127.

Jones, A. K., & Schwarz, P. Experience Using Multiprocessor Systems—A Status Report. *ACM Computing Surveys*, 1980, *12*, 121–165.

Kaminsky, W. J., & Davidson, E. S. Developing a Multiple-Instruction-Stream Single-Chip Processor. *Computer*, 1979, *12*, 66–76.

Kuck, D. J. A Survey of Parallel Machine Organization and Programming. *ACM Computing Surveys*, 1977, *9*, 29–59.

Kuck, D. J. *The Structure of Computers and Computations* (Vol. 1). New York: John Wiley & Sons, 1978.

Kuck, D. J. High-Speed Machines and Their Compilers. *Proceedings of the CREST Parallel Processing Systems Course.* Cambridge University Press, in press.

Kuck, D. J., Kuhn, R. H., Leasure, B., & Wolfe, M. The Structure of an Advanced Vectonizer for Pipelined Processors. *Proceedings of the Fourth International Computer Software and Applications Conference*, 1980, 709–715.

Kuck, D. J., Lawrie, D. H., & Sameh, A. H. (Eds.). *High-Speed Computer and Algorithm Organization*, New York: Academic Press, 1977.

Kung, H. T. The Structure of Parallel Algorithms. In M. C. Yanits (Ed.), *Advances in Computers* (Vol. 19). New York: Academic Press, 1980.

Lawrie, D. H., & Vora, C. The Prime Memory System for Array Access. *Proceedings of the 1980 International Conference on Parallel Processing*, 1980, 81–90.

497

Lee, R. B.-L. Performance Bounds in Parallel Processor Organization. In D. J. Kuck, D. H. Lawrie, & A. H. Sameh (Eds.). *High-Speed Computer and Algorithm Organization*, New York: Academic Press, 1977.

Leiner, A. L., Notz, W. A., Smith, J. L., & Weinberger, A. PILOT—A New Multiple Computer System. *Journal of the ACM*, 1959, *6*, 313-335.

Minsky, M., & Papert, S. On Some Associative, Parallel, and Analog Computations. In E. J. Jacks (Ed.), *Associative Information Techniques*, New York: Elsevier, 1971.

Ortega, J., & Voight, R. Solution of Partial Differential Equations on Vector Computers. *Proceedings of the 1977 Army Numerical Analysis and Computer Conference*, 1977.

Padua, D. A., Kuck, D. J., & Lawrie, D. H. High-Speed Multiprocessors and Compilation Techniques. *IEEE Transactions on Computers*, 1980, *C-29*, 763-776.

Paul, G., & Wilson, M. W. An Introduction to VECTRAN and Its Use in Scientific Programming. *Proceedings of the 1978 LASL Workshop on Vector and Parallel Processors*, 1978, 176-204.

Peterson, J. L. Petri Nets. *ACM Computing Surveys*, 1977, *9*, 223-252.

Ramamoorthy, C. V., & Li, H. F. Pipeline Architecture. *ACM Computing Surveys*, 1977, *9*, 62-102.

Reghbati, E., & Corneil, D. G. Parallel Computations in Graph Theory. *SIAM Journal on Computing*, 1978, *7*, 230-237.

Robinson, J. T. Analysis of Asynchronous Multiprocessor Algorithms with Applications to Sorting. *Proceedings of the 1977 International Conference on Parallel Processing*, 1977, 128-135.

Satyanarayanan, M. Commercial Multiprocessing Systems. *Computer*, 1980, *13*, 75-96.

Seeber, R. R., & Lindquist, A. B. Associative Logic for Highly Parallel Systems. *AFIPS Conference Proceedings*, 1963, *24*, 489-493.

Slotnick, D. L., Borck, W. C., & McReynolds, R. C. The SOLOMON Computer. *AFIPS Conference Proceedings*, 1962, *22*, 87-107.

Stone, H. S. Parallel Processing with the Perfect Shuffle. *IEEE Transactions on Computers*, 1971, *C-20*, 153-161.

Stone, H. S. (Ed.). *Introduction to Computer Architecture.* Chicago: SRA, 1975.

Thompson, C. D., & Kung, H. T. Sorting on a Mesh-Connected Parallel Computer. *Communications of the ACM*, 1977, *20*, 263-271.

Thornton, J. E. Parallel Operation in the Control Data 6600. *AFIPS Conference Proceedings*, 1964, *26* (Pt. II), 33-40.

Thornton, J. E. *Design of a Computer, the Control Data 6600.* Glenview, IL: Scott, Foresman, and Co., 1970.

Thurber, K. J. *Large Scale Computer Architecture.* Rochelle Park, NJ: Hayden Book Company, Inc., 1976.

Tomasulo, R. M. An Efficient Algorithm for Exploiting Multiple Arithmetic Units. *IBM Journal of Research and Development*, 1967, *11*, 25-33.

Watson, W. J. The TI ASC—A Highly Modular and Flexible Super Computer Architecture. *AFIPS Conference Proceedings*, 1972, *41* (Pt. I), 221-228.

Williams, S. B. A Relay Computer for General Application. *Bell Laboratories Record*, 1947, *25*, 49-54.

Wisniewski, J. A., & Sameh, A. H. Parallel Algorithms for Network Routing Problems and Recurrences. *University of Illinois at Urbana-Champaign, Department of Computer Science Report No. 79-997*, 1979.

Wulf, W. A., & Bell, C. G. C.mmp—A Multi-Miniprocessor. *AFIPS Conference Proceedings*, 1972, *41*, 765-777.